Volume One
SELECTED SCRIPTURE SUMMARIES
From the Whole Bible

WORKS BY DR. LOCKYER —

All the Men of the Bible
All the Women of the Bible
All the Kings and Queens of the Bible
All the Apostles of the Bible
All the Children of the Bible
All the Promises of the Bible
All the Prayers of the Bible
All the Doctrines of the Bible
All the Miracles of the Bible
All the Parables of the Bible
All the Books and Chapters of the Bible
All the Trades and Occupations of the Bible
All the Holy Days and Holidays
The Sins of Saints
The Unseen Army

Lockyer Bible Preacher's Library I

Twin Truths of Scripture, Volume 1
Twin Truths of Scripture, Volume 2
Triple Truths of Scripture, Volume 1
Triple Truths of Scripture, Volume 2
Triple Truths of Scripture, Volume 3

Lockyer Bible Preacher's Library II

Ancient Portraits in Modern Frames I: Bible Biographies
Ancient Portraits in Modern Frames II: Church History Biographies
Selected Scripture Summaries I
Selected Scripture Summaries II

Volume One
SELECTED SCRIPTURE SUMMARIES
From the Whole Bible

Herbert Lockyer

BAKER BOOK HOUSE
Grand Rapids, Michigan

PHOTOLITHOPRINTED BY CUSHING - MALLOY, INC.
ANN ARBOR, MICHIGAN, UNITED STATES OF AMERICA
1975

To
Dr. E. Schuyler English
Gifted Expositor of the Word, Who Was Among My
Earliest Friends in America, and Who, When Editor
of *Our Hope*, Encouraged Me to Write Some of These
Summaries for that Renowned Periodical Now,
Unfortunately, Defunct.

"After all, the chief proof that the Bible is good food is the eating of it."

— GENERAL GORDON

Contents

Preface

The adjective in the title of these volumes explains its contents. The word *select* means to take from a number of the same or an analogous kind by preference. That is what this book is—a selection taken from a mass of studies belonging to the same realm. For well over sixty years it has been my great privilege to preach and teach the Word over the British Isles, and also throughout America, in churches and mission halls and in Bible colleges and institutes. In turn, it has been my joy to serve as an evangelist, pastor, and for the last thirty-five years, as Bible teacher-at-large.

My great, undying passion has been prayerfully and carefully to study God's incomparable Word, and to communicate to others truth revealed to my own mind by His Spirit. And in all kinds of opportunities, one has been encouraged by the absorbing interest of believers in a sane and satisfying exposition of Scripture. In an extensive Bible conference ministry, often with the use of a blackboard to carry outlines of themes presented, it has been most gratifying to watch the delight of an audience as these were expounded.

For over half-a-century I have amassed a quantity of material on many Scriptural subjects, and now, conscious as I am that, having gone well beyond the "four score years," heaven is not too far distant, I felt that a host of Bible searchers would like to share some of the treasures I discovered in God's inexhaustible storehouse—the Bible, the brightest and most precious gems in the crown of literature. May your meditation of these outlined truths be as sweet to your taste as they were to mine! As for my estimation of the

Holy Scriptures, I add a hearty Amen! to the lines of Robert Pollock—

> This Holy Book, on every line
> Marked with the seal of high divinity,
> On every leaf bedewed with drops of love
> Divine, and with eternal heraldry
> And signature of God Almighty stamped,
>   From first to last.

First Summary
The Presence of Humor in Scripture

You may wonder why we have chosen such a theme to introduce these Scripture summaries. The simple reason is to show that although the Bible is God's Word, divinely inspired, yet it is written in human language, and its humorous element reveals how closely it is related to human life, particularly, human emotions. In her *Northanger Abbey,* Jane Austin reminds us that "the liveliest effusions of wit and humor are conveyed to the world in the best chosen language." This observation is certainly true of the Bible brand of humor. Samuel Butler, who boasted, "The phrase *unconscious humor* is the one contribution I have made to the current literature of the world," contends that "the most perfect humor and irony is generally quite unconscious." It would seem that this is so with those in the Bible who used the humorous and ironic in the service of truth.

Humor is defined as "a mental quality which apprehends and delights in the ludicrous and mirthful." Some men are naturally humorous. Others, quite unconsciously, are capable of exhibiting a dry humor. Jonathan Swift in a letter to Mr. Delany, had the lines—

> Humour is odd, grotesque and wild
> Only by affectation spoiled;
> 'Tis never by invention got;
> Men have it when they know it not.

C. H. Spurgeon, that Prince of Preachers, knew he had such a gift and used it wisely and well. Cicero expressed the sentiment that "joking and humor are pleasant and often of extreme utility." Spurgeon's preaching and teaching sparkled with humor which he could also use to great advantage, as his *Lectures to Students* and *John Ploughman's Talks* reveal. The story is told of a minister who called to see Spurgeon about a member of his church who was strongly opposed to his ministry. This troublemaker always sat in the front row of the church, and as soon as the minister announced his text, this man put his fingers in his ears, and so continued to the end of the sermon. The distracted preacher asked Mr. Spurgeon what he should do in these trying circumstances, and he replied, "If I were in your plight I think I would ask the Lord to send a fly to light upon his nose." The troubled minister saw the humor of the situation, and found relief in a hearty laugh.

It may be open to question whether there is any intentional humor in the Bible. Without doubt, many of its writers had a sense of humor, yet such a natural expression of mirth is by no means conspicuous in what they wrote. The Bible makes no reference to court jesters, clowns, or funny men. Certainly there are references to "laughter," but it is usually associated with scorn, mockery, derision, rather than with unadulterated merriment. When God is referred to as laughing it is in derision (Ps. 2:4). What divine sarcasm there is in the scorn of the impotence of those who try to overturn His throne! Who, with a watering pot, is able to put out the stars, or roll back the burning orb of the midday sun into night (Ps. 37:13)? God laughs at all human folly and awaits the day of retribution.

When God fashioned man, He gave him face muscles with which to laugh. "God hath prepared laughter for me" (Gen. 17:17; 21:16, margin); " ... ye shall laugh" (Luke 6:21; see Job 9:23; Ps. 126:2). Solomon reminds us that there is "a time to laugh," as well as cry, even though he later added that "sorrow is better than laughter." This king who wrote that "a merry heart doeth good like medicine," would never have subscribed to the Ordinance of the Second Council of

12

Carthage—"If any monk or clerk utters jocular words causing laughter let him be excommunicated." Can we not detect a touch of humor in some of the figures of speech Solomon employed to drive home a truth? For instance, what bitter contempt is found in the statement applied to the slacker, "Go to the ant, thou sluggard, consider her ways and be wise" (Prov. 6:6). Here the ant is before us as an example of industry and energy and economy—a contrast to humans who are lazy and indolent (see Prov. 26:14-15). Then there is the illustration about the crib being clean where no oxen are found (Prov. 14:4). This is an extension of the lesson of the ant and the sluggard. It is easy to be lazy, hard to go hungry. If a farmer has no oxen, of course, the crib will be clean—no fodder to furnish and no litter to clean out. But think of what is lost by not having the strength of the oxen to plow the field and pull the loads! Monks may return to a monastery for a life of contemplation and be clear and clean of the dust and turmoil of the world, but the world suffers from their absence from it and their work in it.

Solomon also used the figure of a living dog being better than a dead lion (Eccles. 9:4). Dead, the king of beasts loses its strength and majesty. The dog, although held in low esteem in the East, is superior to a dead lion in that it can be tamed and made to fulfill a good purpose. Humor is likewise found in the allegory Solomon gives us of a great king who came against a city and besieged it, and how one poor wise man within the city delivered it by his cunning (Eccles. 9:14-18; see also 10:10). Throughout the Bible, then, the many facets of humor—wit, satire, irony, retort, ridicule, and other forms of the ludicrous can be traced. Discussing this humorous element in Scripture, Dr. A. T. Pierson observes—

> Humour has its legitimate place, province, and office, even in sacred things. Being one of the faculties in man, it affords a medium and a channel of approach and appeal. Ridicule is sometimes a keener

and more effective weapon than argument—the only answer which some assaults on truth or errors in teaching and practice deserve. But like other sharp weapons, it requires careful handling, and it is one of the marks of perfection in the Word of God that we are instructed by example as to its proper uses and the avoidance of its abuses.

The Gospels tell us that "Jesus wept," but are silent as to His laughter and wholesome humor. Surely He must have had an engaging smile to attract the children to His knee. He knew that sarcasm was a potent weapon and He used it most effectively. But He never employed humorous, ironic figures of speech merely for effect. The humor He used did not draw attention to itself, or exist only for its own sake. Think of His metaphor about a camel trying to go through the eye of a needle; or of blind men leading the blind, and all falling into a ditch; or of describing Herod as a cunning cruel fox! For withering irony our Lord's somewhat humorous illustrations are incomparable.

Going back to the Old Testament, can we not detect intentional humor in the spectacular and impressive conflict between Elijah and the prophets of Baal on Mount Carmel (I Kings 18)? The pagan prophets called in vain for fire to kindle the sacrificial bullock. Elijah, mocking them, said, "Cry aloud: for he is a god; either he is talking, or pursuing, or he is in a journey, or *peradventure he sleepeth and must be awaked.*" The sting is in the tail of such an ironic taunt, for how could a *god* talk so loud as not to hear the cry of his suppliants, or fall into a dead sleep and not be able to hear?

Another bit of unconscious humor can be traced in Gideon who had *seventy sons.* No wonder! "He had many wives" (Judg. 8:30)! We moderns may smile at some of the quaint language of the old translators of the Bible, but humor is there. We are told that Asa was diseased in his feet and that the disease spread, so much so that he sought, not the Lord, but the physicians for relief from his loathsome malady. With what result? "Asa slept with his fathers" (II Chron. 16:12-15). Had he sought the Lord, the implication is that he might not have joined his departed relatives so soon. The same touch of humor is seen in the incident related by Jesus of a woman suffering for twelve years from an issue of blood, and who "suffered many things of many physicians," and who when she had spent every penny she had was worse than before (Mark 5:25-26). They were physicians of no value (Job 13:4).

The same quaint touch can be found in the account of the slaughter of the Assyrians who became *dead corpses* (II Kings 19:35). How expressive is the redundancy here! David, too, knew how to use terms humorous yet ironic. We have, for example, his protest to Saul about pursuing him as a *dead dog,* and as a *flea* (I Sam. 24:14; 26:20). These homely but vivid similes are readily understood by Orientals. Nothing was so loathed by the Hebrews as a dead dog, and David accuses Saul of treating him as such. As for the figure of the flea, the original is more emphatic, "a single flea." Fleas were a universal pest in Palestine where they abounded in a degree not known elsewhere. Saul was hunting for David as "one flea"— description of extreme insignificance. David was a flea not easily caught, one who easily escaped, but who, if he had been caught, would have been poor game for the royal hunter.

Samson stands out in Scripture as an example of the mischievous *abuse* of the ludicrous. Dr. A. T. Pierson speaks of him as "the representative wag of Scripture, in whom humour runs mad, the element of the ridiculous in this case being carried to the extreme, as if for warning. Samson's riddle about the carcass of the lion has an element of wit about it, just as bitter sarcasm is found in his condemnation of the Philistines for plowing with his heifer—a reference to his wife (Judg. 14:14-18)." After his slaughter of the Philistines, Samson celebrated his victory by an utterance in which he skillfully played on words. "With the jawbone of an ass, heaps upon heaps, with the jaw of an ass have I slain a thousand men" (15:16). The original Hebrew for "ass" is almost equivalent to that of the word for "heaps." Wordsworth reproduces the verse, "With the jaw bone of an ass, a mass, two masses," etc. But a Jewish writer suggests as an approach to the witty original the setting—*"I ass—ass—inated them."*

Another humorous incident can be found at the fords of Jordan where the Gileadites forced the Ephraimites to pronounce the Hebrew word *Shibboleth.* They had difficulty, however, in pronouncing the *sh,* just as a German friend of mine has difficulty with the English *w* and always pronounces it as a *v,* so "wonderful" is "vonderful" to him. Because the Ephraimites could not frame to pronounce Shibboleth right and said "Sibboleth," the loss of the *h* cost them their lives (Judg. 12:6). Dr. Pierson remarks that "this word has passed into our language to indicate the test word, pet phrase, or trifling peculiarity, which becomes the watchword of a party or the test of orthodoxy, and may give rise to bitter warfare between sects and persecuting bigotry and intolerance."

Isaiah's account of the abysmal folly of idolatry cannot be equaled. What humor, in the form of irony, the prophet manifested when he described the idolator as one feeding on ashes as out of part of a tree he carves out a god to worship (see Jer. 10:1-16), and another part he burns to warm himself and to cook his food. Thus, "the log he burns and turns to ashes is identical with the god he adores" (Isa. 44:9-20). Further, there is a hint of comedy in poetic retribution as in the case of Adoni-bezek who was paid back in his own coin (Judg. 1:5-7); and in the experience that befell Haman when he perished on the gallows he had prepared for Mordecai (Esther 8:7). Paul likewise knew how to use divine sarcasm. In many of his paradoxes he also betrayed a sense of humor, as, for example, when he wrote about "idle tattlers and busybodies"

(I Tim. 5:13). They were idle in all that was good, but industrious in evil. "Hands hanging down for want of work, but tongues always swinging with gossip—active in meddling and mischief making." Paul's illustration about "itching ears" has a humorous touch about it as he employed it as a ludicrous rebuke in his exposure of error and vindication of the truth (II Tim. 4:3). An itch in the ears is as bad as in any other part of the body, perhaps worse. Behind the apostle's amusing metaphor is a reference "to swine that, having the scurvy, seek relief for itching ears by rubbing them against stone heaps." Thus Paul ridicules those who like to hear false teachers who give them mere pleasure (Acts 17:19-21) and do not offend by truths that grate on the ears and disturb the conscience. It was Horace, the Roman poet and satirist who said—

> For a man learns more quickly and remembers more
> easily that which he laughs at, than that which he
> approves and reveres.

Second Summary
The Emphasis on Determination in Scripture

All who read the Bible carefully are impressed by the fact that certain words stand out like a range of mountain peaks against the sky of Scripture. And such a word study is most profitable as we gather together references to an outstanding word, noting the significance of each peak as we pursue our search. One such word is a strong, resolute, and forceful term occurring in some form or other over thirty times in the Bible. It is the word *determination. Termination* implies an ending, but *determine* means to set down limits or bounds to something, as when you determine to perform a task. From the several places where this compelling word occurs we have divine determination, satanic determination, and Christian determination.

Divine Determination

The idea of fixity, inflexibility, tenacity of purpose is characteristic of the nature of God. His resolution to stand by or adhere to His promises and prophecies is prominently featured in Scripture. "I am the Lord, I change not" (Mal. 3:6). Here is a summary of some of the passages dealing with this specific trait in the divine character. "God hath determined to destroy thee" (II Chron. 25:16).

The word translated "determine" in this instance carries the idea of giving counsel. The unknown prophet declared the doom of Amaziah because of his idolatry. God had given His counsel and He would abide by it because of His intense hatred for the graven images which robbed Him of His glory

18

and honor. With ruthless determination He was out to destroy all that aspired to the place He alone should occupy on the throne of the human heart. This is the thought expressed by the prophet Isaiah in these pages—"For the Lord God of Hosts, shall make a consumption, even determined, in the midst of all the land" (10:23). "He hath determined against it" (19:17). "A consumption, even determined upon the whole earth" (28:22). Godly reformers, burdened about the social evils of their times, have reflected something of this divine determination to exterminate them. "Seeing his days are determined" (Job 14:5).

The term as used here means "to move sharply," "cut off." This reveals the true thought of the passage, namely, that the days of the patriarch were measured, appointed, cut off. As "God is the length of our life and days," then, seeing He is the Lord of life, He determines how long a man shall live. If it is His purpose to take away a child from any home, then no power can withhold the fair flower from being removed. As He gave, so He can take away. If it is His desire that a person should go the whole length of the allotted span, or beyond it, then He cannot be robbed of His purpose. Our span of life is as long as God determines. We stay or go at His pleasure and bidding—"He hath determined the times before appointed, and the bounds of their habitation" (Acts 17:26).

Luke the historian uses the word *horigo* for the English "determined." The implication at this point is that the seasons referred to which God ordained for seedtime and harvest, summer and winter, day and night which are fixed by divine decree, make the earth a fitting abode for men. He also fixes, or determines, the bounds of their habitations, or where they cannot dwell. This is why different nations live in different parts of the globe. Thus God determines not only how long a man shall live but where he shall live. "Seventy weeks are determined . . . desolations are determined . . . that determined shall be poured upon the desolate . . . then that that is determined shall be done" (Dan. 9:24, 26-27; 11:36).

The Revised Version gives the word *decreed* for *determined*. These passages in Daniel's prophetic book revolve around the stupendous truth relating to the end of Gentile reign or dominion on the earth. While it is not possible to outline in this present summary all that is involved in the various aspects of Gentile rule and overthrow as Christ returns to usher in His glorious reign, the truth emphasized by the prophet is that the Stone out of the mountain—the type of the power of Christ in judgment—is the divinely decreed method of the consummation of Gentile history.

As the righteous judge, He will be inflexible, unwavering, unyielding in His purpose to abolish all that is wrong, and to diadem that which is right. Meantime, amid the increasing corruption of the world, we are to be patient seeing the Judge is at the door (James 5:9). "My determination is to gather the nations . . . to pour upon them mine indignations" (Zeph. 3:8). All the glories awaiting the redeemed, and all the desolations involved in the overthrow of the anti-Christian forces by the all-conquering Christ must be fully realized, seeing He has decreed them. "The Son of man goeth, as it was determined" (Luke 22:22).

Horigo is also employed in this passage related to divine determination. This word means "to mark out, to divide, make, or set a boundary." It is the foundation of our English word *horizon,* implying "that which bounds." Here, *determination* is linked with *termination,* or *conclusion,* "the end of the way." Luke expresses the same truth of Christ's determination to die, and of the firm resolve of cruel men to crucify Him. "Him, being delivered by the determinate counsel and foreknowledge of God" (Acts 2:23); and "to do whatsoever thy hand and thy counsel determined [Revised Version, "foreordained"] before to be done" (Acts 4:28).

The Greek word *proorigo,* means, "to mark out beforehand," here the Revised Version translation "foreordained." Christ came as the Lamb slain *before* the foundation of the world. *Born* a Saviour, He was actually "born crucified."

Such a death as Jesus died was, therefore, irrevocable, for God had decreed it from the past eternity as the means of the sinner's salvation. The divine and human factors involved in the death of the cross is expressed by Peter in his sermon— "Him, being delivered by the determinate counsel and fore-knowledge of God, ye have taken, and by wicked hands have crucified and slain" (Acts 2:23).

When we read that Jesus set His face steadfastly toward Jerusalem, we have evidence of His cooperation with God in such a decreed death. There must have been the look of unshakeable resolve on that strong face of His as He walked so assuredly to Calvary. Christopher Smart, of the seventeenth century, in his majestic poem "Song of David," hints at this in the last verse—

> Glorious—more glorious is the crown
> Of Him that brought salvation down
> By meekness, call'd Thy Son;
> Thou that stupendous truth believ'd,
> And now the matchless deed's achiev'd
> Determined, dared, and done.

Perhaps a word or two are in order as to the two distinct aspects of the mystery of the cross referred to in Peter's declaration.

The Historical Aspect—"Ye have taken and by wicked hands have crucified and slain."

This blackest crime of all history was perpetrated by those who were morally responsible for the dark deed of the cross. Jew and Gentile alike took part in a cruel action, as deliberate as it was diabolical. They would not have this Man to reign over them. Peter declared that Pilate was determined to let Jesus go (Acts 3:13), but that the Jews desired a murderer in His place. Pilate pronounced Jesus innocent, and knew

21

that it was not right to keep Him as a prisoner; yet he allowed his determination to weaken, evaporate, and parted with Christ against his better judgment.

The Divine Aspect—"Delivered by the determinate counsel . . . of God."

The cross, then, was no afterthought on His part but was "marked out beforehand." In the dateless past, "love drew salvation's plan." Peter makes no effort to demonstrate the logical consistency of these two aspects, but simply presents them as facts. Later on we read, "For of a truth against thy holy child Jesus, whom thou hast anointed, both Herod, and Pontius Pilate, with the Gentiles, and the people of Israel, were gathered together, for to do whatsoever *thy* hand and *thy* counsel determined *before* to be done" (4:27-28). Such a passage indicates that God made the passions which the enemies of Jesus indulged in, and perverted, to be the instruments of working out His will. When men suppose they are choosing their own way, the end is shaped by God, rough hew them as men will. Yet they must bear the blame for their misdeeds in spite of the fact of God's foreordained purpose.

Satanic Determination

If fixity of purpose is characteristic of God's purpose in the extermination of evil, and in the preservation of His redeemed children, Satan is just as determined to destroy all divine aims and to further his own diabolical ends. He is unshaken, unwavering, immoveable, and staunch in his plan to go to eternal doom dragging as many deluded souls with him as he can. Saul is a tragic example of satanic resolve, as a casual glance at his career quickly proves. Saul's constant hatred toward David is a reflection of Satan's antagonism toward Christ and His own.

"Evil is determined by [Saul]" (I Sam. 20:7, 9; 5:17). The threefold repetition of this phrase indicates how deep-seated Saul's determination to kill young David was. Because King David is a fitting type of Christ in many ways, we can see in Saul's decided effort to slay David, a glimpse of the hatred Satan manifested toward Christ in the days of His flesh.

"Evil is determined against our master" (I Sam. 25:17). "Evil is determined against [Haman] by the king" (Esther 7:7). Several passages emphasize the association of *evil* with determination, and they all prove how the enemy of our souls is unyielding in his persistence to rob us of the best God has for us. But in this fact we can rest that if we are truly the Lord's: Satan cannot rob us of Him for we are His forever, and no one—not even Satan—can pluck us out of His hand. What he does strive to do is to plunder us of the fullness of blessing the Lord seeks to bestow upon His own. Therefore, it is imperative for us to be constant in our endeavor to live near Calvary, for He who died there is our only shelter from the dark, sinister, and persistent forces of evil to impede our spiritual progress.

Christian Determination

Constancy and resoluteness are to be the hallmark of the saint, as well as of the Saviour, and, in a wrong sense, of Satan. A group of passages outline our need of the same constant, unbending, immoveable attitude toward all that is of God. It is a most unworthy kind of determination when a Christian is set in his purpose not to put wrong things right, or not to fully obey every express command because of his own preconceived ideas and prejudices. But Scripture extols the right kind of determination which is as a flame from the divine beacon.

> His way once chose, he forward thrust outright
> Nor turned aside for danger or delight.

23

Asahel, who refused to turn aside from following Abner, sealed his dogged perseverance not to turn aside to the right-hand or to the left with his heart's blood (II Sam. 2:19-24). No wonder those who passed the spot where Asahel fell down dead because he would not budge, stood still in reverence. May fixity of purpose, tenacity, courage to adhere to the truth of God through thick and thin, be ours!

"And Solomon determined to build an house for the . . . Lord" (II Chron. 2:1).

The Revised Version gives us "purposed to build." It was the ambition of Solomon's father, David, to erect such a house of worship, but he was divinely prohibited to accomplish this worthy aim because he had shed blood. Yet, before his death, David made full provision for the building of the temple, and when Solomon came to the throne he manifested a deep-seated determination to erect a magnificent structure for the worship of God.

Solomon presents us with an expressive type of the present, undiverted purpose of the Holy Spirit to complete the building of the church which is the Lord's body. For almost two millenniums now, the Spirit has been unceasing in His efforts to consummate the expressed purpose of Jesus to build His church. As the shadow of judgment appears to be falling upon the world, and the rapture of saints not far distant, it would seem as if the last living stones are being added to the building of God, His habitation through the Spirit. May a similar dogged perseverance be ours in the work of the Lord! Let us not be like the man Jesus pictured who began to build but was not able to finish.

"The disciples determined to send relief unto the brethren which dwelt in Judea" (Acts 11:29).

The church today could do with a little more of the determination of the church at Antioch as it sought to help the needy saints elsewhere. In the last few years there has been a tremendous upsurge to relieve the distressed, famine-stricken, and impoverished millions in various parts of the world. Christian and secular organizations have been, and are, conspicuous in saving many from starvation. Luke, however, was writing of the Christian community at Judea in dire need of relief, and, as the Lord's, we must not forget our prior responsibility to relieve our brothers and sisters in Christ who are in severe distress, physically and financially. We must set our minds to do good to those in the household of faith who are afflicted in many ways. If we cannot send relief to the brave, persecuted saints in China and Russia, we can intercede for them that God will rebuke the persecutors for the sake of His own.

"They determined [Revised Version: "appointed"] that Paul and Barnabas . . . should go" (Acts 15:2).

A question of most vital importance is associated with the appointment of Paul and Barnabas by the church at Antioch to go up to Jerusalem. God had opened the door of faith to the Gentiles, independent of the observance of ceremonial rites and laws. But many of the Jews were unwilling to cast aside the prejudices of the old religion of Judaism, and were thus unwilling to receive the Gentiles freely. But the church had been brought into existence through the free, unmerited favor of God, and as the apostles had nailed their colors to such a mast, they were determined never to surrender them.

We cannot but admire the unyielding perseverance of those early saints to magnify the grace of God, and to doggedly maintain that salvation was without works. The word used here for "determined" means to arrange, or set in order as soldiers. God has arranged the truths of His free grace, and dying love, in orderly fashion, and it is our solemn responsibility to declare to legal-bound souls the freedom salvation imparts.

"Barnabas determined to take with them ... Mark" (Acts 15:37).

The Greek and some of the best authorities give the weaker word "wished," or as the margin of the Revised Version puts it, "was minded," for the stronger term "determined." There must, however, have been a most resolute purpose on the part of Barnabas to take John Mark, although he had proved himself somewhat unsatisfactory for missionary service. Because of the sharp division over this matter, two very close and splendid workers separated. John Mark, of course, was the nephew of Barnabas, and as blood is thicker than water, the family relationship may have perverted Barnabas's better judgment.

Both Paul and Barnabas were equally determined not to give way on the matter of Mark, yet it would seem as if Paul was right in his resolve, seeing the church commended his decision. The sorrowful feature is that from that cleavage, Barnabas passed out of sacred history and is never heard of again. Often an unbending and decided attitude on certain matters between friends where a vital principle is at stake results in a lamentable separation. If the honor of Scripture, and the glory of God are involved, then there must be an unflinching stand, no matter how great the cost of such consecrated determination. This was the spirit of Martin Luther when he chose to leave Rome—"Here I stand! God help me! I can do no other."

" ... it shall be determined [Revised Version: "settled"] in a lawful assembly" (Acts 19:39).

According to E. Bullinger, the word employed here for "determined" implies "to let loose (as dogs), of letters to break open, to solve." The town clerk's judicious handling of the uproar preserved Paul from a rough mauling by a mob of enraged Ephesians. A legal mind saved Paul by urging the complainers to take the matter in question to a court where it could be rightly decided.

"For Paul determined to sail by Ephesus" (Acts 20:16).

The reason behind the apostolic resolve was the desire to be in Jerusalem on the Day of Pentecost—a day of great memories. Would that we had the same impelling motive to remember the Lord in His appointed way, and to prosecute His command to evangelize the lost!

"I have determined to send Paul" (Acts 25:25).

Back of the pompous declaration of Festus regarding Paul's appearance before King Agrippa was the fulfillment of God's prophetic utterance at Paul's conversion. "He is a chosen vessel unto me, to bear my name before . . . kings" (Acts 9:15).

"It was determined that we should sail into Italy" (Acts 27:1).

In this instance we have an illustration of how God used a human agency to bring the apostle Paul to Rome, thereby fulfilling His servant's great desire "to see Rome also," and also to give him the opportunity of preaching the gospel in the then "mistress of the world." Determination brought Paul to Rome where ultimately he died for the Lord he dearly loved.

"For I determined not to know any thing among you save Jesus Christ and him crucified" (I Cor. 2:2).

This forceful word, occurring so often as it does in Paul's life, proves him to have been a man of resolute will, and of unshakeable convictions. Renan, the brilliant French skeptic,

27

referred to Paul as "the ugly little Jew." But he must have had a face that, once seen, was never forgotten, a face bearing the imprint of inflexibility, tenacity, and fixedness of purpose. The photograph of David Livingstone, the renowned Scottish missionary to Africa, is a study of unflinching courage. What an unbending, unwavering, and determined countenance! After that dramatic meeting between Livingstone and Stanley in the dark continent, the resolute explorer-missionary refused to return to England in spite of Stanley's plea. "I still have much work to do," Livingstone said, and on he trudged until one day just before dawn the natives found his lifeless form kneeling by the crude bed, his head resting upon his gnarled, clasped hands.

Can you not picture Paul's face as he condemned the Corinthians for their puffed-up pride and fleshly wisdom, and recorded the great evangelical determination "not to know any thing, save Jesus Christ, and him crucified"? Not only was Paul bent on refusing to speak on any other theme, but he will *know* no other. It was without controversy a portentous determination to have the crucified Saviour fill the whole horizon of his mind and heart.

Among all the "determinations" of Scripture this, surely, is the immediate and abiding one—a dominating ideal we must never surrender if we, too, would be true knights of the crucified Son of God. Probably, the determination of Paul to limit his Christology to "even him as being crucified" represents a temptation conquered, a soul-conflict won. To such an one as the apostle, it would be a trial of spirit to contemplate service in such a city as Corinth. As Dinsdale T. Young expresses it—

> Corinth was a centre of fashion. Shall he essay to appeal to the fashionable crowd with Christ *crucified* as the central theme? Will he not repel them thus? May he not emphasize other aspects of Christ which will be attractive and not repellant? Thus the

evil one would ply him. But the God of peace crushed Satan under his feet and his splendid, "I determined" rings out. Corinth was an aesthetic city. Its architecture is a proverb still, and its brasses are famous now. Corinth was an intellectual city. Its typical Greek love of philosophy all men know.

Corinth was an opulent commercial city too. Shall he not soften the truth and smooth his message? Will not taste, and culture, and materialism, and wealth resent the preaching of "Him" crucified? But, "I determined" cries this hero of the cross. He will cry out and shout in the delicate ears of Corinth nothing but the crucified Lord.

Corinth, with all its art and culture and affluence was abominably corrupt. To "Corinthianize" was a synonym for lust. The city seethed with guilt, and was sodden with sin. Its cheek was painted gaily, but its heart was diseased.

Corinth was "a hyperbole of sin," and Paul was a good physician able to diagnose accurately and prescribe unerringly. He knew that to dilate on Christ's teachings and character and lovely deed, would not effect the salvation of the gay town. Only Christ "as having been crucified" could accomplish such a miracle.

There are those who reject this brave determination of Paul as a very narrow one indeed. But such a message of dominating verity is by no means circumscribed, but one "spacious with firmamental infinity. The very catholicity of God breathes in this evangelical determination to preach a crucified Christ." If you read through the apostle's two Letters to the Corinthians you will find that he wrote to them on some twenty different subjects, yet here he is affirming that the *redeeming* Christ is the true center of Christian preaching. May we be found swearing new devotion to Him who died on that wondrous cross for our redemption! May we share Paul's great evangelical determination to preach a crucified Christ, and to live a crucified life!

"I determined this with myself, that I would not come again to you in heaviness" (II Cor. 2:1).

The matters on which Paul had made up his mind and had set himself out on his resolute course to follow was the subject previously stated when he had been called upon to exercise severity of discipline upon a sinning brother. He resolved to remove all such irregularities, so that his visit might be mutually agreeable. The church at Corinth had been too lax in condoning things the early church had to deal with in a drastic manner in order to preserve its spiritual influence in heathen surroundings. In these apostate days, when the professing church seems so impotent to arrest the rising tide of infidelity and iniquity, all because of her departure from the faith as delivered to the saints, leaders need something of the apostolic determination to lovingly discipline those who openly flout the authority of Scripture.

"I have determined there to winter" (Titus 3:12).

Why Paul had firmly made up his mind to winter at Nicopolis we are not told. The name means "City of Victory," and the town was built in honor of the victory Augustus achieved over Mark Antony at Actium. Perhaps the apostle was impressed with the tremendous spiritual need of the place, and because of this determined to spend the winter months there, making it a city of victory for his Lord. Amid the winter of sin, bitter antagonism, and personal trials, he positively decided to live in that city. When winter comes, no matter in what shape and form, may it be our unending desire to live in our spiritual *Nicopolis*—Calvary, our city of continual victory over the world, flesh, and the devil.

Third Summary
The Divine Inability in Scripture

It may come as a surprise to you to learn that the Lord God Almighty is found saying, "I cannot" (Isa. 1:13). Faith delights to feed upon the ability of God, and to rest in the affirmation of Job concerning Him, "Thou canst do every thing" (Job 42:2). Yet, as we are to see, there are some things that God cannot do. The story is told of Napoleon who wanted cannons conveyed over the Alps and consulted his engineers as to the project. They said that the task was impossible. "Impossible," snapped Napoleon, "never mention that hateful word in my presence again. It is not in my vocabulary." But we know from what followed that the word was very much there.

"Impossible" *is* a word in God's vocabulary. Certainly His power is unlimited in the material world. He could roll back the sea for Israel, make the sun stand still for Joshua, and turn it back on its course for Hezekiah. The miracles of Jesus prove that "all power in heaven and on earth" was His. In the material and natural realms, "the sweet omnipotence of love" is clearly manifest. But when it comes to the moral and spiritual realms, God is confronted with glorious impossibilities, as Joseph was when he said to his lustful temptress, "I cannot do this great wickedness." G. Bernard Shaw, in *Man and Superman* has the phrase, "He who can, does. He who cannot teaches." God can do mighty things—and does. But there are some things He cannot do, and this teaches us the significance of His inability.

31

> "The new moons and sabbaths . . . I cannot away with; it is iniquity, even the solemn meeting" (Isa. 1:13).

The evident teaching of the narrative is that certain religious observances and ordinances were intermixed with sin and iniquity, and that God abhorred such a mixture. It was hateful to Him, and He could not, therefore, sanction or condone unreal ceremonialism or hypocrisy. The same severe condemnation is found in the scathing denunciation of the hypocrites by Jesus in Matthew 23. If there is anything heaven cannot stand it is sham, or mere make-believe. Those who profess to be holy must be honorable. Life must be pure if it is to be pleasing to God.

Our modern age is one of unreality, superficiality, a mixture of true and false, and there is dire need of preachers to cry out with Jeremiah, "Cursed be he that doeth the work of the Lord deceitfully" (48:10). As we diagnose the seemingly religious life of many today we find that some go to church and assume a religious exterior in order to advance their social, material, and financial position. Others go to cover up their shortcomings. A garment of religion covers unholy transactions. Church associations divert attention from unworthy practices. Then there are those who connect themselves to a church, not out of any deep need of personal worship, but simply out of habit. There are others who minister in holy things, but who are yet unregenerate, and hostile to deeply spiritual service. The sons of Eli were priests *before* the Lord, but not *of* Him, for they knew Him not.

Isaiah records the divine inability to have anything to do with the "solemn meeting," simply because the lives of those attending it robbed it of any real solemnity. Did not Jesus say of some who taught in His name, "I know you not"? He had to condemn the church at Laodicea because it had kept

Him outside its so-called sacred precincts. "I stand at the door and knock." What a travesty—a church without the Christ! To a very large degree, modern religion must be hateful to God, and He cannot condone it.

He Cannot Condone Sin

> "Thou art of purer eyes than to behold evil and canst not look upon iniquity [Revised Version: "perverseness"]" (Hab. 1:13).

This estimation of the divine character does not mean that God cannot see sin. He does see it as no other can, and is grieved. When Jesus beheld the gross sin of Jerusalem, He wept. A skeptic said to a Christian worker, "If I could see what your God sees, my heart would break." The reply was, "God's heart did break at Calvary over all He saw." What the prophet means is that God cannot look upon iniquity with approval, or countenance anything alien to His holy mind and will. Pitying our failures and weaknesses, He cannot wink His eye at them, or gloss them over.

How grateful we should be that we have a God who cannot be lenient with sin! He cannot approve evil because of its dire results, and because of all it cost Him. In these days of growing laxity multitudes have no idea of the sinfulness of sin. Writers, artists, and playwrights make fortunes by appealing to the animal in man. The production of anything suggestive is the best-paying business on the stage and screen. As Christians, we have become so accustomed to sinful sights that we do not feel the shame and abhorrence of evil that we ought to. James tells us, "God cannot be tempted with evil" (1:13). But, alas! we do not share the divine hatred and disapproval of iniquity in any shape or form. Yet to be Godlike is to loathe sin, yet love the sinner, seeking to win him for the One who died to save him from all iniquity.

In these days of intense pornographic pressure, it is increasingly difficult not to look upon iniquity or to behold evil. May purer vision be ours! Said Job, "I have made a covenant with mine eyes." May the Lord enable us to guard our eye-gates so that nothing shall pass through them to destroy our purity and peace of heart.

> O Holy Spirit, keep us pure,
> Grant us Thy strength when sins allure;
> Our bodies are Thy temple, Lord;
> Be Thou in thought and act adored.

He Cannot Consider His Own Comfort

Another glorious impossibility can be found in the taunt flung at the Saviour as He died upon the tree—"He saved others: himself he cannot save" (Matt. 27:43). The foes paid Him an unwitting tribute when they said, "He saved others." What self-abnegation was His! The giving of Himself to others in His ministry among men reached its climax when, at Calvary, He gave His life to save the lost. He gave Himself for our sins. But those rejectors greatly erred when they said, "Himself he cannot save." Because of all He was in Himself as the Mighty God, and Creator of the wood on which He hung, and of those who nailed Him to it, He could have called fire down from heaven upon His crucifiers and stepped down from His cross a triumphant victor.

To those around the cross it appeared to be true—"Look at that blood-spattered man, unable to do anything for Himself, although in the days of His flesh, He was the miracle-worker." But such a limitation was self-imposed. Jesus did not use the power He possessed to relieve Himself from the anguish He endured. He denied self-action. Did He not say that power was His to lay down His life and to take it up again? Therefore, His life was not forcibly taken by cruel men; rather, it was freely given. He could have saved Himself, but, glory to His name, He did not. Had He saved Himself we would have been of all men most miserable. The only way by which Jesus could atone for sin and deliver us from it was to hang there—and hang He did!

The nails that kept Him on that tree were not those made of wood or metal. Those rough spikes were only the symbols of these nails—satisfying the claims of the broken Law, and of God's holiness, justice, and righteousness; self-abnegation, and obedience to the Father's will; passion to redeem man from sin; love, unfathomable love for sinners; determination to conquer the devil and hell. He knew that He would conquer death by dying. These, then, were the nails that kept Him from saving Himself. In his most moving chapter on "Why Do the Innocent Suffer?" Bishop Fulton Sheen, in *Life Is Worth Living,* has the paragraph—

> At the broken Person of Christ on the Cross, we begin to see the full gravity of sin. We see there our own autobiography. The Cross is the desk upon which it is written, His blood is the ink. His nails the pen. His flesh the parchment. We see our evil thoughts in the Crown of Thorns, our avarice is the Hands that are pierced with nails, our wanderings away from the path of goodness is the Feet pinned with nails. And all our false loves are the open and rent side.

Because Jesus did not save Himself, His death was a voluntary one. He did not consider His own comfort, but willingly surrendered Himself to men to do their worst. Does the principle of willing sacrifice govern our lives, or are we prone to save ourselves from identification with His cross? Did not Jesus say that trying to save our lives, we lose them, but that, in losing them for His sake we find them?

> Live for self—you live in vain;
> Live for Christ—you live again.

He Cannot Be Inconsistent with Himself

It was Paul who used the pertinent phrase of Jesus, "He cannot deny himself" (II Tim. 2:13)—of which Bengel, the renowned expositor said, "This impossibility is worthy of praise"—and so it is! In the context, Paul contrasts God with ourselves, "If we deny him . . . he abideth faithful: he cannot deny himself." We deny Him and prove to be inconsistent toward God, ourselves, and others, but there has never been the least flicker in the lamp of divine faithfulness. What a helpless, hopeless world ours would be if an inconsistent God controlled it! How we should give thanks at the remembrance of His unstained holiness! Had there been the slightest flaw in His divine character, then God would not be infallible, or have any right to act as God.

But the Almighty, Perfect One cannot act contrary to His own being and nature. He must be righteous and just in all His ways. "Your Father in heaven is perfect," was the testimony of His Son. He cannot, therefore, be untrue to Himself. He would be inconsistent if He treated saved and unsaved alike, failing to punish sin. (The laws of our country demand justice—shall we deny to God what man himself demands?) He would be inconsistent if He allowed those redeemed by the blood, and regenerated by the Holy Spirit to be finally lost, seeing that Jesus said, "No man is able to pluck them out of my Father's hand."

He would be inconsistent if He did not heed the penitent cry of a lost soul, for He said, "Whosoever shall call upon the name of the Lord shall be saved." He would be inconsistent if He did not answer prayer in accordance with His will, for He promised, "Ask, and ye shall receive." Too often, our bonds and promises are quickly made, and as quickly broken, but God can never go back on any promise He has made.

The greatest hindrance in effective Christian witness today is that of inconsistency. Equity has fallen upon the streets. What we are often contradicts what we say. We deny ourselves. May God grant that our character and conduct will ever be harmoniously blended, of one piece, as was the garment Jesus wore!

He Cannot Lie

The idea of God's inability to depart from truth pervades Scripture. "The Cretians are always liars," Paul says, and by way of contrast, "God . . . cannot lie" (Titus 1:12, 2). "God is not a man that he should lie" (Num. 23:19). "The strength of Israel will not lie" (I Sam. 15:29). "It [is] impossible for God to lie" (Heb. 6:18). What a great comfort it is for the saint to know that, as he continues living in a world of liars, he has a God who cannot lie! Scripture often reminds us that He is the God of truth and, therefore, hates all forms of lying, dishonesty, deceit, and craftiness.

"Lying lips are an abomination unto the Lord: but they that deal truly are his delight" (Prov. 12:22). It might have been in haste that David said, "All men are liars," but is it not true that such an estimation describes present day humanity? We have business and commercial lies; political lies; religious lies, such as Ananias and Sapphira were guilty of. But God cannot lie—the Word declares it; the fulfillment of His promises confirms it; experience affirms it. Among those finally excluded from the Kingdom are "liars" (Rev. 21:8, 27). May we be constantly delivered from all semblance of lying—even from telling what we call "white lies"! By His grace and power we must aspire to be like Him—a God that cannot lie!

He Cannot Save Apart from the Human Will

The reason sin intruded into God's fair universe was because, when God created man, He did not fashion him as a machine with no power of choice. God endowed man with freedom of will, and the history of sin is the use of this gift against the Giver.

> Our wills are ours, we know not why.
> Our wills are ours, to make them Thine.

But Adam and Eve became sinners when they willingly thwarted the divine will. God could not keep our first parents in that original Paradise against their will, seeing He had endowed them with liberty of choice. Jesus recognized this aspect of divine inability when He said of those who rejected His love and mercy—"How often would I have gathered thy children together . . . and ye would not" (Luke 13:34). Then we read that when He came into His own country "he did not many mighty works there because of their unbelief" (Matt. 13:58).

When it comes to the deliverance of a soul from the tyranny of sin, the battle is fought in the region of the will. God is willing to save. The preacher seeking to win souls manifests the divine will. The devil, however, exerts his will against the divine will, and works upon the will of the one who hears the gospel. Once a soul is willing to be saved, the battle is won. An awful responsibility, therefore, rests upon the sinner to say, "I will arise and go to my Father." But if he lingers in his sin, and is indifferent to the divine entreaty, then the sinner seals his own doom, for God cannot save him against his will. He never forces an entrance into the human heart. "*If* any man open the door . . . I will come in to him."

In Tonbridge, Kent, there is a monument to a company of gypsies, who, after picking hops in a field, set out to cross from one side of the Medway to the other when the river was in flood. They were drowned. A young man crept into a trench where the bodies were laid out, and kneeling down beside one corpse cried, "Mother, mother, I tried to save you; I did all a man could do to save you, but you would not let me." Is this not also the divine wail? Think of the Master's sob of unwanted love over Jerusalem sinners when, in effect, he bemoaned, "I did all a God could do to save you, but you would not let Me." But what instant emancipation there is when the sinner reaches the point of surrender, and cries—

> Nay, Lord, I yield, I yield
> I can no longer hold.
> I sink by dying love compelled,
> And own Thee—Conqueror!

Fourth Summary
The Virtue of Thoroughness in Scripture

One of the arresting features of Scripture is the way simple, ordinary phrases seem to leap out of the page and compel us to stop to discover sublime truths from the homely words that go to form them. For instance, after Joshua assumed the leadership of Israel we read that "he left nothing undone of all that the Lord [had] commanded Moses" (Josh. 11:15). The phrase, "he left nothing undone," testifies to the thoroughness with which Joshua carried out the divine instructions committed to his late chief, Moses, the servant of God. He did not complete *some* of those commands but *all* of them. As a true soldier, Joshua's love of obedience would not allow him to rest until he had fulfilled every detail of the last words of Israel's lawgiver. Conscientiousness in carrying out the divine will is, therefore, the conspicuous trait in Joshua's character. But the sentence "he left nothing undone" bristles with most suggestive thoughts and applications.

The Perfection of Creation

In the divine record of creation we read, "Thus the heavens and the earth were finished and all the host of them" (Gen. 2:1). On the seventh day, the Creator rested from His work, and as He looked at the completed product said, "It is very good." It was thoroughly perfect, with no loose ends to be tied up. In the adaptation of both man and beast to the world in which they were to live, God left nothing undone, even down to the minutest details. It is not difficult for faith to believe that the world and man, formed by a

40

definite creative act, were perfect as they came from the hand of the Creator. Nothing was forgotten or overlooked. Thoroughness stamps creation.

The Completeness of Provision

Once settled in the Land of Promise allocated among the tribes of Israel, Joshua recorded, "There failed not ought of any good thing which the Lord had spoken unto the house of Israel; all came to pass" (Josh. 21:45). Here again is evidence of thoroughness in divine dealings. What the Lord had promised with His lips, He fulfilled with His hands. There was the total fulfillment of all He had declared. He had left nothing undone in respect to provision for the pilgrim journey of His people. And what is descriptive of God's dealings with Israel is true of our individual lives, for each of us daily enjoys the totality of His benefactions. If we find ourselves in straits, facing varying needs, God reveals Himself as Jehovah-Jireh who has left nothing undone in all that is necessary for our well-being.

The Finality of Revelation

The solemn warning about adding to the words of Scripture, or taking away any of its words, is proof that the Bible is the complete, final, and authoritative revelation of the mind of God to the mind of man (Rev. 21:18-19). "The Law of the Lord is perfect," for He left nothing undone when He inspired holy men of old to set forth "the prophecy of the Scriptures" (II Peter 1:20-21). All we need to know about God, the Saviour, sin, the human heart, life beyond the grave, the destiny of earth, are set forth with a thoroughness we cannot escape. The reason why the Bible is so up-to-date is because God left nothing undone in His description of the world, present, as well as past. Possessing greater wisdom than the wiseacres of today, God knew all about our twentieth century when He inspired the prophets and apostles to set down the truths He wanted the world to read. Momentous happenings of our time were predicted millenniums ago, and prove how absolute Scripture is in its panorama of the ages.

The Fullness of Redemption

When it came to our deliverance from the guilt and power of sin, and the awful consequences of rejecting divine claims, Jesus left nothing undone in the matter of our salvation and security. As He died on the cross, He cried, not as a victim but as a victor—"It is finished!" The superb work of emancipation for the sin-bound was superbly and thoroughly accomplished. Once and for all, by His death and resurrection, Jesus made a full and final provision for a sinning race. Now, all that a sinner can do is to accept by a naked faith the perfect redemption so freely provided. Nothing can be added to such a matchless gift of grace.

> "It is finished!" Jesus cries,
>   I will trust! I will trust!
> As He bows His head and dies!
>   I will trust! I will trust!
> All my load on Him is laid;
>   And my debt He freely paid;
> He my peace with God has made;
>   I will trust! I will trust!

The Ideal of Service

The old adage that if a thing is worth doing it's worth doing well certainly sums up the thoroughness in the attainment of aims on the part of many Bible saints, none of whom left anything undone. Receiving full and complete instructions as to the creation of the tabernacle and the institution of its services, we read that "Moses finished the work," even down to the formation of the necessary tent pins. With such an accomplished task the glory of God filled the sanctuary, for He always crowns the perfect with honor. Boaz certainly did nothing by halves when it came to the redemption of Ruth and the security of her as his bride. "He did not rest until he finished the thing" (Ruth 2:18). To Solomon was granted the privilege of building a temple for the Lord, and through the years of erection, the king was most thorough in the provision of all that was necessary for such a task, and labored on till he "built the house and finished it" (I Kings 6:9, 14). Nehemiah was another who left nothing undone until his vision of a restored city was realized: "So the wall was finished," and that in spite of sneers and scoffs (Neh. 6:5). Paul, inspired by the dying declaration of Jesus—"It is finished" (John 17:6)—could come to his own end by affirming, "I have finished the course" (II Tim. 2:7). How we need the same thoroughness in our service for the Master! Yet how sadly we miss.

The Inspiration of Life

It was the renowned Cicero who said, "Let us do nothing in a spiritless fashion, nor anything timidly, nor anything sluggishly." Ovid, another Roman philosopher, remarked, "Finish thoroughly the work you have set yourself." Would that these words could form your epitaph and mine—"He left nothing undone"! What an inspiration for a full, God-honoring life this reputation that Joshua achieved is for us! Too often, things we have done should have been left undone. All of us are conscious of mistakes and failures we would not make if we could live our life over again. On the other hand, there are some things left undone we should have done. All of us need to join in the Confession contained in *The Book of Common Prayer*—

We have left undone those things which we ought to have done; And we have done those things which we ought not to have done; And there is no health in us.

We are guilty of sins of omission as well as of commission. When David spoke of "secret sins," he referred to those he had committed unconsciously. Whether we are cognizant of it or not, all of us are guilty of partial obedience, imperfect consecration, and defective allegiance. There is a lack of thoroughness, or stickability, about our efforts. We are like the man the Master referred to in one of His peerless parables who "began to build but was not able to finish" (Luke 14:30). Near the town of Ancrum is a site known as "The Baron's Folly," so-named because the nobleman set out to build a magnificent castle but relinquished the task, and the few stumps of stone testify to his lack of constancy.

The historic city of Edinburgh was determined to erect a monument on Calton Hill to the memory of the Scottish soldiers who fought in the Peninsular War and at Waterloo. Such a memorial was to have been a reproduction of the Parthenon at Athens, at a cost of some fifty thousand pounds—a large sum in those days. Out went the appeal, but the response was meager, and after sixteen thousand pounds had been spent the work was suspended. The twelve great pillars, standing out in the skyline and costing one thousand pounds each, look like some ancient ruin. Although admired by architects and builders who have a "feeling for stone," that uncompleted memorial is referred to as "Pride and Poverty," or as "Scotland's Disgrace."

Are we not guilty of beginning to build but not being able to finish? Is not our pathway through life strewn with broken pillars where there should have been a worthwhile edifice? What God expects of us is what He Himself manifested at creation, namely, *consummation*. There are three observations to be made in connection with the fact that our sins of omission prevent completion—

First, they are many in number.

In his *Diary,* the revered Andrew Bonar wrote at the conclusion of one year, "This year omissions have distressed me more than anything." As we come to the end of a year or a life, we have need to be distressed over what we have left undone. The biographer of Charles Darwin said of the renowned scientist, "He never wasted a few spare minutes from thinking that it was not worth while." His golden rule was, "Take care of the minutes," hence, he became rich and accurate in many realms of knowledge.

Do we not think of some things we might have done—tears we might have dried, loads we might have lifted, heartaches we might have eased, souls we might have saved, time we might have used more profitably? Too often, we leave little acts undone in the home and neglect those we should have helped before death claimed them. We evade manifest obligations and work which we ought to face. With what fiery energy the bees, birds, and butterflies carry out their special commission entrusted to them in the natural realm. But we, alas! have gaps, inertia, laziness, procrastination, imperfection, lack of thoroughness, stumps where there should be a stately castle.

Second, they are not to be slighted.

Things left undone are often of great consequence. Mighty issues hang on little things. Emerson speaks of "the science of omitting as a necessary science if things are vulgar, unseemly and nonessential." But to treat some of the small things of life as trivial is suicidal. "A little thing is a little thing: but being faithful in a little thing is a great thing." Did not Jesus say that "he that is faithful in least is faithful in much"? And the former is the gateway to the latter. Too often, however, we leave undone large and noble matters and concentrate on the inferior and unnecessary. We strain at gnats but swallow camels. For instance—

> We shirk work demanding courage and sacrifice, and condescend to please our own pride, or further our own selfish pleasures.
> Great principles are left out of character, because they seem difficult to acquire and maintain.
> Great duties are ignored because they involve heroism, suffering, and self-sacrifice.
> Great opportunities are forfeited because they demand endeavor, resolution, thoroughness, and promptitude.
> Great service is declined because it entails separation from worldly pleasures and pursuits, and utter consecration.

Third, they are to be accounted for.

Can it be that we are as deeply concerned as we ought to be over the things we have done amiss, but less troubled about the things we have left undone? God will hold us responsible for what we have not done, as well as what we have done. It is useless to say we have no gifts, no time, no opportunity to serve, for this is but a way of glossing over the shirking of personal responsibility. Each of us, no matter how simple and ordinary we may be, has a God-given task to complete that no other can do.

> There's a work for Jesus
> Ready at your hand,
> 'Tis a task the Master
> Just for you has planned,

46

Haste to do His bidding,
Yield Him service true;
There's a work for Jesus,
None but you can do.

May grace be ours to crowd into life more passion, purpose, perseverance, and precision! Let us strive to be more prompt, definite, resolute, and thorough. Having put our hand to the plow may we never halt till the end of the furrow is reached. Then, when we reach heaven, it will be said of us as it was of Joshua, "He left nothing undone"!

Fifth Summary
The Significance of Singularity in Scripture

The adjective *singular* means, "individual, distinctive, exceptional, peculiar to oneself." These ideas are embedded in the recurring phrase, "as for me." Doubtless you have observed the frequent occurrence of this arresting triad in the lives of various saints in Bible days, and noticed how they sparkle like gems in the crown of Scripture. These three words bring before us a certain contrast, or separation, as the speaker places himself apart from others. Looking around he sees other men following this and that line of thought and action, and they appear to be in the majority. Their sentiments have all the weight and force of fashion behind them, for what they do has been done from time immemorial. Therefore, he cannot help it if he takes another line under divine compulsion, and risks being thought odd.

However singular, opposite, or peculiar it may seem to say, "As for me," all of those who uttered these words felt that they must set out on another road, or pursue a different course than that the others were taking. Let others live and act as they may, but, "as for me," it must be otherwise. For instance, when David said, "As for me," his life was like a star, dwelling apart. That such a singularity is Godlike is proven by the first occurrence of the phrase where it is applied to God—"As for me, behold my covenant is with thee" (Gen. 17:4). No matter how Abraham had been selfishly treated by Lot, and Abraham himself had been guilty of deception, God was different in that He had set His heart upon Abraham as the progenitor of a mighty race. As we are to find, the quotation marks a strange and forceful spiritual singularity in the lives of those who used it. In *Twelfth Night,* Shakespeare has the line, "Let not thy tongue tang arguments of state; put thyself into the tricks of singularity." But as used by Bible saints, singularity has no trick, but is a conspicuous feature of decision and character.

> Each the known track of sage philosophy
> Deserts, and has a byword of his own;
> So much the restless eagerness to shine,
> And love of singularity, prevail.

The Individuality of Devotion to God

"As for me and my house we will serve the Lord" (Josh. 24:15).

Joshua, the ancient leader of Israel is a fitting illustration of the necessity of the personal element in singularity when it comes to spiritual matters. At Shechem he placed before the nation the nature of loyalty to God, and the obligations of such an expected loyalty, and then challenged them to a choice, a choice that must be their own, and not one that even Joshua, loved and honored though he was, could make for them. It would seem as if the people wavered in their choice, and so we reach the climax of Joshua's appeal in the phrase, "As for me and my house." Whatever else he might do for him and his, the die was cast—"We will serve the Lord."

Having firmly established the things of God in heart and home, whether such an action was singular or no, Joshua was determined to abide by his distinctive choice. Yes, and his declaration has had a long and active life, seeing it became the watchword of many a Christian home in which it can still be found as a motto. May such personal devotion to God be ours, although the way of the world runs otherwise, and other homes are ordered by other, less worthy principles. Our hearts and homes are thrice happy if the things of God are as deep springs in individual daily thought and action. Although the world may be against us, let the spiritual singularity of Joshua be ours—"As for me I will serve the Lord"!

The Individuality of Prayer

The compelling phrase we are considering occurs often in the Psalms. Here, for instance, is its triple association with prayer—"As for me, I will come into thy house" (Ps. 5:7). "As for me, I will call upon God" (Ps. 55:16). "As for me, my prayer is unto thee, O God" (Ps. 69:13).

Once again we have the determination of the speaker to stand out from all others, odd though his position may have been thought to be. This "as for me" of dependence upon God contrasts sharply with the way of others. In the first two verses above we have the psalmist's proposal, "I *will* come . . . call," but in the third verse his proposal becomes practice, "My prayer *is* unto thee."

Is not the growing need of our day for men and women to preserve this individuality of prayer, seeing they are surrounded by myriads of prayerless people, even those to whom waiting upon God has no appeal? Let others try to live their lives apart from God, and fashion their own ways—ours must be the determination to watch and safeguard singularity in respect to fellowship with God. Because prayer is contagious and pleaders win pleaders, we must ring out our "as for me" as a holy, personal ambition and save others, thereby, from the sin of prayerlessness. Further on, we have the psalmist saying, "It is good for me to draw near to God" (73:28)—good, not only for ourselves, but also for others as we intercede for them. May Samuel's resolve be ours as we think of saints and sinners "standing in the need of prayer": "As for me, God forbid that I should cease to pray for you" (I Sam. 12:23).

50

The Individuality of Eternal Satisfaction

"As for me, I will behold thy face in righteousness: I shall be satisfied when I awake, with thy likeness" (Ps. 17:15).

Within this Psalm there is sketched for us with awful vividness, the individuality of worldly men, each of whom were satisfied with the pursuit of their own selfish and sensual desires. But in the verse before us the psalmist isolates himself from all worldly and carnal aims, contrasting them in a powerful way with immortality and its satisfaction of mind. Men of the world receive their satisfaction in this life, but the saint is content to wait for his complete gratification in heaven—"*shall* be satisfied."

Thus the truth to be gleaned from the psalmist's particular and peculiar aspiration is, let worldly men of low degree be pleased and satisfied with earthly store; but let ours be the personal hope and eternal pleasure of seeing the King in all His beauty. Let others live for their carnal joy, their earthly possessions, their gold; let them thirst after pursuits which bring a passing contentment. Such people are to be pitied if they die without Christ, for their present pleasures form the only heaven they will ever have. Bless God, those who through faith in the redeeming grace of Christ may appear odd, singular, or peculiar to world-lovers, have a glorious prospect of never-failing satisfaction once they cross the narrow sea of death and see Him whom their hearts have loved since first they met Him.

The Individuality of Christian Forgiveness

David, in another Psalm, describes a most unusual aspect of his spiritual singularity. "As for me, when they were sick, my clothing was sackcloth" (35:13). The "they" he speaks of were the people who had treated him with gross and persistent injustice, and who became "sick," or chastened by God, as they deserved to be. But what about David's attitude? Was he jubilant? Did he say, "Serves you right for the way you treated me"? No, he returned good for evil, and thus fore-shadowed the spirit of Calvary. He bewailed their trouble by clothing himself in the garb of mourning and by fasting and praying for them. Others might have been glad to see them suffer, but not David—his clothing was "sackcloth."

What an example of noble spiritual individuality David left us! We need more of this distinctiveness in forgiving those who have wronged and ill-treated us! How do we treat those who offend and hurt us and how do we feel when they suffer? Is ours an inward gratification to see them being paid back in their own coin? If so, let us stand rebuked by the psalmist's "As for me . . . sackcloth." Others may believe in keeping up the old grudge, never forgiving, remaining aloof, and being glad to see those who ill-treated them afflicted. But as for me, a blood-washed, divinely forgiven sinner, it must be the Calvary way, for the cross reveals the very heart of God with whom is forgiveness that He may be feared. Symbolically, we must put on the sackcloth when we see our enemy sick, seeking, thereby, to win him from his antago-nism. May the Lord enable us to cultivate, more than ever, this feature of singularity, and turn the other cheek! To for-give those who despitefully treat us may appear odd, but it is the way the Master went and we must follow Him.

The Individuality of Divine Support

Still in the Psalms, we find another instance of spiritual singularity, this one related to what God is able to do for those who, in their desires and aims, are separate from sin-ners. "As for me, thou upholdest me in mine integrity" (41:12). Under what circumstances did the psalmist prove that God was able to uphold and sustain although it appeared that he had been left to fight his own battle? Why, he was on a bed of languishing, surrounded, not by kind sympathetic friends consoling him as ministering angels, but encircled by enemies, deaf to his cry for succor and impatient to see his end. As if to add extra infusion of gall to his bitter cup, his own familiar friend had turned his back upon his anguish.

What a picture of unrelieved suffering this Psalm presents! Yet there is no such a thing as unrelieved suffering with the saint of God, because as he gives himself to prayer, he proves the personal divine support available to him in his hour of need. John Wesley used to speak of "the old unfashionable medicine of prayer," and such effective medicine can sanctify and transform a sickbed, making it administer blessing to the afflicted one. Every child of God may know this singular, individual support God offers to all who are upright in heart. The Good Shepherd never forgets even the poorest lamb in His flock. No matter how humble and insignificant we may be, He has us on His heart at all times. Let us, then, lay hold of this precious "as for me," and determine to know God as our personal support, stay, strength, and song! While multitudes around may be ignorant of divine sustenance and feed on their own ways, may ours be the serenity that comes through knowing that God cares for us.

The Individuality of Satan Assault

In an autobiographical psalm, Asaph reveals how narrowly he escaped from falling into a net the wily tempter had set for his feet: "As for me, my feet were almost gone; my steps had well-nigh slipped" (73:2). The psalmist was envious when he saw the prosperity of the wicked and arrogant and almost fell into the temptation of complaining over his own impoverishment as he saw the wealth of others. Is there not an individuality and singularity about the terrible temptation some people face? Each of us has a special kind of temptation, and no saint can hope to escape. Some, of course, are more susceptible than others to the approach of the enemy. May we be delivered, however, from the peculiar temptation of Asaph, namely, that of envy over the prosperity of others. How we need to beware of covetousness, especially if we do not have much of this world's goods!

When you look at others, with their lands and gold,
Think that Christ has promised you His wealth untold.

Gold and grandeur can do nothing for a man beyond the veil. If it could, then Dives, the rich man, would not have gone to hell. The child of God has One who is able to supply all that is necessary for the manifold needs of life. "Be content with such things as ye have: for he hath said, I will never leave thee, nor forsake thee" (Heb. 13:5). Do you know that this is one Scripture that if read backwards means the same— "Thee forsake nor thee leave never will I." If we have yielded to Asaph's temptation and our feet are almost gone, let us hasten to the cross and humbly and repentantly ask for forgiveness and complete deliverance from the tempter. God's delivering grace is for each and all, and He gives individual grace to resist every individual temptation.

The Individuality of Divine Revelation

Although there are many other verses that contain the phrase "as for me," which Bible lovers can pursue with profit, we conclude with these two references from the Book of Daniel.

"As for me . . . this secret is not revealed to me for any wisdom that I have" (2:30). "As for me . . . my cogitations much troubled me" (7:28). There are two phrases in the second chapter of this prophecy, which provide a vivid contrast, "As for thee O King"—"As for me" (2:29-30). Nebuchadnezzar's dream came in the silence of the night, and he was to discover that there was a God in heaven able to reveal secrets. The revelation of the structure of the dream, and also its significance was granted to Daniel, who had no wisdom of his own to interpret it. It was divinely revealed that the thoughts of many hearts might be made bare. The Chaldean astrologers sought to interpret the king's dream by the aid of natural reason, but failed. Daniel was exceptional, singular in that he alone was able under God to unfold the mystery and message of the dream. Is there not an "as for me" in respect to a true unfolding of the Word and ways of God? Is not the Holy Spirit able to take you and me aside and reveal the inner significance of truth? What we receive may be contrary to the accepted theories and ideas of men, but with Daniel we must be singular in saying, "As for me, this secret is revealed unto me, and I must accept, believe, and declare it." Daniel said that his "cogitations" troubled him, and often we are compelled to stand aside and tremble at the overwhelming revelation of truth granted.

As we conclude this particular summary it is necessary to remind ourselves what "as for me" does not mean. Never for a moment is the Christian called to isolation, detachment, singularity for their own sakes, but always for the sake of God and of others. It is the believer's business to be most considerate, sympathetic, courteous, and companionable within the orbit of the will of God. If this is not remembered, the absence of prayer and of sanctified common sense can make one disagreeable, unwelcome, objectionable by their oddity, singularity, mistaking this as fidelity to a principle.

It is imperative to keep a sacred place in the heart for the aim "as for me," when it means consideration and sympathy as different as possible from drift and compromise. If our lives are absolutely governed by a personal surrender to the will of God, then there will come the abandonment of all worldly methods of living and acting, and of all alluring fashions of thought and practice. If the "as for me" of Bible saints is conspicuous in our lives, then, with our feet planted firmly on the revelation that God's Word provides, we will be content to let others live as they may.

Let the multitudes drift into indifference to His Word, His sanctuary, His Holy Day.

Let even those who bear His name be ignorant of His express commands as to the Ordinances, and to personal self-discipline of habits and the need of holy living.

Let it be out of fashion, even in religious circles, to witness definitely for Christ, to seek the salvation of the lost from sin and hell.

"As for me," it must be otherwise. Without pride trumpeting self-exaltation, we must be spiritually singular. I am not my brother's judge as to what he should not do, but my Master's servant whose call I must obey, and so, "As for me, I must serve the Lord."

Sixth Summary
The Wondrous Hiding of God in Scripture

Can we own a God who
. . . Hides Himself so wondrously
As if there were no God?
He is least seen when all the powers
Of ill are most abroad.

Evidently the saintly and seraphic Isaiah, known as "The Evangelical Prophet" could own and love such a God for he, it was, who challenged Him by saying, "Verily Thou art a God that hidest thyself, O God of Israel, the Saviour" (Isa. 45:15). To the prophet, God appeared to remain incognito. From the narrative it would seem as if Isaiah condemned the Lord for neglecting His people when they were in exile and bondage. Somehow He had forgotten them, or they, Him; yet now with clearer light it is possible to trace His footprints. Although apparently unseen and indifferent, prophet and people alike came to discover that the unseen One was actively ruling and overruling in all their past history. The verse before us pulsates with great thoughts, so let us try to take some honey out of this piece of the rock of impregnable Scripture. We love and serve a God who delights in hiding Himself in order that our discovery of Him may enrich our lives.

His Being

God, in His own divine essence, no human being has seen. He dwells in glory inaccessible, and hides Himself from the gaze of inferior beings, as Paul indicates in his letters to young Timothy, "Now unto the King, eternal, immortal, invisible" (I Tim. 1:17). " ... the blessed and only Potentate, the King of kings, and Lord of lords, who only hath immortality dwelling in the light which no man can approach unto; whom no man hath seen, nor can see" (I Tim. 6:15-16). Then John declares that, "No man hath seen God at any time ... " (1:18). The nearest any human has come to seeing Him who is invisible is Moses, for on that mount, God said to his honored servant who desired to see Him, "Thou canst not see my face: for there shall no man see me and live. ... Thou shalt see my back parts: but my face shall not be seen" (Exod. 33:20, 23). Even the seraphim in His august presence have to veil their faces before the blinding glory of His radiant holiness. We have a faint idea of the dazzling glory of Deity at the Transfiguration when the disciples were partially blinded through the inherent glory of Jesus flashing forth.

> True Image of the Infinite
> Whose essence is concealed,
> Brightness of uncreated light,
> The heart of God revealed.

His Creation

Solomon reminds us that "it is the glory of God to conceal a thing" (Prov. 25:2); and the prophet says, "There was the hiding of his power" (Hab. 3:4). What are the great discoveries of men in the realm of science but the unfolding of what God originally hid in the universe. He, it was, who deposited the gold, silver, diamonds, coal, and other minerals and beneficial treasures in the earth, leaving man to find what He had hidden. "There is nothing new under the sun" because all was known to God who placed it there. This is what man is continually doing, bringing to light by laborious search what God stored away in His creation. Kepler said, as he made fascinating studies of the starry heavens, that he was only "thinking God's thought after Him," or, discovering what God had hidden.

His Book

As we think of Scripture, the description of Isaiah is most apt, "Verily thou art a God that hidest thyself." The prophet also witnesses that God reveals the unseen and unknown, "I have showed thee new things from this time, even hidden things" (48:6).

David prayed, "Hide not thy commandments from me" (119:19). He did not want God to keep the inner, hidden sense of divine truth from him. Often it seems as if He hides Himself in His Word and "showeth himself through the lattice." Prejudice, disobedience, and sin can keep Him hidden from our gaze. It is only as we are obedient to the voice of the Holy Spirit that He can enable us to trace the Lord.

> Beyond the sacred page,
> I seek Thee, Lord.

In the days of His flesh, Jesus made it clear that unbelief prohibits revelation: "But they understood not this saying, and it was hid from them" (Luke 9:45). "If thou hadst known . . . now they are hid from thine eyes" (Luke 19:42). It is one thing to read the Book of God superficially, as literature, but a different thing altogether to know and love the God of the Book, and knowing the Author enables us to see the glory gilding the sacred page. The psalmist prayed, "Open my eyes, that I may behold wondrous things out of thy law"—things that have always been in the Word since it was written, but which the Holy Spirit alone can enable us to find. And when we do, then we rejoice as those finding great spoil. Further, quietly and unseen by others and unobserved by ourselves, our life, loves, beliefs, and habits are changed through the sanctifying Scriptures.

59

There are times in your experience and mine when it does seem as if Isaiah's words are true, about God hiding Himself. In the midst of his anguish Job cried, "O that I knew where I might find him!" (23:3). To the patriarch it seemed as if God had either departed from him, or was veiling His face from the eye of faith.

Take Mystery

The frequent complaint of saints of old is that expressed by David, "Why hidest thou thyself in times of trouble?" (Ps. 10:1; see 44:24; 88:16). When in dire need Mary and Martha sent for Jesus, He delayed His journey to Bethany and hid Himself, as it were. Why? Why is God silent in the hour of grief? Thanks be to the Saviour Himself who at Calvary cried, "Why?"—"My God, my God, why hast thou forsaken me?" There are mysteries, perplexities, and problems in human life that our finite minds cannot explain, and hidden purposes in many experiences that no skill can unravel. It is consoling, however, to walk in the dark with God. Moffatt translates Isaiah's estimation of the divine character, "Verily thou art a God that hidest thyself," as "Yours indeed is a God of mystery, a God that saves." Even in the mystery, He is working out His beneficent, saving purpose. Now, we live in a world of mystery, but the Paradise of Revelation awaits us, as Paul reminds us in the comforting words, "For now we see through a glass, darkly; but then, face to face." But although God may veil His aims in all He permits, He never makes a mistake as we shall discover when He unrolls the canvas and explains the reason why.

> Judge not the Lord by feeble sense
> But trust Him for His grace;

Behind a frowning Providence,
He hides a smiling face.

Take Prayer

David urges God to give ear to his prayer, and not to hide Himself from his supplication (Ps. 55:1). In a daring way, the psalmist pleads with God not to turn His face away as if resolved not to listen to his cry. Are there not times when it seems as if the divine ears are not open to our supplication? Have we not experienced the problem of unanswered prayer? Have we not prayed for necessary, legitimate things, yet received no answer? Although the Scripture assures us that He is the God who hears and answers prayer, somehow it appears as if He has hid Himself from our need, and has forgotten to be gracious. In spite of our agonizing cry, He does not hasten to relieve us of our adversity or trial.

What we must not forget is the fact that there can be a radical cause for God hiding Himself from our supplication. We cannot expect to have the smile of His face and His ears open to prayers if our life is displeasing to Him. If we regard iniquity in our hearts, then He cannot hear us. Lack of divine favor, then, should lead us to search our ways. "Thou hidest thy face, they are troubled" (Ps. 104:29). In spite of His miraculous ministry, many people did not believe Jesus, and He departed from them, and hid Himself from them (John 12:36-37). May we so live that His ears will always be open to our prayers! If, however, some remain unanswered, when we see Him we'll know the reason why.

Unanswered yet? Faith cannot be unanswered,
    Her feet are planted firmly on the Rock;
Amid the wildest storms she stands undaunted,
    Nor quails before the loudest thunder shock.
She knows Omnipotence has heard her prayer,
    And cries, "It shall be done"—sometime, somewhere.

His Christ

When we come to the Saviour, God's beloved Son, we touch the deepest truth of Isaiah's word about God hiding Himself, for in Christ, God truly hid Himself. "God was in Christ reconciling the world unto himself." To Moses, God said, "There shall no man see me and live." It is only as we see God in Christ that we can live both now and in eternity. "No man hath seen God at any time; the only begotten Son, which is in the bosom of the Father, he hath declared him" (John 1:18). Jesus Himself could say, "He that hath seen me, hath seen the Father," for He came as the culmination of the revelation of God. Often in the Old Testament God veiled Himself in angelic form, and appeared to men, but He became incarnate in Jesus. "Veiled in flesh, the Godhead see." The only One privileged to see the face of God is the One who reveals the divine character. He came as the express image of God's person. Does He not live and have His being in a silent, hidden, mysterious way in your heart and mine? Are we not indwelt by the unseen blessed Spirit? Conversely, our lives are hid with Christ in God.

His People

Paul reveals a mystery hid from the ages: "Christ in you the hope of glory" (Col. 1:26-27). There is the veiling of Him in our own being. The world cannot see the Father, Son, and Holy Spirit; yet all three are resident in your life and mine, for every true believer is a mysterious cabinet of the Trinity. When Jesus was here among men, He "could not be hid," and when He appeared it was quickly noised abroad that He was in the house (Mark 2:1; 7:24). We cannot hide the fragrance of a rose, the heat of a fire, the glory of a sunset. Thus it is with Christ and ourselves. If we are living in unbroken fellowship with the three Persons of the Blessed Trinity they are bound to express their hidden presence through our lives, and those around us will swiftly discern the charm of our God-possessed life. Let us pray that He will bury Himself deep in our being, and then reveal His love through us to a world of sin.

Seventh Summary
The Gospel of Nevertheless in Scripture

A good, serviceable Bible concordance is the best commentary when it comes to word study. Dr. A. J. Gordon, one of the outstanding Bible expositors of the last generation, wrote, "In Scripture, words, like blazed trees in a forest, are sure guides through the labyrinth of Revelation. *Lamb, blood, faith, forgiveness, peace*—these are God's words: and whoever will take one of them and trace it through the Bible, threading together on this single word, as on a cord, the various texts where it occurs, will find both a wondrous continuity, and a wondrous unity thereby established."

It is this excellent advice we are taking with the word *nevertheless*. It occurs some thirty times in Holy Writ, and is actually three words in one, Never-the-less, meaning, "not the less," or "notwithstanding," or "however," or "none-the-less," or "yet." Scattered throughout the pages of the Bible, this cheery word, *nevertheless,* challenges our thought and invites meditation. As S. E. Burrow put it—

> In the dark patches of life—when things are difficult and clouds darken the horizon—it speaks to us, either of a possible alternative or an ultimate advantage. There may be a night of failure, but the morning shall find the nets full to overflowing! It bids us not to be wholly concerned with the present, for there is a "nevertheless afterward" in the programme for which it is worth waiting. It is a friendly word—is this *nevertheless*—for it urges us to look out for the brighter side, and to wait for the compensa-

tion which the all-loving Father holds in reserve for His children, so that all things shall work together for good.

As we examine many of the references where *nevertheless* appears, we shall find how the word is associated with the various aspects and experiences of Christian service.

As used by Nehemiah, the model worker, the word represents difficulty in service, for this exile in Babylon was not only deeply concerned about his fellow-Jews in faraway Jerusalem who were suffering "great affliction," but was equally distressed concerning the city of his fathers—"the walls of Jerusalem broken down, and the gates burned." Nehemiah not only wept and mourned, but fasted and prayed. God heard His servant's cry, and moved the heart of the king to grant Nehemiah leave of absence that he might repair the walls and encourage his brethren. But setting about the task, he met with much opposition and ridicule, and found the going hard. What did he do—compromise with the foes who tried their utmost to stop the rebuilding plan? Let Nehemiah himself answer, "Nevertheless we made our prayer unto our God, and set a watch against them day and night" (4:7-9). Here we have the *Nevertheless of Steadfastness.* Satan tries in so many ways to discourage the child of God, and often faith is sorely tried; but victory is secured as he shelters behind the "nevertheless" of Nehemiah, and just goes on working, watching, and praying.

While there are other Old Testament references to this word, wealthy in meaning and content, let us confine ourselves to many of its appearances in the New Testament.

"The King was sorry, nevertheless for his oath's sake" (Matt. 14:9)

This was the *Nevertheless of Doublemindedness.* Herod was more afraid of the taunt of assembled guests than he was of the voice of conscience. The careless oath he made should have been broken, for a holy man's life was at stake. While John's cruel death reminds us of the cost of fearless discipleship, he should not have died, and would not have been murdered if Herod's last struggle with conscience had not created a false regard for public opinion. Associated with this "nevertheless" is not only the doom of the Baptist, but the gross licentiousness of Herod and his court.

"Nevertheless not as I will, but as thou wilt" (Matt. 26:39; Mark 14:36)

The circumstances surrounding this *Nevertheless of Surrender* are familiar. Jesus was born to die, for He came as the Lamb slain before the foundation of the world. Virtually, then, He was born crucified, and during His public ministry He often spoke of the decease He was to accomplish at Jerusalem. Conscious of all that awaited Him, He did not falter, but set His face steadfastly toward His cross. His cry for the removal of the bitter cup was but the natural cry of human weakness, and it was quickly followed by submission and surrender to the will of His Father. Because God is infinitely wiser than we are, knowing what is best for us, this Gethsemane "nevertheless" must condition all our petitions.

"Nevertheless, I say unto you, Hereafter shall ye see the Son of man sitting on the right hand of power, and coming in the clouds of heaven" (Matt 26:64)

The contrast before us in the context is most impressive. Jesus had been standing before Caiphas, and, wrongly accused, He was sentenced to die. Defiantly, however, He rings out the truth that the tables would be changed and that He would sit as the righteous judge, and sinners would be made to stand before Him to receive, not false justice as had been heaped upon Him, but only what their sin truly deserved. His foes gave Him a cross, but that was to be the way to His throne. "Nevertheless . . . hereafter"! How comforting is the *Nevertheless of Glory!*

"Nevertheless at thy word I will let down the net" (Luke 5:5)

Peter, the spokesman of the apostolic band, as an experienced fisherman knew that night was the right time to fish, even though on this particular night not one solitary fish found its way into his net. So when the sun rose and shone upon the waters—the wrong way to fish—Peter was a little amazed when Jesus said to these discouraged fishermen, "Put out to sea again, and let down your nets for a draught." Yet, although he might have questioned the wisdom of his Master, there came his *Nevertheless of Obedience.* With what result? Because he was willing and humble enough to forego his own judgment and ignore his fishing knowledge and experience and obey his miracle-working Lord, he reaped a bountiful harvest from the sea that fine morning. Peter was obedient to Christ's command even though it was contrary to the accustomed order of things. The fisherman's wrong time for fishing was Christ's right time.

"Nevertheless I must walk to day, and to morrow, and the day following" (Luke 13:33)

Is there not something defiant and challenging about this *Nevertheless of Immortality?* Herod, "that fox," as Jesus called him, tried hard to kill Him before His time to die on the cross, but He knew that He was immortal until His work was done. The time and manner of His death had been planned in a past eternity, and not even a bloodthirsty king could quicken His end. Let Satan, demons, and men do their utmost to thwart Calvary, He knew that He would walk "today, to morrow, and the day following," and then die as decreed. Do we believe that if we live in obedience to the will of God we too are immortal until our course is finished?

"Nevertheless when the Son of man cometh shall he find faith . . . ? (Luke 18:8)

The original is a little more emphatic and explicit—"Shall he find *the* faith?" When Christ returns He will find plenty of faith—faith in heresies, in superstitions, in self-righteousness and self-sufficiency, and, conversely, personal faith in Himself by the few in comparison to those who are iniquitous and apostate. But the question is, will He find "the faith," . . . that is, adherence to the whole body of revealed truth, to " . . . the faith which was once delivered unto the saints" (Jude 3)? Is not this *Nevertheless of Loyalty to the Fundamentals,* scorned even in religious circles today? Apostasy is responsible for the evident spiritual impotence of the church in a world of need. By the time Christ returns, "the faith" will be a very scarce commodity indeed.

"Nevertheless let us go unto him" (John 11:15)

The word, as used here by Jesus, marks an interruption and transition, and indicates a reference to something else. He knew all about the fatal sickness of Lazarus whom He loved, yet He did not hasten to his relief. He said to those who were mourning the death of Lazarus, "I am glad for your sakes that I was not there, to the intent ye may believe"—meaning that His delay was not a denial, even though His friend had died. Thus, there came the *Nevertheless of Glorious Assurance,* and you will see that nothing can defy the Lord of power. Sometimes we are confronted with what seem to be gigantic or impossible tasks, but when, nevertheless, we go to them in the power of Him who conquered death, faith is amply rewarded.

"Nevertheless among the chief rulers also many believed on him" (John 12:42)

How the heart of Jesus must have been cheered as some of the chief rulers declared their willing acceptance of Him as their Messiah! In spite of the spiritual blindness of the Jewish nation as a whole, there were those whose eyes were opened to see in Him the One eagerly anticipated, and who manifested the *Nevertheless of Acceptance*. There has always been the remnant who recognize the validity of the spiritual.

"Nevertheless I tell you the truth" (John 16:7)

The emphasis here is on the pronoun, "*I*, who knoweth all." As the truth, He could not do anything else but tell the truth. What He had told them filled the hearts of the disciples with sorrow, for He spoke of His departure. They were also perplexed by His statement that it was "expedient," or a good thing for Him to leave them. Too often, we cannot see the beneficial purpose in some things God takes from us, and how even the most untoward experiences of life work together for our good. As scholars in His school we have to learn the lessons associated with the *Nevertheless of Expediency*.

"Nevertheless he left not himself without witness" (Acts 14:17)

Paul and Barnabas, in restraining the people of Lystra who wanted to worship them as gods because of their miraculous power, thundered out against the nation's idolatry, utter godlessness, and selfishness, and then declared that even amid such God had not left Himself without witness. Divine goodness was not only manifested in nature, but in the darkest scene there is something to remind the darkest heart of God as the Creator. In our corrupt time, as the shadow of judgment gathers around a world far from God, He has not left Himself without a witness among people in every walk of life. There are still the thousands who have not bowed the knee to Baal, and who are embraced in the *Nevertheless of Testimony*.

"Nevertheless the centurion believed the master and owner of the ship, more than those things which were spoken by Paul" (Acts 27:11)

Perhaps it seemed more natural to trust an expert than a missionary. But Paul had a divine intuition, and so advised against the advice of the owner of the ship. His warning, however, was not accepted and the *Nevertheless of Rejection* resulted in disaster. The centurion in charge of the prisoners, who would not accept the word of a man of faith, must have been humiliated when Paul's prophecy came true. We do not doubt that the centurion showed all due deference to Paul, nevertheless he believed not the apostle, but the master of the ship. He came to learn that God often works contrary to experience.

"Nevertheless we have not used this power; but suffer all things lest we should hinder the gospel of Christ" (I Cor. 9:12)

How noble and sacrificial is this *Nevertheless of Self-denial!* As Jesus never performed a miracle to bring personal relief in time of need, so the apostles were embued with the same spirit. Paul could have taken what was justly due, but he exercised a self-imposed poverty in order that his self-abnegation might make the gospel more effective. In the cause of Christ, it is not a matter of what we can get out of it that counts, but what we can put into it in the shape of self-sacrifice. Later on, Paul has another "nevertheless," proving that he never made gains out of those he ministered to.

70

"... nevertheless, being crafty, we caught you with guile"
(II Cor. 12:16). The more he spent for them, and loved them,
the less those Corinthians seemed to spend on Paul. Yet, with
inspired craftiness, he won many of them for his Master.

"Nevertheless God ... comforteth those that are cast down" (II Cor. 7:6)

In Macedonia Paul found himself troubled on every side,
with fightings without and fears within. There was so much
to discourage and distress this brave herald of the cross, but
he took fresh heart when he saw Titus. Not only was Paul
divinely consoled in spite of his trials, but in the coming of
Titus, a brother was born for adversity. No matter how black
the night, there is always the *Nevertheless of Consolation,*
someone whose presence is a balm and benediction.

"Nevertheless I live, yet not I" (Gal. 2:20)

The word as used here makes an antithesis, and is conspicuous as an injunction. Death and life are joined together.
Among the paradoxes of our Christian faith there is the most
pertinent: Dead yet alive! Crucified yet existent! Are we
sharing in this *Nevertheless of Co-Crucifixion and Co-Resur-
rection?* Are we dead indeed unto sin, and fully alive unto
God?

"Nevertheless I am not ashamed ... " (II Tim. 1:12)

Living in the "Nevertheless what saith the Scripture?"
(Gal. 4:30), Paul was never ashamed of, nor apologized for
his forthright witness. Remember that at this time, Paul was a
prisoner in Rome. He knew there was no release for him, and
that as a prisoner he was doomed to die. As the end drew
near for him to be offered, the past came up before his
mental vision. There were many things in his old life as a

persecutor he deeply regretted, but they were all under the blood. He never regretted, however, his sacrificial and faithful ministry as a preacher. He was never ashamed of the gospel of Christ, and could face martyrdom resting on the *Nevertheless of Satisfaction*. "I have fought a good fight."

"Nevertheless the foundation of God standeth sure . . . " (II Tim. 2:19)

Paul could foresee the trials facing the church, and the hurt and damage before her because of apostasy and persecution, but he had no fear as to her continuance. He knew that because she is eternal she is indestructible. Even the gates of hell cannot prevail against her. The *Nevertheless of Safety* here seems to suggest that although many would be shaken by false teaching, yet God's firm foundation would stand immovable. What a bracing "nevertheless" this is for the days of spiritual declension in which we live! The vast majority neglect the church, others deem it to be an outworn institution, and so despise and condemn it. Yet in spite of seeming decay and the hostility of men, His true church stands secure. Individual, material church buildings may vanish and denominations cease to be, but the church of the living God composed of born-anew souls can neither wither nor perish.

"Nevertheless afterward it yieldeth the peaceable fruit of righteousness" (Heb. 12:11)

The writer to the Hebrews tells us that there is a loving purpose behind the discipline of life. "Whom the Lord loveth he chasteneth." Such chastening may come in different ways—the pain of loss, of failure, of disappointment—the keener pain of being slighted by friends, of being misunderstood, and consequently misjudged by them—the sorrows and trials of life. What unspeakable comfort it is to know that

Jesus passed this way before us when He lived our life on earth. "He was tested in all points like as we are," and is therefore "able to succour those who are tested." Is it not balm to our soul to remember that He endured the contradiction of sinners against Himself?

Our peril during a season of testing is to dwell unduly upon it and become resentful and bitter of spirit, and thus lose our joy and become powerless for service. We must never forget that all chastening is parental, and for our present and future good. Our all-loving Father has us under His watchful eye, and designs that we should become not only like Him, but also like His beloved Son "who learned obedience by the things which he suffered." While for the moment divine chastening is not joyous but grievous, there is the *Nevertheless of Enrichment*—a spiritual enrichment resulting from submission to the divine will, even when it seeks our highest good through pain.

"Nevertheless we, according to His promise, look for new heavens and a new earth, wherein dwelleth righteousness" (II Peter 3:13)

Presently, as Peter makes clear in the context, we live in an age of scoffers, and of those who walk after their own lusts, and who challenge the promises of Scripture, and make light of its doctrines, particularly that of Christ's return with its consequent bliss for His own and terrible judgment for His foes. Concerned and distressed as we ought to be over the utter abandonment of the world to the lustful pursuit of carnal pleasures, we must face the future undismayed, for Peter gives us the *Nevertheless of Hope*. Things may be dark and distressing today, but God has promised a universe in which righteousness will prevail. The worldling being "without God" is "without hope." But those of us who are Christ's through His atoning work "look beyond this vale of tears to that celestial hill" with glad and grateful assurance. Peter's glorious "nevertheless" keeps us calm and confident amid the chaos, turmoil, and dissolution of things of this world.

"Nevertheless I have somewhat against thee, because thou hast left thy first love" (Rev. 2:4)

In His first letter to the churches, our Lord has some admirable things to say about the church at Ephesus. It was an almost perfect church. It had borne much for His sake. It had manifested superb patience. It had not become weary in well-doing. Yet the Lord had this *Nevertheless of Complaint* against her. She had *left,* (not "lost") her first love—and this was no little thing to fail in, no slight fault. Paul makes it clear that the decay of love is the decay of that without which all other graces are as nothing (I Cor. 13).

After parading the commendable virtues of the church, Christ intervenes with His "nevertheless." No person or church bearing His name is absolutely good or utterly bad. He marks the worst in the best, and the best in the worst and gives credit where it is due. What does He see to commend or condemn in you and me? Has He anything against us as His professed followers? May we so live that He will never have to write this "nevertheless" over our spiritual experience!

Eighth Summary
The Spiritual Depths in Scripture

Among the 150 psalms forming the Psalter, one of the most remarkable is Psalm 78, proving as it does that its composer was a most unusual historian. Faithful in descriptive details, he reviews the providential dealings of God toward the children of Israel as they journeyed through the wilderness. How he delighted to dwell upon the wonders of that pilgrimage from Egypt to Canaan, when miracles were wrought for the physical welfare of the people almost every step of their passage through desert land! One instance of divine provision for the host is found in the phrase, "[God] . . . gave them drink as out of great depths" (78:15).

This observation emphasizes one aspect of the goodness and power of God; for what the psalmist had in mind was not a mere trickle, which satisfied the thirsty travelers for a little, but a boundless, inexhaustible supply of fresh water. It is this fact that we want to use as an illustration of the infinite supply God has for His pilgrims today. If the supply is limited it is from our side, not from His. We can have as much of God as we desire. Has the wonder, then, of His marvelous fullness flashed upon our minds? Are we to be found drinking out of the great depths?

> Praise to the Holiest in the height,
> And in the depth be praise;
> In all His words most wonderful,
> Most sure in all His ways.

Before we come to examine some of the depths of Scripture, there are two introductory thoughts worthy of emphasis—

Superficial Days

What a superficial age ours is! People, alas! are easily satisfied. Small pools suffice for the majority. These are days of flimsy beliefs and behavior; days of flippancy and frivolity, and of a shallow experience. Too many are all show, lacking depth. We have a scarcity of deep characters. Robert Burns, the Scottish poet has a verse which, perhaps, is self-revealing—

> Good Lord, what is man! for as simple as he looks,
> Do but try to develop his hooks and his crooks.
> With his depths and his shallows, his good and his evil,
> All in all, he's a problem must puzzle the Devil.

In our Lord's Parable of the Sower, He spoke of the seed withering away because it had "no depth of earth." How descriptive this is of multitudes today! They do not "dwell deep" to use Jeremiah's words (49:8, 30). We fear that even in Christian circles there is too much superficiality, especially now among some young believers who crave pop-music for hymns, and a very light spiritual fare. But they will never achieve much for the Kingdom unless they launch out into the deeps of the precious things of faith and of the Spirit. The man whose house stood when the floods came was the one who "digged deep" below the sand (Luke 6:48). Job was asked the question by Jehovah—"Hast thou entered into the springs of the sea? or hast thou walked in search of the depth?" (38:16). May we ever be found walking in "search of the depth"—digging, dwelling, drinking, drawing deeply of His bountiful springs!

Satisfying Depths

One sweet thought which emerges from this beautiful Psalm of Pilgrimage is the display of the splendor of divine provision. Imagine Israel crowding round that smitten rock saying, "This cannot last long. The gushing stream will soon dry up." But when they discovered that in spite of the vast quantity they drank, the water still flowed on, glad and grateful surprise possessed their hearts. The spring was inexhaustible, for what the people could see was fed by channels they knew nothing about and could not see. Thus it is with grace! The idea behind the psalmist's allusion to "great depths" is that of striking or boring through rock to the great ocean on which the earth was supposed to rest—great depths are the reservoir of water hidden in the earth. (See Gen. 7:11; Ps. 33:7; Prov. 8:24.)

The refreshing supply, gushing up from earth's innermost storehouses, never ceases to run. Those streams in the desert were so plentiful in quantity because they were miraculous in origin. Torrents, not driblets, came from the rock, and so the psalmist was lost in admiration at the abundance God provided. When Abraham cast out Hagar, the bondwoman, he gave her a bottle of water. When it was exhausted, God gave her a well. Our supplies are never exhausted because their origin and source is God and, being fathomless and boundless, they remain to satisfy the saints in succeeding ages. Giving never impoverishes God, nor does withholding from us enrich Him. The story is told of Archbishop William Temple when he was a student at Rugby. "Are you not," one of the masters asked him in discussing one of his schoolboy essays, "a little out of your depth here?" "Perhaps, sir," was the confident reply, "but I can swim." The waters that flowed from the sanctuary which Ezekiel mentions, commenced as a trickle but became waters deep enough to swim in. Let us, then, think of some of these deep waters, out of our depth altogether, but in which we can swim.

Depth of Life's Experiences

Tennyson, in *The Princess,* wrote of

> Tears, idle tears, I know not what they mean,
> Tears from the depth of some divine despair.

Is this not the sentiment of the psalmist when he penned the words, "Out of the depths have I cried unto thee, O Lord" (130:1)? Who has not with the writer, some time or other, out of the great depth of soul-need cried to heaven? How often we are made to drink of the depth of sorrow, disappointment, or anguish over sin. Paul commended the churches of Macedonia because in spite of their "deep poverty" they were conspicuous for the riches of their liberality (II Cor. 8:1-2). The blind unbelief of the Pharisees caused Jesus to sigh "deeply in his spirit" (Mark 8:13).

David speaks of "deep calling unto deep" (42:7), and from the depths of our human need we must ever draw from the depth of divine grace. In his appraisal of Shakespeare, Coleridge said, "The body and substance of his works came out of the unfathomable depths of his own oceanic mind." But our unfathomable depths are not in ourselves, but in Him who is the boundless source of every precious thing. Our cares, tears, trials, toils, and graves may be some of the depths we plumb, but life's experiences, although adverse, must not sink us in the depths of despair, depression, and doubt. They should send us for spiritual refreshment to the great depths of God's love, grace, and sufficiency. "He led them through the depths" (Ps. 106:9). No matter what deep trials we may encounter, we can constantly drink of the Rock who follows us (I Cor. 10:4). Wordsworth in *Laodamia* says—

> The gods approve
> The depth, and not the tumult of the soul.

Of this we are confident, God our Father approves when in spite of the tumult of the soul, we are found drinking out of the great depths of His provision.

Depths of Satan

Scripture has a triad of passages relative to these satanic depths that Jesus knew something about. "Her guests are in the depths of hell" (Prov. 9:18). " . . . deeper than hell" (Job 11:8). "Which have not known the depths of Satan . . . " (Rev. 2:24). Have we had experience of the depths of Satan that our Lord drank from in those fierce temptations in the wilderness? Saintliness and satanic attacks go together. The more we drink of the great depths of divine grace and power, the greater will be the assaults of Satan. But He who emerged from the depths of Satan more than a conqueror is able to make us sharers of His victory. The only souls He uses to roll back the tides of iniquity in the world are those who have met and conquered the devil in their own lives.

We are exhorted not to be ignorant of the enemy's devices and wiles, and of the terrible blight he causes. General William Booth startled his officers one day, when speaking to them on evangelism, by saying, "I wish I could send you all to hell for a fortnight." What he meant was that if they could live for two weeks amid the groans and moans of the damned in the depths of hell, they would return to earth with a passion for souls. It was said of Dante, that as he moved silently along the street, people would say, "He has seen hell." Knowing of the diabolical purpose of Satan to ruin our beings, corrupt our desires, cripple our testimony, blast our lives, let us drink continuously out of the great depths of Calvary's victory over his dominion. Christ was manifested to destroy the works of the devil, which He did through His death and resurrection. Therefore, as a defeated foe he can be resisted by faith.

Depths of Scripture

Having reached the period of widespread apostasy predicted in the New Testament, we are not surprised at the way the Bible is being treated in religious circles. Its inspiration is denied; its authenticity, ridiculed; its authority, despised. Historical persons and events are treated as myths. Facts are dealt with as fiction. Of itself, the Bible says, "Every word of

God is true," but many theologians scorn such a claim. By the time he takes out of the Word all the supposed myths, legends, discrepancies, inconsistencies, suppositions, and errors, the Modernist has little left save the covers. How refreshing and consoling it is to turn from the ramblings of apostates to the psalmist's wonderful estimation of God's works and words: "O Lord, how great are thy works, and thy thoughts are very deep" (92:5).

Those of us who love and revere Scripture, deeming it to be the divine revelation of God, are yet sometimes guilty of a light, cursory, casual, and superficial reading of it. We do not seem to have the time or inclination to explore its sublime depths. Scripture is not like the shallow, trashy literature of today—too muddy and polluted to offer a refreshing draught for thirsty minds. Within Holy Writ are unfathomable depths we can never plumb, truths and thoughts too high for us to reach. But all we need to know, the Holy Spirit is willing to show us. Further, the more immersed we become in its teachings, the more we are known as "a people of a deeper speech" (Isa. 33:19). The Spirit who searcheth the deep things of God is with us to reveal the deep and secret things (Dan. 2:22; I Cor. 2:10).

Scripture is not a set of petty maxims. It has no surface views of God, man, sin, and judgment. Its truths, themes, and doctrines are the deepest to engage the greatest intellect ever made. Here is knowledge too high for man to attain (Ps. 139:6).

> Here may the wretched sons of want
>   Exhaustless riches find;
> Riches above that earth can grant,
>   And lasting as the mind.

We believe the Bible to be the Word of God, not merely containing it, but His Word, in its entirety, and that "*all* Scripture is given by inspiration of God." The Greek word for "inspiration" means "God-breathed," the breath of God being used as a symbol of His power as He acted upon those who wrote the Bible, guiding them as to what they should write or speak. It is a significant commentary on the doctrine of inspiration in any age of the church, that the nearer one lives after the pattern of the holy men who wrote the Bible, the more devoutly one clings to their view of inspiration (I Cor. 2:13; II Tim. 3:16). Without doubt—

> A glory gilds the sacred page,
>   Majestic, like the sea:
> It gives a light to every age;
>   It gives, and borrows none.
>
> The Hand that gave it still supplies
>   The gracious light and heat:
> Its truths upon the nations rise:
>   They rise, but never set.

Depths of Deity

When we come to the blessed Trinity, we reach an ocean that is boundless in extent and fathomless in depth, for in each Person "the fulness of the Godhead bodily" can be found (Col. 2:9). It was F. W. Faber who taught the church to sing—

> My God, how wonderful Thou art!
>   Thy majesty how bright;
> How beautiful Thy mercy-seat
>   In depths of burning light!

Let us see if we can descend into the luminous depths of Deity by separating the three members of the Godhead.

The Grace of God

> Depth of mercy! can there be
> Mercy still reserved for me?

81

Yes, such a depth can never be exhausted. Micah tells us that God is able to cast all our sins into the depths of the sea of His forgetfulness (7:19). In this depth, our sins are beyond the reach of man or devil. "Thy judgments are a great deep" (Ps. 36:6), and God can cast your sin and mine into the depth of the sea, because sin was deeply embedded in the sacred body of Jesus at Calvary where He bore our judgment and drank the bitter cup for us. In some mysterious way He was made to drink of the wrath of a righteous God.

> None of the ransomed ever knew,
> How deep were the waters crossed

and He plunged into them for our sake, and by His stripes we are healed. At the cross, the Rock was struck, and out of its riven side streamed oceans of grace and forgiveness. Are we experiencing the deep and ever-deepening grace of God? It would seem as if for many the experience of His saving power is so shallow that they merely dip a toe in the lake, when they should be swimming in the mighty sea. With the woman of Samaria they say, "The well is deep and I have nothing to draw with." But they can draw out of the never-failing depths if only they are willing to obey and surrender. The full purpose of grace, however, is not completed when the Lord rescues us from the depths of sin. Through His matchless, boundless grace, we are to be raised to the heights of glory. "I will bring my people again from the depths of the sea" (Ps. 68:22). The sea can be used as a type of our restless, agitated world, and out of its depth of sin and sorrow we are to be caught up to meet the Lord in the air. Even the actual sea will give up its Christian dead.

The Love of Jesus

What a fathomless ocean we have in Jesus who came as the personification and revelation of the love of God for a world of sinners lost, and ruined by the Fall! No satanic depth can separate the blood-washed from such inexhaustible love (Rom. 8:38-39). Paul prays that those who have Christ deep in their hearts by faith may comprehend all the dimensions of the love of Christ—its breadth, length, depth, and height. Then he has this paradox, " . . . to know the love of Christ which passeth knowledge" (Eph. 3:17-19). How can you know the unknowable? O the depths of the riches of divine love!

> O Love, that wilt not let me go,
>   I rest my weary soul in Thee;
> I give Thee back the life I owe,
> That in Thine ocean depths its flow
>   May richer, fuller be.

Not only is the Saviour's love a bottomless abyss, but all His words, works, and ways spring from the depths of His deity, and well up out of the vast reservoir of His untainted holiness. We may drain a vessel of its contents, but we can never exhaust the hidden springs from which the vessel is filled. Samuel Rutherford expressed it thus, "How little of the sea can a child carry in his hand? As little as I am able to take away of my great Sea, my boundless and running over Christ Jesus." May we ever be found drinking deeply of His love, His self-abnegation, His sacrifice, His glory and majesty!

> Oh, the deep, deep love of Jesus,
>   Vast, unmeasured, boundless, free;
> Rolling as a mighty ocean
>   In its fullness over me.
> Underneath me, all around me,
>   Is the current of Thy love;
> Leading onward, leading homeward,
>   To my glorious rest above.

The Ministry of the Spirit

Paul indicated something of the inexhaustible depths in

the sacred Third Person of the blessed Trinity when he said, "But be filled with the Spirit" (Eph. 5:18). What a limitless ocean He is! In Scripture, water is a type of the refreshing ministry of the Holy Spirit; so when Ezekiel wrote of a river that could not be passed over, waters constantly rising, waters to swim in, he gave us a fitting illustration of the fullness of the Spirit (47:5). Then the prophet asked the pointed question, "Son of man, hast thou seen this?" Have we experienced the fullness of the blessing of the gospel of Christ the Spirit can make possible? Because He is the reservoir of power, limitless in supply He does not want us to be content with water to our ankles, or up to our knees and loins. His purpose is to fill us with His fullness. But have we an ever-increasing thirst for the rivers of living water to be found in Him? Listen to Him as He says, "Drink abundantly, My friends." In one of his hymns on *The Holy Spirit,* Charles Wesley writes,

> God, through Himself, we then shall know
>   If Thou within us shine;
> And sound, with all the saints below
>   The depths of love divine.

Ninth Summary
The Aspects of Fear in Scripture

Cervantes, the fifteenth century novelist, tells us that "fear has many eyes." Wordsworth, the eighteenth century poet, wrote—

> Fear hath a hundred eyes, that all agree
> To plague her beating heart.

The simile of several eyes is but another way of describing the quantity of fears that plague the human heart. But that there is victory from all fettering fears is proclaimed by David, "I sought the Lord, and he heard me, and delivered me from all my fears" (34:4). The setting of this psalm gives a preacher sufficient material for a sermon on cowards. Pursued by King Saul, David was smitten with fear. Then we read that "sore afraid of Achish," he pretended he was mad while in the presence of the Philistine king (I Sam. 21:12-13). But in the psalm, David tells us how he turned to God when at a dead end, and He emancipated him from the fear of both Saul and Achish. A peculiarity of the psalm is the labor the author bestowed upon it, for in the Hebrew its twenty-two verses are cast in alphabetical order, and uses fear in five different ways in four of its verses (34:4, 7, 9, 11). Four different meanings are likewise given of the word:

Terror

It is this agitated emotion that we find in passages like "Fear and dread shall fall upon them" (Exod. 15:16). "Then the men feared the Lord exceedingly" (Jonah 1:16). This idea of terror can be used in a wrong way, as, for instance, when we read that the shepherds were sore afraid, and that the angels told them not to fear (Luke 2:10). Such a terror-stricken condition is unhealthy, and robs the soul of peace, trust, confidence, and power. But *terror* is also used in a right way. We are not to be "highminded, but fear" (Rom. 11:20). We must "serve God acceptably with all reverence and fear" (Heb. 4:1; 12:28).

Reverence

Several times the word *fear* implies reverence of soul—a reverential trust with hatred of evil. This is filial fear, the holy feelings of the renewed heart toward God. "The fear of the Lord" is a common phrase used often (Ps. 111:10; Prov. 3:7; 8:13, etc.). Such a fear produces trust, loathing of sin, reverent submission to divine providences, and a ready obedience to all God's gracious commands. It also bids us keep our heart tender, our soul safe, and our life continuously adjusted to the divine will.

Timidity

In writing to young Timothy as he commenced his ministry as an evangelist, Paul reminded him that God had not given him "the spirit of fear," but of "power" (II Tim. 1:7). The veteran preacher counsels the young man just beginning to preach to be firm, courageous, and not timid or hesitant in the face of foes. He must never be guilty of drawing back, but launch out into the deep, and thus fully commit himself to the cause of Christ.

Caution

Noah, we read, "moved with fear" (Heb. 11:7), went on building the ark. In spite of the ridicule and unbelief of the multitude to be drowned by the Flood, Noah went on quietly, cautiously with his God-given task. Christ's intercessions were heard of God "in that he feared" (Heb. 5:7). Daily, it was His concern to be cautious as to the accomplishment of God's will. When the mob threatened Paul's life, the captain dealt with the unruly crowd in a cautious, tactful manner. The Latin word for "caution"—*lavere*—means "to be on one's guard." *Cautious,* says Webster, implies "attention to examine probable effects and consequences of acts so as to avoid danger."

Idle Fears

Aesop says that we might—"better die once for all than to live in continual fear." But the tragedy is that the majority of our fears are imaginary. We live in dread of experiences that never come to pass. The psalmist describes those who were in "great fear, where no fear was" (Ps. 53:5). How foolish it is to be troubled over troubles that never appear, and to worry over things that never happen! Never trouble trouble, till trouble troubles you, is sound advice. How useless it is to try to cross bridges before we come to them! The good Lord deliver us from the fear of what may overtake us, and give us grace to live in the present, even moment by moment, knowing that the future is His concern.

> Lord, for tomorrow, and its needs
> I do not pray:
> But keep me, guide me, hold me, Lord,
> Just for today.

Those heartbroken women at the tomb of Jesus entertained an idle fear when they asked, "Who shall roll us away the stone from the door of the sepulchre?" But when they looked, the stone was out of its groove, the door was wide open, and an angel was seated on what the women had feared. A physician, who was also something of a psychologist, and who knew that many of his patients made themselves ill by worrying over the future, displayed a large motto in his consulting room for all to see and read—

DON'T WORRY,
IT MAY NOT HAPPEN

If we truly believe that our times are in the Lord's hands, then we also believe He knows all about the future and will suffer no trial to overtake us without His permission. And what He allows, no matter how grievous, is for our good and His glory.

> Ye fearful saints, fresh courage take;
> The clouds ye so much dread
> Are big with mercy, and shall break
> In blessings on your head.

Fear of Things

This aspect is more tangible than the one just considered in that we know that inevitable dreaded consequences are associated with certain experiences. Scripture gives us many instances of the "hundred eyes" of fear.

Fear of Physical and Material Loss

Cried Job, "For the thing which I greatly fear is come upon me" (3:25). The loss of work, of money, of health, are foreseen by many and bring despair. But if we are God's children, why worry in the day of adversity? Have we not the promise about there being no want to them who fear Him (Ps. 34:9-10)?

Fear of Opposition and Hatred of Others

Because of His stern condemnation of the Pharisees, Jesus

knew that animosity would accrue, but He had no fear, for in spite of demons and men, He finished His course. Our allegiance to Him, and spirituality of life are bound to arouse the antagonism of a godless world, but we have nothing to fear for He will preserve our life from the enemy (Ps. 64:1). The Angel of the Lord is encamped near us, and is, therefore, at hand to deliver us when assailed (Ps. 34:7).

Fear of Calamities

Out on those storm-tossed waves, thinking they would perish any moment, the disciples might have been justifiably afraid, but Jesus rebuked them, "Why are ye so fearful, O ye of little faith?" They should not have been alarmed, seeing "the Master of ocean, and earth, and sky" was in their boat. Faith and fear cannot live together. When the storms of life are raging, if Jesus is at the helm of your little craft, then all will be well.

Fear of Persecution and Death

It must have seemed hard for the disciples to accept the fiat of Jesus, "Fear not them which kill the body" (Matt. 10:28). He knew that His own body would be killed, but He had no fear. He could reecho the declaration of the psalmist, "I will not fear what flesh can do unto me" (Ps. 56:4). Similar defiance can be ours, if we believe that God is ever at hand to protect us from our foes. With boldness we can say, "The Lord is my helper" (Heb. 13:6).

Fear of National and Political Changes

Describing the end-time period of Gentile history Jesus said that, "Men's hearts [would fail] them for fear" (Luke 21:26). Are we not living in this predicted fear-driven world? Whether we think of statesmen and rulers or industrialists and workers or parents and children, hearts are possessed by fear as to the condition of human society. But for those who rest in their omnipotent Lord, there is the confidence that though the earth be removed they need not fear (Ps. 46:2). They have a courage born of truth, and a grace of fearlessness which springs from the revelation of God's almightiness. Such courage is the helm that keeps the soul according to the divine compass, and makes us safe regardless of adverse events.

Fear of Man

Solomon reminds us that "the fear of man bringeth a snare" (Prov. 29:25). Such a phase of fear is common to saint and sinner alike. It was characteristic of many in the New Testament as well. There were those Galileans who came to believe in the fearless Christ—"Howbeit no man spake openly of him for fear of the Jews" (John 7:13). Joseph of Arithmathea, who sacrificed his new tomb for the burial of Jesus, was "a disciple ..., but secretly for fear of the Jews" (John 19:38). After the resurrection, "the disciples were assembled together for fear of the Jews" (John 20:19). The psalmist could say, "Whom shall I fear ... of whom shall I be afraid?" (Ps. 27:1). Alas! many are secret disciples for fear of what the worldly minded around them may say. They have the light, but keep it under a bushel. Such fear is a sign of a craven, cowardly heart. But God is able to impart courage, or nerve which enables us to do His bidding in spite of ridicule and contempt. As they looked upon John Knox after his death, and passed by his coffin, people said, "There's the face that never feared the face of man." If we fear God we have no reason to be afraid of any man.

When professed believers realize their obligations of being more pronounced in their witness and more committed to the Lord, but withhold their full allegiance because of the fear that this will interfere with business prospects, they are guilty of keeping back part of the price. When a Christian feels he should be separated from worldly pleasures and pursuits, but fears to make the break in case he is laughed at or snubbed for a seeming holier-than-thou-attitude, then his fear of man is a snare. Peter was afraid to own His Lord in the hour of His suffering, but Pentecost made all the difference, for on that historic day he so condemned the Jews with the crime of history that as they witnessed his boldness they marveled. No wonder they were amazed, knowing of his previous denial of Jesus. There are others who are almost persuaded to become Christians, but cowardice keeps them back from surrendering to Christ. They are afraid of the jeers they may receive, and so, lacking the courage of their convictions, the fear of man keeps them in the peril of dying without the Saviour.

Slavish Fear of God

Scripture makes it clear that there are wrong ways, as well as right ways, of fearing God. Job confessed, "Therefore am I troubled at his presence, when I consider, I am afraid of him" (23:15). But Paul reminds us that we "have not received the spirit of bondage again to fear" (Rom. 8:15). When the psalmist said, "But there is forgiveness with thee, that thou mayest be feared," he referred to a holy, reverential fear—the mark of one whose many sins have been forgiven. Filial fear of God is a duty, and causes us to shrink from sin, keeps us from straying, and enables us to avoid all that is offensive to our Holy Father. Servile fear, or dread of God, drives us from Him, as it did our first parents. But this is not the sort of fear that can make us holy. This aspect of fear springs from selfishness.

Often dread of God is based on ignorance of God's nature and a wrong conception of His character. He is not a God with a mailed fist, a tyrant, a despot, a hard Being bent on the vengeance and destruction of sinners. Once we receive the

91

Spirit of adoption we cry, "Abba, Father!" What a glorious change from cowering before Him! In his exaltation of the Saviour, after the birth of his son, Zacharias exclaimed, " . . . that we being delivered out of the hand of our enemies might serve him without fear" (Luke 1:74). Here the concept of dread is meant, for the saints must ever serve the Lord with reverence. Such fear is the beginning of wisdom. Are you afraid of God? "I remembered God and was troubled," the psalmist confessed. Sinners are half-way on the road to salvation if they are afraid, or troubled, as they remember the thrice Holy One. But such fettering fear vanishes when they come to know Him as the God of love who gave His only begotten Son for their salvation. This loving, gracious God is our God for ever and ever.

> Fear Him, ye saints, and you will then
> Have nothing else to fear;
> Make you His service your delight,
> Your wants shall be His care.

Fear of Death

Doubtless this is the most common aspect of fear. Sometimes even true believers are afraid to die and fail to fear the grave as little as they do their bed. The writer of Hebrews speaks of those "who through fear of death were all their lifetime subject to bondage" (2:15). Death, of course, is the greatest fact of life. As soon as we are born we start our journey to God's green acre, but whether death is a friend or a foe depends upon our relationship to God. Sinners are afraid to die, and have good reason to be. Those who are not ready, through grace, to die, have cause to dread the grave. Conscience makes cowards of many, who blatantly rejected God, when they come to the swelling of Jordan.

Christ, through death, destroyed him who had the power of death. Willingly, He tasted death for every man, and robbed it of its sting (I Cor. 15:35; Heb. 2:9, 14). Why, then, fear man's last enemy since the sting is gone? Our relationship to Christ determines our attitude to death. To those who live and die without Him as Saviour, death is a terrible foe ushering them into a Christless eternity. But if He has been received as "the resurrection and the life," then death is a kind friend leading us into the presence of Him who is alive forevermore.

> I fear no foe, with Thee at hand to bless;
> Ills have no weight, and tears no bitterness:
> Where is death's sting? Where, grave thy victory?
> I triumph still, if Thou abide with me.

Fear of Hell

It was a sermon on hell that convicted the renowned missionary, Mary Slessor, of her sin and led her to accept Christ as her Saviour. It is to be regretted that this solemn truth of Scripture is seldom preached today. Yet the fear of hell is deep and real in many hearts. Would that we could have more of such fear in these materialistic days! How dare we be silent about warning the lost of "the blackness of darkness for ever," when we have Scriptures like these? "Fear him which is able to destroy soul and body into hell" (Matt. 10:28). "The rich man also died . . . in hell . . . in torments" (Luke 26:22-23). "But a certain fearful looking for of judgment and of fiery indignation" (Heb. 10:27). "It is a fearful thing to fall into the hands of the living God" (Heb. 10:31). "But the fearful . . . shall have their part in the lake which burneth with fire and brimstone: which is the second death" (Rev. 21:8). "The wicked shall be turned into hell, and all the nations that forget God" (Ps. 9:17).

Men may try to do away with future judgment, or treat hell in a jocular manner, but because it was a grim reality to Jesus, and He died to save sinners from such a doomed, eternal abode, it is a subject that should be preached with all the compassion of the Saviour. This fear of hell is tormenting, but perfect love can cast out such fear (I John 4:18). Submission to divine claims removes all fear of perdition. "There is therefore now no condemnation to them which are in Christ Jesus" (Rom. 8:1). Faith kills fear. Trust casts out terror. After seeking the Lord, David was delivered from *all* his fears (Ps. 34:4), even the fear of death for although he would have to walk through death's dark vale, he would fear no evil. Through grace, may our song be—

> The fear of hell has gone forever,
>> No more to cause my heart to grieve.
> There is a place, I do believe,
>> In heaven for me, beyond the river.

Tenth Summary
The Fact and Features of Depression in Scripture

Florence Nightingale, The Lady of the Lamp, tells how on her way to the Crimean War she heard from the sailors a weird story of birds with black wings, and blue breasts that flew over the Black Sea during stormy weather. Sometimes they perched on the masts of the ship, but they never were caught. On dark nights they would go to Mohammedan graveyards and roost among the green boughs of the cyprus trees, mingling their doleful notes with the sighing of the wind, making thereby weird, eerie sounds. Moslems declared that the spirits of the wicked lived in the birds and that the sorrowful notes were the wailing of the dead.

To most lives, these birds with their black wings and blue breasts come, and we hardly know from whence they come. They are hard to capture and destroy, and almost turn hearts to the cemetery. Sad, heavy-hearted, we are not able to define the burdens depressing us. In other words, fits of depression, despondency, melancholy overtake us and we have "the blues"—a colloquial expression for deep despondency and depression of spirit. It is said that "blues" is a contraction of "Blue Devil," or an evil demon. In the opening verses of Psalm 77, it would seem as if the writer knew all about "the blues," and also their radical cure. Read the first nine verses and you can hear the flutter of a whole flock of those birds with their black wings. It would seem as if God allowed the author of the psalm to have "the blues" in order that he might give us a divine analysis of his state of mind. Having diagnosed the disease, he gives the cure—how to pluck the feathers out of the black wings of the blue-breasted birds symbolizing a melancholy frame of mind and despondency of heart.

The more we read the Bible the more fascinated we are by its relevance to human life. In a most impressive way it covers the whole gamut of feelings and emotions common to mankind and takes account of human frailties. For instance, some of the outstanding characters are portrayed as being subject to spiritual depression, heaviness, and dejection. As C. Ernest Tatham puts it,

> One might think of some of God's picked servants of old, men whose names come down the centuries perfumed with Heaven's aroma and who have affected the lives of myriads for blessing. We are not to think of these as sort of demi-gods or even supermen, but rather that they themselves were compassed about with infirmity, men of like passions with us. In spite of their accomplishments for God and His glory, they were quite imperfect vessels.

Biblical Illustration of Depression

Many of the best men of the Bible, because of their periodic lapses into "the blues," reveal that they were only men at the best. They were touched with the feeling of our infirmities.

Take Moses

This outstanding figure of the Old Testament, a giant among men, the great lawgiver and instrument of divine miraculous power, surely knew nothing about gloominess or despondency. Such a friend and servant of God must have had a continuous mountaintop experience, and no downcast valley. But think of the complaint he poured into the ears of God when he succumbed to the feeling of despair, "Wherefore hast thou afflicted thy servant? And wherefore have I not found favor in thy sight, that thou layest the burden of all this people upon me. . . . I am not able to bear all this people alone, because it is too heavy for me" (Num. 11:11, 14).

Men of lesser grit would have fainted under such a burden long before Moses did. In his downcast frame of mind, he momentarily forgot that it was Jehovah who had been bearing the multitude of murmuring Israelites for so long. Looking at the horde of complainers and taking his eye off God, Moses gave way to the feeling of discouragement. Often excessive labor results in a wearied body, exhausted frame, and a tired brain. Such a condition can rob the harp of the sweet music of joy. If one has had extra strain in caring for and nursing others, with all that this entails in loss of regular hours, irregular meals, and loss of sleep, it is not to be marveled at if the nerves become overstrung and a feeling of dolefulness ensues. Ian Maclaren, the Scottish novelist loved to use the bright motto—"Be kind. Everyone is fighting a hard battle." Those who are hard-pressed need all the sympathy we can offer.

Take Elijah

The stern, rugged figure of this prophet dominates the theocratic period of Israel's history. What a stalwart defender of faith in Jehovah he was! Solitary yet brave, he stood alone, and when he called down fire to consume the sacrifice, 850 defiant priests saw the nation forced to its knees sobbing, "The Lord, he is the God; the Lord, he is the God." We would have expected such a champion to follow up such a tremendous conquest with a terrible onslaught upon the hosts of evil. But the physical exhaustion of building an altar, dividing the bullock, running miles, and the psychological tension of his confrontation with the maniacal priests of Baal, were too much even for this strong, fearless prophet, and so we see him plunging into the deepest valley of reactionary melancholy and depression.

After Carmel there came the juniper experience, with its reaction to the contest with the priests of Baal, and Elijah's yielding to the feelings of despair. Sitting under the tree with dejected countenance, he mournfully laments, "O Lord take away my life; for I am not better than my fathers." While on the mountain, defying the godless priests, he spoke about "Jehovah, God of Israel." Now under the tree of despondency, he laments, "I, even I only." After his life had been so remarkably used of God, he now begs Him to take away his life; yet he was afraid that Jezebel might oblige instead. He was defiant on Mount Carmel, yet he ran away from the threat of an evil-minded woman. How would you react in similar circumstances?

Take David

The Psalms are full of sighs, moans, and laments. Perhaps it is because of what they have to say about depression and melancholy feelings that we love them. How true to life they are! A depressed age like ours has need to face the question— "Why art thou cast down?" David not only wrote about spiritual despondency, he experienced it. From the time he was a shepherd-lad when he tackled and killed wild beasts attempting to destroy his father's sheep and slew Goliath the Philistine giant, noble exploits had been his. Forced to flee because of Saul's jealousy, God covered David's head in the day of battle, and was his shield. All plots against him failed.

But even such a warrior experienced that human endurance has its limitations, and one day he failed to see Him who is invisible, and who was able to undertake for him to the end. So he dejectedly moaned and mourned, "I shall now perish one day by the hand of Saul: there is nothing better for me than that I should speedily escape into the land of the Philistines; and Saul shall despair of me to seek me any more in any coast of Israel: so shall I escape out of his hand" (I Sam. 27:1).

A quaint writer says of Psalms 42 and 43, which are credited to David and are one in style and sentiment, that in them, "David is chiding David out of the dumps." As can be seen, these two doleful psalms form a soliloquy, which means a person talking to himself about himself. Tossed and ruffled within his soul and with turbulent waves destroying his inner peace, David asks himself why he is in such a dark, sad state. "Why art thou cast down, O my soul?" There was no reason why he should be disquieted within for he had a thirst for God and was the recipient of His loving-kindness (42:1). Robert Louis Stevenson once wrote, "The world is so full of a number of things, I'm sure we should all be as happy as kings." But David, although a king, was not happy.

Do not these two psalms fully express the frequent feeling of many, and should we not, like David, seek to chide ourselves out of a fit of depression? For nothing is so detrimental to health and happiness as unrelieved despondency and downheartedness. This is the state of mind which Shakespeare could describe only as "the dumps, so dull and dreary." Three times over David asks himself the reason for the melancholy emotion surging within his soul. Twice he asked in vain, for trouble and anxiety came rolling back in spite of a moment's respite, but the third time the answer came in the form of triumph—"I shall yet praise him, who is the health of my countenance."

Take John the Baptist

This Elijah-like prophet that Jesus so highly commended exercised a remarkable ministry as the forerunner of Him whom he acclaimed as "the Lamb of God who taketh away the sin of the world." Although he lived and labored in the desert, he gathered a great congregation in his wilderness habitat. (Modernistic preachers turn a congregation *into* a

99

wilderness. Giving stones instead of bread, they empty churches of hungry souls.)

The Baptist's magnanimity is seen when Jesus entered His public ministry, and John's task as the forerunner was ended—"He must increase but I must decrease." Because of his fearless preaching on sin and repentance, the Baptist found himself in prison, and it seemed as if, for the time being, all his hopes of the establishment of the Kingdom he had taught were fast disappearing. So he dispatched two of his disciples to Jesus with the question, "Art thou he that should come, or look we for another?" What a doubtful question to ask, especially as John himself had introduced Jesus as the Lamb who had come into the world to die for sin!

Mystified, perplexed, downcast, and depressed, and sensing the brutal death before him, this greatest of all the prophets (Matt. 11:11), succumbed to a bout of dejection. There has only been one perfect Servant of God, who, even in the face of bitterest opposition, never gave way to gloom and despair. It is the Saviour of whom Isaiah prophesied, "He shall not fail nor be discouraged" (42:4). This was the One who, facing His dejected disciples, could say, "Be of good cheer; I have overcome the world." Our victory over all forms of depression is found in meditating on Him whose blessed life was a joyous one throughout—"For consider him that endured such contradiction of sinners against himself, lest ye be wearied and faint in your minds" (Heb. 12:3). The secret of His freedom from inner disturbed emotions that result in despair was His constant, unbroken fellowship with His Father and the anticipation of the joy set before Him. Therein lies our victory as well. May we covet the blessing the Lord gave to the church at Ephesus, "for my name's sake [thou] hast laboured, and hast not fainted" (Rev. 2:3).

Various Causes of Depression

The saintliest of men often find themselves in the Cave of

Despair or the Slough of Despond. It is the common lot of all to sit at some time or other beneath the willow tree. Solomon reminds us that "man is born to trouble, as the sparks fly upward." We serve a God, however, who is never cast down or weary, and who offers Himself as the "lifter up of [our] head." Satan, sin, and circumstances are responsible for dolefulness, but Jesus is able to relieve all who are oppressed, and depressed, of the devil (Acts 10:38). What, then, are some of the reasons for human disquietude and dispirited feelings?

Impaired Health

Paul knew something of this for he had a thorn in the flesh which caused him pain. Whatever this infirmity of the flesh was, the apostle had to endure it constantly, because its removal was denied even though he prayed that it might be. The more longstanding an ailment, the more it makes inroads upon our peace of mind. Countless numbers of God's children are subject to physical disabilities which He does not remove—a fact to bear in mind in these days of professed healers of all diseases. Strong, healthy, vigorous men often fail to understand the depressing influence of feeble health and how the spirit droops under the weight of such a burden, and of how lack of physical vitality produces a melancholy frame of mind.

If we are hale and hearty we should strive to help by our sincere sympathy those weighted down by suffering. "We then that are strong ought to bear the infirmities of the weak." If we are carefree and able to sing for joy, let us not forget the moan of the afflicted. But if bodily aches and pains are yours and shadow your spirit somewhat, take heart from the counsel of God, and hope in God, who is the health of your countenance. May we ever remember those who, because of their infirmities, are not able to travel to God's house, and may we visit them in their affliction!

101

While it may sound somewhat paradoxical, yet it would seem as if some people are not happy unless they are unhappy. The psalmist sighed, "my soul refused to be comforted" (Ps. 77:2). Although, in the day of his trouble, he sought the God of Comfort, yet he did not receive comfort because he did not desire it. He preferred his discomfort, sorrow, and despondency to the peace of God. Doubtless you have met those who are not content unless they are miserable and depressed. They somehow hug their grief, and glory in their sorrow, and attract to the windows the birds with the black wings and feed them instead of starving the doleful creatures. Like Rachel of old they refuse to be comforted. They have the unhappy knack of looking on the dark side and of living in the shadows. When you urge them to look on the bright side, they lament that there is not a bright side. Well, grace can be theirs to polish up the dark side they seem to prefer.

It is inevitable that all of us will have sorrow of some sort or other, but let us not sin against the divine Comforter by refusing His consolations. We speak about "getting over" sorrow. Somehow we dislike the term. What is better is "getting into" the trials of life to find right in the heart of them the dearest of all friends—the Man of Sorrows Himself. It is only thus that we are preserved from the despondent aspect of grief, and learn that—

> Not a shaft can hit,
> Till the God of love sees fit.

When dear ones are removed there is the tendency to nurse our sorrow, and linger in the valley of weeping until we become pathetic and burdensome. Tears continue to be our meat day and night, and the clouds never vanish from our heart. We sigh and moan, as if no one else had ever lost a loved one. Our gloom is never alleviated. Are we not guilty of the sin of selfishness when we weep and wail as if we were alone in our sorrow?

A Complaining Spirit

The more we complain, the more cause we have for complaining, and a disgruntled heart is never a glad one. The psalmist said, "I complained, and my spirit was overwhelmed" (Ps. 77:3). The prophet anticipates the time when there will be "no complaining in our streets." Alas! today our streets are full of grousers and grumblers. Nothing others can do ever pleases them. They complain about their food, or the weather, or their circumstances. How such mournful murmurers need the spirit of the old lady who had only two teeth, but who was grateful that one tooth was opposite the other, so that she was able to bite! The squid is a kind of cuttle fish that blackens the water about it so that it can hide itself in it. Not only does it shut out its own vision, it obscures the vision of others as well. Just so, the complaining spirit darkens the life and robs the heart of sunshine around.

Insomnia, or Sleeplessness

This black-winged bird hovers over many a bed, especially in these days of pressures. Too often we seek relief in drug and drink addiction. "Thou holdest mine eyes waking" (Ps. 77:4). If God prevents sleep, as He did in the case of King Ahasuerus, it is for a beneficial purpose. But unnecessary worry, despondency, and melancholy exact a sad toll in sleepless nights; and loss of "care-charming sleep, thou easer of all woes," makes it difficult for anyone to be cheerful. Tossing and turning, the sleepless one may rise and flood the dark room with light, but there is a darkness of mind that sleeplessness only accentuates. Because the psalmist blamed God for the darkness, inner darkness became denser.

Often the saints of God, who have long waking periods, do

not suffer temperamentally or physically because they spend the sleepless hours in meditation, worship, and communion with Him who neither slumbers nor sleeps. Frances Ridley Havergal, a constant sufferer, left it on record that some of the sweetest hours of her life were the nights of sleeplessness when her heart was awake to God, and her thoughts were filled with praise. Yes, God is able to give to His beloved sleep, but happy are those who can turn restlessness into restfulness, and whose heart reposes in God amid the shadows of night. If, through our own sin or folly, sleep deserts us, then despondency continues through the day that follows.

Ours should be the experience of the psalmist when he reminds us, "I call to remembrance my song in the *night:* I commune with my own heart" (Ps. 77:6). Instead of a sigh during sleepless hours there was a song as he remembered God's past goodness. How victorious we are when we are able to sing songs in the night! Is it not true that sorrow's crown of sorrow is the remembrance of happier things? "Son, remember!" was the solemn word given to the rich man in hell, and the memory of what he might have been and done was a flame tormenting him. Further, there are many who were once like nightingales, filling the air with music, but who now screech like owls and are so doleful. The greater the delight, the more intense the depression when the delight vanishes.

Unfaithfulness of Others

If it be true that David wrote Psalms 42 and 43 at the time of the rebellion of his favorite son, Absalom, then we can understand the cause of his darkened soul. The king was an exile on the east of Jordan, fleeing from his head-strong son, and such a sudden, disappointing crisis broke the father's heart. His depth of despair was as a sword in his bones (Ps. 42:10). Paul also was a lonely man, and this loneliness was intensified by friends who acted unfriendly. There are allusions in his Letters to unfaithful companions, for instance, Demas who forsook him. The feeling of sadness and gloom these unworthy partners caused him is poignant—"All that are in Asia turned away from me." "All forsake me." "I was left alone in Athens." Is your heart heavy because friends have proved false? Deceived, are you dejected? Well, do not allow your despondency to deepen into contempt. Dispirited and forsaken though you may be, perhaps while you are sighing God is preparing a still better friend for you.

Mysterious Providences

In a remarkable way David personified his sorrow when he said, "My tears have been my meat day and night, while they continually say unto me, Where is thy God?" (42:3). Seeing all His waves and billows had gone over him (42:7), he found himself cast down because of the apparent inactivity of God to help him. Had He, as his Rock, forgotten him in the hour of deep need? At Calvary, we have an echo of the *whys* of this psalm, in the divine *why*—"My God, my God, why hast thou forsaken me?" Often we find ourselves in a state of gloom and despair because of God's seeming indifference not only to some of the glaring sins and injustices in human society but also to personal problems. Yet He is always in the shadows planning and working out His purposes.

Personal Sin

Multitudes are doleful, disconsolate, and despondent because of their iniquitous state. They are not right with God; they are not ready to meet Him in eternity; and they are depressed—and have every cause to be. Would that they would become so distressed and depressed over their sins that the peril of dying would drive them more speedily to their only refuge—the Fountain at Calvary opened for sin and uncleanness! Or, it may be that you have experienced the joy that came with your salvation from sin's penalty and thrall-dom, but now you have lost that joy, and find yourself sharing the despair of the prodigal son, "When I remember these things, I pour out my soul in me," and as you think of the past, and how you basked in the sunshine of His presence, you pour out your soul in sighs and moans. "Oh, that I were as in months past" (Job 29:2). What else can you expect but remorse and unhappiness of heart if you are not walking in the light as He is in the light? Believe with David, that God is able to restore unto you the joy of His salvation.

Advancing Age

Many experience that the evening-tide of life brings shadows and heart-grief. Youth is the time of smiles and sunshine, as it ought to be; but old age is a tragedy to many who live alone. With time on their hands they have plenty of time to think, and become disconsolate. The older some become, the more susceptible they become to the feelings pulsating in the breast of David when he found himself cast down and so disquieted in mind. Days are long for the aged, and there is time to brood and repine. A description of such loneliness can be found in a private letter Dr. Dinsdale Young sent to a friend in which he said, "Alone—all alone, no wifely or daughterly hand to serve me in my old age." Yet although age is leaving its mark after the storms and billows almost engulfed your frail bark, tranquility of heart can be yours if you are resting in Him who said, "To old age I will carry you." How inspired are the lines of Browning in *Rabbi ben Ezra*—

> Grow old along with me!
> The best is yet to be.
> The last of life, for which the first was made:
> Our times are in His hand
> Who saith, "A whole life I planned,
> Youth shows but half; trust God;
> See all, nor be afraid."

Victory over Persistent Downheartedness

A most vital and practical question many ask is, How can we defeat spiritual gloom and lift ourselves into, and keep ourselves in, the sunnier sky of cheer? As there is enough despair in the world without adding to it, we should strive after a cure for personal melancholy and dejection. John Gay, quaint poet of the seventeenth century, in *The Beggar's Opera* has the couplet—

> If the heart of a man is deprest with cares,
> The mist is dispell'd when a woman appears.

Doubtless the visit of a kind, understanding, and sympathetic friend can exercise a soothing influence over us when we are cast down, but there is a Friend who sticketh closer than a brother who can relieve us as no other. What wise philosophy there is in the verse of one of Sankey's hymns—

> Go bury thy sorrow, the world hath its share;
> Go bury it deeply, go hide it with care:
> Go think of it calmly, when curtained by night,
> Go tell it to Jesus, and all will be right.

There are, at least, three elements in the antidote for spiritual despondency.

First, we must recognize the fact that depression is tragic.

Such an emotion works havoc in our own life and robs those nearest to us of the pleasure and joy they ought to derive from our company and fellowship. Dejection is the worst feeling we can have, because it magnifies trouble, and drags at and prevents our doing our daily work in an acceptable manner. It makes a mountain out of a mole-hill, shadows blessings, makes the hard things of life more prominent than the good things, robs us of God's smile, weakens His promises, cripples our testimony, and arrests our spirituality.

Second, we must bury our sorrow in the thought of others.

A sure avenue of relief when gloom settles on our spirit, is to go out and visit others as dejected as ourselves, or worse, and seek to encourage them. Too often we parade our personal grief to the exclusion of the cares, agonies, heart-grief of others. Doubtless you have read of the man whose moan was loud because he had no hands, but who met another man with no feet, and thus learned the lesson of sympathy. A radical cure, then, for a brooding, repining spirit is to forget our morbid self, and get out into the world broken by its sins and sorrows, and help bear the burdens of others.

Third, we must turn to God.

Here, alone, is perfect relief. If tempted to be low-spirited, we must follow the example of David and tighten our grip on God, then our soul will shine with the light of heaven. Listen to his voice, "Then will I go unto the altar of God, unto God my exceeding joy: Yea, upon the harp will I praise thee, O God my God" (Ps. 43:4). He alone can erase the furrows on the brow, and the tearstains from the cheek, and the burden from our hearts. By His grace we can lift up our head and smile at the storm.

In seasons of undue depression and disquietude the proper remedy is to expostulate with our soul directly. "Why art thou cast down, O my soul?" Chiding ourselves for dolefulness we should say, "Up, fainting heart, look out of the window and think of the never-failing God, and of all the good things in life." We must sweeten the inner chamber of the soul with sprigs of the sweet herb of hope. "Hope thou in God: for I shall yet praise him for the help of his countenance." The aspect of any event depends largely upon the beholder's point of view. If one's hope is in God, then this stimulates and calms the disturbed soul. Trouble in life would be less disturbing if we were more convinced that God is ours and that we are His.

The successful way of gaining and maintaining a fixed temper of tranquility is constant retreat into the deep, hidden chamber, the secret place of the Most High where storms cannot harass, and where we experience perfect peace.

> "Be all at rest!" for rest alone becometh
> The soul that casts on Him its every care.

How slow we are to imbibe the lesson of casting all our care upon God! Although we cannot expect to be immune from the trials of life, yet like the apostle we can be sorrowful yet always rejoicing, and bid our disquieted spirit to lean upon His bosom who calmed the angry waves. If your harp is hanging on a willow tree, take it down, right now, and strike up a new song unto the Lord for His unfailing grace.

> Hidden in the hollow
>   Of His blessed hand,
> Never foe can follow,
>   Never traitor stand;
> Not a surge of worry,
>   Not a shade of care,
> Not a blast of hurry,
>   Touch the spirit there.

Eleventh Summary
The Importance of "the North Side" in Scripture

It may surprise you to know that the north is not only one of the four cardinal points of the horizon—it is also a quarter that is full of symbolic import. This end of the earth's axis is frequently mentioned in the Bible, its first reference being in Genesis 13:14, and the last in Revelation 21:13.

North—the Sacrifice Side

Offerings had to be slain on "the side of the altar north-ward" (Lev. 1:11; Ezek. 40:46). Sacrifices killed on the southward side were deemed polluted. In the Church of England, the north side is the altar side, and the side on which the word is read.

As the north represents the dark side of the earth, the Scriptures are as a light shining in the world's darkness. The north, as the death-side, is emphasized throughout the Bible.

1. Abraham lived on the north side—"Lift up thine eyes . . . northward" (Gen. 13:14). Sojourning in a strange country with its tents and testings, Abraham knew all about the death-side of obedience to God. When he allowed Lot to choose the best of the land, Abraham died to self-choice.

2. David lived on the north side—"Promotion cometh neither from the east, nor from the west, nor from the south" (Ps. 75:6-7). Why is the north omitted, the only quarter true promotion can come from? The only way up is down—in humility.

3. Jesus lived and died on the north side. Jerusalem was built on the north of Mount Zion. Job tells us that God

110

stretched out the north over the empty place (26:7). Jesus died at Golgotha—the place of a skull, a phrase suggesting emptiness and nothingness.

4. Israel knew about the north side. "I will say to the north, give up" (Isa. 43:6). Sacrifice and surrender from which we shrink are associated with the north, the altar side.

North—the Unwelcome Side

Job, another child of the north, wrote of cold coming out from this quarter (37:5). The Arctic regions are spoken of as the Frozen North. The north is never a pleasant side to explore, spiritually as well as geographically. Death to sin and to all carnal and worldly pleasures brings icy treatment from friends, even religious ones, who know not what it is to live without the camp with Christ (Heb. 13:13). You should rejoice if your separation unto God is resulting in the frozen rivers of friendship. As Jesus watched the retreating forms of those who were unwilling to pay the price of full discipleship, He asked, "Will ye also go away?"

North—the Beneficial Side

The Bible says that the north has its bright side as well as its bleak aspect.

1. Golden sunshine is there. "Fair weather cometh out of the north" (Job 37:22). The ancients regarded the northern spheres as the residences of gods. Sacrifice has its golden pleasures and privileges.

2. Beauty and joy are there (Ps. 48:2). Zion, on the north side, was beautiful for situation. A joy, not of earth, is ours as we identify ourselves with the crucified Christ.

3. Fellowship is there. "The table . . . upon the side . . . northward" (Exod. 40:22). Friends may isolate us because of our allegiance to Christ, but He is ever with us (Heb. 13:5).

4. Tranquility is there. Zechariah tells that it is possible to

experience a quiet spirit even in the north country (6:8). Spiritual isolation may be ours, but in Him, there is peace.

North—the Governmental Side

Jeremiah hints that the north symbolizes "evil" and that God will deal with it (1:14). Joshua found a valley of giants in the north (15:8; 17:15). Look up passages like Ezekiel 1:4; 8:3-5; 9:2; Daniel 11:13-15; Joel 2:20 for other implications of the north as the judgment side. "The King of the North" is to play a prominent part in the formation of the Northern Confederacy.

Solomon reminds us that "the north wind driveth away rain" (Prov. 25:23). God's north wind of justice always drives away the rain of hostility and danger. The priests occupied a chamber with a northern prospect (Ezek. 40:46; 46:19). It may not be a bright prospect but it is always a blessed one. "Lift up thine eyes *northward*"—God is there (Ps. 89:12)!

Twelfth Summary
The Repetition of Surnames in Scripture

Does it surprise you to learn that the Bible has a good deal to say about surnames? In His commission to Cyrus, the Gentile king, God declared that He had "surnamed" him (Isa. 45:4).

The word *surname* means "an additional name." It represents the family name of a person. Archbishop Trench reminds us that something may be learned from knowing that the "surname," as distinguished from the "Christian" name, is the name over and above; not "sire" name—a name received from the father, but "sur" name (super-name).

It is reckoned that in England alone there are over forty thousand different surnames, or one to every five persons. Surnames were introduced into England by the Normans, and were adopted by the nobility in A.D. 1100.

An Honorary and Symbolic Title

As the custom of bestowing family names was unknown among the Jews, the Old Testament usage of "surname" simply means a flattering or honoring title. Gentiles were so envious of the riches of the Jews that they were anxious to be surnamed Israel, that is, enrolled as members of the Jewish nation (Isa. 44:5).

God surnamed Cyrus "my shepherd," appointing him, thereby, as His instrument of restoration (Isa. 44:28).

Elihu declared that he would not give "flattering titles" or "surnames" unto men. He himself was not overawed by Job's social position (Job 32:21).

113

In the New Testament we have many instances of the use of a surname. Simon surnamed Peter (Acts 10:5, 32); James and John surnamed Boanerges (Mark 3:17); Judas surnamed Iscariot (Luke 22:3); Barsabas surnamed Justus (Acts 1:23); Joses surnamed Barnabas (Acts 4:36); John surnamed Mark (Acts 12:12, 25); Judas surnamed Barsabas (Acts 15:22).

A Label Denoting the Bearer's Life and Labors

There are those whose surnames remind them of what they were or should strive to be. Nobility of task is associated with surnames like Elijah the Tishbite; Nehemiah the king's cup-bearer; John the Baptist; James the Lord's brother; Luke the beloved physician; Zena the lawyer.

In some cases we find the retention of an old name after the reason for it has passed away. An example of this is found in I Samuel 27:3; 30:5; II Samuel 3:3, where Abigail is called the wife of Nabal, even though her husband was dead.

Let us now group together those who are particularly labeled, and who are always identified by their label.

Rahab the Harlot (James 2:25). Why is this appendage carried over into the New Testament? Why not call her Rahab of the Scarlet Thread, or Rahab the Woman of Faith (Heb. 11:31)? Why is she branded forever as a woman of shame? *Matthew the Publican* (Matt. 10:3; Luke 5:27). Is this not another unkind reminder? Why not forget those unjust days? Did he not become one of the evangelists? Then why carry the stigma of a disreputable occupation? *Simon the Leper* (Matt. 26:6; Mark 14:3). Was he not cleansed of his foul disease? Then why not let the reminder of his leprous past fade away? *Mary Magdalene, out of whom went seven devils* (Luke 8:2). If it is against the principle of the gospel to rake up a person's past once they have been forgiven, is it not unchristian to remind a once devil-driven soul of a once polluted body? *Nicodemus, the same who came to Jesus by night* (John 3:1-2; 7:50; 19:39). Why always speak of the

114

fear and cowardice of the ruler who came to befriend Jesus? *Paul the persecutor* (I Tim. 1:13; Acts 22:4). Why is he not always spoken of as "Paul the apostle"?

Perhaps the old labels are carried to remind them of what they once were, and to keep them humble before God. The pit from which they were digged must not be forgotten (Isa. 51:1; I Cor. 6:9-11). Gypsy Smith used to keep his old rusty knife with which he made clothes-pegs to remind him of what he once was. It is blessed to know that all who reach heaven are to lose their old names and possess new ones (Rev. 19:12, 16).

Thirteenth Summary
The Cameos of Divine Tenderness in Scripture

The direct interpretation of the passage "even as God" (Eph. 4:32), concerns the infinite tenderness of God, expressed in His willingness to forgive the sinner for Christ's sake. And here we have a somewhat significant phrase, *"for Christ's sake."* Christ is always the medium of divine supply, as well as the one Mediator between God and man. Laban confessed to Jacob that he had learned that the Lord had blessed him for *his* sake. In like manner we are always and only blessed by God for Christ's sake.

The Being and attributes of God remain a profound study. The Almighty is incomprehensible, yet the most single-hearted can accept the revelation concerning Him. And in our study of the divine character, we must be careful to maintain a full-orbed vision of God, seeing there is a tendency in some quarters to dwell upon one attribute to the belittlement of another. For example, often His mercy is magnified at the expense of His majesty.

One of the most beautiful and comforting among God's transcendent attributes is that of His tenderness. This part of His nature brings Him near, making Him so real and dear. And not only so, but "tenderness" is sadly needed in these harsh, loveless days when it is a scarce commodity among men.

Dictatorships crucify tender feelings and outrage that which is noble in life. Communism, Nazism, Fascism, yes, and even Materialism, dry up the sweet, the loving, the gracious, and the gentle. Look at the hard, repulsive, unlovely faces of some of the would-be dictators! Such proud men may have greatness, but it is a greatness born of brute force, not of gentleness.

Well, here is the apostle Paul, the once-arch persecutor, urging the Ephesians to emulate the tenderness of God. Do our lives reflect this attractive attribute? Or do we find ourselves hard, bitter, unfeeling, loveless, and unsympathetic? Are we characterized by a lack of gentleness, even of God's gentleness with its power to make us great? Contact with the tenderness of God can soften and refine character. John, the Son of Thunder, was transformed into the Apostle of Love. It is still true that Christ is able to make the rebel a king and a priest. The dying thief was perhaps a murderer, a desperado equivalent to a modern gangster, a stranger to all that was delicate. Yet, at the sight of Jesus who, as He died, exhibited the tenderness of God in praying for His enemies, the repentant thief was so broken up and transformed that, as Robert Browning puts it, " 'Twas a thief who said the last kind words to Christ."

And, if we have lost the tenderer feelings of human nature, it is for us to repair to the source of all gentleness, even the tenderhearted God Himself. "Gentleness," Paul reminds us, is a "fruit of the Holy Spirit." He it is, the blessed Holy Spirit, who alone can enable us to manifest such a Godlike quality.

As the Scriptures present us with several aspects of divine tenderness, it is helpful to faith to combine the pictures so beautifully drawn.

The Eagle that Fluttereth

"As an eagle stirreth up her nest, fluttereth over her young, spreadeth abroad her wings, taketh them, beareth them on her wings: so the Lord alone did lead him" (Deut. 32:11-12).

Three aspects of the eagle's purpose are here indicated by Moses.

First of all the eagle stirs up her nest, compelling the eaglets to fly. Wings grown in the nest on the crag must learn to fly, so out go the young. Destroying the nest, twig by twig, the old eagle's desire is to make the nest too uncomfortable for the eaglets. And it is thus that God sometimes acts toward His own. The nest has to be torn to pieces, especially when the soul becomes too settled among the things of the world.

In the next place, the mother eagle flutters over her young in order to teach by example how to fly. It might well seem as if the eaglets are falling down into a bottomless abyss. The mother, however, is determined to induce her brood to use their wings. She, of course, is near and ready to swoop down to the help of her own. And thus it is with God. He stirs up our nests and makes us use our wings. We become too earthbound. Yet we were made to fly. May we spread our wings and trust ourselves to God.

Then we notice that the eagle spreads abroad her wings. In this way she protects, defends, hides her own in case of attack. With her wings the mother bird can drive off assailants, carry her young on her wings or back, and soar away. At a considerable altitude she will drop the eaglets, compelling them to find their wings, and then, if through any cause they cannot use their wings, she rapidly darts down and places her body beneath her young that they may alight and rest upon it. And what a beautiful glimpse of the tenderness of God this presents as He shelters us with His strong wings! If He cuts us loose from something to which we have clung, He is near to preserve us from falling.

The Father Who Pitieth

"Like as a father pitieth his children, so the Lord pitieth them that fear him. For he knoweth our frame; he remembereth that we are dust" (Ps. 103:13-14).

The Fatherhood of God is indeed a sublime truth, but it is efficacious only as it rests upon the kindred truth of the Saviourhood of Christ. Of course, there is a sense in which God is the Father of all. It is He who is responsible for our creation (Mal. 2:10). But in a spiritual sense He is the Father only of those who are reconciled to Him by God the Son. He also declares Himself to be a Father of the fatherless.

There is always a lack in life if one has never had a father's benign and beneficial influence. Are you living with God as your Father? A father's compassion belongs in an eminent degree to God. He displayed it in the gift of His beloved Son and in His sufferings for a sinful race. "In his love and in his pity, he redeemed them" (Isa. 63:9).

Human fathers know how to pity their children when they are in distress. And the tenderness of a father will carry him to great lengths in order to extricate his child from trouble. His tenderness is also expressed in strength, wisdom, and provision. A mother's tenderness is manifested in love, patience, and comfort. Faith is thrice happy when it can sing:

> I know my heavenly Father knows
> The storms that would my way oppose.

The Bridegroom Who Rejoiceth

> "As a bridegroom rejoiceth over the bride, so shall thy God rejoice over thee" (Isa. 62:5).

Here we have another sacred glimpse into the tender heart of God. How does a bridegroom rejoice over his bride? Watch him as he slowly moves toward the altar to claim his bride. What holy joy and deep satisfaction are his as he awaits the union which will indicate the climax of love!

Believers are spiritually joined in marriage to Christ. The Bride is His church (Rev. 21:9), and He is coming to claim His own. Once a bridegroom takes his bride he is supposed to possess her till death do them part. He endows her with all his worldly goods and they become each other's. Thus it is with ourselves. The figures of bride and bridegroom typify the union and communion existing between Christ and His own. As the Bride, the church has been married to the Bridegroom forever. He has endowed her with all He has; and ere long, beloved, He will return to claim His Bride.

The Mother Who Comforteth

"As one whom his mother comforteth, so will I comfort you" (Isa. 66:13).

As a good mother is the "holiest thing alive," we here have another precious insight into the heart of God. It is to the mother that the child usually runs when there are tears to be kissed away. And God calls Himself *El Shaddai,* the Breasted One. This is a delicate and sacred expression. A mother's breasts impart sustenance to her child. And in the perplexed, troubled hours of life it is blessed to know that we can lean upon the heavenly bosom for comfort and relief.

A child, still fretful in spite of a father's efforts to calm and soothe, is soon asleep upon the soft pillow of a mother's breast. Of course, the wonder of God is that He is able to function as father and mother, seeing He made them both. He combines all the qualities of noble-hearted fatherhood and gentle motherhood. As the Father He can inspire courage and fortitude, while in the troubled hours of life God's mother-side is sufficient for comfort and peace.

The Shepherd Who Seeketh

"As a shepherd seeketh out his flock . . . scattered abroad . . . in the cloudy and dark day" (Ezek. 34:12).

The metaphor of a shepherd is a favorite one of the Lord's (Ps. 23:1; 80:1). The prophets exhibited the compassion of Christ under the same figure, "He shall feed his flock like a shepherd" (Isa. 40:11), and Christ Himself used it, "I am the good shepherd" (John 10:11), while the apostles represented Him in the same way (Acts 20:28; Heb. 13:20; I Peter 5:4). In Luke 15 the tenderness of the Shepherd is revealed in His willingness to give His life in order that straying sheep might be found. Are you a lost sheep? Have you strayed? Then the seeking Shepherd, who is the Saviour, is waiting to place you tenderly upon His shoulder and bring you home to God.

The Refiner Who Sitteth

"He shall sit as a refiner and purifier of silver" (Mal. 3:3).

A refiner deals with the molten mass as if it were a child. His precious ore requires careful and delicate handling. Here, then, are depicted the sanctifying influences and graces of Christ. The refiner *sits*. He must sit, seeing that his eye is steadily fixed upon the furnace. If the silver remains too long in the heated crucible, it will be injured. So he sits. He is in no hurry for the purification of his metal. And it is needful for us to go into the furnace of trial and affliction. But Christ is constantly at the side of His own. His eye is steadily intent upon His work of purifying us in love and wisdom. The refiner knows that his silver is ready when he can see his own image reflected in the heated metal. Thus is it with the heavenly Refiner. He knows that His work of purification is completed in His own when He can see His own face reflected.

> Work on then, Lord, till on my soul
> Eternal light shall break;
> And in the presence glorified
> I satisfied shall wake.

121

The Hen that Gathereth

> "...as a hen gathereth her chickens..." (Matt: 23:37).

Here Christ compares His saving, preserving mercy to a hen covering her brood with her wings in time of danger. He knew that the Roman Eagle was about to desolate Jerusalem; thus He pleaded with the inhabitants to seek the shelter He so willingly offered. Doubtless the Master had often watched the mother bird calling her young beneath her sheltering wing (and how they would rush for protection!), but here were defenseless souls who refused His protection. And of what folly sinners are guilty when they reject their only possible avenue of escape from sin and eternal darkness!

Further, the figure of the hen reveals the tenderness the Lord Jesus exhibited in the days of His flesh. He went about continually doing good. We see Him saving men and soothing, calming the troubled minds of the distressed. Always in touch with a world of familiar objects, such as the hen, Christ exhibits Himself as the all-compassionate Lord.

The Nurse Who Cherisheth

> "We were gentle among you as when a nurse cherisheth her own children" (I Thess. 2:7).

The gentleness of the apostle Paul was born in the tenderness of God. This is why meekness, love, and compassion characterize his writings. He lived near to the heart of his Lord. This portion, where he speaks of himself as a gentle nurse, is one of the most affecting in all his Epistles. The reference, of course, is to a nursing mother, seeing that to "cherish" means to support or nourish. And Paul was able not only to bring souls to spiritual birth, but to nourish them thereafter with the sincere milk of the Word.

122

The nursing profession is a most noble and sacrificial one. Surgeons and physicians are certainly valuable, yet they themselves readily confess that after an operation a great deal depends upon the kind of nursing their patients receive. And new-born souls require a great deal of care. If they are to become strong and robust, then they must be constantly nursed. As a nurse, God offers to make our bed in sickness, which means that He yearns to make us the recipients of His tender care. Alas, we are too often spiritually weak. Our low condition requires constant attention. Yet so great is His grace that He deals kindly with our erring hearts, nursing us back to robust health.

This meditation on divine tenderness, however, would be incomplete if we failed to say that if the forgiveness of God's tender heart is spurned, then another side of His divine nature is seen. Justice, unbending and unchanging, divine justice which was satisfied on Calvary's cross for all who believe, must operate upon the individual if love is finally rejected. For if a soul dies without Christ, for whose sake God is willing to forgive, then the righteous judgment of God is caused to fall upon the guilty sinner. Therefore let us urge sinners to be wise and respond to the tenderness of God, so gracious in its invitation to flee from the wrath to come.

Fourteenth Summary
The Teaching About Guidance in Scripture

There is no aspect of life about which we have to be so careful as that of "guidance." No matter in what realm we dwell, there is nothing so solemn and necessary as the knowledge of the mind of God.

Some good folks there are who positively assert that they are being guided by the Lord, when subsequent events prove that they simply are following their own inclinations and interpret this to be the will of God. It is little short of sacrilegious to hear the casual way some Christians talk about being "led." Their guidance, we fear, does not come from a heavenly source.

True and unmistakable guidance, however, is promised us in the Scriptures. "I will instruct thee, and teach thee in the way which thou shalt go; I will guide thee with mine eye" (Ps. 32:8). Of course, if this guidance is to be ours, our eyes must be constantly turned toward the Lord. Wandering vision will mean that we shall stumble and lose the pathway of His purpose. It is unfailingly safe to believe that "where God's finger points, God's hand will lead the way." Let us give ourselves, then, to some attempt at an understanding of what the Bible has to say about this all-important matter of guidance.

The Guide

When journeying through unknown regions, it is important to have an efficient guide. Who is He, then, who is offering Himself as our guide? What are His qualifications to act in such a capacity? Well, the prophet Isaiah leaves us in no doubt as to His wisdom and ability: "The Lord shall guide thee continually" (Isa. 58:11).

There are two things that beget confidence in the Lord's guidance. First, there is the perfection of His character, He is all-wise and, as the omniscient One, He knows all things and can therefore lead us aright. Then there is the perfection of His love. A loving heart directs His guiding hand. And He always gives the very best to those who leave the choice with Him. There are times when we are puzzled, as though He errs; but after the mists roll away, we shall bless the hand that guided and the heart that planned.

One must hasten to say that the continual guidance of the perfect Guide rests upon the basis of our acceptance of Jesus Christ as Saviour and Lord. It is true that James says: "If any of you lack wisdom, let him ask of God," but divine help is offered only to "any of you" who are previously referred to as "my brethren." A person lacking in faith or unstable has no right to expect anything from the Lord (James 1:2-8).

The guidance of God, which is the sure portion of those who know the Lord, is not promised to those who live their lives outside the domain of His grace. If we know Him as Saviour then we have every right to seek and expect divine guidance. And once we are His the Holy Spirit begets spiritual sensitiveness as to divine requirements. We become instinctively aware of the mind of the Lord. Abandoning ourselves to Him, and trusting ourselves to His wisdom, we find that life becomes profoundly blessed.

> And now I have flung myself fearlessly out
>   Like a ship on the stream of the Infinite Will;
> I pass the rough rocks with a smile and a shout,
>   And I just let my Lord His dear purpose fulfill.

The Guided

When Isaiah declares that the Lord guides continually, he

makes it very clear that those who are guided are a special class: God's people (Isa. 58:1-11). And for those redeemed and regenerated there are certain features about the matter of guidance essential to be observed. If these phases are recognized, there need be no doubt or uncertainty about the knowledge of God's will.

We must realize our utter inability to decide for ourselves what we ought to do.

We must confess our lack of wisdom, for the promise of help is not for those who are wise in their own conceits or puffed up with their own knowledge and ability. If we have no deep sense of the need of divine guidance, then, of course, we shall not know what it is to throw ourselves upon God. Self-evolved plans will be ours, and self-choice is grievous to Him who has promised to guide us with His eye. Friction and failure are ours when we scheme our own way through life. One step prompted by self can impoverish a whole career. Setting out upon a false track, we find ourselves away from the center of God's will. Misinterpreting our own desires as the will of God, we often embark upon hazardous enterprises which end in catastrophe. To come to the end of ourselves and accept the Lord's plan for life may cut clean across our own self-conceived plans, but "the Lord's choice is always a choice one."

There must be an inherent desire to know the will of God, and then the willingness to accomplish that will when it is fully known.

Years ago the late S. D. Gordon wrote in my autograph album: "The greatest passion that can burn in the human heart is to know the will of God and get it done." We must have no bias. Our own will and desire must be set aside. With the Saviour we must pray: "Not my will, but thine be done."

Often there is the temptation to make circumstances fit in with what we imagine to be the will of God for us. Sometimes we declare that the Lord told us to do a certain thing or to go to a certain place when such an action was simply the creation of our own mind.

We must definitely pray and wait for guidance.

Asking God, we must wait for His direction. And what sad mistakes we could avoid if only we prayed more! There are no short-cuts or royal roads to guidance. In response to prayerful waiting upon God, guidance can be ours in all affairs, whether personal, domestic, business, or spiritual. Furthermore, as we wait we come to learn that the *stops* as well as the *steps* of a good man or woman are ordered of the Lord.

We must have a positive expectation that God will grant our petition for guidance.

We must ask "nothing doubting" as James expresses it. For those who pray, wait, and believe, guidance is sure and certain. Expecting the Lord to lead, we quickly discern His voice as He says: "This is the way, walk ye in it."

Alas, this is where we so often fail! We pray, and then begin at once to wonder whether God *will* guide. Doubt and impatience assert themselves. If guidance is delayed, we take matters into our own hands. Contrariwise, when we trust ourselves absolutely to the wisdom and hands of our Guide, He never fails to lead us aright.

We must follow a step at a time.

"Take step by step by the Spirit" (Gal. 5:25, Bishop Moule's rendering). God always leads step by step.

> O'er each step of the onward way
> He makes new scenes to arise.

Taking the present step, we must leave all further steps until the time comes to take them. Peace and contentment are ours as we proceed to take the next step that God reveals to us in answer to prayer.

> I do not ask to see the distant scene,
> One step enough for me.

We are tempted to regard *one* step of little consequence, yet subsequent steps are vitally affected by the movements of the moment. Eternity alone will reveal the value of single steps. It will then be discovered that God builds a life, not in a moment, but moment by moment. All the great achievements of our modern age represent slow and steady growth. Mushrooms may spring up in a night to wither just as quickly; the oak takes hundreds of years to grow and is rendered impervious thereby to the ravages of storm and time. Therefore, let the unchanging determination of Job be ours. "My foot hath held his steps, his way have I kept, and not declined" (Job 23:11). Let us lay hold of the promise: "As thou goest step by step the way shall open up before thee." And let us never forget to take each step with the feet of prayer and obedience.

Divine guidance is always direct guidance.

There is no uncertainty about the leading of the Spirit. God is light and casts no shadows. If we follow our own impulses or the wishes of others, then we shall move in a mist. It is here that we can detect the weakness of "guidance" as taught by the Oxford Group Movement. A quiet time is urged upon the "grouper" at the beginning of the day, when with a mind blank and a pencil in hand, he must wait for "leading." Yet a moment's thought will suggest the fact

128

that a blank or static mind is an easy prey for Satan as, alas, so many "groupers" have discovered. All mental impressions are not of God. Nothing is more clearly taught in the Scriptures than that there are evil spirits which have access to the human mind. To act contrary to the Scriptures is an evidence that that guidance is not of God, for He will never lead us to speak or act in a way that is antagonistic to His revealed will and written Word.

The Guidance

Divine guidance, like the Guide, is perfect, good, and gracious. Enoch, we are told, walked with God. "It became his life's ambition and the sovereign aspiration of his soul to company with the Eternal, and by such an act he put himself in alignment with the divine purpose and plan and received sure and certain guidance."

The guidance of God is certain.

Isaiah declares: "The Lord shall guide thee continually" (Isa. 58:11). But the paramount question is: How does He guide? Here we reach the heart of our study.

First of all, God guides by His Word, and guidance from this source is certain. There is nothing hazy about the leading of the Scriptures, for as a lamp to our feet and a light unto our path, they show us where and how to walk. Quite often all the guidance one needs is the plain unadorned Word. In special circumstances, it is surprising how the Holy Spirit will cause certain passages to become luminous. For example, if one is troubled about separation from unworthy and unspiritual associations, a passage like II Corinthians 6:14-18 offers immediate and unmistakable guidance.

Again, God guides by the Holy Spirit. It was the Spirit who guided Philip to the chariot of the eunuch (Acts 8:27). Paul was likewise subject to the leading of the Spirit (Acts

16:6-7). The Holy Spirit is an unerring guide. Knowing the mind of God concerning every phase of our lives, the Spirit can prompt us to do those things well-pleasing to the Father. And such an infallible Guide will never lead us to do anything contrary to the will of God as revealed in the Scriptures. Is it not blessed to know that we can habitually learn to discern the voice of the Spirit and secure thereby a life devoid of bitter mistakes and wrong turnings?

Of old God sometimes guided His people by dreams and visions. After receiving the prompting of the Spirit Paul was led into Macedonia (Acts 16:9-10). Dreams, however, are a very uncertain method of guidance and do not form part of God's usual procedure, especially now that God's full revelation is given us in the completed Scriptures.

There are times, also, when God guides by circumstances both ordinary and extraordinary. Abraham's servant could say: "I being in the way the Lord led me"; and, time and again, guidance comes as we exercise sanctified common sense amid surrounding circumstances. The position that we are in sometimes interprets God's will. For example, here is a young man who has a desire to be a missionary but is doubtful whether he is being led out to the regions beyond. He has aged parents who are not fit to be left alone and who, if his provision were withdrawn, would inevitably suffer. In such a case, home circumstances offer sufficient guidance. Until conditions change, this young man should see that his duty is to care for his own.

F. B. Meyer often recalled an experience he had crossing the Irish Channel on a dark, starless night. "I stood on the deck by the captain," he says, "and asked him, 'How do you know Holyhead Harbour on a night like this?'

" 'Do you see those three lights?' he replied. 'Well, those three must line up behind each other, and when we see them so aligned, we know the exact position of the mouth of the harbor.' " And Meyer made the following application:

When we want to know God's will there are three things

which always occur: God in the heart impelling you forward; God in His Book corroborating whatever He says to the heart; God in circumstances which are always indicative of His will. It is nothing short of folly to set out upon any course until all these three agree.

The guidance of God is personal.

Let us look at Isaiah's pronouncement again: "The Lord shall guide thee continually." *Thee!*—yes, you, my friend, no matter how humble and lonely you may be. God's eye is on the sparrow, and He watches you, too. He loves and cares for *you,* and is willing to guide you as if you were the only one in His universe requiring guidance.

Perhaps some of you have been tempted to think that you are far too insignificant for God to notice. "How can it be possible," you ask, "for a God so great to condescend to guide me in the common, ordinary, everyday affairs of life?" Well, He has promised to guide me, yes, even me. Therefore, let us trust Him to lead us over life's rugged pathway. Say to Him: "Hold Thou my hand, I am so weak and helpless I dare not take one step, without Thy aid," and unerring guidance will be yours.

The guidance of God is continual.

Surely we ought to underline the word "continually" in Isaiah's promise of divine guidance! For the majority of us, guidance is fitful and spasmodic. At times, we are truly led of God; at other times, we choose our own will and way. But guidance is offered not only for the great problems of life, but for all the little matters which demand a knowledge of the will of God as well. He promises to guide us, not sometimes but always; not only in the crises of life but all the way and all the time. And this continual guidance can be relied upon until we reach the end of our earthly pilgrimage. Then, the loving hand of the Guide having led us thus far, He will lead us from the dusty lanes of earth to the golden streets of heaven.

If we are uncertain of the way to take for any earthly journey, it is helpful to have written directions, but what freedom from anxiety is ours if we have the leadership and personal companionship of a friend who knows the way. Guideposts are one thing; guides, another. And blessed be His name, we have the Lord as our Guide to the country whither we are journeying!

The guidance of God is satisfying.

If we enjoy the certain, personal, continual, guidance of God, then we shall know what it is to have our souls satisfied even in times of parching drouth, and to have our bones made fat; we shall be like a watered garden, and like a spring of water whose waters fail not (Isa. 58:11). Others may lose their way, but we are led aright. Others may be barren, but we are fruitful. Drouth may overtake us, straitened circumstances and testings may come, yet with the good hand of our God upon us we can have a source of refreshment unknown to those who have only a self-planned life.

Beloved, let us "cease meddling with God's plans and will." Touch anything of His and you mar His work. You may move the hands of a clock to suit you but you do not change the time; in like manner you may hurry the unfolding of God's will, but you harm and do not help the work. You can open a rosebud, but by so doing you spoil the flower. Leave all to Him. Hands off! "Thy will, not mine. . . ."

Conscious of our proneness to stray when left to ourselves, let us lovingly depend on our heavenly Guide to lead us "o'er moor and fen, o'er crag and torrent 'til the night is gone." Let us follow His way, which is always the best way.

God bade me go when I would stay
    ('Twas cool within the wood);
I did not know the reason why.
I heard a boulder crashing by
    Across the path whereon I stood.

He bade me stand when I would go.
    "Thy will be done," I said;
They found one day at early dawn,
Across the way I would have gone,
    A serpent with a mangled head.

No more I ask the reason why.
    Although I may not see
The path ahead, His way I go;
For though I know not, He doth know,
    And He will choose safe paths for me.

Fifteenth Summary
The Number of Probation—Forty—in Scripture

A good deal of nonsense, as well as wisdom, has been written on the subject of life's beginning at forty. Life begins at forty! True life can begin long before forty is reached if only one is willing to begin with God. Life as He means it to be lived can only commence when the Spirit of Life enters to regenerate the soul.

Not so long ago I read of one who discredited the idea that life began at forty. John W. Deering was executed in the Utah State Prison for killing a man. Deering reached his fortieth birthday less than two months before his capital punishment. He is reported to have said as he was about to suffer for his crime, "Those . . . who talk about life beginning at forty—I'll prove they are lying. . . . Death is death and that's the end of everything. That's all there is to it." Well, this murderer knows now the reality of the unseen and the eternal. At forty either damnation or eternal bliss commenced for him.

The purpose of this study, however, is to prove that God begins at forty; that the number as employed in the Bible has more than an arithmetical value. From earliest years the figure has enshrined a deep symbolism. Doubtless many superstitions associated with the number arise from the Scripture's use of it.

Of course, in the interpretation of the science of numbers all straining and fanciful interpretations must be avoided. Alas, some have been guilty of subtle trifling with the arithmetic of the Bible, thereby bringing such a theme into disrepute.

Calmly and sanely, then, let us examine the special and

sacred number of forty, and discover some of its symbolical associations, admitted from ancient times in many realms of thought.

The Symbolism of the Number

That the figure suggests a marked stage usually related to some great event, period, or experience, can be proved from many of its connections. For instance, it is held that forty years constitutes a generation or epoch, the end of which witnesses maturity. And then, from time immemorial the number has been universally recognized as important both because of its frequency of occurrence in the Bible and the uniformity of its association with a period of probation, trial, separation, chastisement, and humiliation.

The Rabbis regarded forty years as the age of understanding, the age when man reveals and reaches his intellectual prime. The mischievous cry of our age is, "Too old at forty." Yet this is the period of fullest energy and highest achievement. Macaulay in his *Essays* remarks: "No great work of imagination has ever been produced under the age of thirty to thirty-five years, and the instances are few in which any have been produced under the age of forty. Taking the writings of authors generally, the best and most valuable of their works have been produced within the last seventeen years of their lives."

The Koran, the bible of Moslem, says that man attains his strength when he comes to forty, as it was at this age that Mohammed, after leading a life of meditation, took to himself the title of "The Prophet of Mecca."

Tiberius is credited with the saying that "man is a fool or physician at forty." It was at forty that Moses went into the solitude of Midian to learn that he was nobody. Isaac was forty years old when he took Rebekah to wife (Gen. 25:20) and Esau was the same age when he married Judith (Gen. 26:34).

Perhaps the wisest of all things said about the age of forty is in Cowley's essay, "The Danger of Procrastination": "There is no fooling with life when once it turns beyond forty."

Other associations of the number are interesting to observe. Forty days represented the usual period required by the Egyptians for embalming. Ancient physicians were wont to ascribe many strange changes to the period of forty. Saint Swithin's Day betokens forty days rain or sunshine. The alchemists looked on forty days as the charmed period when the philosophers' stone and elixir of life were to appear. Quarantine for certain infectious diseases used to extend to forty days. A tranquil rest or nap after dinner is spoken of as "forty winks," implying, of course, an indefinite number.

The Scriptural Significance of the Number

Jerome, who was one of the first to note the importance of forty, declared that this number is always one of affliction and punishment. But that it is not always associated with chastisement will be evident as we proceed. Without doubt the number plays a large part in the sacred Word, and is one of the most conspicuous employed.

At times forty is a round figure. The use of a definite numerical expression in an indefinite sense, that is, a round number, is prevalent in many languages. For example, we say, "a hundred and one" or "a thousand and one" things. Now, we do not mean the exact figures we quote, but use them in an indefinite sense, implying that we are not sure of the quantity. The Persians spoke of "forty years" when they really meant many years. It would seem as if the lax use of numbers was frequent among Israel and their neighbors (cf. Acts 4:22). There are occurrences suggesting a conventional use of the figure when "forty" is not exactly meant. The forty days of Jonah (3:4), read "three days" in the Septuagint. In Acts 13:18 we have "about the time of forty years."

Coming to the typical significance of the figure, a safe guide in the study of the symbolism of numbers reminds us that forty is the product of five and eight and points to the action of grace (5) leading to and ending in revival and renewal (8). This double truth is evident when the number is related to a period of probation and testing. When associated with enlarged dominion or extended rule, this is so in virtue of its factors four and ten and in harmony with their signification, namely, material completion (4) and perfection of divine order (10).

Classifying the figure, it will be found that it falls into five groups, all of which are related to probation.

Probation by Trial

To receive the Law, Moses was in the Mount for forty days and forty nights (Exod. 24:18; 34:28; Deut. 9:9-11). Dr. Joseph Parker's apt comment on Moses' somewhat long absence from the people is worth reciting. "The few commandments which we once called the Law could be written in less than a minute each; it was not the handwriting but the heart-writing that required the time."

After the sin of the golden calf Moses was before the Lord forty days and forty nights (Deut. 9:18-25). It may be that the leader of Israel remembered the forty years he had to spend in Midian after his own sin in slaying the Egyptian and burying him in the sand. That the period of forty years spent in the wilderness was one of grief to God and yet one of gracious discipline can be proved by comparing such passages as Deuteronomy 8:2-4; Psalm 95:10; Nehemiah 9:21; Hebrews 3:9, 17. During those forty years, old Israel died out and a new Israel took its place (Num. 32:13).

The forty days' search of Canaan resulted in a penal sentence of forty years (Num. 13:25; 14:33-34; Ps. 95:10): "Each day for a year shall ye bear your iniquities, even forty years."

137

In the strength of the "angel's food" he received, Elijah was empowered to witness for forty days and forty nights (I Kings 19:8). It was in the same way that the Lord Jesus was nourished.

Nineveh experienced that judgment is always mixed with mercy: "Yet forty days, and Nineveh shall be overthrown" (Jonah 3:4). During this period of probation, the prophet warned the people of coming doom. God in His goodness, however, gave the Ninevites time to repent.

Great preparations have great issues. Thus in compliance with the type and example of Moses, the great law-giver, and Elijah, the reformer, our Lord fasted for forty days and forty nights, during which period He was tempted of the devil (Matt. 4:2; Luke 4:2). The testing of the Lord Jesus differed from that of Moses and Elijah, seeing that they were not subjected to such onslaught on the part of the satanic hosts as our Lord endured during His dark period.

Probation by Humiliation and Punishment

In the record of the Flood, forty is characterized as a number sanctified by judgment and mercy. "I will cause it to rain upon the earth forty days and forty nights" (Gen. 7:4; cf. 7:17). This period was likewise a time of trial for the faith of Noah. Forty days had to expire before Noah opened the window of the ark.

Under alien rule, servitude was permitted in order to chastise Israel for her sins, and bring her back to God. "The Lord delivered them into the hands of the Philistines forty years" (Judg. 13:1).

Ezekiel has to remain on his right side for forty days to symbolize the forty years of Judah's transgression, a day for a year, which with the three hundred and ninety days on his left side make the four hundred and thirty years of Israel's sojourning in the land of Egypt (Exod. 12:40-41; Gal. 3:17; Ezek. 4:5-6).

A fitting type of atonement in which Christ can be seen bearing and putting away our iniquity can be discovered in the forty sockets of silver (Exod. 26:19, 21).

The "forty stripes save one" (Acts 25:2; II Cor. 11:24) bring us to an interesting Jewish requirement. Jews were forbidden under Mosaic law to inflict more than forty stripes on an offender, so for fear of breaking the law they stopped short of the number. If a scourge contained three lashes, then thirteen strokes would equal thirty-nine (Deut. 25:3).

Probation by Prosperity in Deliverance and Rest

Israel under Othniel had rest for forty years (Judg. 3:11); under Barak had rest for a similar period (Judg. 5:3, 31); under Gideon had quietness for another forty years (Judg. 8:28); and under Eli had a beneficial rule for forty years.

Probation by Prosperity in Enlarged Dominion

This aspect has been pointed out by another: Israel was under Saul "by the space of forty years" (Acts 13:21) (apostasy is typified by this period); Israel enjoyed David's reign for forty years (II Sam. 5:4) (militancy characterized this era); Israel enlarged her dominion under Solomon's forty years' rule (I Kings 11:42) (prosperity as a type of the millennium is herewith seen, when Christ as the Prince of Peace will reign for a thousand years)—that is, twenty-five forties.

Lesser kings reigned for a similar period. Jeroboam reigned forty-one years (II Kings 14:23); Jehoash reigned forty years in Jerusalem (II Kings 12:1).

Probation by Waiting

Under this aspect, several associations of the number are drawn together to prove the thought of preparation.

Goliath exhibited himself with pride for forty days. Such a

139

period meant an anxious wait for Israel. But as the days slipped by, the giant gathered greater courage and confidence. "The Philistine drew near morning and evening and presented himself forty days" (I Sam. 17:16). Is this not a typical presentation of Satan's temptation of Christ in the wilderness?

Forty played a large part in the life of Moses, who lived for one hundred and twenty years, that is, three forties. We find him forty years in Egypt learning to be *somebody;* forty years in Midian discovering that he was *nobody;* forty years in the wilderness realizing that God was *Everybody.* "When he was full forty years old it came into his heart to visit his brethren. . . . When forty years were expired" (Acts 7:23, 30). The first two forty year periods fitted Moses for his mission as Israel's deliverer.

Then there came those forty days of lingering upon the mount which, being a time full of testing, approved Moses as a fit person for his prophetical and mediatorial office. Dr. Joseph Parker asks, "What is the meaning of all this withdrawal? The meaning is reception. There must be a time of intaking, there must be periods when we are not giving out but when we are receiving in. Sometimes we do everything by doing nothing." But what a hard lesson this is to learn!

Under this section we can likewise place the great forty days between the resurrection and ascension of our Lord (Acts 1:3): "Being seen of them forty days." What wonderful days of fellowship and instruction they must have been for the disciples!

This period, however, was a somewhat strange one since it belonged neither to the life of Christ on earth nor to the history of His church. Those forty days formed a mysterious borderline between the preresurrection and the postresurrection of the church. It was, of course, a period necessary to confirm the faith of Christ's disciples, and to strengthen the proofs of the resurrection. The forty days He was seen of His own bore witness to the reality of His work and the genuine-

140

ness of His mission. They were also days of special instruction, for they gave the Master time to impart the full commission for the future government of His church. And in the life of our Lord, the period had its counterpart in the temptation of the wilderness (Luke 4:2) which was symbolic of Christ's perpetual triumph in times of conflict.

What Christ actually did during the forty days He tarried among men as the risen Lord is a matter of conjecture. As with the forty days in the wilderness, so this period was one of solitude and of communion with the Father. Christ, however, was no longer tried and tempted by contact with Satan. Death and resurrection had given Him complete immunity from satanic approach. Doubtless those waiting days were days of intercession in the desert places and heights of Galilee (Luke 4:42; 6:12).

Dr. Parker reminds us that "this is the period of testimony, the period of revelation, the period of true preaching of the Kingdom of God, and it may be that we require forty days and forty nights, representing an indefinite space of time, in which to prove our own resurrection with the Lord." But the beauty of *this* dispensation is that we have the risen Lord with us not only for forty days but "every day" and "all the days" (Matt. 28:20). He is the abiding Friend, Saviour, and Lord throughout our days and nights. One need not be forty years of age before receiving Him as Saviour; rather, receive Him early in life if you would know constant peace and would be *sure* of your eternal destiny before it is too late. Neither need one wait for forty years to pass before going forth to witness in His name. No—nor forty days, but now, today. For God is ready to begin to work in every heart the very moment that heart is ready to receive and yield to Him.

Sixteenth Summary
The Blessed Trinity in Scripture

Let us consider in this summary the mode of God's existence. As His mode of Being and operation is of a threefold character, we are compelled, at the outset, to face the mystery of what is called "The Trinity."

Doubtless there are those who have been perplexed by this entrancing theme, asking themselves the question: "Have we one God, or three?" If we are not clear in our explanation of the Trinity, we shall open the door to serious errors. At the very beginning of our meditations, it is needful to observe the following facts:

The Trinity is a mystery.

No perfect knowledge of this wonderful theme is possible to man in his present, finite state. The modes of the existence and operation of the divine Being can never be fully apprehended by human beings. The sacred mystery of the Trinity is one which the light within man could never have discovered. That this truth is infinitely beyond the comprehension of the creature is readily granted.

The Trinity is not fully explainable.

We must further realize that we cannot supply a perfect meaning or definition of the word, person, distinction, or subsistence as used to distinguish between the Father, the Son, and the Holy Ghost. Just as the divine and human natures in Christ who is yet but one Person is inexplicable, so three Persons who are yet but one Godhead cannot be perfectly defined.

The Trinity is a fact.

Although we cannot attain a complete understanding of the manner in which the three personal distinctions of the Godhead subsist, yet the fact is clearly affirmed that in the unsearchable nature of Deity, the threefold distinction exists without distinction or confusion. Here is great depth—the Father-God, the Son-God, the Holy-Ghost-God, yet not three Gods but one God, the three Persons in essence. This is a divine riddle that defies arithmetic, where one makes three and three makes one. Our narrow thoughts can no more comprehend the Trinity in unity than a nutshell will hold all the water in the sea. A man once asked Daniel Webster: "How can you reconcile the doctrine of the Trinity with reason?" The statesman of giant intellect replied: "Do *you* expect to understand the arithmetic of heaven?"

The Trinity is a comforting truth.

When devoutly pondered and reverently believed, the doctrine of the Trinity becomes at once a rock of defense and a spring of comfort and inspiration. The Father is seen as associated with gracious designs toward a sinful world; the Son, as carrying out the divine plan of salvation for sinners; the Spirit, as exercising a sanctifying and transfiguring influence upon the hearts of those who respond to the claims of Christ.

If, as one has said: "We cannot be good Christians without the firm belief of the Trinity," then, by inference, the stronger our faith in the fact of the Trinity, the better our Christianity.

The Trinity is a Scriptural revelation.

This doctrine is taught exclusively by revelation, as neither natural conviction nor material creation could have enlightened us in the matter. A basis for it has often been sought and thought to be found in independent speculation concerning the nature of things in the laws of being and thought, but it is at least safer to those who accept the Scripture and the revealed will and purpose of God to make them the whole basis.

It is from the Scriptures alone, as we shall presently discover, that we learn that the Godhead consists of three Persons: The Father, the great Upholder and Purpose of all things; the Son, the one and only Redeemer of mankind; the Holy Spirit, the indispensable Sanctifier and Enlightener. Each of these having His own distinct sphere of operation is yet found acting together in perfect unison with the Others.

The Trinity is an object of faith.

The Trinity is purely an object of faith; the plumb line of reason is too short to fathom this mystery, but where reason cannot wade, there faith may swim. There are some truths in religion that may be demonstrated by reason: namely, that there is a God; but the Trinity of Persons in the unity of essence is wholly supernatural and must be received by faith.

This sacred doctrine is not against reason, however, but above it. Those erudite philosophers who could find out the causes of things and discourse on the magnitude of the stars, the nature of minerals, and so forth could never, by their deepest search, find out the mystery of the Trinity. It is of divine revelation and must be adored by those who humbly and believingly accept it.

The Trinity is a subject that has engaged the greatest minds during the centuries of the Christian era, but, philosophy (even Christian philosophy) has failed utterly to explore its profound depths and explain its full significance. Augustine gave the study of this mystery the best powers of his mind, and it is related of him that walking along the seashore on one occasion, absorbed in deep contemplation, he found a little lad digging a trench. When asked what he meant to do, the boy replied that he wanted to empty the sea into his dipper, whereupon Augustine asked himself: "Am I not trying to do the same thing as this child in seeking to exhaust with my reason the infinity of God and to collect it within the limits of my own mind?"

While, however, the Trinity defies the powers of the most gigantic minds, yet in another sense the doctrine is as simple and plain as the fact itself, especially when it is received as revealed truth and not as the result of logical deduction but as a doctrine having Scriptural authority as its basis. The doctrine of the Trinity is a profound and vital subject. Without it Christianity could have no existence.

The Term

The word *Trinity,* is not found in the Bible. It was first formally used at the Synod held at Alexandria, A.D. 317, and said to have taken its place in the language of Christian theology for the first time in a Biblical work of Theophilus, Bishop of Antioch in Syria from A.D. 168-183. The holy mystery, however, was long before this a common article of Christian confession, as is seen by the passage in Lucian, greatest Greek writer of the Christian era and the Voltaire of antiquity, about A.D. 160. In his *Philopatris,* he makes the Christian confess: "The exalted God . . . Son of the Father, Spirit proceeding from the Father, One of Three, and Three of One."

Doubtless the term arose from the need for a word to express the doctrine tersely. It properly means "threefoldness," that is, God's threefold manifestation, and it is not, as it is sometimes said to be, an abbreviation of "tri-unity," which is a term belonging to the realm of metaphysics. The word *trinity* is derived from the Latin word *trinitas* and the adjective *trinus,* meaning "threefold" or "three-in-one."

The Truth Itself

It is only when one really sets oneself the task of analyzing all that can be known of this august theme that he realizes how stupendous a task it is. Perhaps it may be as well to proceed along the following lines:

Definitions

Many definitions of the Trinity have been formed by councils and theologians. Possibly a perusal of a few selections may help us to understand more clearly the doctrine. The term itself means "the union of three in one," and is generally applied to the ineffable mystery of three persons in one God—Father, Son, and Holy Spirit.

Irenaeus

One of the earliest confessions is that of Irenaeus who, in his treatise against heresies, demands "complete faith in one God Almighty, of whom are all things; and in the Son of God, Jesus Christ our Lord, by whom are all things and His dispensation by which the Son of God became man; also a firm trust in the Spirit of God who hath set forth the dispensations of the Father and the Son, dealing with each successive race of men as the Father willed."

The Church of England

Article Number 1 of the Church of England affirms: "In the unity of this Godhead there be three Persons, of one substance, power, and eternity; the Father, the Son, and the Holy Ghost."

R. Watson

This eminent theologian defines the doctrine thus: "The

Divine Nature exists under the personal distinctions of the Father, the Son, and the Holy Ghost."

W. B. Pope

Dr. Pope says: "One Divine Essence exists in a Trinity of co-equal, personal subsistences, related as the Father, the Eternal Son of the Father, and the Holy Ghost, eternally proceeding from the Father."

When, however, we speak of three persons and one God, we must never entertain the idea of a confederacy of gods, each possessed of distinct individuality wholly apart from the others (as, say, three persons taken from an audience) but, rather, a Trinity in unity. There is one God, without division in a Trinity of Persons, and three Persons without confusion in a unity of essence. Let us express it thus:

The Unity in Trinity

We must not infer that because the three are always mentioned in the same consecutive order, thus—the Father, the Son, and the Holy Spirit—that one is subordinate or superior to the other. This unity of the Persons in the Godhead consists of two things.

The Identity of Essence

In the Trinity there is a oneness in essence. The three Persons are of the same divine nature and substance. Thus there are no degrees in the Godhead; one Person is not more God than another. The Holy Ghost is equal to the Father and Son, and the Son is equal to the Father and Spirit.

The Mutual "In-Being"

The unity of the Persons in the Godhead consists in the

mutual "in-being" of them, or their being in one together: "Thou, Father, art in me, and I in thee" (John 17:21). A unity in Trinity means, then, that all three are the same.

The Trinity in Unity

If we were to take three persons from a group and put them together by themselves, it would be almost impossible for them, because of their natural make-up, to agree in everything. Little differences of thought or action would inevitably be seen, sooner or later. But there is about the Trinity a most wonderful, beautiful harmony and unity. Not for one moment has one Person crossed the wishes of Another or acted adversely or independently of Another. The Father, Son, and Holy Spirit are all one in thought, holiness, action, love, grace, and so forth. The Trinity is unity. Each does the same.

The First Person

The First Person in the Trinity is God the Father. He is called the First Person in respect to order, not dignity; for God the Father has no essential perfection which the other Persons of the Godhead have not. He is not more wise, more holy, more powerful than the other Persons are. There is certainly priority, but not superiority. God is always mentioned first, then, owing to the order of His manifestation and work.

The Second Person

The Second Person in the Trinity is God the Son, who was begotten of the Father before all time. See Proverbs 8:23-25, where Christ is described as wisdom personified.

The Third Person

The Third Person in the Trinity is God the Holy Ghost, who proceeds from the Father and the Son, and whose work is to illuminate the soul and enkindle the sacred emotions. The essence of the Spirit is everywhere, but more particularly in the heart of the believer. Thus, these Three are one in holiness, love, wisdom, eternal nature, and unity of personality. We can express this most perfect unity thus:

(1) *The Father is the Original Source of all things.*
   Genesis 1:1 suggests it: "In the beginning God. . . ."
(2) *The Son is the Medium of all things.*
   " . . . hath committed all judgment unto the Son" (John 5:22).
(3) *The Spirit is the Agent of all things, the One whom the Son uses to bestow the blessings of God.*
   Ephesians 2:18 is a verse that combines this remarkable Trinity in unity.

Thus the order of divine performance is *from* the Father, *through* the Son, *by* the Holy Spirit. To illustrate this divine unity one might use the demonstration of the power-station, cable, and electric lamp or machine. Concerning Trinitarian unity Dr. Handley Moule has this very comprehensive statement:

> The oneness of Godhead is altogether unique and implies a unity of the Eternal Content ineffable, absolute, so that nothing can be more truly one; and necessary, that is to say, such that Its eternal reason for so being is in Itself. . . . In one respect, One; It is in another aspect Three; three eternally harmonious Wills, Agents, Persons, inasmuch as there is between Them knowledge, will, and love. Each has as His nature the entire Divine Nature which is quality, not

quantity; Each is truly God; Each is necessarily and eternally One in Being with the Others; there are not Three Gods. Each is not the Other; there are Three Persons.

Heresies

In our thinking concerning the Trinity we need to be aware of at least five errors.

Arianism

This teaching contends that the Godhead consists of one eternal Person who, in the beginning before all worlds, created in His own image a super-angelic being, the only begotten Son, the beginning of the creation of God. The first and greatest Creature evolving through the created Son was the Holy Ghost.

Semi-Arianism

This teaching holds that the Son was a divine Person of glorious essence, like to, but not identical with, that of the Father, and from eternity begotten by the Father by a free exercise of will and power; and therefore subordinate to, and dependent upon him.

Socinianism

This system regards God the Father as the only God, one in Person as well as essence; and Jesus Christ as a mere man, though an inspired Prophet and called Son of God only on account of His miraculous conception in the womb of the virgin; and the term Holy Spirit only as another name for the one God, the Father. The more common, modern, and significant title of this system is Unitarianism.

Christadelphianism

This heresy says that God is one Power, the increate Father, by whom all things have been created. Jesus Christ, born of the virgin Mary through the begettal of the Holy Spirit, became Son of God. The Holy Spirit is considered to be simply an energy or power from God. This system makes Christ a created being, and denies the personality of the Holy Spirit.

Millennial Dawnism, now Jehovah's Witnesses

This teaching makes Christ, before His earth life, a created and superior angelic being, and during His earthly life, God. This system is practically silent on the Person of the Holy Spirit.

Illustrations of the Trinity

Up to a certain point illustration is lawful and helpful, but the Trinity in unity being the mode of existence of the Eternal is a thing essentially unique and is therefore lifted far above the possibility of complete comparison or illustration. The student and teacher, therefore, will do wisely to deal very sparingly with such treatment of this doctrine. He will always guard what he does in the way of illustration with a remembrance of the unique nature of the subject and that we have no *perfect* analogy of the Trinity.

Perhaps some of the most striking analogies of this profound truth are:

The Human Constitution

Man is a tripartite being, having spirit, soul, and body—three parts yet one person. There is also a trinity in the Scripture of the self-life—heart, mind, and will.

The Sun

In the sun's light we have triple rays giving light, heat, and chemical effects. In the body of the sun there are the substance of the sun, the beams, and the heat; the beams are begotten of the sun, the heat proceeds both from the sun and the beams; but these three, though different, are not divided; they all three make one sun. So is the blessed Trinity—the Son is begotten of the Father, the Holy Ghost proceeds from both; yet though They are three distinct Persons They are but one God. In the atmosphere we also have three in one—light, heat, and air.

Material substance

Matter, we know, exists in solids, liquids, and gases.

Nature

Saint Patrick, the Irish saint, found his Irish audiences utterly unable to take in the idea of the Trinity till he presented a shamrock leaf to them, which, with its three green leaves on one stem, gave them their first intelligent conception of the Godhead—three Persons but one God: One in purpose, and in operation, abiding in and with us. We come adoringly to the Father, through the Son, and by the Holy Spirit.

Another natural illustration of this divine truth is that of the plant with its threefold section of root, stem, and fruit or flower, the last being the revealed part of the whole. Thus we close this aspect of our study by returning to a thought already expressed, namely, the primacy of order. God is first. The Spirit is last because He is the last Person of the Godhead to be fully revealed, and also because it is He who brings to fruition the purposes of the Father and the Son. "He is called the Third Person, not in order of time or dignity of nature but in order and manner of subsisting."

So God, the Father, God the Son,
And God the Spirit we adore,
A sea of life and love unknown,
Without a bottom or a shore.

Scriptural Evidence

Coming to the unfolding of the doctrine of the Trinity in the Word of God, one must accept the candid statement that our only authority on this mysterious subject is the Bible; therefore, let us carefully weigh its teaching. An unbiased study reveals the trinitarian view as a view transcending reason but in no way contradicting it.

Old Testament Gleams

This doctrine has been of necessity unfolded gradually in the Scriptures, for each step in the development of the truth had to be made clear before another could be taken. Hence we find in the Old Testament one God who is Creator and Lord. In the New Testament the incarnation reveals Jesus as God who was with God, the Saviour of men. After the event of Pentecost, the Holy Spirit is revealed as God and Indweller of the church.

In the Old Testament, then, there are no dogmatic announcements of this truth, but hints, strong gleams or foreshadowings of it, which gather more definiteness as time rolls on, until revelation is complete. Among the strong gleams the following can be cited:

(1) The History of Creation (Gen. 1:26): "Let *us* make man in *our* image, after *our* likeness."
(2) The Fall of Man. After the fall, the same plural form is used (Gen. 3:22): " . . . the man is become as one of *us.*"
(3) The *Confusion* of Tongues. At Babel, God said,

"Let *us* go down, and . . . confound their language" (Gen. 11:7).

(4) The Priestly Benediction. The threefold benediction of the High Priest (Num. 6:24-26) is held by the Jews of old to teach their doctrine.

(5) The Call of Isaiah. In Isaiah the threefold ascription of praise offered to God teaches the Trinity (6:3). Also, the same plural form is seen (6:8)—"who will go for *us*?"

(6) The Commission of the Messiah. In the commission of the Messiah, as announced by Himself (Isa. 48:16), we have another strong gleam of the Trinity: "The Lord God, and his Spirit, hath sent me."

(7) Divine Titles. One illustration of how divine titles are used of all the three Persons of the Trinity can be found by comparing Exodus 20:2, "the Lord thy God," John 20:28, "My Lord and my God," and Acts 6:3-4.

(8) *Elohim*. This plural noun used some five hundred times by Moses (and in another form some five thousand times in the New Testament), accompanied continually by a verb in the singular, reveals the oneness of Deity and the plurality of Persons.

(9) Manifestations of God. There are, in the Old Testament, several manifestations of God which are described as being at once Himself and His Messenger or Angel. Thus God is at once Sender and Sent—God and God's Angel, and these can only be understood as signifying a plurality of Persons in the Godhead, that is, in the account of Jacob's wrestling (Gen. 32), where we read: "Jacob was left alone; and there wrestled a man with him" (v. 24). "And Jacob called the name of the place Peniel: for I have seen God face to

face" (v. 30). "He had power over the angel, and prevailed" (Hos. 12:3-4).

Other instances of this can be found in Genesis 16:10; 18:3, 30; 20:11; Exodus 3:2; 23:20-21; Numbers 22:32; Joshua 5:14; 6:1; Judges 2:12; etc. From these passages it is clear that plurality in the Godhead was taught from the beginning. How otherwise can these passages be explained, where God uses the plural pronouns as if speaking of others acting in harmony with Him, or in which the same Person is called Jehovah and the Captain, Angel, or Messenger of Jehovah, or where God is said to be sending the Messiah, to whom divine honors and titles are ascribed (see Jer. 23:6; Isa. 7:14; 9:6; Mal. 3:1).

The New Testament Unfolding

It is the special care of the New Testament to unfold what the Old Testament conceals in respect to the Trinity, and thus it teaches with more distinctness this doctrine, inasmuch as the names, Father, Son, and Spirit, both separately and jointly, are used; and, further, that the Father is God, the Son is God, and the Spirit is God.

In the New Testament, where the references to three Persons are clear and explicit, the doctrine is assumed rather than taught. New Testament writers display a simplicity and assurance, when speaking of the Trinity, proving that it was no novelty to them.

Thus the whole teaching of the New Testament is built upon the assumption of the Trinity and its allusions to the Trinity are frequent, cursory, easy, and confident. The New Testament is trinitarian to the core. Let us quote a few evidences:

1. Our Lord's Baptism (Matt. 3:16-17): The Father's voice from heaven; and Spirit's descent, the anointing received; the Son at Jordan, object of the Father's testimony, subject of the Spirit's anointing.
2. The Baptismal Formula (Matt. 28:19): Here we have one name, indicating Trinity in unity, but three Persons.
3. Gifts and Administrations Within the Church. I Corinthians 12:4-6 acribes such to Father, Son, and Spirit respectively.
4. The Apostolic Benediction (II Cor. 13:14). A deeply taught servant of God has said:

It is a comforting and observable fact, that the three Persons of the Trinity are never brought together in the Bible without a result of blessing. We have instances in which each Person, standing by Himself, is an aspect of fear. The Father we see clothed with thunders on Sinai; the Son as the falling stone that grinds to powder; and the sin against the Holy Ghost shall never be forgiven. But there is not an instance upon record in which the three Persons stand together without an intention of grace. And it is a magnificent thought, that the completeness of the Deity in all His essence and in all His operation, is never mentioned but for mercy. The whole doctrine of the Trinity is a subject, not of understanding but of faith. We must come to Him in such a spirit as that which fills the mind of the angels when they cry: "Holy, Holy, Holy, Lord God Almighty, which was, and is, and is to come." This is to rise from prayer to worship, from supplication to adoration.

5. The Guide to Prayer (Eph. 2:18): This passage

gives not only the clearest possible declaration of the Trinity but also marks the sole ground of prevailing prayer.

6. The Development of the Church (Eph. 4:4-6): Here such upbuilding is ascribed to the cooperation of the three Persons in the Godhead.

7. The Appeal of Love (Rom. 15:30): This is a silent assertion of the Trinity giving additional beauty to Paul's writing. See also Philippians 2:1, where "consolation of love" refers to the Father, with II Thessalonians 3:5, where "the Lord" means the Holy Ghost. Another exhortation combining the Trinity is in Romans 8:9.

8. The Doxology of Revelation (Rev. 1:4-6).

9. The Worship of Heaven (Rev. 4:6), where we have the triple ascription of praise.

10. The Work of Salvation. Luke 15 shows us the Father, Son, and Holy Spirit at work. The three-fold "verily" of John 3 brings the Trinity together: "verily" of the kingdom of God (v. 3); "verily" of the birth of Christ (v. 5); "verily" of the Spirit's witness (v. 11). (See II Thess. 2:13-14; Titus 3:4-6; I Peter 1:2.)

Bearing in mind all that we have gathered from the Old and New Testaments on the subject of the Trinity, we can say that the general trend of teaching can be stated thus:

(1) *In Creation* we witness the cooperation of the Father; the Word; the Spirit.

(2) *In Redemption* God is the Father in the source of grace—He *sends;* Jesus is the grace—He *comes and administrates;* the Holy Spirit is the medium of grace—He *communicates, applies, and seals.*

The practical conclusion of our meditation is evident. This great doctrine of the Trinity avails nothing if locked in the brain—"What shall it profit thee?" Of what value is it to study the Trinity if we ourselves are displeasing to the Trinity? If there be one God subsisting in three Persons, then let us give equal reverence, love, and obedience to all Three. Let us—

1. *Obey God the Father,* even as Christ Himself did (Deut. 27:10; John 4:34; Acts 5:29, 32; II Cor. 10:5).

2. *Obey God the Son* (Ps. 2:12), Kiss of Obedience. What He commands is for our interest and benefit.

3. *Obey God the Holy Ghost.* As He is God, let us render unto Him the tribute of homage and obedience due unto His name (Acts 26:19; I Peter 1:2).

Man himself is a trinity—body, soul, and spirit.

Man is assailed by a trinity—the world around, the flesh within, and the devil beneath.

Man is guilty of a trinity—the lust of the flesh, the lust of the eyes, and the pride of life.

Man is saved by a Trinity—the Father, the Son, and the Holy Spirit.

Seventeenth Summary
The Antagonism of Satan in Scripture

If there is one passage more than any other which summarizes the subtle working of Satan to overcome the child of God, it is the phrase Daniel gives us, "He shall wear out the saints of the Most High" (7:25). "Saint" was a favorite term of the prophet in speaking of the believer. His sevenfold use of it forms a profitable study. It is the saint, more than the sinner, that Satan concentrates on. Because he already possesses the sinner, he does not give him much thought; but because of the holy calling and character of the saint, Satan waits for every unguarded moment to wear down resistance to his power.

The direct application of Daniel 7 concerns the period of Great Tribulation. The ten horns represent the ten-kingdom empire John refers to (Rev. 17), which is a period marked by the hostility of the Antichrist towards the Tribulation saints, ended only by the return of the Ancient of Days to deliver them. The chapter as a whole describes the diabolical plan burning in the savage heart of Satan since he was deposed as Lucifer before the creation of man. For well-nigh six millenniums now, he has been at war with the saints, and he knows that his time is short, so he is manifesting greater wrath for those redeemed by the blood of the Lamb.

There are two aspects of satanic antagonism mentioned by Daniel, "war with the saints" (7:21), and "wear out the saints" (7:25). The first implies a more open, a more active antagonism; while the second suggests a more subtle, insidious and crafty method of thwarting the purpose of God concerning the saints. We speak of a "wearing out process." Job refers to water wearing away the stones (14:19), and this is the method to be most feared by the child of God, namely, the gradual, silent, yet effective force of the enemy. Many saints stand firm in the day of battle against his mighty attacks and assaults, and emerge victorious from his war against them, but who, alas! are ultimately conquered by the imperceptible, unconscious forces of the foe. They are not overthrown in open conflict, but are slowly robbed of their spiritual vitality. Let us try to diagnose the wearing-out process Satan employs. How does he sometimes succeed in wearing out the saints of the Most High?

Through Prolonged Trials

If ever a saint was subject to the process we are considering, it was Job who was forced to cry, "My soul is weary of my life" (10:1). The psalmist also became weary of his groaning (Ps. 6:6; 69:3). A saint who is subjected to continuous bodily suffering and trial, and has a load that never seems to lift, is apt to become worn out. Constant pain confuses the mind, and in many cases leads to depression, or a heavy feeling of exhaustion. Such a condition sometimes leads to negligence of the spiritual means of grace and religious exercises which help to keep the soul in repair. If suffering is not relieved or removed, the spirit becomes burdened, faith is gradually weakened, melancholy sets in—a frame of mind Satan can work upon to great advantage.

This morbid spirit unfits one.

It causes the wheels of the chariot to come off. If the strings of a lute are wet, they can produce no sweet music. And if we are unnecessarily sad and cast down, then the spiritual lute is wet and cannot make the saint joyful, even in tribulation.

160

This morbid spirit sides with Satan against God.

It opens the floodgate of doubt regarding God's love and care. Faith is silently yet surely worn out, and the brightest saint ends his days in darkness.

This morbid spirit breeds discontent, and ends in death.

We have known most earnest saints to find relief in self-murder. Despair set in, and deepened until utterly worn out by this satanic method, they ended their existence. How we need to pray for spiritual discernment enabling us to detect the ambush of the evil one and overcome him by the blood of the Lamb!

Through Providential Dealings

There are at least two verses which indicate how Satan employs other tactics in his wearing-out process. Solomon exhorts us, "Neither be weary of his correction" (Prov. 3:11). Isaiah expressed the feelings of God in this condemnation, "Thou hast been weary of me, O Israel" (43:22). How true these verses are to experience! The constant chastenings of the Almighty either wear out or nerve up the believer. There are those who permitted providential dealings to make them more virile, strong, and active for God. They are used as steps to climb closer to Him. But the sad story is that too often they wear out those saints who fail to understand the sanctifying purpose God has in permitting untoward experiences to befall them (see Gen. 45:5).

Satan is constantly active, employing all his gathered wisdom and experience in soul-destruction, to disturb the faith in a child of God, and to stop its actings. He knows only too well that if faith in God is not operative, all other graces suffer, just as a watch does if its mainspring is out of order. In these hard-pressed days we meet too many derelict saints who are worn out and useless because they strive against the divine Potter who seeks to mold them into His image. They fought and resisted the divine will and plan for their life until they became exhausted, and are now laid aside, useless, like a worn-out vessel.

Through the Greatness of Life's Tasks

We can never be too watchful against the craftiness and duplicity of Satan. The first and last glimpses we have of him in Scripture is as a "deceiver," and perfection of deceit and subtlety is his. There are two further passages that enlighten us as to the cunning methods he employs to destroy the power of saints, and succeed where others fail. "Thou art wearied in the greatness of thy way" (Isa. 57:10). "Be not weary in welldoing" (Gal. 6:9). If we think that our high and holy calling as saints is impossible of realization, and that no matter how we strive and struggle to be like Christ, failure will dog our footsteps, then after a series of sinnings and repentings we will end up by saying, "I'm giving up. It's no use trying to be a Christian."

Because of the great cleavage between the ideal and the actual we become disappointed, and life is robbed of joy and hope and confidence. God has far too many saints who were once strong, robust, and alert in His cause, but who are now worn out, spiritually crippled. They resemble an institution full of worn-out men and women incapacitated for life's duties and for further service. May grace be ours to wear well, and to emulate the example of Paul who could say, "By the grace of God, I continue." There are two ways by which we can prevent the weariness that life's responsibilities sometimes brings.

Substituting Submission for Suppression

A constant striving in the battle against sin is the error of

162

saint and sinner alike, for holiness, like salvation, comes as a gift. It is one of the stratagems of Satan to wear out the saints, exhaust them through multitudinous efforts to sanctify themselves. They must learn to submit, to cease struggling and wearying themselves. Victory is not to be found in our own efforts but in yieldedness to heaven's will—in trusting, not trying. We must cast our daily doings down at Jesus' feet.

Substituting the Holy Spirit for Human Energy

Nothing can wear out a Christian worker like self-energy, or fleshly efforts. How necessary it is to remember that it is not what we are able to do, but what the Holy Spirit is able to accomplish through us! Many are rushed off their feet not by God, but by Satan, and they become worn out. Others become worn out from doing nothing. Idleness in Christian service is also detrimental to one's spiritual health. Experience leads us to confess to being more tired on holiday than when working. Yet some appear to enjoy one long, spiritual holiday, and little relish service for God and souls.

Through Domestic Difficulties

Esau's choice of wives from another nation was a grief of mind to his parents. It caused Rebekah to say that she was "weary of my life because of the daughters of Heth," and that if Jacob made a similar choice then, "what good shall my life be to me?" (Gen. 26:34; 27:46). Hannah was another who experienced great sorrow of heart because of trying conditions at home (I Sam. 1:5-23). Satan is ceaselessly active in our homes, wearing out, silently yet gradually, many who would be saintly in such a narrow circle. Through constant cares, difficulties, trials, and domestic affairs, there comes an imperceptible weakening of spiritual force and character. It would seem as if Satan is busiest here producing in those who were once so bright in the Master's service, spiritual inertia.

Within the home there are those who, like the earthly brothers and sisters of Jesus, do not believe in His claims. Possibly there is a son or daughter, so ungrateful and unfeeling, like Absalom who tried to rob his father David of his throne. There may be unsaved ones like the sons of Eli the high priest, who know not the Lord, and the daily conflict becomes a wearying load for Christian parents.

Here, then, is the real test if one's home life is not to be broken up. Constant intercession and appropriation of grace to live for God untouched, unmoved amid all the perplexities, vicissitudes, and burdens of the family circle; and to never wear out, spiritually, but to maintain a deep unruffled calm and peace of mind in spite of a surge of care and blast of duties. If Jesus is the Head of the home and all within it love and obey Him, then such a home will be a foretaste of heaven.

> O happy house! where Thou art not forgot,
>   Where joy is flowing full and free;
> O happy house! where every wound is brought,
>   Physician, Comforter, to Thee.
> Until at last, earth's day's work ended,
>   All meet Thee in that home above,
> From whence Thou comest, where Thou hast ascended,
>   Thy heaven of glory and of love!

Through the Daily Routine

Not only do clothes and articles wear out through constant usage. In nature, too, there is a gradual deterioration of the material. "Change and decay in all around we see." As with the wear and tear of life, so is it with the daily round and common task. Sameness and lack of change can produce inertia. When Jethro saw how Moses bowed down under his very heavy daily load, he said, "Thou wilt surely wear away" (Exod. 18:18). Even Jesus was "weary with his journey," and sat on a well where He found both physical and spiritual refreshment (John 4:6). And we are exhorted to "consider him, lest ye be wearied and faint in your minds" (Heb. 12:3).

Is it not amid the responsibilities of everyday life that we can detect the insidious efforts of Satan to weaken our spiritual strength? We have the same old duties to face, floors to scrub, tables to serve, clothes to mend, and mouths to feed, and if one is not careful the day's charge becomes a dread. Yet if all is done for God's glory we can say, "Blessed be drudgery!" We are never worn out by the monotony of life's duties, although they are commonplace, if we lift them up to a higher plane. True, we shall be often weary *in* our work, but never weary *of* it. We often say that it is "better to wear out than rust out." It is better still to reach God's ideal and *last out*. Edward Thring, one of the greatest of English schoolmasters, wrote the following prayer when a student at Cambridge, "Oh, God, give me work till the end of my life, and life till the end of my work for Christ's sake, Amen!"

How apt and full of spiritual suggestion is the appealing question of Jeremiah to those who failed by the way—"If thou hast run with the footmen, and they have wearied thee, then how canst thou contend with horses? And if in the land of peace, wherein thou trustedst, they wearied thee, then how wilt thou do in the swelling of Jordan?" (Jer. 12:5).

Since there is no discharge in the war against the rulers of the darkness of this world, how imperative it is to learn the secret of victory and freshness, and the laws of spiritual health, endurance, and sustenance whereby we can stand the strain of such a conflict. As life becomes more tense, and society more corrupt, people appear to be more devil-driven, and even the saintliest find it increasingly harder to live the divine life. The Scripture presents a twofold secret for our comfort.

165

First, there is a waiting upon Him who is never weary.

How precious is the promise Isaiah has for our hearts, "They that wait upon the Lord shall renew their strength, They shall mount up with wings as eagles; they shall run, and not be weary; and they shall walk, and not faint" (40:28-31). The word the prophet uses for "renew" can be translated "exchange." No matter how worn out we may be, weariness can be exchanged for divine strength enabling us to face life's responsibilities with gladness and unflagging zeal. May grace be ours to maintain spiritual freshness no matter how we have to run or walk!

Second, there is the constant infilling of the Holy Spirit.

Whether it be in the home, or where we labor for our daily bread, or in the work of the church, an unfailing source of freshness and alacrity, will enable us to resist the wearing out process of Satan—we will be "strengthened with might by His Spirit in the inner man" (Eph. 3:16). When He is at the center of our life then all that would disturb us at its circumference is successfully dealt with, and we become more than conquerors over satanic antagonism. The mighty Spirit is more than a match for those hellish forces that seek to weaken our spiritual life. The healthier a person is, the more he is able to resist germs that would weaken his physical power. If the Holy Spirit keeps our inner life buoyant, strong, fertile, and fresh, then the wearing-out tactics of Satan are nullified, and we are triumphant. How assuring are those lines of Wordsworth—

> Dive through the stormy surface of the flood
> To the great current flowing underneath;
> Explore the countless springs of silent good;
> So shall the truth be better understood,
> And thy grieved spirit brighten, strong in faith.

Eighteenth Summary
The Record of Romance and Redemption in Ruth

The love story of Ruth is one of the most wonderful, perfect, and touching narratives in Scripture. Easily read in twenty minutes, it is a book that all classes and conditions of people can read with pleasure and profit, seeing that it combines many traits of human life and character. The charming Book of Ruth provides us with the history of a nation, the history of a family, and the history of a soul. Without doubt, it is one of the rarest gems in the realm of literature.

The Book of Ruth is a book that every family ought to read when gathered together, for the story of a wrong step, taken by a Jewish family long ago, will serve to save family life from disaster. Elimelech and Naomi went down to Moab and met sorrow and tragedy. We have no right to move even from one house to another, as well as from one community to another, without the clear guidance of God's Spirit. If we acknowledge Him in *all* our ways, He will direct our paths.

The Book of Ruth is a book that every young woman should read, for it emphasizes the fact that in religious matters, there is no escape from a personal decision. One cannot just *drift* into grace with a companion or a church. Within this Hebrew idyl we have Ruth's decision which leads to nobility and royalty, and also the decision of Orpah, which results in obscurity and oblivion.

The Book of Ruth is a book that all sorrowing hearts can profitably meditate upon. A common grief bound three weeping widows together. "Fellow feeling makes us wondrous kind."

The Book of Ruth is also a book that all true lovers can

learn a great deal from, for it reveals the grief of mixed marriages on the one hand, and on the other, the blessedness of the sacred union when two marry in the Lord. An unequal yoke is forbidden in Scripture. What sorrows must be faced when a Christian marries a non-Christian; or a Protestant a Catholic!

The Book of Ruth is a book that all disappointed souls should read. It is one of the best books in the Bible for backsliders to peruse. Naomi, down in Moab, felt the misery of her separation from her own people in Bethlehem. How could she be happy in Moab after having lived in Bethlehem? How can a backslider find pleasure in the world after having tasted the joy of salvation? When, ultimately, Naomi returned to her native land, it was the beginning of the barley harvest. It is always barley-harvest when a backslider cries: "Restore unto me the joy of thy salvation" (Ps. 51:12).

The Book of Ruth is a book that we should persuade all masters and servants to read, knowing that, from one of its underlying principles, the solution of industrial problems in labor circles may be discovered. The delightful relationship existing between master and servants in a dark, chaotic period of Israel's history is one of the superb episodes of the Bible. As Boaz walked through his fields and met his servants, he smiled upon them and said: "The Lord be with thee." And they replied: "The Lord bless thee." In these days of selfishness and greed, we sadly need the revival of the mutual understanding seen in Ruth.

The Book of Ruth is a book that all Bible students should read, since it is rich in typical teaching. Within it there are types of Christ, of Israel, of the church, and of the believer. Here is a favorite book for Bible teachers to expound.

In Boaz, we have a type of Christ. Think of how he is described in the Book of Ruth—as lord of the harvest; dispenser of bread; kinsman-redeemer; man of wealth; advocate; bridegroom; life-giver—titles to which our Lord lays claim.

In Ruth, we have a type of the church. Bought with a

168

price, the Moabitess yet became the bride of the one who purchased her. In this connection, read Ephesians 5:21, 23.

In the union of Boaz and Ruth, we have a type of the composition of the church. Boaz was a Jew; Ruth, a Gentile. Yet both became one. Within the true church regenerated Jews and Gentiles become one. In Christ, there is neither Jew nor Gentile.

Bethlehem means "house of bread" and represents our fullness of supply in God.

Moab means "waste," or "emptiness," and typifies the emptiness, disappointment, disillusionment of worldly pleasures and pursuits.

Outstanding, attractive characters make up a good story. Without them a tale has no appeal. Let us, therefore, try to portray the conspicuous characters making up the Book of Ruth. In Old Testament days, names were associated with the experiences and circumstances of the people. This is why so many given names are rich in spiritual significance. An illustration of this is to be found in I Samuel 25. Abigail, pleading before David for her worthless, churlish husband said: "As his name is, so is he. Nabal is his name, and folly is with him." In effect, Abigail said: "Pay no attention to my husband; he is a fool by name and a fool by nature." Let us seek, then, to gather the story of the Book of Ruth around the outstanding characters the book contains.

Elimelech

The father of the Jewish family, prominent in the Book of Ruth, has a most suggestive name. *Elimelech* means "My mighty God is King." Doubtless it was given him by godly parents when Israel wholly followed the Lord. Such a name was an evidence of their faith in the sovereignty of Jehovah. Elimelech, however, belied the name he bore. It is one thing to possess a good name, but a different matter to have a life correspondingly as good as the name. Elimelech had the best

169

of names, but he did not act as if God was his King. Had he believed in the sovereignty of God, he would have stayed in Bethlehem, and that in spite of famine. But one may argue that there was only one right thing for Elimelech to do; rather than see his family perish from starvation as famine gripped the land, he went down to Moab where there was plenty of bread. Elimelech, however, was a Jew and, as such, he had the promise that in the days of famine he would be satisfied. Had he truly believed that God was his King, he would have remained in Bethlehem, knowing that need could never throttle God. God used the ravens to feed Elijah; He can spread a table in the wilderness.

Are we true Elimelechs? Do we live and act as if God is All-Sovereign, and able to do exceeding abundantly above all we could ask or think? Let us rest in the present tense of such a significant name, "My God *is* King." While His sovereignty is yet to be displayed, He is presently high over all. "The Lord God omnipotent *reigneth.*"

Further, if we bear a good name, one full of spiritual significance, may grace be ours to live the life corresponding to such a name.

Naomi

Having taken her husband "for better or for worse," what else could Naomi do but take her two children and follow Elimelech into Moab? She was a prey to circumstances over which she had no control. It was she, however, who had to bear the brunt of the wrong step her husband took. Hers was the greater loss in that emigration into a heathen land.

Naomi means "pleasant, agreeable, attractive," and suggests all that is charming. And she must have had an unusual personality to have drawn to her heart a lovely girl like Ruth, and held her close with the cords of love. Evidently Ruth the Moabitess had no difficulty in living with her mother-in-law.

The tragedy of Naomi, however, was the fact that ten

years in Moab, away from God and His people, dried up her finer feelings—so much so that when she ultimately returned to Bethlehem, her old friends met her with the salutation: "Why, here comes Naomi!" But her disposition had so changed that she replied: "Call me not Naomi, call me Mara." Bitterness had taken the place of beauty. Naomi could not bear the contradiction between the name she bore and the thing she had become. No longer was she delightful to know. Disobedience and grief had coarsened the one-time attractive woman.

Can this be the tragedy of someone reading these lines? You, too, look back and think of the days you were easy to live with. You had a winsomeness of character that drew others to your side. A spiritual or natural charm was yours that made you a channel of influence; but things are different now. You stepped out of God's will, became disobedient to the heavenly vision and, consequently, courted grief and adversity like Naomi of old. And today you are hard, cynical, disagreeable, and irritable. All sweetness of disposition has vanished. Spurgeon used to speak of "sweet sinners" and "sour saints." Have you become a sour saint? Well, the old-time charm can be restored if only you will return to your charming Lord. He alone can restore the years the cankerworm has eaten, and once again make you "lovely and pleasant" in your life.

Mahlon and Chilion

Into that Jewish home in Bethlehem two boys were born, with somewhat strange names: *Mahlon,* meaning "sickly," or "invalid"; *Chilion,* meaning "pining one," or "wasting away." It may be these two were twins and from their birth were frail and weak. Naomi had to guard them from a rigorous life. They required much attention and constant care. This much is evident—that all the while they remained in Bethlehem, their strength could be guarded, but by going down into Moab and marrying heathen women, they only hastened their end. The fast, idolatrous life of Moab was too much for their none-too-robust constitutions, so they found graves in foreign soil. Their sin in marrying Moabitish women may have been the cause of their premature deaths (see Deut. 7:3; 23:3).

The curse of church life and work today is the presence of far too many Mahlons and Chilions—professing Christians who have been sickly since the day of their spiritual birth. How frail and puny they are! Spiritual anemics! Theirs is not robust health. They are akin to those Corinthians whom Paul expected to be full grown so that he could feed them with strong meat. Alas, their spiritual stomachs could not take it, so he had to resort to the milk bottle! We are persuaded that what many church members require is not a pastor but a nursemaid constantly to carry and coddle them. They are so carnal and, therefore, so easily displeased and peeved. Unless stroked the right way, and given full recognition they turn up their noses, and quit at the slightest provocation. Babies are lovely to look at but, if they remain babies, they become abnormalities. God save us from spiritual babyhood.

Orpah

Scholars are divided as to the exact significance of the name, *Orpah*. Some say it means "stiff-necked"; others affirm her name signifies "duplicity," or "doublemindedness." The latter seems to fit in with her character, seeing that her actions prove her to have been somewhat double-minded. While under the roof of Naomi, Orpah was obliged to yield temporary, external allegiance to the God of Chilion, her husband. A crisis on the Bethlehem-Judah road, however, revealed her unwillingness to pay the price of complete surrender.

Orpah knew what to expect if she went all the way into Bethlehem, so she went back to her own people, her own land, and her own gods (1:15-16). Naomi had promised her daughters-in-law no easy road. Orpah knew that the Jews hated the Moabites. She doubtless left Moab under an emotional impulse, but her heart was divided. She left Moab as a place but carried Moab in her heart. The psalmist speaks of his heart as being fixed. Orpah's difficulty was that of a heart that was mixed. She wanted Bethlehem but loved Moab, and being double-minded, was unstable in all her ways.

Ruth

Ruth has always been the writer's favorite female Bible character. Several interpretations have been given of her name. "Fullness" and "satisfaction" have been suggested and are in keeping with her experience. Although she left Moab empty, how full she became! Ruth went all the way in surrender and was crowned with riches, honor, and an imperishable memory. When Orpah left Naomi and Ruth, she went out into oblivion. This was not the experience of Ruth! In Bethlehem, her own life was full, and she filled the lives of others. To Naomi she was better than seven sons.

The meaning of *Ruth* that we like most is that of "a closely drawn friend." Truly she stands out as the personification of true friendship. Why, there is no episode in all literature comparable to that on the Bethlehem-Judah road, when Naomi pled with Orpah and Ruth to go back to Moab. She knew what it would mean for these young widows to cross the dividing line. Orpah planted a cold, loveless kiss upon Naomi's brow, and went back to her heathen ways. Ruth, however, clave unto her mother-in-law and cried: "Intreat me not to leave thee, or to return from following after thee: for whither thou goest, I will go; and where thou lodgest, I will lodge; thy people shall be my people, and thy God my God. Where thou diest, will I die, and there will I be buried: the Lord do so to me, and more also, if ought but death part thee and me" (1:16-17).

Steadfastly minded to go with Naomi every step of the

way into the unknown, she stands out in contrast to the fickle-minded Orpah. Remember that, at that time, Naomi was a bitter woman, and it takes grace to befriend an embittered person. Thus Ruth's exhibition of undying friendship is a classic. God knows that we have so-called friends who leave us like Orpah. There are others, however (and the Lord bless them!), who cling to us like Ruth clung to Naomi.

Have you ever been impressed with the fact that Calvary was also enacted on that road back to Bethlehem? *From* Naomi, one woman went out into obscurity, whereas another went *with* Naomi to honor and joy. From the side of the crucified Son of God, one thief went into perdition, the other went into paradise.

Boaz

In a true love story, the heroine meets a good man, marries, and they live happily ever after. So it is in this classic account. The unfolding story can be briefly told. Back in Bethlehem, Naomi was too old to work, yet she must live. Ruth, then, with characteristic kindness and thoughtfulness, went out and labored in the fields of Boaz, where it was her "hap" to come under the notice of her master.

It is evident that the somewhat elderly bachelor evinced more than a passing interest in the beautiful Moabitess. Naomi, who proved herself to be a good matchmaker, brought about the meeting of Ruth and Boaz in the latter's threshingfloor. There it came about that Ruth's property by marriage was redeemed by Boaz, and in turn she became the bride of the man who redeemed her possessions.

Of the Biblical meaning of *Boaz* there is no question. It has been said that his name represents "fleetness, alacrity." Without doubt Boaz acted promptly in the protection, redemption, and marriage of Ruth. All who love the Lord should be "alive and quick to hear each murmur of His voice." Promptly the Word and will must be obeyed. In the description of the temple, however, we are told that the name of its left pillar was Boaz, for in it is strength (I Kings 7:21). Boaz was true to his name. He was strong in love, grace, courage, and integrity. Between the lines of the story he stands out as a strong, reliable man, dependable in every way. May we covet all that his name implies! In this age of apostasy, we are apt to be too weak and vacillating. We need to be strengthened with all might in the inner man. We must "be strong *in the Lord.*"

Obed

Ruth's complete surrender to the God of Israel was rewarded with complete satisfaction and joy. Although a Gentile, she became the bride of a Jew and the mother of one from whom the Messiah was to spring. God blessed Ruth with a son, Obed by name, a name which, although the neighbors had a share in choosing, must have been Ruth's personal choice.

Obed means "a servant who worships." It illustrates Ruth's experience. She started life in Bethlehem as a servant, laboring in the fields of Boaz, but she was a servant who worshiped. "Thy God," she said to Naomi, "shall be my God."

Can we say that we are among God's Obeds? Are we servants who worship? Two classes to be distinguished in our churches are those who serve but seldom worship, and those who worship but fail to serve. We have met preachers who are so busy doing Christian work that they have little time to pray, meditate, and cultivate spiritual aspirations. Somehow they forget that, while the seraphim have six wings, four are used for worship, and only two for service.

The art of worship has been sadly neglected in Protestant circles. We hold no brief for the Roman Catholic Church. We love some Roman Catholics but abominate the system they represent. This much, however, must be said for Catholic churches and cathedrals—they are notable for the atmosphere

175

of worship. Silence, even though it is the silence of death, pervades the buildings. You never see Roman Catholic worshipers indifferent, chattering to each other, or gazing around. Catholic churches have no need of a notice in the vestibule reading: "Please observe silence." Such a notice is found, however, in some Protestant churches. Why, the first moments in some of our church services suggest the rabble of a marketplace rather than the house of God where the Lord waits to meet His people. Church members need to hear more sermons on worship. "Oh, *worship* the Lord!" But Catholicism does not preserve the right balance. It teaches people to worship but not to go out and serve a world of sin and need. Ruth worshiped. She also knew how to toil and glean for herself and others.

As a servant who worshiped, Ruth was amply rewarded. She became the mother of Obed. Obed became the father of Jesse. Jesse became the father of David. David became the ancestor of Jesus Christ. It is thus that Ruth finds honorable mention in the human genealogy of our Lord Jesus (Matt. 1:5).

As our heavenly Boaz, Christ is the One who has the right to reign as King. As the mighty God, He is King. He is also the One whose grace makes us pleasant and attractive. His matchless love begets true friendship. His gentleness makes us great and strong to obey. His holiness calls forth the worship of our hearts and the service of our lives.

Thus we have the sweet, charming love story of Ruth, the letters of whose name spell out the truth of each chapter, making up the book bearing her name.

R stands for *resolve,* which characteristic summarizes chapter 1. Ruth was determined in her resolve to decide for God and His people: "Thy people shall be my people, and thy God, my God." Many children of Christian parents need to make a similar resolve.

U can represent *unselfishness,* a trait which is so prominent in chapter 2. Ruth's chief concern was for Naomi, an aging widow who was not able to glean in the fields. Without hesitation, Ruth left the land of her nativity and, among unknown people, labored to support Naomi and herself in her adopted land.

T brings us to *trust,* and this is the virtue emphasized in chapter 3. Ruth began to reap a rich reward from Him under whose wings she had come to trust. When the matter between Boaz and herself was developing, Naomi urged Ruth to "sit still" until Boaz had finished the thing concerning Ruth and himself. Ruth, as a trusting soul, could afford to sit still. If we know what it is to trust in the Lord with all our heart, then our strength is to sit still.

H indicates *honor,* so prominent in chapter 4, where Ruth learns that they who honor the Lord are honored by Him. As we have already seen, Ruth became the ancestress of our blessed Lord. Hers is an imperishable memory. The Book of Ruth is a commentary on the divine declaration: "They who honor me, will I honor, saith the Lord."

One cannot close this meditation without drawing attention to a most unusual tract by S. Fox, a missionary in India, written many years ago. Its title is "Ruth, Chapter 5, Verse 17." And this is what he says in the tract:

> It was in the town of Guntur, about two years ago, that I was asked to address a large meeting one evening in the church building. I suppose there were between five and six hundred people present. The meeting was addressed in Telugu, and the elderly Indian pastor was chairman. I was led to speak on Ruth and Boaz. I pointed out that Ruth was a twice-married woman. Her first marriage to Mahlon being fruitless, she was later married to Boaz. And at once God blessed this union and she became the happy mother of a child, who was the progenitor of David and of Christ Himself. I joined this with the passage in Romans 7 wherein we are told that we

have died to the law that we might be married to another, even to Christ. The purpose of the union being that we might bring forth fruit to God. I brought before my audience many points and sought to force them home:

1. Barrenness can give place to fruitfulness.
2. Weakness can be changed to strength.
3. Sorrow changes to joy when we find our Boaz, the Rich Man and the Strong One of Bethlehem—a true type of Jesus Christ. He was born of a woman, born in the same place, born under the law, to bring us eventually to the place of sonship and adoption; delivering us from the curse of the law.

Then further, at the close of the address I said, "Now turn, if you can, to Ruth, chapter 5 and verse 17, and read, if you are able to find it, the story of how Ruth, grown tired of Boaz, after a time leaves him and goes back to Moab; digs up her old husband, hangs the dead bones of Mahlon around her neck, and says, 'This is the one for me.' " Sad to say, many, not knowing their Bible, began at once to search for this strange passage, for it does sound strange, doesn't it? Even the old pastor, right before his congregation, began to fumble to find Ruth 5:17. I waited. A few, at once sensing something wrong, looked into my face to find out if I was serious, for they knew there were only four chapters in the Book of Ruth. Then I drove home the point as follows:

"Friends, you will not find that verse, and please God, may you never find the experience either, for both are out of bounds."

Yes, what an awful thing for the Christian to leave grace and return to law! Or to leave the place of blessing, and backslide into the world. It is like opening up the grave of the dead, and mixing with dry bones, or worse, with that which is putrid and corrupting. What a picture of a backslider, with a dead body around his or her neck! No, the body of sin is for us destroyed, that is, it has no power over us, and is, in the plan of God, removed, crucified, and buried. May we, by the help of this New Husband and Lord, live the risen and glorified life.

Nineteenth Summary
The Twelve Gates in Nehemiah

The prophet Isaiah exhorts us to "go through, go through the gates" (Isa. 62:10) which is what we have to do as we study Nehemiah's restorative work. Jerusalem of old was beautiful for its situation, a city compact together and surrounded by walls. Entrance into the city was effected by twelve gates, corresponding in turn to the twelve gates of the New Jerusalem (Rev. 21:21).

The gates of a city were places of greatest concourse for business and judicial proceedings, also for idling. They were centers of public life. Markets were held around them. The special commodities traded in gave the gates their distinctive names. Legal tribunals were also held at these gates. Prophets and teachers went to them with divine messages.

On the other hand, the gates were noted as the rendezvous for gossip. While the maidens and married women of the city went to the wells for conversation, the men found their way to the gates to exchange their tales and confidences.

Through the disobedience of His people, God suffered the city, its walls and gates, and the temple to be destroyed, and the people themselves brought into bondage. After their deliverance from captivity, Ezra was commissioned to rebuild the temple, and Nehemiah's task was to repair the walls and gates of the city. Thus we come to glean a few spiritual lessons from Nehemiah's circuit of the walls and the work he accomplished. Let us follow the patriot as he went from gate to gate.

The Sheep Gate

Doubtless this first gate received its name from the fact that sacrificial lambs were led through it (3:1). Beyond this gate was an adjoining pool where the sheep were washed before being slain (see John 5:2).

In the spiritual pilgrimage, all must start at this gate, suggesting as it does a constant witness to the fact that without the shedding of blood there is no remission of sins, no cleansing. Christ was led as a lamb to the slaughter. He was both the Lamb and the Shepherd, and His Person and work form the starting place of all true restoration and redemption. After making the circuit, Nehemiah finished up where he had started, namely, the sheep gate (3:32). So Christ and Him crucified is the commencement and the consummation of all things. D. L. Moody used to say that "souls were always saved in the church where the blood of Jesus is preached." Thus we start with Him, and when we see Him in glory, it will be as the Lamb, slain from the foundation of the world.

The sheep gate is also a reminder of our need as sheep who have gone astray. Here is the wicket gate all must pass through if they would reach the Celestial City. It may be humiliating to confess that we are silly sheep, yet we must begin where God does. One can pass through the church-gate but not through the sheep-gate.

We are told that the priests sanctified this gate. Thus the sacred character of Nehemiah's task was impressed on his workers at the earliest possible moment. God localized His presence in the temple and, girded with divine strength, the people had to repair all avenues leading to His sacred courts.

The Fish Gate

This was the gate that fish from the Jordan River and the Sea of Galilee were brought to. Fishmongers would gather at this gate to market the harvest of the waters (3:3). The fish

181

gate always follows the sheep gate. We are saved to serve—forgiven to fetch others—won to win. Andrew, as a true fisher of men, first found his own brother. Not all, however, who pass through the sheep gate enter the fish gate. They fail in their responsibility to bring others to Christ. They forget the royal commission of going into their little piece of the world to preach the gospel by lip and life. The "fish gate" is one that needs constantly to be kept in a state of repair.

In the Scriptures, fish have most interesting associations. Zephaniah cried from the fish gate (1:10). Do we? Peter learned a lesson on divine provision when he caught that fish with the silver piece in its mouth. Peter, ever impulsive, said "I go a fishing," and he caught 153 fish in his net, symbolic, perhaps, of the haul he landed at Pentecost. The fish Jesus cooked for His disciples' breakfast taught them something of His divine solicitude. The early martyrs used the sign of the fish to represent Jesus as they suffered for Him in their catacomb cells.

The Old Gate

Some authorities feel that this gate received its name because it belonged to ancient Salem, which was said to have been built originally by Melchizedek. "The Old Gate" is identified with three other gates:

The College Gate (II Kings 22:14)

It was here that Huldah the prophetess lived and taught. What do we know of the tuition to be received at "The College of the Feet" where Mary studied?

The Corner Gate (II Chron. 26:9)

The margin has it, "The gate of it that looketh." This gate

reminds us of Him who is the chief corner stone (I Peter 2:6). Christ is the Cornerstone of all things.

The First Gate (Zech. 14:10)

As the gate of the old city it suggests Him whose goings forth are of old. He came as the Ancient of Days.

Too many in these apostate days no longer tarry at the old gate. The old paths have been forsaken (Jer. 6:16). The fundamentals of the faith have been forsaken. The old gate of the gospel of redeeming grace is now deemed antiquated and unnecessary. Solomon in his wisdom said, "Remove not the ancient landmarks" (Prov. 22:28). Those of us who believe the Scriptures must needs mend and mind this old gate. We must arise and build. There are those among us who have never left such a gate. It has no need of repair in our experience. The old, old story of Jesus and His love is still our message and our hope.

The Valley Gate

This fourth gate (3:13), opening before the Valley of Hinnon, was repaired by the inhabitants of Zanoah, a name which means "broken." In the experience of the saints of God it typifies the humility needed in the service of the Master. Too often we are proud of our gifts, position, and achievements. We are guilty of a pride of race, or face, or grace, or lace, or pace. We sing about going down into the valley with Jesus, but we know nothing of that brokenness of spirit which results in blessing (Ps. 51:10). The valley is a sign of death (Ps. 23:5). Are we dying daily to pride, haughtiness, and self-glorification? We talk about being "up and doing." We might accomplish more if we were down and dying. Christ humbled Himself. Are we living in the Valley of Humility? Do we wear the apron of humility that Peter spoke of (I Peter 5:6)?

183

The Dung Gate

One commentator tells us that outside of this gate lay piles of sweepings and offscourings of the streets. The refuse and filth of the city was doubtless carried through this gate to be burned nearby (3:14). Such a gate symbolizes rejection and reproach for Christ's sake. "Thou hast made us as the offscouring and refuse in the midst of the people" (Lam. 3:45). Nehemiah went through this gate. He was scorned, despised, ostracized, treated with contempt (2:19).

Paul passed through the dung gate. He was counted as the filth of the world, and the off-scouring of all things (I Cor. 4:13). The best the world could offer was but dung in his sight. Christ stooped to this unwelcome gate. He was spat upon, despised, and made to endure all manner of shameful indignities, and the reproach broke His heart.

Martin Luther, commenting upon Matthew 5:10-12, pictures the disciples of the Lord arriving at the gates of heaven and being met there by the Master Himself. One of the questions He asks each one who arrives is, "Wert thou an abomination to the whole world as Mine have been from the foundation of the world?" What kind of reply could we give to such an interrogation? All who welcome the dung gate are in for a rich reward.

The Fountain Gate

Near to the pool of Siloam, this gate is now known as "The Virgin's Fount" (3:15). It was next to the dung gate, where it always is in man's spiritual experience. "Thou hast saved and cleansed and filled me." The fountain ever flowing is a type of the Holy Spirit's ministry in and through the believer (John 4:14; 7:37-39). Out from within the believer, rivers of living water flow to refresh the dry, arid wilderness around. Once cleansed and thoroughly identified with Christ in His reproach, the Spirit flows through us unchecked.

The Fountain Gate was over against the sepulchre, which is also true to type. Calvary and Pentecost are adjacent. It is only as we lay in dust life's glory dead that from the ground there can blossom red a life of fruitfulness. The Spirit-controlled life is ever a channel of spiritual refreshment. We cannot be Pentecost Christians unless we are prepared to become Calvary Christians. Out of the smitten rock the water flowed. Death leads to life. The cross results in a crown. Water from the Spirit-possessed life causes everything to live, whithersoever it flows. Is "the fountain gate" fully operating in your life and service?

The Water Gate

It was from this part of the wall that superfluous water from the temple reservoirs was carried off, and possibly used to irrigate surrounding land (3:26). Water is a figure of the cleansing, irrigating power of the Word of God. (See John 3:5; 13:1-16; 15:3; Eph. 5:26.) Our Lord could say of His disciples, "Now ye are clean through the word which I have spoken unto you." The psalmist also speaks of the cleansing efficacy of the Word: "Wherewithal shall a young man cleanse his way? by taking heed thereto according to thy word" (Ps. 119:9).

Praise God, this gate is in no need of repair. The infallible Word needs no building up or improving. The Scriptures cannot be broken. In the estimation of the modernist, the water gate is very much in need of repair, and he tries to patch it up. But how mutilated the Bible is, once he has finished with it! Because of its perfection, the Word of God is able to repair and restore broken lives. "The law of the Lord is perfect, converting the soul" (Ps. 19:7). If it were not perfect, it would never be able to convert a soul. Everyone born of the Spirit, then, is a fresh evidence of the veracity and divine inspiration of Scripture.

The Horse Gate

Through this particular gate on the eastern wall, horses entered the city (3:28). Horses, in Nehemiah's day, were principally used for warfare—"as the horse rusheth into the battle" (Jer. 8:6). We are told, however, that the Lord delighteth not in the strength of the horse. He takes pleasure in those who fear Him (Ps. 147:10-11).

We now come to the warfare of the believer. Because we live in a world of evil and of satanic delusion, our life is one of conflict, and the conflict is becoming more intense. The wrestling is fierce. As good soldiers of Jesus Christ, we have to be tough.

The blessed truth to remember, however, is that we are marching, not *on to* victory, but *from* victory. By His death and resurrection Christ secured a glorious victory for His saints, which they must daily appropriate if they would be more than conquerors. Now they overcome the enemy by the blood of the Lamb. Principalities and powers may muster their unseen array, but resting in Christ's victory, we are more than conquerors. If we would triumph over all our foes, trials, and adversities, we must bring the cross to bear upon them all. When Christ cried, "It is finished," He secured for men not only a perfect redemption, but a full victory over all the powers of hell.

The East Gate

This gate was so named because it was on the east of the temple and was connected with it. It also faced the rising sun (3:29). The Shekinal glory left the east gate, and returned again to it (Ezek. 43:1-2)—"Afterward he brought me to the gate, even the gate that looketh toward the east: And, behold, the glory of the God of Israel came from the way of the east: and his voice was like a noise of many waters: and the earth shined with his glory."

For the believer, the east gate represents the coming of Christ in glory.

> "Upheld by hope" in darkest day
> Faith can the light descry;
> The deepening glory in the East
> Proclaims deliverance nigh.

The dawn is purpling in the east. The Sun of Righteousness is about to rise. Are our faces toward the sunrise? Are we living at the east gate? Through this gate we are to enter the City of God. Some writers identify this gate as "The Gate Beautiful" at which the beggar sat pleading for alms. Made of Corinthian brass, it is said that this magnificent, massive gate required twenty men to close it. Of this we are confident, there is no gate so beautiful to the believer as "the east gate" which will bring him to the "glorious daybreak" (Mal. 4:2).

The Prison Gate

The Revised Version translates "the prison gate" as "the gate of the guard" (3:25; 12:39; II Kings 11:6). It is assumed that the court of prison was at this gate. Prisoners would be pilloried at it, or led to jail through it.

In a sense, we are all prisoners. Though regenerated, we yet are confined in this body of death. We are prisoners of hope. Our captive spirit longs to soar to heights above. How many there are who live in a body crippled by pain and disease! What a happy release awaits them!

Alas, too many of us are prisoners in another way! We are bound with the fetters of indulgence, carnality, formality, prejudice. We do not stand fast in the liberty wherewith Christ has made us free. We are entangled with the yoke of bondage. Yet Christ is able to loose all such prisoners. "If the Son therefore shall make you free, ye shall be free indeed" (John 8:32, 36). It is possible for one to have life but not liberty. Lazarus enjoyed both when Jesus said, "Loose him and let him go."

> Make me a captive, Lord,
>> And then I shall be free;
> Force me to render up my sword
>> And I shall conqueror be.

The Gate of Ephraim

This northern gate (8:16; 12:39), was also as "the gate of Benjamin" (Jer. 37:13). Originally it was named after Joseph's son, Ephraim, a name meaning "double fruit." It was given by Joseph as a tribute to God for His goodness. "God hath caused me to be fruitful in the land of my affliction." So affliction, as well as adversities, can bear fruit to the glory of God.

"The Ephraim gate" fittingly follows "the prison gate," for if we are fully delivered from the prison house of sin and self, we can bear double fruit. "Being made free . . . ye have fruit." How can we bear more fruit and much fruit if we are bound with the fetters of doubt, fear, and pride? What does it mean to be God's Ephraim? Well, double fruit consists of the fruit of holiness in life, and the fruit of souls in service. The one phase of fruit is dependent upon the other.

Further, it is not by strain or effort that we become doubly fruitful. We do not *produce* fruit, we only bear it. Fruit is not the fruit of the Christian, but the fruit of the Holy Spirit. Neither is this double fruit the result of imitation; it is rather *manifestation*. It is the outcome of the One who dwells unhindered within us.

The Gate of Miphkad

Professor Sayce, the renowned archeologist, located this gate at the north-eastern corner of the temple hill (3:31). It was also known as "the registry gate," implying that it was the place of visitation, the appointed place of meeting. Probably it was the gate where the judges sat to register and review, and then settle all disputes and controversies.

For the believer, the Miphkad gate can typify the Bema, the Judgment Seat of Christ, where all differences and disputes between believers will be adjusted. How grateful we are that the Judgment is to be a private one. The Lord and His own will be together. He will not expose our dirty linen to the gaze of the world. As we linger amid the shadows, we are apt to criticize one another. But let us strive to judge nothing before the time.

Two classes are referred to as being occupied with the repair of the gate of Miphkad, namely, the goldsmiths and the merchants. Christ offered Himself as Goldsmith—"Buy of me, gold tried in the fire." He likewise spoke of Himself as a Merchant offering "white raiment" and "eyesalve." If we know Him in this dual capacity, then we need have no fear when we meet Him at His "gate of Miphkad."

Nehemiah completed his circuit where he began, at "the sheep gate." Christ, who was led as a sheep to the slaughter, is the center and the circumference of all. His cross is the *summun bonum* in life.

The gates, being twelve in number, suggest the perfection of government, and these twelve gates we have considered are His gates. If we enter them in penitence and praise, with the government of every part of our life upon His shoulders, then, when the pearly gates open for us, ours will be an abundant entrance into His presence.

Twentieth Summary
The Evidence of Divine Providence in Esther

The Book of Esther, which is placed last in the ancient *Megilloth,* shares with the Song of Solomon the distinction of not mentioning God or any divine name. It is thus that we call Esther, "The Book Without God." Yet, as we are to see, God is present everywhere in Esther. Verily, He is a God who delights to hide Himself!

Because of the lack of God's name there were those who questioned the fitness of including Esther in the Sacred Canon. But think of what we would have missed if Esther had been excluded! The book contains an historical account of tremendous importance in the annals of Jewish history. Throughout the centuries God had carefully nurtured His people in order to preserve the royal seed from which the Saviour was to come. The Assyrians and Babylonians had done much to destroy the Jews as a nation, but if Haman's wicked plot to completely exterminate the Jews had suc-ceeded, God's plans and the destiny of man would have been considerably altered.

Connection

Approaching the book as a whole, there is a significant feature to be noted in the use of the "now" or "and" com-mencing the book. In the ancient Hebrew order of Old Testa-ment books, Esther follows Ecclesiastes, a book with which it has no possible connection whatever. This tell-tale "and," then, is like a body mark on a lost child, proving that Esther has strayed from its original connection.

In our English Bible, Esther follows Nehemiah but, as one scholar suggests, it should be placed between chapters 6 and 7 of Ezra, seeing that there is a gap there of some sixty years. "Chronologically, though the book comes after Nehemiah, the events of the book antedate Nehemiah by about thirty years. Esther made possible Nehemiah." Esther, then, can be placed within the interregnum between Ezra 6 and 7 seeing it describes the position of those Jews who were contented to stay in Babylon.

Author

What Origen said of Hebrews can be applied to Esther, "God alone knows who wrote it." Augustine and other Early Fathers ascribed the book to Ezra. The Talmud declares that Esther was composed by "the great men of the synagogue." Several students suggest that Mordecai wrote the book. And the phrase "Mordecai wrote these things" (9:20), proves him to be a penman. The record of his acts, however, suggests that the book was not written until Mordecai had passed away (10:2). Doubtless Mordecai left written material of the events of his day from which Esther was compiled.

From exact information given of secret and delicate matters it would seem as if the book had been written by a Jew, long resident in Persia, who was closely acquainted with court life at Shushan.

Many wise Jews affirmed that Esther was dictated by the Holy Spirit and add, "All the books of the Prophets and all the Writings shall cease in the days of the Messiah, except the Volume of Esther, and lo, that shall be as stable as the Pentateuch and as the constitution of the oral law which shall never cease."

Title

The book we are considering received its name, not because Esther was the authoress of it, but because she is the principal person mentioned within it. Here is the entrancing record of a Jewish orphan girl whose name was changed as she became the queen of a Persian king.

Scope

The period covered by Esther is around sixty years, and falls in between the going up of Zerubbabel from Babylon to Jerusalem and that of Ezra's restorative ministry, and, as we have already observed, can be placed after the sixth chapter of Ezra.

Purpose

A fourfold purpose can be traced in the writing of this book, and of its inclusion within God's Word:
1. To show the condition of the Jews who remained at Babylon.
2. To set forth the overruling providence of God.
3. To manifest God's unchanging love for His covenant people.
4. To declare God's power to overthrow the devices of the wicked.

Authenticity

It may come as a matter of surprise to many to learn that this wonderful little book has been the object of fierce opposition and has received much ill treatment at the hands of many enemies.

One destructive critic, for example, says that the narrative of Esther "consists of a long string of historical difficulties and improbabilities, and contains a number of errors in regard to Persian customs."

Another modernistic writer calls it "a poem" based upon a very slight foundation of fact.

Yet another scholar reserves his opinion as to Esther's authenticity and "waits to see whether any documents are hereafter discovered which will confirm and elucidate this isolated court story, with all its various details, and if so, to what extent."

Well, archaeology has silenced this critic. The palace where the scenes of this book were enacted has been excavated, and the various places mentioned have been identified and many events verified.

There is another who writes of Esther as "a story which, in fact, is a tissue of improbabilities and impossibilities."

Still others affirm that the book is the work of pure imagination, and establishes the pride and arrogance of the Jews.

Martin Luther, under whose cloak many of the opponents of Esther hide, was a hostile foe of the book. In his *Table-Talk* he says, "As to the Book of Esther, I would it did not exist, for it Judaizes too much, and has in it a great deal of heathenish naughtiness."

The Jews themselves, however, have always regarded Esther as true history, uniting it with Daniel, Ezra, and Nehemiah. In fact, they hold it in such peculiar esteem as to declare it to be more precious than the Prophets or Proverbs, or the Psalms, and destined to outlast all the Hebrew Scriptures, excepting the Pentateuch.

The strongest proof of the book's authenticity is the continuance of the Feast of Purim, which was instituted to celebrate the deliverance of the Jews from Haman's cruel clutches, and which was observed as we know from II Maccabees 15:36, at no greater distance than the time when the events occurred. The unbroken observance of this feast is the most powerful evidence of Esther's reliability, for the Jews would hardly observe for ages such a solemn festival if the incidents recorded around it were only a fable or a romance.

Key Verses

In the study of any book within the "Divine Library" one should be on the lookout for a key verse, crystallizing the teaching of the book in question. There are two such verses in Esther. The first indicates the inscrutable providence of God. "For if thou altogether holdest thy peace at this time, then shall there enlargement and deliverance arise to the Jews from another place; but thou and thy father's house shall be destroyed: and who knoweth whether thou art come to the kingdom for such a time as this?" (4:14). Mark the phrase "who knoweth." May ours be the hope and trust in God, and in His overruling grace evidenced in Esther's rise to power.

Then there is the truth regarding the certain retribution of the wicked as found in 7:10: "So they hanged Haman on the gallows that he had prepared for Mordecai. Then was the king's wrath pacified." The New Testament commentary on this passage is in Paul's word about reaping what we sow. "Be not deceived; God is not mocked: for whatsoever a man soweth, that shall he also reap. For he that soweth to his flesh shall of the flesh reap corruption; but he that soweth to the Spirit shall of the Spirit reap life everlasting" (Gal. 6:7-8).

Key Thought

Without doubt Esther is the book of the Bible that conspicuously sets forth the providence of God in human affairs. Here we have what Dr. A. T. Pierson calls "the romance of providence." In his introduction, Dr. C. I. Scofield says of Esther, "The significance of the Book of Esther is that it testifies to the secret watch-care of Jehovah over dispersed Israel. The name of God does not occur, but in no other book of the Bible is His providence more conspicuous. A mere remnant returned to Jerusalem. The mass of the nation preferred the easy and lucrative life under Persian rule. But God did not forsake them. What He here does for Judah, He

194

is surely doing for all the covenant people." As a whole, the book illustrates the truth—He knows! He Loves! He Cares!

Key Phrases

Five times over Haman is referred to as "the Jews' enemy" (3:10; 7:6; 8:1; 9:10-24), a designation applied to no one else in Scripture. In his desire to destroy the Jews, Haman stands out as a fitting type of the Antichrist.

Esther is also a book of feasts. "The great feast" to which Vashti refused to come, it has been discovered from unearthed inscriptions, was held to consider the expedition against Greece for which Xerxes spent four years in preparation. He fought the famous battles of Thermopylae and Salamis two years before he married Esther. Esther remained his queen for about thirteen years.

The "feasts" in order are:

Ahasuerus's Feasts	(1:3; 1:5)
Vashti's Feast	(1:9)
Esther's Feast	(2:18)
Esther's Banquet	(5:4, 12, 14; 6:14; 7)
Jews' Feast	(8:17; 9:17-19)
Purim Feast Established	(9:20-32)

Characteristics

In the teaching of this dramatic book attention will be drawn to several unique features. For example, some of the longest verses in the Bible are to be found in Esther. There are seventy-five words in 3:12 and ninety words form 8:9.

Chapter 10, made up of only three verses, is one of the shortest chapters in Scripture. Compare Psalms 133 and 134.

The action of Haman in seeking to exterminate all the Jews (3:6), marks another assault of Satan against the nation from which the Seed of the woman was to come. The two unseen and unnamed actors in the book are God and Satan. Satan was the instigator of the hatred and antagonism of Haman. With Genesis 3:15 before him, the devil, foiled again and again in attempts to destroy the "seed royal," now endeavors to put an end to God's redemptive purpose by slaughtering all the Jews. God, however, defeated the evil designs of Satan at every turn, and made the wrath of man to praise Him. As the Preserver, He saw to it that "the seed" was kept intact.

Another interesting feature of the book is that of the existence of a postal service. It may be that the inauguration of our present-day efficient postal system goes back to the time of Esther. Away back in those ancient times there were postmen who were runners on foot (3:13-15; Jer. 51:31). There were also couriers on horseback (8:10).

Evidently the Persian system for the delivery of letters was perfect. Stables, we are told, could be found along the various routes, at such distances as a horse could accomplish in a day. All the stables were provided with a number of horses and grooms. A postmaster, presiding over each stable, would receive the dispatches along with the tired men and weary horses, and then send on the messages by fresh riders. Sometimes there was no delay in the conveyance of an urgent message, even at night, for night carriers would take up the work of day carriers and thus continue and complete the route. One surmises that there must have been many a weary wait for the postman in those days when there were no trains or airplanes.

Another characteristic feature of Esther is that of "casting the lot" (3:7; 9:24). It has been pointed out that the Persian word for *pur* is "lot." There may be a reference here to the "monthly prognosticators" Isaiah mentions (47:13). Haman sought the counsel of those who professed to know the lucky and unlucky days of the calendar, when he determined upon the wholesale massacre of the Jews. The lot fell upon the twelfth Hebrew month, Adar, which is equivalent to our

March, and on the thirteenth day of that month. One wonders whether this is one of the origins of the superstition regarding thirteen as being an unlucky number. Certainly that thirteenth day of Adar was a very unlucky day for Haman.

The main point in the story of Esther, however, is that of the overruling providence of God. Haman's wicked purpose was circumvented. And to celebrate their deliverance, the Jews instituted the Feast of Purim, which is called "The Feast of Lots" (9:20, 32). Such a feast became a national institution by the general consent of Jews everywhere (9:27), and has remained a solemn Jewish festival throughout the ages. One of the Jewish proverbs is "The temple may fail, but the Purim never." This feast falls in early spring, a month before the Passover, and occupies two days as fixed by Mordecai and Esther, the thirteen and fourteenth of Adar. The day preceding Purim is observed as a fast day in commemoration of Esther's fast before going in, uninvited, to the king (4:16). And at the feast the Book of Esther is read as part of the celebration. We are told that at the mention of Haman's name the Jews hiss and spit as a sign of their contempt for such an enemy. At the conclusion of the book as it is now read by the Jews, there is an appropriate benediction, possibly added by the Greek translators. It reads, "Blessed art Thou, O Lord our God, King of the universe, Who hast contended our contest, judged our cause, avenged our wrongs, requited all the enemies of our souls, and hast delivered us from our oppressors. Blessed art Thou, Who hast delivered Thy people from all their oppressors, Thou Lord of Salvation."

A prophetic note is sounded in the words "should not fail" (9:28), for the feast has never ceased—a testimony, surely, to the inspiration of the book.

The change of names is another noticeable feature of Esther. Evidently it was customary for Eastern monarchs to change the names of those whom they honored. *Joseph,* meaning "increase," was changed to Zaphnath-paaneah, signifying "A revealer of secret things" (Gen. 41:45). Esther's Jewish name was Hadassah, meaning "myrtle" (2:7). Her Persian name, *Esther,* means "a star." May ours be the passion to grow fragrantly as the myrtle, and shine as brightly as a star! Some of the ancient rabbis, however, declared that *Esther* meant "to hide," seeing that she was hidden in the house of Mordecai, her guardian; and because her nationality was concealed until the crucial moment (2:10). The greatest of all Monarchs is found to have changed Jacob to Israel, and Saul to Paul. As for ourselves, a new name awaits us in glory.

It will also be found that there is a striking absence of any reference to prayer, praise, Palestine, Jerusalem, or the temple in the book. The Law is likewise unmentioned, unless we take 3:8 as a possible exception. The nearest approach to religion is in the care of Mordecai for Esther (2:7, 15).

The most conspicuous feature of Esther is, of course, the entire absence of God's name. Such an omission, accountable by the fact that it was taken from Persian records, was offensive to the Jews. Probably it was on this ground that it was the last book to be admitted into the Hebrew Canon, and why the Greek translators inserted prayers and various religious expressions.

Various reasons have been assigned for the peculiar omission of any divine name:

1. It has been suggested that the absence of the name of God from the book arose from the increasing scruple against using divine names during the period between Malachi and John the Baptist.

2. Other scholars attribute such an absence out of deference to the fashion of the Persian court, or to a shrinking from irreverence on the part of the writer, who may have viewed it as irreverent to introduce God without necessity into a history which was addressed as much to Persians as to Jews. The book, it would seem, was not so much intended for sacred history as for secular.

3. Perhaps the true reason is to be found in Deuteronomy

31:16-18 where God declares that if His people forsake Him, He would hide His face from them. The Talmud says, "Where do we get Esther in the Law?" and the answer is, "In Deuteronomy 31:18, 'And I will surely hide my face.'" Often *face, name, presence,* are synonymous terms.

4. Another writer has this interesting suggestion to make. More than sixty years had passed since Cyrus had given the Jews permission to return. The vast majority of the people nevertheless remained where they were. Some, like Nehemiah, were restrained by official and other ties. The rest were indifferent, or declined to make the necessary sacrifices of property and of time. God, in His providence, will watch over and deliver the last class, but He will not permit their names and His to be bound together in the record.

It is impossible to read Esther without realizing that although God is not directly referred to, He is the chief actor behind the scenes. As Matthew Henry observes, "If the name of God is not here, His finger is." While we have nothing but history recorded here, all history is *"his-story."* As one writer expresses it, "His is a secret control of the affairs of His people: a hidden hand shifts the scenes. Only the eye of faith sees the divine factor in human history, but to the attentive observer all history is a burning bush aflame with the mysterious Presence."

The absence of God's name, then, need cause no alarm, for "it is that there should be one book which omits the name of God altogether to prevent us from attaching to a mere name a reverence which belongs only to the reality."

A gifted Bible expositor has sought to prove that God is in Esther in a secret way. His name is like buried treasure in the book. The four letters J.H.V.H. represent the Hebrew for *Jehovah.* Here are four passages in which, it is affirmed, God has deposited His name.

The English paraphrase of "all the wives shall give" (1:20) would be "*D*ue *R*espect *O*ur *L*adies shall give to their husbands." Here we have LORD backwards.

The command, "Let the king and Haman come this day (5:4), can be expressed, "*L*et *O*ur *R*oyal *D*inner this day be graced by the king and Haman."

The lament, "Yet this availeth me nothing" (5:13), is given as "Sa*D*, fo*R* n*O* avai*L* is all this to me."

Further, "Evil was determined against him by the king" is translated, "For he saw that there was evi*L* t*O* fea*R* determine*D* against him by the king."

By the same reasoning the divine title, I AM represented thus E.H.Y.H. is found in 7:5, "Wher*E* dwellet*H* the enem*Y* that dwellet*H*."

When the name is put forward, it suggests that God is ruling and causing another to act. When the name is put backward it signifies that He is overruling the counsels of others for the accomplishments of His own purpose. To our way of thinking, such an interpretation seems to be somewhat strained but we state it for what it is worth.

Chief Characters of the Book

What a portrait gallery Esther presents! Here are characters widely diverse in nature and purpose.

Ahasuerus

King Ahasuerus was Xerxes of secular history, famous Persian monarch, 485-465 B.C. "The points of moral resemblance in the character of Xerxes, as represented by Grecian history, coincide with the character of Ahasuerus in this book." In this monarch we have a man of uncertain judgment, of wild passion, weak mind, and cruel disposition. His name means "victorious" but he belied the name he bore insofar as the conquest of his baser instincts were concerned. Ahasuerus married Esther 478 B.C. He died thirteen years later. It is said that he was murdered by night by his chamberlain, the captain of the guard. Esther lived far into the following reign of Artaxerxes, her stepson, son of Xerxes. It was under Artaxerxes that Nehemiah rebuilt Jerusalem.

Vashti

The first queen of Ahasuerus has often been misrepresented because of her failure to obey her husband. But she stands out in the story of Esther as a woman of excellent modesty, chaste dignity, and of strong determination.

There was a rule in Oriental society that no woman might appear in public without having her face veiled. Thus had she obeyed the request of her drunken husband, Vashti would have lost her modesty and the respect due to her. Her name, meaning "beautiful," was exemplified by her character. As Dr. Alexander Whyte expressed it: "Her beauty was her own and her husband's and not for open show among hundreds of half drunken men." We, therefore, commend Vashti for her courageous refusal to cast her pearls before swine. "Who will come into this picture gallery of God and admire the divine portrait of Vashti the Queen, Vashti the Veiled, Vashti the Sacrifice, Vashti the Silent?"

Esther

This young, beautiful, patriotic Jewess who gave her name to the book we are considering passes before us as a woman of clear judgment, of magnificent self-control, and capable of the noblest self-sacrifice. Esther is a type of the Messiah of Israel in that she was willing to die for her people.

Haman

A descendant of the Amalekite kings (Num. 24:7; I Sam. 15:8, 32) Haman was seven devils rolled into one. He sold himself to Satan for the destruction of God's covenant people. He has been described as "a man of utmost vanity,

201

blindest prejudices, and capable of the deadliest enmity; a time-serving, selfish, implacable, swaggering bully; a man whose mind was covered over at the top, so as to shut out all lofty aspirations; and close in at the sides, so as to shut out all kindness; and open only at the bottom, for the incoming of base passions, pride, haughtiness, and hate."

Mordecai

This faithful Jew was a Benjamite, a descendant of Saul (2:5). Thus, part of his task was to end the war against Amalek (Exod. 17:16) which was a work entrusted to Saul, another Benjamite (I Sam. 15:2-23). In this connection compare 3:1 with 7:10 and 9:10.

Mordecai is one of the chief actors in the story. With a love so deep for his own people, he was a constant and faithful guardian of their interests. There was no trace of vanity or worldly ambition in his make-up. He was unmoved by success and prosperity. Neither money nor honor could buy him. Amid varied and trying circumstances, Mordecai loyally played his part. He consistently refused to give any man the worship due only to God.

In one of the apocryphal chapters Mordecai is found appealing to God in the following manner, "Thou knowest, Lord, that it was neither contempt nor pride, nor for any desire of glory, that I did not bow down to proud Haman, for I would have been content with good will for the salvation of Israel to kiss the soles of his feet: but I did this that I might not prefer the glory of man above the glory of God, neither will I worship any but Thee." His name signifies "worshipful" or "dedicated," and his life fully illustrated his devotion to God.

Lessons

It is evident to the casual reader of Esther that it abounds

202

in conspicuous lessons. Possibly the best way to glean these lessons, is to gather them around the characters the book portrays.

```
        V   E   H   M   S   N   G   C   R   P
        A   S   A   O   C   O   A   O   E   E
    T   S   T   M   R   E       L   U   V   A
    H   H   H   A   D   P   S   L   N   E   C
    E   T   E   N   E   T   L   O   T   N   E
        I   R       C   R   E   W   E   G
                C   A   E   E   S   R   E       GOD
    B   C   C   H   I       P               C
    O   H   H   A       C       C   D   C   H
    O   A   A   P   C   H   C   H   E   H   A   AMID
    K   P   P   T   H   A   H   A   C   A   P
        T   T   E   A   P   A   P   R   P   T
    O   E   E   R   P   T   P   T   E   T   E   THE
    F   R   R       T   E   T   E   E   E   R
                    E   R   E   R   E   R
    E               R       R       C           SHADOWS
    S                               H
    T                               A
    H                               P
    E                               T
    R                               E
                                    R
```

Key Thought: THE REALITY OF THE DIVINE
                    PROVIDENCE

Chronologically, the book comes in between chapters 6 and 7 of Ezra.

Principal Characters

Ahasuerus . . . . The Vainglorious King
Vashti . . . . .The Veiled Queen
Esther . . . . The Valorous Heroine
Mordecai . . . . The Virtuous Patriot
Haman . . . . The Vaunted Favorite

The record of this sensuous, tyrannical monarch supplies us with several striking lessons. For example, we have:

The Curse of Drink (3:5; 7:10).

What shame and sorrow drink creates wherever it flows! Its hellish influence is not confined to any class. It is here found entering the palace of Shushan, destroying the nobility of a king and bringing grief to the heart of a gracious queen. It was drink that so controlled Xerxes that he was willing to expose Queen Vashti to the gaze of a crowd of coarse revelers. Ahasuerus's action was an outrage on all the customs and privileges and proprieties of his age. He would never have acted in this manner if he had not been flushed with wine.

The tragic story of drink is that in every walk of life, woman is sure to suffer when man becomes intemperate. Where drunkenness reigns she is treated coarsely, her feelings are outraged, her delicacy is wounded, her rights are denied. Often her health and very life are endangered when men drink.

Ahasuerus was a threefold slave. He was—

A Slave of His Appetite (1:10)

As a king, Ahasuerus ought to have set a pattern of dignified demeanor. How quickly strong drink degrades!

A Slave of His Passions (1:12)

Drink aroused the demon within the king. But as Solomon reminds us, "He that is slow to anger is better than the mighty."

A Slave of His Pride (1:15-22)

While perhaps Xerxes loved Vashti, pride would not permit him to revoke an unjust decree. Later in Scripture, Herod, another drunken monarch, was sorry over what he decreed concerning John the Baptist.

But there is another way in which we can treat the autocratic Xerxes. In these ten chapters made up of 167 verses the word "king" occurs over one hundred times, "his kingdom," twenty-six times; and his own name, twenty-nine times. Seven features of the royal monarch can be applied to Christ as King:

(1) Universal dominion (1:1; 10:1)
(2) Made feasts (1:3, 5, etc.)
(3) Showed riches (1:4)
(4) Vessels diverse (1:7)
(5) Rewards service (3:1; 6:1; 10:2-3)
(6) Holds out sceptre (5:2; 8:4)
(7) Punishes the wicked (7:9-10)

Another lesson one can gather as he thinks of Ahasuerus is that of the reproach of ingratitude emphasized in 6:1-14.

Then there is the use of little things. "That night the king could not sleep" (6:1). Why? The simple answer given by a boy was, "Because God wouldn't let him!" Upon that sleepless night turned the whole history and fortune of the Jews. How true it is that "little is much if God is in it." But while there was a sleepless monarch, there was also a wakeful Providence. And the Bible is eloquent with the truth that God uses small things to accomplish His purposes. Therefore, the day of small things must not be despised. We have:

(1) A left-handed man (Judg. 3:21; Ehud)
(2) An ox-goad (Judg. 3:31, Shamgar)
(3) A tent-peg (Judg. 4:4, 21, Jael)
(4) A millstone (Judg. 9:53, Abimelech)
(5) Pitchers and trumpets (Judg. 7:20, Gideon)
(6) Jawbone of an ass (Judg. 15:16, Samson)
(7) Loaves and fishes (John 6:9, a lad)
(8) A sleepless night (Esther 6:1, Ahasuerus)

And that no flesh might glory in His presence (I Cor. 1:20, 27; II Cor. 12:9), God has used the most unlikely people. It was a miner's son, Martin Luther, who, under God, shook the world. It was a cooper's son, John Calvin, whom God used to build up the church in faith. It was a shepherd's son, Zwingli, who established the Reformation in Switzerland. It was the son of a plain burgess, John Knox, who turned Scotland upside down. It was the daughter of a drunken father, Mary Slessor, who became the uncrowned queen of Calabar. It was a shoe salesman, D. L. Moody, who rocked two continents for God.

What we learn from Vashti

From the disposition of this courageous queen we observe:

(1) A violation of a national custom
(2) An outrage upon her womanly modesty
(3) A derogation from her wifely dignity
(4) A slur upon her royal station

The twofold lesson to be learned from Vashti's unwillingness to satisfy a drunkard's desire is the emancipation of womanhood and the cost of a noble stand.

What we learn from Esther

Many lessons can be gleaned from this queen. It was a pity that such a fine woman had to succeed just as fine a woman as Vashti. In Esther's waiting for audience with the king, we have an illustration of prayer. We do not have to wait, however, for the waving of a golden sceptre. In Esther, also, we have the growth of a soul. Note her progress:

(1) Hadassah the orphan
(2) Hadassah the captive in Babylon
(3) Hadassah the beautiful maiden
(4) Esther the queen

Points of resemblance in soul-winning are also present in Esther's passion for others:

(1) Esther was bowed down with a crushing load of sorrow.
(2) Esther felt that no one besides the king had power to help her.
(3) Esther was willing to stake all upon one bold appeal.

Esther can also be taken as a type of the composition of the church, in which Jew and Gentile are merged. Ruth, as a Gentile woman, had a Hebrew husband. Esther, as a Hebrew woman, had a Gentile husband.

In dealing with young girls, the story of Esther can be used with telling effect. The necessity of obedience and the results of good training are evident in Esther's career.

As to the fact of Esther's revenge upon Haman, Dr. H. H. Halley says, "The book does not say nor intimate she did right in that particular. It merely states the fact, a fact common in the history of every nation. If you will accept the Book of Esther as a simple, historical statement, and not be overmuch exercised to find a moral in it, you can see that it is an important link in the chain of events that led to the re-establishment of the Hebrew nation in their own land preparatory to fulfilling their Messianic mission of bringing Christ into the world."

What we learn from Haman

If one were an artist, what material he could find for several striking pictures in the Book of Esther! For example, think of the morning when Haman entered the palace and met the king and, learning that he wanted to honor someone, made the bestowment as high as possible, thinking that Ahasuerus had him in mind. Pride, however, goes before a fall. Haman was called to pay honor to the Jew he hated, Mordecai. From this dramatic reverse we can learn the folly of selfish ambition.

Remembering that Haman was a descendant of Amalekite kings (Num. 24:7; I Sam. 15:8, 32), and that Mordecai was a Benjamite, we are taken back to the sorrow of partial obedience. The work entrusted to Saul is completed. God's war against Amalek is over (Exod. 17:16).

And when we come to the hanging of Haman upon the gallows reared for Mordecai, we have a grim illustration of the certainty of retribution. "His own iniquities shall take the wicked himself" (Prov. 5:22). Other instances of the principle of retribution are before us in Agag (I Sam. 15:33); Adoni-bezek (Judg. 1:7); Judas (Matt. 27:3-5); (see also Num. 32:23; Gal. 6:7-8).

What we learn from Mordecai

The varied circumstances of this noble man and true guardian of Jewish interests are suggestive of many lessons. Carried away as a captive by Nebuchadnezzar, Mordecai's name, which means "bitter bruising," is most apt. But he rose from obscurity to a position of great honor. From Mordecai we learn "the grace of patience," "the goodness of God," "the power of godliness," and "the reward of godliness."

Here was a man who refused to bow to man, and Haman knew that with all his growing power, position was of no avail so long as Mordecai failed to bend the knee.

What we learn from the book as a whole

The danger of material prosperity is one lesson we glean from Esther. There were indulgent Jews who preferred the glamorous life of Babylon to the worship of God in Jerusalem.

Shushan offers a fitting type. Purity is evidenced by the name, which means "A city of the lily." Shushan was the palace of the king. The church is our Lord's Shushan. Shushan was perplexed, and the church is experiencing perplexing times. She has enemies both within and without, eager to overthrow her. Shushan rejoiced, and the church has had her periods of joyous revivals.

Thinking of the Jews, it is interesting to use seven characteristic features given us being typical of believers: Light, joy, gladness, usefulness, honor, and safety are aspects we can trace as we follow the fortunes of God's ancient people in this book.

The postal service mentioned in Esther can also be used in many profitable ways. Preachers, for example, should be diligent, as hastened by the King's commandment. They should also be faithful whether their message is one of life or of death.

Points to be noted in the two postal deliveries are these: First, a message of death was carried to the people (3:13). Such a somber message was universal and brought trouble, bitterness, humility, weeping (3:13; 4:1-3). Second, a message of life had to be sent out in haste. And this word was universal and produced light, gladness, joy, feasting, good days (8:11, 16-17).

Coming to the overruling providence of God, one realizes that although there is no trace of His name in the book, yet He is everywhere. His absence is only apparent. What happened to Israel proves that God reigns. Summarizing the lessons in this connection, we can say:

1. There is an unseen hand behind our human affairs.

> There's a divinity that shapes our end,
> Rough hew it as we will.

2. Both evil and good have their ultimate rewards.

3. The prosperity of the wicked is unsafe and unsatisfying, and it ends in adversity.

4. The adversity of the good is a trial of faith, issuing in prosperity.

209

5. Retribution is administered with poetic exactness.

6. The most minute events are woven into God's plan.

7. Providence is not fate, but consists of wise and loving benevolence. Freedom and responsibility go together.

Thus, as we take leave of this "Book Without God," we close with the lines—

> Careless seems the great Avenger,
> History's pages but record
> One death-grapple in the darkness
> 'Twixt old systems and the Word.
> Truth forever on the scaffold,
> Wrong forever on the throne,
> But that scaffold sways the future,
> And behind the dim Unknown
> Standeth God, within the shadow,
> Keeping watch above His own.

Twenty-first Summary
The Prominence of Wisdom in Proverbs

"He that would be holy, let him read the Psalms; he that would be wise, let him read Proverbs." So said Dwight L. Moody in speaking of the Bible book we are now considering.

The Psalms speak of the necessity of a clean heart before God; the Proverbs, of a right spirit in our dealings with each other. In the Psalms, we have devotion; in Proverbs, duty. And this is as it should be, for holiness, devotion, and spirituality, such as we gather from the holy Psalms, are meant, in the purpose of God, to fit and equip us for the ordinary duties and common relationships of life, such as the Book of Proverbs bids us face.

This interesting development has been referred to in many different ways. For example:

> After the teaching of devotion in the Psalms, this book [Proverbs] comes in well for admonition and guidance in practical life. . . . The Psalms are to thrill and animate the heart, the Proverbs to direct the way that we should take. . . . David was not more thoroughly trained to be the psalmist of Israel than Solomon was qualified to be the master of practical admonition (Fraser).
>
> What the Psalms are to devotional life, the Proverbs are to practical life (Pierson).
>
> From the throne-room of the Psalms, we pass into the business-house of the Proverbs (Anon.).

Men of all branches of life have recognized in Proverbs a book of excellent worth. Its practical wisdom and potent influence for righteousness in all matters relating to home, business, and commerce have placed it in a premier position among the greatest books in wisdom literature. If there are any who fail to see anything wonderfully wise and yet sublimely simple in Proverbs, let him remember what Carlyle said to a young man who declared that there was nothing in the Book of Proverbs: "Make a few proverbs," said Carlyle, "and you will think differently of the book."

Therefore, if we desire to be wise, let us give ourselves more diligently to the study of this treasure house of wisdom.

The Title

The Hebrew word for "Proverbs" is *Mashal*. This word has a twofold significance.

The primitive sense of the word is taken from a root meaning "likeness" or "comparison," as if the first sense of it was that of the principle of analogy underlying it, e.g., Proverbs 25:19: "Confidence in an unfaithful man in time of trouble is like a broken tooth, and a foot out of joint." It is therefore akin to the word "parable" or authoritative saying, and hints that moral truths are taught by comparison or contrast.

It is now connected with the verb "to rule," "to master," "to govern"; hence the word is applied to words which are to rule and govern the life (e.g., Gen. 1:18; 3:16; Exod. 21:8). Thus, the Book of Proverbs is not merely a collection of human wisdom but of divine rules for earth from heaven.

Matthew Henry's comment is apt at this point: "The word *Mashal* here used for a proverb, comes from a word that signifies *to rule* or *have dominion,* because of the commanding power and influence which wise and weighty sayings have upon the children of men. . . ."

This particular word, *Mashal,* is used of: (1) an allegory (Ezek. 17:2); (2) a discourse (Num. 23:7-8); (3) a taunt (Isa.

14:4); (4) an argument (Job 29:1); (5) a byword (Jer. 24:9); and (6) a lament (Mic. 2:4).

Ere we leave this point, it may be fitting to understand what a proverb is, and then carry this meaning with us through the rest of our study. Perhaps the best way of stating the matter is the following: "Proverbs are wise sayings, contained in short sentences, which can easily be remembered, and the Book of Proverbs is a collection of wise sayings, given by divine inspiration, and written in poetic style."

Our English word *proverb* means "a brief saying in the stead of many words" *(pro-verba)*, and implies pithiness in parallelism. Proverbs have been mottoes that mold life and history. Is it not somewhat strange that a very expressive thing about our own language is the use of proverbs? For instance, think of the condensed wisdom that we have in proverbs that we daily use, such as: "There's many a slip betwixt cup and lip"; "Kill two birds with one stone"; and, "A bird in the hand is worth two in the bush."

The power of proverbs such as these lies in their form; they are short, sharp, incisive, impressive. They assume truth, attract attention, and imprint themselves on the memory and are, therefore, easily remembered.

Turning to the preface of the Book of Proverbs, we find mention of three terms which describe the special aspect of a "proverb," repeated illustrations of which we find through the book.

To understand a proverb (1:6)

Here the word *proverb* indicates, as we have suggested, "a similitude," that is, an illustration of life and truth drawn from material things, e.g., "As cold water to a thirsty soul, so is good news from a far country."

Figure or dark saying ("interpretation," 1:6)

Knotty saying or riddle ("dark sayings," 1:6)

Such meanings suggest intricate sayings, like Samson's riddle of Judges 15:12. To our Lord, a proverb was equivalent to an obscure saying (John 16:29).

Besides the form of a simple proverb, the thought may take the form of (1) a fable (Judg. 9:7; II Kings 14:9); (2) a riddle (Judg. 14:12; I Kings 10:1-2); (3) a satire (Isa. 14:4; Hab. 2:6); and (4) a parable (Isa. 5:1-2).

The Authors

The current opinion is that Solomon was responsible for all the sayings that compose the Book of Proverbs. Although he was not the composer of the entire collection, he was certainly the compiler.

During King Solomon's reign, in a special degree, the people awoke to the life, industry, intercourse, and wealth of the world around them and, with such awareness, there came a literary development as well, when the value of the proverb as a vehicle of instruction came to be recognized. The king himself was versatile and had distinct literary tastes, speaking "three thousand proverbs" and of "songs . . . a thousand and five" (I Kings 4:29-34).

While Solomon was the principal author or compiler of the Book of Proverbs, yet a close examination of the book reveals it to be a series of compilations made at different times, confessedly also, to a considerable extent, the work of a number, perhaps a whole guild, of writers. It would appear that there are six sources from which these proverbs have been gathered, and then, under the guidance of the Holy Spirit, placed together into one perfect whole, thus forming a complete book of practical wisdom.

"The proverbs of Solomon the son of David, king of Israel"
(1:1)

This title is apparently intended to cover the whole book,

214

which may bear out the thought that possibly Solomon grouped all the proverbs together as we have them. Some old Jewish writers affirm that Solomon wrote The Song of Solomon when he was young; Proverbs in the midst of his days; and Ecclesiastes when he was old.

Another interesting feature about this title is that it differs from Ecclesiastes. Here it is "Solomon the son of David, king of Israel" because he ruled over all Israel. But in Ecclesiastes, it is "Preacher, son of David, king in Jerusalem," because then, as Matthew Henry observes, his influence had grown less upon the distant tribes, and he confined himself very much to Jerusalem.

"The proverbs of Solomon" (10:1)

These words are repeated, as if in some special sense the collection, commencing here, deserved it. Possibly those set forth in this section were of his own composition.

"These are also proverbs of Solomon, which the men of Hezekiah, king of Judah, copied out" (25:1).

Some think that these proverbs were culled out of the three thousand proverbs which Solomon spoke (I Kings 4:32), leaving out those that were physical and that pertained to natural philosophy, and preserving such as were divine and moral. In this collection, some have noticed that special regard was given to those observations which concern kings and their administration.

"The words of Agur, the Son of Jakeh" (30:1)

Although some have tried to connect this announcement with Solomon, asserting that it was a kind of *nom de plume* that he used, yet it is evident that this person, whoever he was, was not Solomon. He is connected by many scholars with the Massa mentioned in Genesis 25:14 as a son of Ishmael. His home would therefore be somewhere in north Arabia.

"The words of King Lemuel" (31:1)

Here again many have sought to connect this man and ruler with Solomon, affirming that he is expressing the wonderful love and regard that existed between his mother, Bathsheba, and himself. It would appear, however, that the wise, unknown monarch referred to was, like Agur, a descendant of Ishmael, and therefore, like Agur, a king of the same tribe.

"The words of the wise" (24:23; see 1:6; 22:17)

The proverbs bearing this title apparently are ascribed to sages in general, thus indicating that in this time of peace and prosperity, a class of men had arisen differing alike from the priest and prophet, men who studied the practical questions of life in their bearing upon individual conduct, and who cultivated beauty of style in their imagination.

The Scope

Perhaps no better statement of the scope or design of this book can be given than the inspired words found in 1:2-4:

> To know wisdom and instruction,
>> To perceive the words of understanding;
> To receive the instruction of wisdom, justice, and
>> judgment, and equity;
> To give subtilty to the simple,
>> To the young man, knowledge and discretion.

Such words seem to indicate that the general idea of the book is to instruct the young at their entrance into public and active life. But have we not, in Proverbs, rules for the

216

guidance of all, whether young or old? Can we not all find in this book that which will "inspire deep reverence for God, a fear of His judgments, and an ardent love for wisdom and virtue"?

Dr. Arnot has a series of expositions dealing with many of the Proverbs, and the title of his book denotes the true scope of Proverbs, *Laws from Heaven for Life on Earth.* He writes:

> Proverbs is a book of wisdom for the path of us all; and it is God going over the path with us. In Ecclesiastes you have King Solomon going over the path alone in his own experience; but in Proverbs, you have God going over the path with us, pointing out the dangers, the need of care in this direction or in the other. And he who will be a wise man in the one who has his mind and heart and conscience fully equipped with the wondrous truth in this Book of Proverbs.

Ridout observes that there are thirty-one chapters in the book, one chapter a day, for a month. Says he:

> If you will take it, and read a chapter every day for a month, carefully and prayerfully, and note the words of wisdom that are in it, I need not assure you of what value it will be to you. If you will do this again and again your profit will be greater, for it is not a book that you can close and put away, but one that you can live by as a guidebook, through the world.

Characteristics

One peculiarity of the book is that it seems to stand alone. If it was taken out of the Bible altogether, it would still be complete and whole as a book of wisdom. "We are not," says Bishop Hopkins, "to expect generally any connection, either of sense or sentences, in this Book of Proverbs. Other parts of

217

Scripture are like a rich mine, where the precious ore runs along in one continued vein; but this is like a heap of pearls, which, though they are loose and unstrung, are not therefore the less excellent and valuable."

Another characteristic is its literary style. The wonderful poetic beauty of this book is a marked feature. Dr. James M. Gray takes the following illustrations from *The Literary Study of the Bible* as an example of its poetic worth. In 4:10-19 (RV), we have a poem on "The Two Paths," appearing thus:

> Hear, O my Son, and receive my sayings;
> And the years of thy life shall be many.
> I have taught thee in the way of wisdom,
> I have led thee in paths of uprightness;
> When thou goest, thy steps shall not be straitened;
> And if thou runnest, thou shalt not stumble.
> Take fast hold of instruction;
> Let her not go;
> Keep her;
> For she is thy life.
> Enter not into the path of the wicked,
> And walk not in the way of evil men;
> Avoid it,
> Pass not by it,
> Turn from it
> And pass on.
> For they sleep not, except they have done mischief,
> And their sleep is taken away, unless they cause some
>   to fall;
> For they eat the bread of wickedness,
> And drink the wine of violence.
> But the path of the righteous is as the shining light,
> That shineth more and more unto the perfect day.
> The way of the wicked is as darkness,
> They know not at what they stumble.

There is yet another characteristic of the book that one may refer to. Proverbs is an anthology of sayings or lessons of the sages—on life, character, and conduct; and it embodies the distinctively educative strain of Hebrew literature. Professor Plumtree remarks that "for the most part it seems to stand, like the proverbs of other nations, on the ground of a prudential, practical morality. Men are warned against sensuality, drunkenness, slander, indebtedness, on the ground that they will find themselves involved in disaster, or shame, or inconvenience. The rewards and punishments of the life to come are hardly mentioned."

Key Verse

This is found in the prologue and is never lost sight of throughout the book. In fact, the rest of the book is a development or expansion of the theme it embodies: "The fear of the Lord is the beginning of knowledge" (1:7).

It is interesting to notice that the word "beginning" may be translated "chief part." And so it is, for no matter what wisdom a man may have, if he lacks the true reverence of the Lord, and holiness, then what true knowledge has he?

Key Words

By gathering the key words together, one is quickly guided as to the teaching of the book: "wisdom" occurs fifty-two times; "wisely," three times; "wise," sixty-five times; and "fools," "foolishness," and equivalents occur seventy-nine times. From this one can see that the central thought of the book is that goodness is wisdom, and wickedness is folly.

"Righteousness" also finds a prominent place in the book, occurring (with the word "righteous") seventy-five times.

Key Thought

The phrase in the key verse that we have mentioned, "the

fear of the Lord," occurs thirteen times throughout the book. Combining this with the key words referred to, we come to understand that there can be no virtue in our dealing with others unless this is based on religious motives. Practical wisdom, resting on and arising out of religious character, is the leading thought of the inspired volume of Proverbs.

Keynotes of Doctrine

Wisdom, which stands for goodness
Foolishness, which stands for wickedness
Righteousness, which stands for life.

Value

One cannot overestimate the supreme value of Proverbs, both as a book to stimulate our faith in God and as a standard of practical morality. First of all, the religious value is important in that its teachings are peculiarly clear and spiritual. Jehovah is set forth as:

The Creator and Governor of the universe and the Disposer of human destinies (3:17; 8:22-29).
Incomprehensible alike in His nature and His works (25:2; 30:3-4).
Active in universal providence (5:21; 15:3; 25:2; 30:3-4).
Controller of outward fortunes and the minds of men (10:22; 21:1).
Declared to be holy, just, and loving; to command and reward piety and virtue, and to abhor and punish all sin, not only here but also in eternity (3:33; 10:3-29; 12:2; 14:32).

Regarding its practical value, Matthew Henry tells us that Proverbs is a book that helps us "to form right notions of things, and to possess our minds with clear and distinct ideas of them; to distinguish between truth and falsehood, good and evil; and to order our conversation aright in every thing."

Analysis

Owing to the miscellaneous character of the book, a detailed outline of it is impossible. However, this brief outline may be followed:

1. Preface, introducing the subject of wisdom (1:1-6)

2. In praise of wisdom (1:7-9)

A Father's counsel to his son. The frequent repetition of the phrase "my son" implies the tone of a father or a sage bringing stores of wisdom and experience to the young.

Another outstanding feature of this section is the personification of wisdom in chapter 8. Such a description of wisdom is interpreted as declaratory of Christ. Proverbs 8:22-26, with John 1:1-3 and Colossians 1:17, can only refer to the eternal Son of God.

3. Maxims bearing on the nature, value and fruits of good and bad conduct in various relations to life (10:22- 16:33)

All the proverbs in this section, the longest section of the book, are molded strictly to the couplet form (one triplet only [19:7] being an apparent exception, due probably to the loss of a line), each proverb a parallelism in condensed phrasing, in which the second line gives either some contrast to or some amplification of the first.

4. Some words of the wise (22:17-24:22)

In this short section the proverb literature seems for the first time to have become, as it were, self-conscious, to regard itself as a strain of wise counsel to be reckoned with for its educative value.

5. Further words of the wise (24:23-34)

The wise sayings under this section refer to wise intercourse and ordered industry.

6. More proverbs of Solomon (25-29)

Here there is a tendency to group numbers of proverbs on like subjects (25:2-7). The proverbs in this portion are chiefly antithetic and comparative.

7. The sayings of Agur (30)

The form of Agur's proverbs is peculiar, verging indeed on the artificial. He deals mostly in so-called numerical proverbs ("three things . . . yea, four"), a style of utterance paralleled elsewhere only in 6:16-19.

8. The words of Lemuel (31)

The words of Lemuel are a mother's plea to her royal son for chastity, temperance, and justice—the kingly virtues. The form used here is the simple Hebrew parallelism, not detached couplets, but continuous.

The last twenty-two verses constitute a single poem in praise of a worthy woman, extolling especially her household virtues. In form, these verses begin in the original with the successive twenty-two letters of the Hebrew alphabet, a favorite form of Hebrew verse. Matthew Henry calls this section "a looking glass for ladies."

Much, much more could be said about this unrivaled compendium of wisdom and counsel, the Book of Proverbs, but space does not permit. Read this condensation of the wisdom of the ages. Read it again and compare your life with it. It is as practical for the daily walk as is the Book of Psalms for the daily worship.

Twenty-second Summary
The Foregleams of the Church in Solomon's Song

Among the many allegorical interpretations of this love song from the pen of King Solomon, the one stating that it pictures "Christ and His church" is the most prominent. Many spiritual writers, like Robert Murray McCheyne, maintain that these two lines are evident: The Lord, the Beloved One in union with His church, His Bride. The book can be divided and treated thus. Six beautiful similes are employed to describe the various aspects of the Beloved and the Bride. The direct application of the book, especially its sixth chapter, is Solomon's fascination for the Shulamite and her loyalty to her shepherd-lover. What an expression of gratitude for her unique character this chapter contains! But the language of the book is symbolic of the Christian church, as well as the individual believer's association with the Lord. There are some writers who discern in verses 4 and 10 of chapter 6, a gradual unfolding of the truth of the church.

The Church Supernal

"Beautiful . . . as Tirzah, comely as Jerusalem" (6:4). This suggests her position in the heavenlies. In the purpose and plan of God she is to be without spot. "He hath chosen us in him before the foundation of the world, that we should be holy and without blame before him in love" (Eph. 1:4). What an ideal He has for the church!

The Church Patriarchal

"Looketh forth as the morning" (6:10). Abraham is

spoken of as "the father of all believers." Jesus said of him, that he "rejoiced to see my day" (John 8:56). In the patriarch we have the first dawn of the character of a called-out body—the promise of the Messiah made known to a dark world.

The Church Levitical

"Fair as the moon" (6:10). While Old Testament saints had light it was but dim and imperfect. Theirs was a partial revelation of God's redemptive purpose. So many of the ceremonies of the tabernacle were shadows of the coming Sun of Righteousness who did not arise until He took upon Himself frail flesh to die. Ancient types and emblems were as a looking through the lattice.

The Church Evangelical

"Clear as the sun" (6:10). The birth of Christ who came as a light to lighten the world was the bursting forth of the Sun upon its darkness. With His coming, and also the advent of the Spirit, there came the spread of the gospel, with its radiant beams being scattered abroad.

The Church Triumphal

"Terrible as an army with banners" (6:10). This aspect can apply to the completion of the church and her translation at the Second Coming of her Head, when He will lead in triumph the innumerable host of the redeemed with all the dazzling splendor of an exceedingly great army. We now come to examine more closely the precious truths associated with the Beloved's expressive designations of the one He loved.

225

The Beauty of Pleasantness

"Thou art beautiful, O my love, as Tirzah." The name *Tirzah* means "pleasantness," and was so called because it was pleasantly situated and of proverbial beauty. The Septuagint translates the phrase as "fair as pleasure," while an old Bible version puts it as, "Thou art pleasant even as loveliness itself." Tirzah was an old, lovely royal city, which had been the royal residence for the kings of Israel from Jeroboam to Umri before the capital was removed to Samaria.

Nothing is so attractive as pleasantness, as David's eulogy of Saul and Jonathan illustrates when he spoke of them as being "lovely and pleasant in their lives, and in their death . . . not divided" (II Sam. 1:23). There are those who seem to delight in saying and doing unpleasant things. But God loves all that is beautiful and pleasing. It is profitable to trace the stream of pleasantness as it quietly flows through Scripture.

> Think of the pleasure God gave to man—"The Lord God made to grow every tree that is pleasant to the sight" (Gen. 2:9).
> Think of the pleasure man can give God—"The offering of Judah and Jerusalem shall be pleasant unto the Lord" (Mal. 3:4).
> Think of the pleasure we can give each other— "Behold, how good and how pleasant it is for brethren to dwell together in unity" (Ps. 133:1).

Did not God create the church to be a beautiful and pleasant sight in the midst of all the ugliness and wretchedness of sin? Tirzah was the ten tribes that revolted after the death of Solomon. But the day is coming when all Israel will be united, and her Beloved will say of her, "Israel My Glory!" As for His church, the blemishes of divisions and of worldliness may mar her beauty, but the time is fast drawing near when the beauty of her Lord will be upon her, and she will be His spotless Bride. Our personal responsibility as members of His Body is to reflect His beauty and pleasantness.

> Let me show forth Thy beauty, Lord Jesus,
> Like sunshine on the hills;
> Oh, let my lips pour forth Thy sweetness
> In joyous sparkling rills.

The Comeliness of Peace

"As comely as Jerusalem." The name *Jerusalem* itself means, "the dwelling of peace," and throughout Scripture the city is emblematic of peace, although it belied the name it bore. Within it was the temple, and it was known as "the city of the living God . . . the joy of the whole earth," having protecting mountains round about her. What is more comely than peace? Think of Jesus asleep on a pillow in that boat tossed about on the water by a fierce storm! Is this not a type of His church as she witnesses in an agitated world? "In the world ye shall have tribulation . . . in me . . . peace." How can this heavenly, God-glorifying peace become ours?

By resting, continually in the Lord

"Thou wilt keep him in perfect peace, whose mind is stayed on thee, because he trusteth in thee" (Isa. 26:3).

By loving His Word

"Great peace have they which love thy law, and nothing shall offend them" (Ps. 119:165).

Must we not confess the absence of this comely peace in the corporate life of the church today? John reminds us that the world recognizes us as Christ's disciples if we love one another. Although we lustily sing, "We are not divided, all

227

one body we"—the sentiment is far from a common experience, for too often instead of fighting together against one common foe, we are found fighting one another. Surely, if we claim to be at peace with God, it is incumbent upon us to be at peace among ourselves, and as a whole, as "comely as Jerusalem."

The Hope of Faith

"Who is she that looketh forth as the morning?" This arresting figure of speech suggests several precious thoughts. For instance, it speaks of—

Freshness

"Looketh forth as the dawn." Dawn is the time of day associated with exhilaration due to the bracing morning air. The shadows of night have vanished, and we open the windows to let the fresh air in. As those who profess to be members of His church we should always present the blush and bloom of spiritual health. The emblem before us can represent the dawning of grace within the soul—our first love, thereafter shining more and more till the perfect day.

Morning Watch

The word "looketh" is used of the Lord—"looking down from heaven," and of man "looking down on earth as through a window." Our life can only be holy, and our testimony effective as we "look forth every morning." Commencing each day with the upward look results in all necessary strength for what the day may hold for it. Anointed with fresh oil we are able to go out into the world confident that the chariot wheels will not drag heavily. Grace will be ours to walk, and not faint.

All who love the thought of the Lord's appearing "look forth every morning" for Him to redeem His promise to return. With the beginning of another day, we look up and ask, "Will it be today, Lord?" For His true church, the dreary night will soon be past, and meridian splendor will be hers—a morning without clouds. Many who looked forth every day for redemption in Israel rejoiced when they saw the Babe. The long, weary night of sorrow and rejection for God's ancient people will vanish and their glorious morning will dawn when they look upon Him whom they pierced and mourn.

The Purity of Witness

"Fair as the moon." Solomon, a master in the use of poetic imagery, implies "whiteness" by the moon, and "heat" for the sun. With the moon there is the thought of brilliance and purity, so we speak about "the silvery moon." While the moon fulfills many functions, there are two that can be distinguished and applied to our hearts.

It shines at night during the sun's absence.

Before the Sun of Righteousness appears, it is the privilege and responsibility of the church to witness during His absence amid the gathering darkness of a condemned world. As the night is far spent, we must redouble our efforts to shine as lights in a world lost in darkness and sin.

The moon has no inherent light.

Instead, it reflects what it receives from the sun. It sends forth borrowed light and illuminates the dark places of earth. In like manner, we have nothing of our own to give the world. In our testimony for the Lord we simply restore a borrowed ray. "We give thee of thine own." We must never forget the question, "What hast thou, that thou didst not receive?"

The Energy of Love

"Clear as the sun." The sun is noted, not only for its light and clarity, but also for its burning heat and energizing properties and mighty strength. "Let them that love him be as the sun when he goeth forth in his might" (Judg. 5:31). John saw the countenance of the Lord he dearly loved as "the sun shining in his strength" (Rev. 1:16). The sun is the mightiest factor in the life of earth for everything man and beast require are dependent upon it. Two functions can be stressed:

The sun scatters disease.

What a boon to physical health sunshine is! The sure way to kill spiritual diseases is to live under the life-giving beams of Him who is our Sun. "The Lord God is a sun." The church, likewise, should be as "clear as the sun," putting forth all spiritual energy as she wars against all that is dark and sinful in the world.

The sun gives warmth.

How we all love to bask in it! Travel agents entice us to follow the sun as holidays are contemplated. The world is a cold place to live in and the function of the church is to glow and shed forth that warmth of love toward those living in the winter of their sin. A children's hymn says, "Jesus wants me for a sunbeam," and it is His purpose that all of us who are truly His should be as sunbeams scattering the warmth of divine love wherever we go. It would seem that the church today is more like an iceberg than a sunbeam.

The Influence of Unity

"Terrible as an army with banners." The term *terrible* means "awe-inspiring," or "dazzling." Twice over Solomon uses this descriptive simile (6:4, 10), and its underlying thought is that of bannered hosts, mighty in strength, from whom foes flee. The Shulamite is portrayed as having powerful eyes, and the Beloved found himself conquered, awed, dazzled by her personal charms (6:5). Can we not see in the language Solomon uses here, the church as a militant force? We sing, "Like a mighty army moves the church of God," and all the various conservative denominations can be looked upon as different regiments forming one army and serving one Sovereign. But is the world being charmed, conquered by the witness of the church? Must we not confess that because of her comprise and pursuit of worldly policies and methods she has lost her power to win the world for God?

Terrible! We may shrink in adopting this term to describe the power of the church, but the question must be faced, "Has she the voice of authority, striking terror in the hearts of the godless, and commanding respect?" During World War I, politicians declared that if the church had been the voice of national conscience, fearful carnage would have been prevented. The church ought to be a force, not a farce; active, not artistic; courageous as well as comely; powerful as well as pure; God's battle-axe and weapon of war.

The church should have power to make the ungodly tremble and bring them to their knees. Describing the power of the early church, Paul spoke of those who fell down on their faces to worship God, and reported that God was indeed in His valiant witnesses (I Cor. 14:23, 25).

The church should have power to overcome the world. John, known as "The Apostle of Love," could yet thunder out divine condemnation. He wrote that all who are "begotten of God overcometh the world" (I John 5:4). Hear him as he challenges the church, "This is the victory that overcometh the world, even our faith!"

The church should have power to master Satan, the terrible foe of mankind. God-begotten, she should know how to resist the devil in his efforts to damn mankind. Alas! however, overcome by the world, the church is destitute of the power she once had to turn the world upside down.

Banners! In times of war, regimental banners or colors have proved a great inspiration to those who fought for the country they represented. The banner of the church is a blood-stained one—it is the cross. "It was God's good pleasure through the foolishness of preaching [a crucified Saviour] to save them that believe" (I Cor. 1:21, RV). At Calvary Christ destroyed the works of darkness, and 'neath the banner of the cross, the church is ever terrible. Thrilling stories are told of banners being the symbol of courage, unity, and confidence during raging battles. It should be so with the church militant—

> Rouse then, soldiers,
> Rally round the banner!

The weapons to use are not carnal, but mighty through God for the pulling down of satanic strongholds (II Cor. 10:5). Further, the church has, as an army with banners, a most invincible Captain, or "Leader-in-Chief," as the Dutch version of Hebrews 12:2 puts it. And because He is the unconquered Leader, the church should be found sharing His victory. The church's living Head is her glorious Victor, her Prince divine, her dauntless King, the One who destroyed the works of the devil. Hear His shout of triumph—"I have overcome the world!" His church's obligation is to reap the fruits of His grim conflict with hell, and serve Him in a hostile world as "terrible as His army with banners."

The Atmosphere

An Introduction to Meteorology

Frederick K. Lutgens
Edward J. Tarbuck

Second Custom Edition Prepared Exclusively for De Anza College

Taken From:

The Atmosphere: An Introduction to Meteorology, Tenth Edition
Frederick K. Lutgens, Edward J. Tarbuck

Custom Publishing

New York   Boston   San Francisco
London   Toronto   Sydney   Tokyo   Singapore   Madrid
Mexico City   Munich   Paris   Cape Town   Hong Kong   Montreal

Cover Art: courtesy of Photodisc/Getty Images.

Excerpts taken from:

The Atmosphere: An Introduction to Meteorology, Tenth Edition
by Frederick K. Lutgens, Edward J. Tarbuck
© 2007, 2004, 2001, 1998, 1995, 1992, 1989, 1986, 1982, 1979 by Pearson Education, Inc.
Published by Prentice Hall
Upper Saddle River, New Jersey 07458

Printed in the United States of America

10 9 8 7 6 5 4 3 2 1

2008400148

LM

**Pearson
Custom Publishing**
is a division of

www.pearsonhighered.com

ISBN 10: 0-558-13303-7
ISBN 13: 978-0-558-13303-0

BRIEF CONTENTS

GEODe: Atmosphere

A copy of the *GEODe: Atmosphere* CD-ROM is packaged with each copy of *The Atmosphere, Tenth Edition.* This dynamic learning aid reinforces atmospheric science concepts by using tutorials, animations and interactive exercises.

 This *GEODe: Atmosphere* icon appears throughout the book wherever a text discussion has a corresponding activity on the CD-ROM.

CONTENTS

3 TEMPERATURE   64

4 MOISTURE AND ATMOSPHERIC STABILITY   96

5 FORMS OF CONDENSATION AND PRECIPITATION   130

6 AIR PRESSURE AND WINDS   166

7 CIRCULATION OF THE ATMOSPHERE 196

8 AIR MASSES 232

9 WEATHER PATTERNS 250

10 THUNDERSTORMS AND TORNADOES 284

11 HURRICANES 318

15 WORLD CLIMATES   428

16 OPTICAL PHENOMENA OF THE ATMOSTPHERE   470

PREFACE

There are few aspects of the physical environment that influence our daily lives more than the phenomena we collectively call *weather*. The media regularly report a wide range of weather events as major news stories—an obvious reflection of people's interest and curiosity about the atmosphere.

The record-breaking 2005 hurricane season saw Katrina, Rita, and Wilma, among others, grab the headlines. Hurricane Katrina was by far the most costly U.S. weather disaster in both deaths and dollars in more than a century. It came on the heels of an extraordinary 2004 hurricane season that saw storms named Charley, Frances, Ivan, and Jeanne slam into Florida. Of course, hurricanes are not the only weather events to make the news. Nor'easters in New England, heavy rains triggering mudflows in California, drought and tornadoes in the Midwest, wildfires in parts of the West, and dense fogs that cause chain-reaction freeway pileups are all part of the news.

Not only does the atmosphere impact the lives of people, but people have a significant impact on the atmosphere as well. By altering the composition of Earth's atmosphere, people have diminished the stratosphere's ozone layer and created serious air-quality problems in urban and rural areas around the world. Moreover, many scientists warn that human-generated emissions are largely responsible for global warming, one of the most serious environmental issues facing humankind in the twenty-first century.

In order to understand the weather phenomena that affect our daily lives and the serious environmental problems related to the atmosphere, it is important to develop an understanding of meteorological principles. A basic meteorology course can take advantage of our interest and curiosity about the weather as well as our desire to understand the impact that people have on the atmospheric environment.

The Atmosphere: An Introduction to Meteorology, Tenth Edition, is designed to meet the needs of students who enroll in such a course. It is our hope that the knowledge gained by taking a class and using this book will encourage many to actively participate in bettering the environment, and others may be sufficiently stimulated to continue their study of meteorology. Equally important, however, is our belief that a basic understanding of the atmosphere and its processes will greatly enhance appreciation of our planet and thereby enrich the reader's life.

In addition to being informative and up to date, a major goal of *The Atmosphere* is to meet the need of beginning students for a readable and user-friendly text, a book that is a highly usable "tool" for learning basic meteorological principles and concepts.

Distinguishing Features

Readability

The language of this book is straightforward and *written to be understood*. Clear, readable discussions with a minimum of technical language are the rule. The frequent headings and subheadings help students follow discussions and identify the important ideas presented in each chapter. In the tenth edition, improved readability was achieved by examining chapter organization and flow and writing in a more personal style. Large portions of the text were substantially rewritten in an effort to make the material more understandable.

Illustrations and Photographs

Meteorology is highly visual. Therefore, photographs and artwork are a very important part of an introductory book. *The Atmosphere, Tenth Edition,* contains dozens of new high-quality photographs that were carefully selected to aid understanding, add realism, and heighten the interest of the reader. Among these are many new satellite images that provide a unique perspective of many atmospheric phenomena.

The illustrations in each new edition of *The Atmosphere* keep getting better and better. In the tenth edition more than 100 pieces of line art are new or revised. The new art illustrates ideas and concepts more clearly and realistically than ever before. Dennis Tasa, a gifted artist and respected science illustrator, carried out the art program.

Focus on Learning

The Atmosphere, Tenth Edition, consists of two products—a traditional college textbook and *GEODe: Atmosphere,* an interactive CD-ROM. Both contain helpful student learning aids.

End-of-Chapter Review.   When a chapter has been completed, five useful devices help students review. First, the *Chapter Summary* recaps all the major points. Next, the *Vocabulary Review* provides a checklist of key terms with page references. Learning the language of meteorology helps students learn the material. This is followed by the *Review Questions* section, which helps students examine their knowledge of significant facts and ideas. In most chapters, *Problems,* many with a quantitative orientation, follow the review questions. Most problems require only basic mathematical skills and allow students to enhance their understanding by applying skills and principles explained in the chapter. Each chapter closes with a reminder to visit the website for *The Atmosphere, Tenth Edition* (http://www.prenhall.com/lutgens). It contains many excellent opportunities for review and exploration.

GEODe: Atmosphere.   Included with every copy of *The Atmosphere* is the interactive CD-ROM *GEODe: Atmosphere*. Prepared by the authors in conjunction with Dennis Tasa, this CD was extremely well received by students and instructors who used the last edition of *The Atmosphere*. *GEODe: Atmosphere* is a dynamic program that provides broad coverage of basic principles and reinforces key concepts by using tutorials, interactive exercises, animations, and "In the Lab" activities. A table of contents for the CD-ROM appears in the front matter for easy reference, and a special icon appears throughout the book wherever a text discussion has a corresponding *GEODe: Atmosphere* activity.

Environmental Issues and Atmospheric Hazards

Many of the serious environmental issues that face humanity are related to the atmosphere. This new edition includes up-to-date treatment of air pollution, ozone depletion, global warming, and more.

Because atmospheric hazards adversely affect millions of people worldwide every day, coverage of this topic has been expanded. At appropriate places throughout the book, students will have an opportunity to learn more about atmospheric hazards. Two entire chapters (Chapter 10, "Thunderstorms and Tornadoes" and Chapter 11, "Hurricanes") focus almost entirely on hazardous weather. In addition, a number of the book's special-interest boxes are devoted to a broad variety of atmospheric hazards, including heat waves, winter storms, floods, dust storms, drought, mudslides, and lightning.

Maintaining a Focus on Basic Principles

Although many topical issues are treated in the tenth edition of *The Atmosphere*, it should be emphasized that the main focus remains the same as that of its predecessors— to foster a basic understanding of the atmospheric environment. In keeping with this aim, the organization of the text remains intentionally traditional. Following an overview of the atmosphere in Chapter 1, the next 10 chapters are devoted to a presentation of the major elements and concepts of meteorology. Chapter 12, on weather analysis, follows and serves to reinforce and apply many of the concepts presented in the preceding chapters. Chapter 13 is devoted to the important issue of air pollution.

The text concludes with two chapters on climate (Chapters 14 and 15) and one devoted to optical phenomena (Chapter 16). Chapter 14, "The Changing Climate,"

explores a topic that is the focus of much public interest as well as scientific research: Is global climate changing and, if so, in what ways? How are people causing or contributing to these changes? The discussions in Chapter 14 have been carefully and thoroughly revised and updated to reflect the fast-changing nature of this sometimes controversial subject.

Highlights of the Tenth Edition

The tenth edition of *The Atmosphere* represents a thorough revision. Every part of the book was examined carefully with the dual goals of keeping topics current and improving the clarity of text discussions. Those familiar with preceding editions will see much that is new in the tenth edition. The list of specifics is long. Examples include the following:

- Chapter 1, "Introduction to the Atmosphere," includes a new, expanded treatment of the nature of scientific inquiry, an updated introduction to atmospheric hazards, and a revised, easier-to-follow discussion of Earth as a system.

- The treatment of temperature controls in Chapter 3 has been strengthened by the addition of several new examples and images.

- Chapters 4 and 5, which focus on humidity, clouds, and precipitation, include revised treatments of dew point and hail and an updated look at intentional weather modification.

- Chapter 9, "Weather Patterns," has a new section on the Alberta Clipper, while Chapter 10, "Thunderstorms and Tornadoes," has updated discussions, maps, and statistics on lightning and tornadoes as well as a new tornado case study (Box 10-3).

- Much of Chapter 11, "Hurricanes," has been revised in light of the extraordinary hurricane seasons of 2004 and 2005. Many new satellite images and photos are included to add relevance and interest.

- A significant portion of Chapter 12, "Weather Analysis and Forecasting," was revised. The goal was not only to make discussions more complete and up to date, but more readable and easier to understand. New figures include the addition of new upper-air charts to help illustrate their role in weather forecasting.

- Chapter 14, "The Changing Climate," has an expanded section on how climate change is detected. It includes a more complete look at the use of proxy data. The treatment of global warming has been updated to include data and examples from 2004 and 2005. The revised section on the possible consequences of global warming takes a closer look at the changing Arctic region. There are eight new graphs, charts, and satellite images to support these new discussions.

Additional Highlights

- "*Students Sometimes Ask...*," a feature that was new in the ninth edition, has been retained and improved in the tenth edition. Instructors and students reacted favorably and indicated that the questions and answers sprinkled through each chapter add interest and relevance to text discussions.

- Although the total number of special-interest boxes in the tenth edition has not changed, eight are totally new and 10 others have been substantially revised.

- The number of satellite images and maps based on satellite data in the tenth edition has been significantly expanded. Such views help add perspective and clarity to many text discussions.

The Teaching and Learning Package

The authors and publisher have been pleased to work with a number of talented people who produced an excellent supplements package.

For the Student

GEODe: Atmosphere CD-ROM. Each copy of *The Atmosphere* comes with *GEODe: Atmosphere* by Fred Lutgens, Ed Tarbuck, and Dennis Tasa of Tasa Graphic Arts, Inc. *GEODe: Atmosphere* is a dynamic program that reinforces key concepts by using animations, tutorials, and interactive exercises. This well-received student-tested product provides broad coverage of basic principles. A special *Geode: Atmosphere* icon appears throughout the book wherever a text discussion has a corresponding *GEODe: Atmosphere* activity. This special offering gives students two valuable products (*GEODe: Atmosphere* and the textbook) for the price of one.

Website. *Atmospheric Science Online* contains numerous review quizzes from which students get immediate feedback. Other activities and resources help expand student understanding of atmospheric processes and phenomena. This website provides an excellent platform from which to start using the Internet for the study of meteorology. Please visit the site at **http://www.prenhall.com/lutgens.**

For the Professor

A wealth of valuable teaching tools is available.

Instructor's Manual 0-13-187472-1. A valuable resource for any professor, the *Instructor's Manual* contains learning objectives, chapter outlines, and suggested answers to the end-of-chapter questions.

Transparency Pack 0-13-187463-2. Includes over 100 full-color illustrations from the text, enlarged for excellent classroom visibility.

Instructor's Resource Center on CD/DVD (IRC) 0-13-187465-9. Provides high-quality electronic versions of select photos and all of the illustrations from the book, as well as customizable PowerPoint™ presentations, MS Word files of both the *Instructor's Manual* and *Tests*, and animations. This is a powerful resource for anyone who is using electronic media in the classroom. Create your own PowerPoint™ presentation with the materials provided, or customize PowerPoint™ with your own materials. Either way, this resource will streamline the preparation of your lectures.

Test Item File 0-13-88958-3. The *Test Item File* contains over 1500 questions covering multiple-choice, true/false, and short-answer questions and is available in print or electronic formats via the *eCatalog, Instructor's Resource Center.*

TestGen EQ/QuizMaster 0-13-187464-0. Computerized test generator that lets you view and edit test-bank questions, transfer questions to tests, and print the test in a variety of customized formats. Included in each package is the *QuizMaster-EQ* program, which lets you administer tests on a computer network, record student scores, and print diagnostic reports.

For the Laboratory

Exercises for Weather and Climate, 6/E 0-13-149701-4. Written by Greg Carbone. This lab manual, which complements Lutgens and Tarbuck's *The Atmosphere, Tenth Edition*, offers students an opportunity to review important ideas and concepts through problem solving, simulations, and guided thinking. This revised edition features an upgraded graphics program and eight computer-based simulations and tutorials that help students better learn key concepts. The lab manual is available at a reduced price when packaged with the text. The accompanying *Solutions Manual* contains all solutions to the labs 0-13-154789-5.

Acknowledgments

Writing a college textbook requires the talents and cooperation of many individuals. Working with Dennis Tasa, who is responsible for all of the text's outstanding illustrations and much of the developmental work on *GEODe: Atmosphere*, is always special for us. We not only value his outstanding artistic talents and imagination but his friendship as well.

Special thanks go to those colleagues who prepared in-depth reviews. Their critical comments and thoughtful input helped guide our work and clearly strengthened the text. We wish to thank:

DONALD ALBERT, *Sam Houston State University*
MICHAEL E. BROWN, *Mississippi State University*
JONGNAM CHOI, *Western Illinois University*
JONATHAN C. COMER, *Oklahoma State University*

TIMOTHY E. KLINGLER, *Delta College*
CHARLES E. KONRAD, II, *University of North Carolina–Chapel Hill*
CHRISTA MELOCHE, *Mississippi State University*
JOHN R. SCALA, *Millersville University*
THOMAS B. WALTER, *Hunter College of the CUNY*
DONALD M. YOW, *Eastern Kentucky University*

We also want to acknowledge the team of professionals at Prentice-Hall. We sincerely appreciate the company's continuing strong support for excellence and innovation. Special thanks to Editor-in-Chief Dan Kaveney. We value his leadership and appreciate his attention to detail, excel-

lent communication skills, and easy going style. The production team, led by Ed Thomas and Debra Wechsler, has once again done an outstanding job. The strong visual impact of *The Atmosphere, Tenth Edition,* benefited greatly from the work of photo researcher Yvonne Gerin and image-permission coordinator Debbie Hewitson. Thanks also to Barbara Booth for her excellent copyediting skills. All are true professionals with whom we are very fortunate to be associated.

Frederick K. Lutgens
Edward J. Tarbuck

DISTINGUISHING FEATURES

The goal of *The Atmosphere, Tenth Edition* is to provide an informative, user-friendly text for introductory atmospheric science. *The Atmosphere* is crafted with a focus on five key areas:

- readability
- illustrations and photographs
- student learning

- environmental issues and atmospheric hazards
- basic physical principles

Readability

Fred Lutgens and Ed Tarbuck are known for their ability to make difficult physical processes understandable for introductory students. *The Atmosphere, Tenth Edition* is accessible to introductory students and contains the level of detail necessary for a survey course in atmospheric science. The frequent heading and subheadings help students follow discussions and identify the important ideas presented in each chapter.

Illustrations and Photographs

Meteorology is highly visual. Therefore, photographs and artwork are a very important part of an introductory book. *The Atmosphere, Tenth Edition*, contains dozens of new high-quality photographs that were carefully selected to aid understanding, add realism, and heighten the interest of the reader. Among these are many new satellite images that provide a unique perspective of many atmospheric phenomena.

Environmental Issues and Atmospheric Hazards

Many of the serious environmental issues that face humanity are related to the atmosphere. This new edition includes up-to-date treatment of air pollution, ozone depletion, global warming, and more. Because atmospheric hazards adversely affect millions of people worldwide every day, coverage of this topic has been expanded. At appropriate places throughout the book students will have an opportunity to learn more about atmospheric hazards.

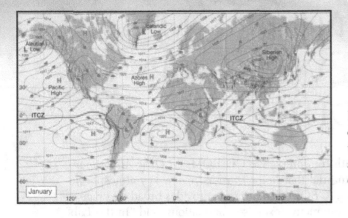

Dennis Tasa, a gifted artist and respected science illustrator, carried out the art program for this and previous editions of the book. In the tenth edition more than 100 pieces of line art are new or revised. The new art illustrates ideas and concepts more clearly and realistically than ever before.

Focus on Learning

When a chapter has been completed, five useful devices help students review:

- Chapter Summary
- Vocabulary Review
- Review Questions
- Problems (in most chapters, many with a quantitative orientation)
- *The Atmosphere, Tenth Edition* Website has review quizzes and activities

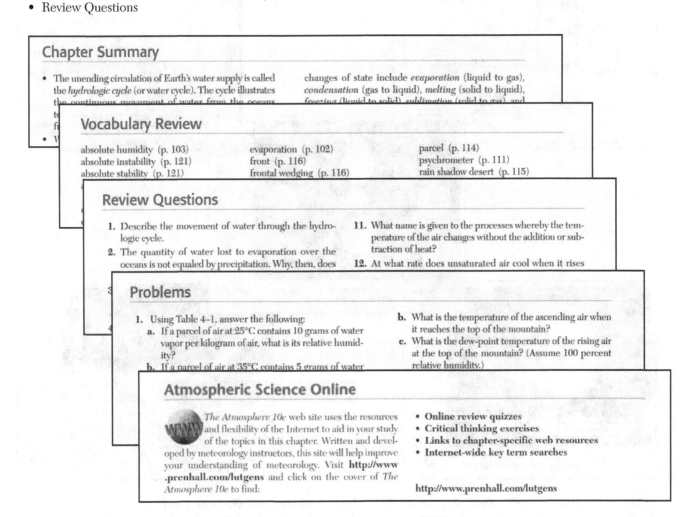

Chapter Summary

- The unending circulation of Earth's water supply is called the *hydrologic cycle* (or water cycle). The cycle illustrates the continuous movement of water from the oceans

changes of state include *evaporation* (liquid to gas), *condensation* (gas to liquid), *melting* (solid to liquid), *freezing* (liquid to solid), *sublimation* (solid to gas), and

Vocabulary Review

absolute humidity (p. 103)
absolute instability (p. 121)
absolute stability (p. 121)

evaporation (p. 102)
front (p. 116)
frontal wedging (p. 116)

parcel (p. 114)
psychrometer (p. 111)
rain shadow desert (p. 115)

Review Questions

1. Describe the movement of water through the hydrologic cycle.
2. The quantity of water lost to evaporation over the oceans is not equaled by precipitation. Why, then, does

11. What name is given to the processes whereby the temperature of the air changes without the addition or subtraction of heat?
12. At what rate does unsaturated air cool when it rises

Problems

1. Using Table 4–1, answer the following:
   a. If a parcel of air at 25°C contains 10 grams of water vapor per kilogram of air, what is its relative humidity?
   b. If a parcel of air at 35°C contains 5 grams of water

   b. What is the temperature of the ascending air when it reaches the top of the mountain?
   c. What is the dew-point temperature of the rising air at the top of the mountain? (Assume 100 percent relative humidity.)

Atmospheric Science Online

The Atmosphere 10e web site uses the resources and flexibility of the Internet to aid in your study of the topics in this chapter. Written and developed by meteorology instructors, this site will help improve your understanding of meteorology. Visit **http://www.prenhall.com/lutgens** and click on the cover of *The Atmosphere 10e* to find:

- **Online review quizzes**
- **Critical thinking exercises**
- **Links to chapter-specific web resources**
- **Internet-wide key term searches**

http://www.prenhall.com/lutgens

A Focus on Basic Principles

Although many topical issues are treated in the tenth edition of *The Atmosphere*, it should be emphasized that the main focus remains the same as that of its predecessors—to foster a basic understanding of the atmospheric environment.

GEODe: Atmosphere CD included with Every Copy of the Tenth Edition

Each copy of *The Atmosphere, Tenth Edition* comes with the interactive CD-ROM: *GEODe: Atmosphere*. *GEODe: Atmosphere* is a highly interactive CD-ROM tutorial that helps learners review key atmospheric-science concepts through a variety of interactive exercises. *GEODe: Atmosphere* provides broad coverage of basic topics in meteorology. The CD includes tutorials, interactive exercises, animations, and "In the Lab" activities.

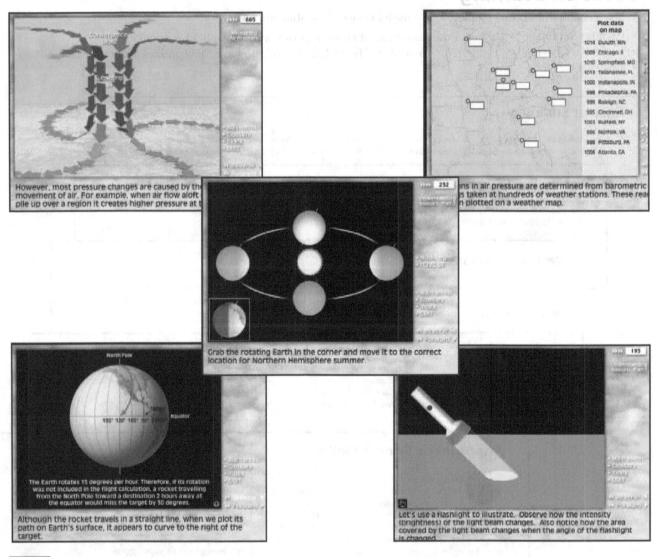

 This special *GEODe: Atmosphere* icon appears throughout the book wherever a text discussion has a corresponding *GEODe: Atmosphere* activity.

LECTURE PRESENTATION TOOLS

Transparencies (0-13-187463-2)

Transparency Set includes over 100 pieces of art from the text, all enlarged for excellent classroom visibility.

Instructor Resource Center on CD-ROM (IRC) (0-13-187465-9)

The *Instructor Resource Center on CD-ROM* provides high-quality electronic versions of photos and illustrations from the book, as well as customizable PowerPoint™ presentations, MS Word files of both the *Instructor's Manual* and *Tests*, and animations from *GEODe: Atmosphere*.

Images are high-resolution, low-compression, 16-bit jpeg files. To further guarantee classroom projection quality, all images are manually adjusted for color, brightness, and contrast. For easy reference and identification all images are organized by chapter.

TEACHING AND LEARNING PACKAGE

Many supplements are available to help you prepare for your course. These range from the traditional supplements you have come to expect to electronic media for use in your classroom.

Instructor Resources

Transparencies (0-13-187463-2)

Includes over 100 full-color illustrations from the text, enlarged for excellent classroom visibility.

Instructor Resource Center on CD-ROM (IRC) (0-13-187465-9)

Provides high-quality eletronic versions of select photos and all of the illustrations from the book, as well as customizable PowerPoint™ presentations, MS Word files of both the *Instructor's Manual* and *Tests*, and animations from *GEODe: Atmosphere*. This is a powerful resource for anyone who is using electronic media in the classroom. Create your own PowerPoint™ presentation with the materials provided or customize PowerPoint™ with your own materials. Either way this resource will streamline the preparation of your lecture

Instructors Resource Manual with Tests (0-13-187472-1)

A valuable resource for any professor, the *Instructor's Manual* contains learning objectives, chapter outlines and suggested answers to the end of chapter questions.

Test Item File (0-13-188958-3)

The *Test Item File* contains over 1500 questions covering multiple-choice, true/false, and short-answer questions and is available in print or electronic formats via the eCatalog, Instructor's Resource Center.

TestGen EQ/QuizMaster (0-13-187464-0)

Computerized test generator that lets you view and edit test-bank questions, transfer questions to tests and print the test in a variety of customized formats. Included in each package is the QuizMaster-EQ program that lets you administer tests on a computer network, record student scores, and print diagnostic reports.

Student Resources

Online Study Guide

This on-line study guide, specific to the text, contains numerous review exercises (from which students get immediate feedback), exercises to expand one's understanding of meteorology, and resources for further exploration. This website provides an excellent platform from which to start using the Internet for the study of meteorology. Please visit the site at **http://www.prenhall.com/lutgens**

LAB MANUAL

Exercises for Weather and Climate
Sixth Edition
Greg Carbone

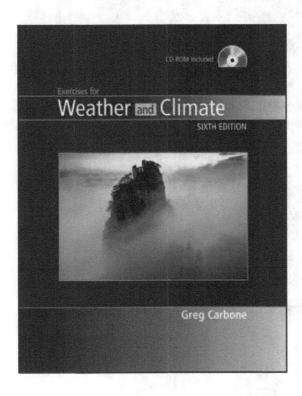

Appropriate for use with any introductory meteorology or weather and climate text, this laboratory manual (0-13-149701-4) consists of 17 exercises that present introductory principles in weather and climate to the student. Collectively the exercises combine data analysis, problem solving, and experimentation; the questions are designed to encourage critical thinking about the fundamental topics of atmospheric processes.

Accompanying *Solutions Manual* contains all solutions to the labs (0-13-154789-5).

Take 20% off *Lab Manual* price when valuepacked with *The Atmosphere, Tenth Edition* (0-13-187462-4).

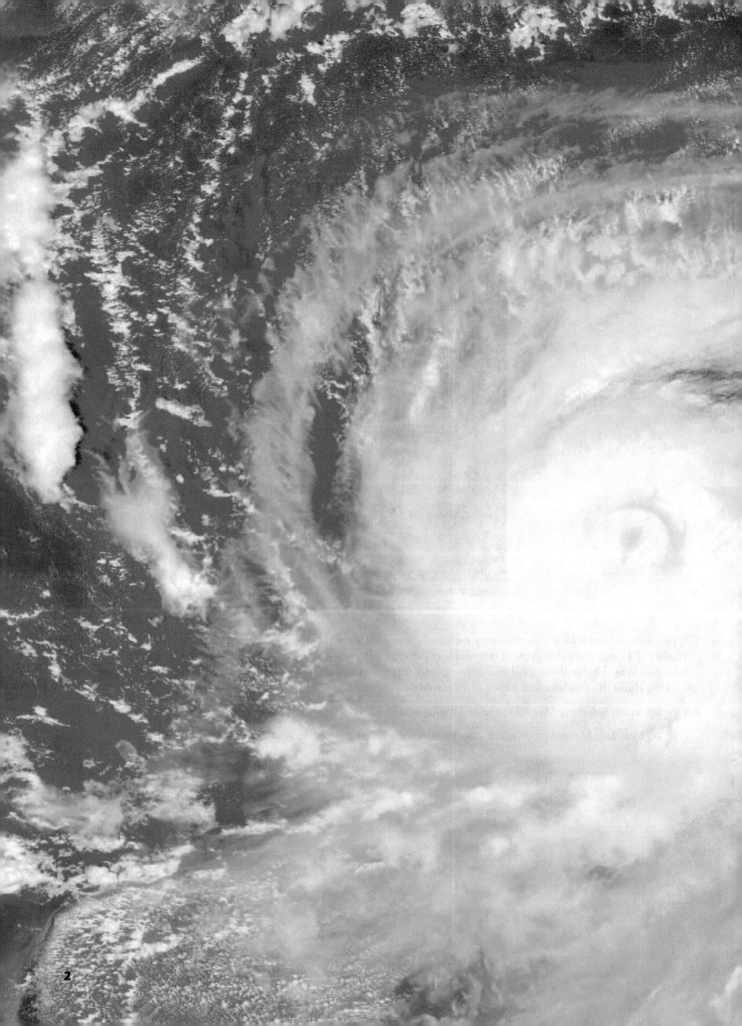

INTRODUCTION *to the* ATMOSPHERE

Satellite image of Katrina in late August 2005 shortly before it devastated the Gulf Coast. *(NASA image).*

Weather influences our everyday activities, our jobs, and our health and comfort. Many of us pay little attention to the weather unless we are inconvenienced by it or when it adds to our enjoyment of outdoor activities. Nevertheless, there are few other aspects of our physical environment that affect our lives more than the phenomena we collectively call the weather.

The United States occupies an area that stretches from the tropics to the Arctic Circle. It has thousands of miles of coastline and extensive regions that are far from the influence of the ocean. Some landscapes are mountainous, and others are dominated by plains. It is a place where Pacific storms strike the West Coast, while the East is sometimes influenced by events in the Atlantic and the Gulf of Mexico. For those in the center of the country, it is common to experience weather events triggered when frigid southward bound Canadian air masses clash with northward-moving tropical ones.

Stories about weather are a routine part of the daily news (Figure 1–1a). Articles and items about the effects of heat, cold, floods, drought, fog, snow, ice, and strong winds are commonplace. Of course, storms of all kinds are frequently front-page news (see chapter opening photo). The hurricane season of 2005 was one for the record books. In late August Hurricane Katrina devastated portions of the Gulf Coast and during the next two months hurricanes Rita and Wilma also made headlines. Earlier in the year, heavy January rains and significant snows pushed rivers in parts of

Indiana, Kentucky, and Illinois past flood stage. Later in January a blizzard buried New England, paralyzing travel and disrupting electrical power (Figure 1–1b). Meanwhile, the Pacific Northwest was experiencing much less snow than average. This was important because melting snows feed the region's streams during the summer, so when little snow falls, drought ensues. By contrast, southern California was hit by day after day of winter storms that led to flooding, mudflows, and huge mountain snows (Figure 1–1c).

These memorable weather events serve to illustrate the fact that the United States has the greatest variety of weather of any country in the world. Severe weather events such as tornadoes, flash floods, and intense thunderstorms, as well as hurricanes and blizzards, are collectively more frequent and more damaging in the United States than in any other nation. Beyond its direct impact on the lives of individuals, the weather has a strong effect on the world economy, by influencing agriculture, energy use, water resources, transportation, and industry.

Weather clearly influences our lives a great deal. Yet it is also important to realize that people influence the atmosphere and its behavior as well. There are, and will continue to be, significant political and scientific decisions to make involving these impacts. Answers to questions regarding air pollution and its control and the effects of various emissions on global climate and the atmosphere's ozone layer are important examples. So there is a need for increased awareness and understanding of our atmosphere and its behavior.

FIGURE 1–1 There are few aspects of our physical environment that influence our daily lives more than the weather. (a) Aerial view of Punta Gorda, Florida, after Hurricane Charley struck on August 13, 2004. This Category 4 storm, one of four to strike Florida in 2004, had sustained winds of 233 kilometers (145 miles) per hour. *(Photo by Rhona Wise/EPA)* (b) Residents of Boston dig out after a blizzard dropped up to two feet of snow in the area on January 23, 2005. *(AP Photo/Michael Dwyer)* (c) Exceptional winter rains in 2005 triggered many debris flows in Southern California, including this one at La Conchita that killed 10 people and destroyed 18 homes. *(Photo by G. Delaurentis).*

(a)

(b)

(c)

Meteorology, Weather, and Climate

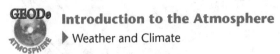

Introduction to the Atmosphere
▶ Weather and Climate

The subtitle of this book includes the word *meteorology*. **Meteorology** is the scientific study of the atmosphere and the phenomena that we usually refer to as *weather*. Along with geology, oceanography, and astronomy, meteorology is considered one of the *Earth sciences*—the sciences that seek to understand our planet. It is important to point out that there are not strict boundaries among the Earth sciences; there are many situations in which these sciences overlap. Moreover, all of the Earth sciences involve an understanding and application of knowledge and principles from physics, chemistry, and biology. You will see many examples of this fact in your study of meteorology.

Acted on by the combined effects of Earth's motions and energy from the Sun, our planet's formless and invisible envelope of air reacts by producing an infinite variety of weather, which in turn creates the basic pattern of global climates. Although not identical, weather and climate have much in common.

Weather is constantly changing, sometimes from hour to hour and at other times from day to day. It is a term that refers to the state of the atmosphere at a given time and place. Whereas changes in the weather are continuous and sometimes seemingly erratic, it is nevertheless possible to arrive at a generalization of these variations. Such a description of aggregate weather conditions is termed **climate.** It is based on observations that have been accumulated over many decades. Climate is often defined simply as "average weather," but this is an inadequate definition. In order to more accurately portray the character of an area, variations and extremes must also be included, as well as the probabilities that such departures will take place. For example, it is not only necessary for farmers to know the average rainfall during the growing season, but it is also important to know the frequency of extremely wet and extremely dry years. Thus, climate is the sum of all statistical weather information that helps describe a place or region.

Maps similar to the one in Figure 1–2 are familiar to everyone who checks the weather report in the morning newspaper or on a local television station. In addition to showing predicted high temperatures for the day, this map shows other basic weather information about cloud cover, precipitation, and fronts.

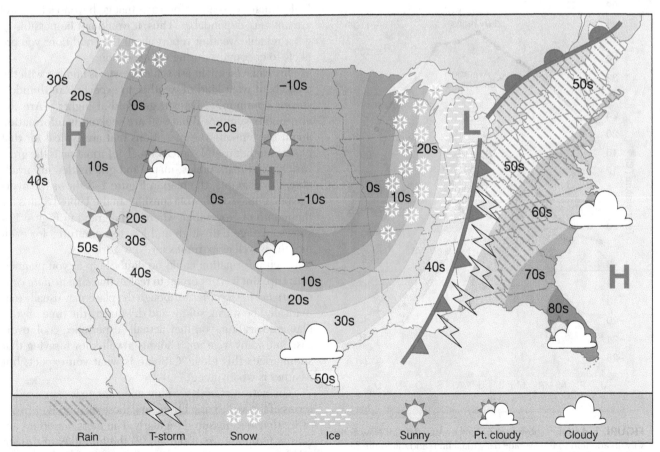

FIGURE 1–2 A typical newspaper weather map for a day in late December. The temperatures shown on the map are the highs forecast for the day.

FIGURE 1–3 Mean percentage of possible sunshine for November. Southern Arizona is clearly the sunniest area. By contrast, parts of the Pacific Northwest receive a much smaller percentage of the possible sunshine. Climate maps such as this one are based on many years of data.

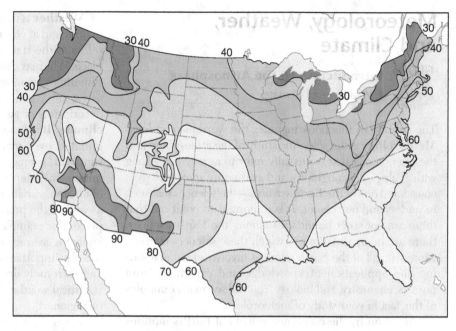

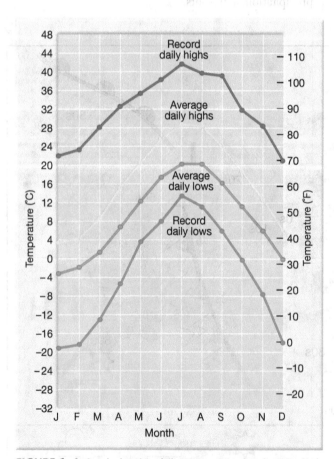

FIGURE 1–4 Graph showing daily temperature data for New York City. In addition to the average daily maximum and minimum temperatures for each month, extremes are also shown. As this graph shows, there can be significant departures from the average.

Suppose you were planning a vacation trip to an unfamiliar place. You would probably want to know what kind of weather to expect. Such information would help as you selected clothes to pack and could influence decisions regarding activities you might engage in during your stay. Unfortunately, weather forecasts that go beyond a few days are not very dependable. Thus, it would not be possible to get a reliable weather report about the conditions you are likely to encounter during your vacation.

Instead, you might ask someone who is familiar with the area about what kind of weather to expect. "Are thunderstorms common?" "Does it get cold at night?" "Are the afternoons sunny?" What you are seeking is information about the climate, the conditions that are typical for that place. Another useful source of such information is the great variety of climate tables, maps, and graphs that are available. For example, the map in Figure 1–3 shows the average percentage of possible sunshine in the United States for the month of November, whereas the graph in Figure 1–4 shows average daily high and low temperatures for each month, as well as extremes for New York City.

Such information could no doubt help as you planned your trip. But it is important to realize that *climate data cannot predict the weather.* Although the place may usually (climatically) be warm, sunny, and dry during the time of your planned vacation, you may actually experience cool, overcast, and rainy weather. There is a well-known saying that summarizes this idea: "Climate is what you expect, but weather is what you get."

The nature of both weather and climate is expressed in terms of the same basic **elements**, those quantities or properties that are measured regularly. The most important are (1) the temperature of the air, (2) the humidity of the air, (3) the type and amount of cloudiness, (4) the type and amount of precipitation, (5) the pressure exerted by the air,

Students Sometimes Ask...

Does meteorology have anything to do with meteors?

Yes, there is a connection. Most people use the word "meteor" when referring to solid particles (meteoroids) that enter Earth's atmosphere from space and "burn up" due to friction ("shooting stars"). The term "meteorology" was coined in 340 BC when the Greek philosopher Aristotle wrote a book entitled *Meteorlogica,* which included explanations of atmospheric and astronomical phenomena. In Aristotle's day *anything* that fell from or was seen in the sky was called a meteor. Today we distinguish between particles of ice or water in the atmosphere (called *hydrometeors*) and extraterrestrial objects called meteoroids or "meteors."

and (6) the speed and direction of the wind. These elements constitute the variables by which weather patterns and climate types are depicted. Although you will study these elements separately at first, keep in mind that they are very much interrelated. A change in one of the elements often produces changes in the others.

Atmospheric Hazards: Assault by the Elements

Natural hazards are a part of living on Earth. Every day they adversely affect literally millions of people worldwide and are responsible for staggering damages. Some, such as earthquakes and volcanic eruptions, are geological. But a greater number are related to the atmosphere.

Occurrences of severe weather have a fascination that ordinary weather phenomena cannot provide. A spectacular lightning display generated by a severe thunderstorm can elicit both awe and fear. Of course, hurricanes and tornadoes attract a great deal of much deserved attention (Figure 1-5). A single tornado outbreak or hurricane can cause billions of dollars in property damage, much human suffering, and many deaths. For example, the four hurricanes that struck the United States in August and September 2004 collectively caused more than $40 billion in damages and 152 deaths. These figures were surpassed in 2005 when Hurricane Katrina struck. Estimates for this single storm are staggering. Although imprecise, the final accounting may approach $300 billion, with more than 1300 deaths.

In a typical year the United States experiences thousands of violent thunderstorms, hundreds of floods and tornadoes, and several hurricanes. According to the National Weather Service, during the 30-year span 1975–2004, tornadoes took an average of 65 lives each year, whereas hurricanes were responsible for about one-quarter as many deaths. Surprisingly (to many), lightning and flash floods were deadlier. During the 1975–2004 period, lightning annually claimed 66 lives, and floods were responsible for an average of 107 fatalities each year.

Of course, there are other atmospheric hazards that adversely affect us. Some are storm-related, such as blizzards, hail, and freezing rain. Others are not the direct result of a storm. Heat waves, cold waves, and drought are important examples. In some years the loss of human life due to excessive heat or bitter cold exceeds that caused by all other weather events combined. Moreover, although severe storms and floods usually generate more attention, droughts can be just as devastating and carry an even bigger price tag.

FIGURE 1–5 The awesome power of a tornado is obvious in this image. Many people have incorrect perceptions of weather dangers and are unaware of the relative differences of weather threats to human life. For example, they are awed by the threat of hurricanes and tornadoes and plan accordingly on how to respond (e.g. "Tornado Awareness Week" each spring), but they fail to realize that lightning or winter storms can be greater threats. *(Photo by Alan R. Moller/Getty Images Inc.-Stone Allstock)*

Between 1980 and 2004 the United States experienced 62 weather-related disasters in which overall damages and costs reached or exceeded $1 billion (Figure 1-6). The combined costs of these events exceeded $390 billion (normalized to 2002 dollars)! Table 1–1 lists the 25 "billion-dollar weather disasters" that occurred during the span 1998 through 2004. As you can see, although hurricanes, tornadoes, and floods stand out, ice storms, drought, heat waves, and hail also figure prominently.

At appropriate places throughout this book you will have an opportunity to learn about atmospheric hazards. Two entire chapters (Chapter 10, Thunderstorms and Tornadoes, and Chapter 11, Hurricanes) focus almost entirely on hazardous weather. In addition, a number of the book's special-interest boxes are devoted to a broad variety of atmospheric hazards, including heat waves, winter storms, floods, dust storms, drought, mudslides, and lightning. To alert you to these discussions, each of the boxes that examines an atmospheric hazard is identified by the same small icon you see at the beginning of this section.

Every day our planet experiences an incredible assault by the atmosphere, so it is important to develop an awareness and understanding of these significant weather events.

Students Sometimes Ask...

According to the graph in Figure 1–6, a single weather event in 1988 caused the greatest total damage for any of the years shown. What was the event?

The costly event was a summer drought and heat wave in the central and eastern U.S., with severe losses to agriculture and related industries. There were also up to 10,000 heat-related deaths. The second-ranking year, 1980, experienced a similar event.

The Nature of Scientific Inquiry

All science is based on the assumption that the natural world behaves in a consistent and predictable manner that is comprehensible through careful, systematic study. The overall goal of science is to discover the underlying patterns in nature and then to use this knowledge to make predictions about what should or should not be expected, given certain facts or circumstances. For example, by understanding the processes and conditions that produce certain cloud types, meteorologists are often able to predict the approximate time and place of their formation.

The development of new scientific knowledge involves some basic logical processes that are universally accepted. To determine what is occurring in the natural world, scientists collect scientific *facts* through observation and measurement. Because some error is inevitable, the accuracy of

a particular measurement or observation is always open to question. Nevertheless, these data are essential to science and serve as the springboard for the development of scientific theories.

Hypothesis

Once facts have been gathered and principles have been formulated to describe a natural phenomenon, investigators try to explain how or why things happen in the manner observed. They often do this by constructing a tentative (or untested) explanation, which is called a scientific **hypothesis** or **model.** (The term model, although often used synonymously with hypothesis, is a less precise term because it is sometimes used to describe a scientific theory as well.) It is best if an investigator can formulate more than one hypothesis to explain a given set of observations. If an individual scientist is unable to devise multiple models, others in the scientific community will almost always develop alternative explanations. A spirited debate frequently ensues. As a result, extensive research is conducted by proponents of opposing models, and the results are made available to the wider scientific community in scientific journals.

Before a hypothesis can become an accepted part of scientific knowledge, it must pass objective testing and analysis. (If a hypothesis cannot be tested, it is not scientifically useful, no matter how interesting it might seem.) The verification process requires that *predictions* be made based on the model being considered and the predictions be tested by comparing them against objective observations of nature. Put another way, hypotheses must fit observations other than those used to formulate them in the first place. Those hypotheses that fail rigorous testing are ultimately discarded. The history of science is littered with discarded hypotheses. One of the best known is the Earth-centered model of the universe—a proposal that was supported by the apparent daily motion of the Sun, Moon, and stars around Earth. As the mathematician Jacob Bronowski so ably stated, "Science is a great many things, but in the end they all return to this: Science is the acceptance of what works and the rejection of what does not."

Theory

When a hypothesis has survived extensive scrutiny and when competing models have been eliminated, a hypothesis may be elevated to the status of a scientific **theory.** In everyday language we may say, "That's only a theory." But a scientific theory is a well-tested and widely accepted view that the scientific community agrees best explains certain observable facts.

Scientific theories, like scientific hypotheses, are accepted only provisionally. It is always possible that a theory that has withstood previous testing may eventually be modified or completely disproved. As theories survive more testing, they are regarded with higher levels of confidence. Theories that have withstood extensive testing, such as the

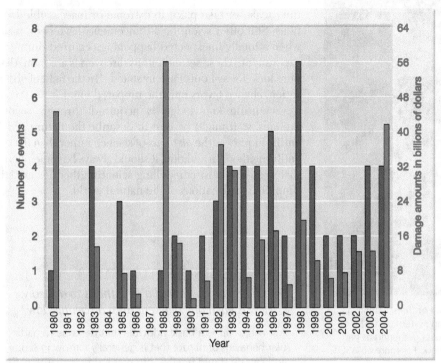

FIGURE 1–6 Between 1980 and 2004 the United States sustained 62 weather-related disasters in which overall damages and costs reached or exceeded $1 billion. This bar graph shows the number of events that occurred each year and the damage amounts in billions of dollars (normalized to 2002 dollars). The total losses for the 62 events exceeded $390 billion! *(After NOAA)*

TABLE 1-1 Billion-dollar weather events 1998–2004*

Event	Date	Damage/Costs†	Fatalities
Hurricane Jeanne	September 2004	$6.5 billion	28
Hurricane Ivan	September 2004	$12 billion	52
Hurricane Frances	September 2004	$9 billion	38
Hurricane Charley	August 2004	$14 billion	34
Southern California Wildfires (drought and winds)	October-November 2003	$2.5 billion	22
Hurricane Isabel	September 2003	$5 billion	55
Severe Storms and Tornadoes in Midwest and South	May 2003	$3.4 billion	51
Severe Storms and Hail in Midwest and South	April 2003	$1.6 billion	3
Drought in 30 states	Spring-Fall 2002	$10 billion	0
Western Fire Season (drought and winds)	Summer 2002	$2 billion	21
Tropical Storm Allison	June 2001	$5.1 billion	43
Midwest and Ohio Valley Hail and Tornadoes	April 2001	$1.9 billion	3
Drought/Heat Wave in South	Spring-Summer 2000	$4.2 billion	140
Western Fire Season (drought and winds)	Summer 2000	$2.1 billion	0
Hurricane Floyd	September 1999	$6.5 billion	77
Eastern Drought and Heat Wave	Summer 1999	$1.1 billion	256
Oklahoma-Kansas Tornadoes	May 1999	$1.7 billion	55
Arkansas-Tennessee Tornadoes	January 1999	$1.4 billion	17
Texas Flooding	October-November 1998	$1.1 billion	31
Hurricane Georges	September 1998	$6.5 billion	16
Hurricane Bonnie	August 1998	$1.1 billion	3
Southern Drought and Heat Wave	Summer 1998	$6.6-9.9 billion	200
Minnesota Severe Storm/Hail	May 1998	$1.7 billion	1
Southeast Severe Weather (tornadoes and floods)	Winter-Spring 1998	$1.1 billion	132
Northeast ice storm	January 1998	$1.5 billion	16

*Source: National Climatic Data Center/NOAA
†To allow for more accurate comparison, dollar amounts are normalized to 2002.

FIGURE 1–7 Gathering data is a basic part of the scientific method. This Automated Surface Observing System (ASOS) installation is one of nearly 900 in use for data gathering as part of the U.S. primary surface observing network. For more on ASOS, see Figure 12–4, p. 350.

theory of plate tectonics and the theory of evolution, are held with a very high degree of confidence.

Scientific Methods

The processes just described, in which scientists gather facts through observations and formulate scientific hypotheses and theories, is called the *scientific method*. Contrary to popular belief, the scientific method is not a standard recipe that scientists apply in a routine manner to unravel the secrets of our natural world. Rather, it is an endeavor that involves creativity and insight. Rutherford and Ahlgren put it this way: "Inventing hypotheses or theories to imagine how the world works and then figuring out how they can be put to the test of reality is as creative as writing poetry, composing music, or designing skyscrapers."*

There is no fixed path that scientists always follow that leads unerringly to scientific knowledge. Nevertheless, many scientific investigations involve the following steps: (1) collection of scientific facts (data) through observation and measurement (Figure 1–7); (2) development of one or more working hypotheses or models to explain these facts; (3) development of observations and experiments to test the hypotheses; and (4) the acceptance, modification, or rejection of the hypotheses based on extensive testing.

Other scientific discoveries may result from purely theoretical ideas that stand up to extensive examination. Some researchers use high-speed computers to simulate what is happening in the "real" world. These models are useful when dealing with natural processes that occur on very long

*F. James Rutherford and Andrew Ahlgren, *Science for All Americans* (New York: Oxford University Press, 1990), p. 7.

time scale, or take place in extreme or inaccessible locations. Still other scientific advancements have been made when a totally unexpected happening occurred during an experiment. These serendipitous discoveries are more than pure luck; for as Louis Pasteur stated, "In the field of observation, chance favors only the prepared mind."

Scientific knowledge is acquired through several avenues, so it might be best to describe the nature of scientific inquiry as the *methods* of science rather than *the* scientific method. In addition, it should always be remembered that even the most compelling scientific theories are still simplified explanations of the natural world.

Observing the Atmosphere

Scientific study of the atmosphere began in the seventeenth century as instruments were developed to measure different elements. The instruments provided data that helped observers begin to gain an understanding of atmospheric processes. In 1593 Galileo invented an early version of the thermometer, and in 1643 Torricelli built the first barometer (for measuring air pressure). By 1661 Robert Boyle discovered the basic relationship between pressure and volume in a gas. During the eighteenth century, instruments were improved and standardized, and extensive data collection began. The acquisition of such data was fundamental to the study of physical processes and the development of explanations about atmospheric phenomena.

It became obvious to those studying the atmosphere that gathering data from only ground-level sites significantly limited understanding. In the late 1700s the only data for conditions at high altitudes came from observations made in the mountains. In 1752 Benjamin Franklin, using a kite, made his famous discovery that lightning is an electrical discharge. Not many years later, kites were being used to observe temperatures above the surface. In the late eighteenth century, manned balloons were used in an attempt to investigate the composition and properties of the "upper" atmosphere. Although several manned ascents were attempted over the years, they were dangerous undertakings. Unmanned balloons, on the other hand, could rise to higher altitudes, but there was no assurance that the instruments carried aloft would be recovered. Notwithstanding the difficulties and dangers, considerable data were gathered on the nature of the air above.

Today balloons continue to play a significant role in the systematic investigation of the atmosphere. Giant balloons are launched regularly, primarily for research purposes (Figure 1–8a). Such balloons can stay aloft for extended periods and represent an important means of carrying monitoring instruments into the region of the atmosphere known as the stratosphere.

Since the late 1920s balloons have carried aloft **radiosondes.** These lightweight packages of instruments are fitted with radio transmitters that send back data on temperature, pressure, and relative humidity in the lower portions of the atmosphere (Figure 1–8b). Radiosondes are sent aloft twice daily from an extensive network of stations worldwide. The data that they supply are essential for making accurate weather forecasts.

Other important means for exploring the atmosphere include rockets and airplanes. After World War II, rockets revolutionized the study of the upper atmosphere. Prior to this time, knowledge of the atmosphere beyond about 30 kilometers (20 miles) came almost exclusively from indirect ground-based measurements. Airplanes also play a significant role in atmospheric studies. High-flying aircraft are capable of reaching portions of the stratosphere. Others are designed to measure such relatively small-scale yet complex phenomena as cloud systems or to fly directly into hurricanes to monitor their current state of development.

Among the methods of studying the atmosphere that are best known to the general public and most useful to atmospheric scientists are weather radar and satellites. Today, when we watch a television weather report, we expect to see satellite images that show moving cloud patterns and radar displays that depict the intensity and regional extent of precipitation (Figure 1–9). Recent technological advances greatly enhance the value of weather radar for the purpose of storm detection, warning, and research. Meteorological satellites give us a perspective of the atmosphere that is unique

(a)

(b)

FIGURE 1–8 Exploring the atmosphere using balloons. (a) Giant balloons such as this one are filled with helium and carry instrument packages high into the atmosphere. (b) A lightweight package of instruments, the radiosonde, is carried aloft by a small weather balloon. *(Photo by Mark Burnett/Photo Researchers, Inc.)*

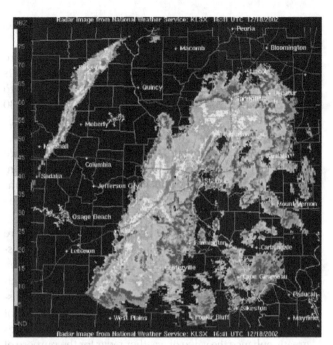

FIGURE 1–9 Radar images show the distribution and intensity of precipitation. This National Weather Service image shows the St. Louis, Missouri, region on the morning of December 18, 2002. The unusual spring-like weather included heavy rain, severe thunderstorms, and a tornado watch. (National Weather Service)

temperatures, precipitation, and changes in atmostpheric composition. Box 1–1 briefly describes one of these modern research satellites, the Tropical Rainfall Measuring Mission (TRMM). Moreover, data relating to phenomena such as the extent of sea ice and glaciers, ocean circulation, vegetative cover, and many other variables are gathered from space.

and invaluable. For example, they provide images that allow us to study the distribution of clouds and the circulation patterns that they reveal (Figure 1–10). Moreover, they let us see the structure and determine the speed of weather systems over the oceans and other regions where observations are scanty or nonexistent. One obvious benefit is that storms can be detected early and tracked with great precision.

In addition to enabling us to monitor storms from space, instruments aboard modern satellites permit us to measure and monitor many variables including winds, solar radiation,

The Atmosphere: A Part of the Earth System

 Introduction to the Atmosphere
▶ A View of Earth

A view such as the one in Figure 1–11a provided the *Apollo 8* astronauts as well as the rest of humanity with a unique perspective of our home. Seen from space, Earth is

FIGURE 1–10 Satellites are invaluable tools for tracking storms and gathering atmospheric data. This image shows severe winter storms that swept across much of Europe on December 16, 2001, delivering bitter cold temperatures, high winds, heavy snowfall, and flooding in some regions. Transportation via road and rail was brought to a halt in parts of many countries while tens of thousands of people were left without power. *(Image provided by ORBIMAGE. © Orbital Imaging Corporation and processing by NASA Goddard Space Flight Center)*

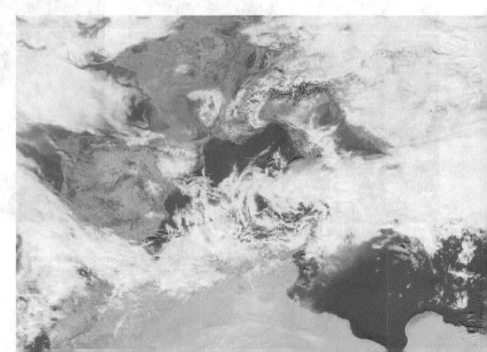

BOX 1-1   Monitoring Earth From Space

Scientific facts are gathered in many ways, including laboratory experiments and field observations and measurements. Satellites provide another very important source of data. Satellite images give us perspectives that are difficult to gain from more traditional sources. Moreover, the high-tech instruments aboard many satellites enable scientists to gather information from remote regions where data are otherwise scarce.

The image in Figure 1–A is from NASA's *Tropical Rainfall Measuring Mission* (TRMM). TRMM is a research satellite designed to expand our understanding of the hydrologic cycle and its role in our climate system. By covering the region between the latitudes 35°N and 35°S, it provides much needed data on rainfall

FIGURE 1–A Satellite image of Hurricane Dennis at 5:59 pm EDT on July 9, 2005. This image of Hurricane Dennis shows the pattern of rainfall intensity. Dark red indicates intense rainfall rates of 50 millimeters (2 inches) per hour. *(NASA/TRMM image)*

and the heat release associated with rainfall. Many types of measurements and images are possible.

The map in Figure 1–B was made using data from the TRMM satellite. In addition to data for land areas, this satellite provides extremely precise measurements of rainfall over the oceans where conventional land-based instruments cannot see. This is especially important because much of Earth's rain falls in ocean-covered tropical areas, and a great deal of the globe's weather-producing energy comes from heat exchanges involved in the rainfall process. Until the TRMM, information on the intensity and amount of rainfall over the tropics was scanty. Such data are crucial to understanding and predicting global climate change.

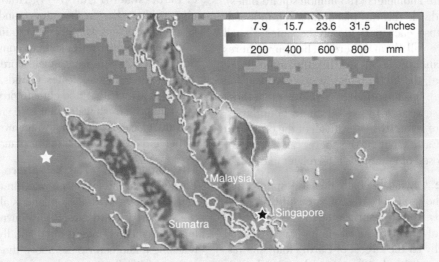

FIGURE 1–B This map of rainfall for December 7–13, 2004, in Malaysia was constructed using TRMM data. Over 800 millimeters (32 inches) of rain fell along the east coast of the peninsula (darkest red area). The extraordinary rains caused extensive flooding and triggered many mudflows. *(NASA/TRMM image)*

breathtaking in its beauty and startling in its solitude. Such an image reminds us that our home is, after all, a planet—small, self-contained, and in some ways even fragile.

As we look closely at our planet from space, it becomes apparent that Earth is much more than rock and soil. In fact, the most conspicuous features in Figure 1–11a are not continents but swirling clouds suspended above the surface of the vast global ocean. These features emphasize the importance of water on our planet.

The closer view of Earth from space shown in Figure 1–11b helps us appreciate why the physical environment is traditionally divided into three major parts: the solid Earth, the water portion of our planet, and Earth's gaseous envelope. In addition, our physical environment supports a vast array of life forms that constitute a fourth major part of our planet.

It should be emphasized that our environment is highly integrated and is not dominated by rock, water, or air alone. It is instead characterized by continuous interactions as air comes in contact with rock, rock with water, and water with air.

Figure 1–12 provides us with one easy-to-visualize example. The shoreline is an obvious meeting place for rock, water, and air. In this scene, ocean waves that were created by the drag of air moving across the water are breaking against the rocky shore. The force of the water can be powerful, and the erosional work that is accomplished can be great.

Earth's Four Spheres

On a human scale Earth is huge. Its surface area occupies 500,000,000 square kilometers (193 million square miles). As indicated, we divide this vast planet into four independent parts. Because each part loosely occupies a shell around Earth, we call them spheres. The four spheres include the *geosphere* (solid Earth), the *atmosphere* (gaseous envelope), the *hydrosphere* (water portion), and the *biosphere* (life). It is important to remember that these spheres are not separated by well-defined boundaries; rather, each sphere is intertwined with all of the others. In addition, each of Earth's four major spheres can be thought of as being composed of numerous interrelated parts.

The Geosphere. Lying beneath the atmosphere and the ocean is the solid Earth or **geosphere.** The geosphere extends from the surface to the center of the planet, a depth of about 6400 kilometers (nearly 4000 miles), making it by far the largest of Earth's four spheres.

Based on compositional differences, the geosphere is divided into three principal regions: the dense inner sphere, called the *core;* the less dense *mantle;* and the *crust,* which is the light and very thin outer skin of Earth. Soil, the thin veneer of material at Earth's surface that supports the growth of plants, may be thought of as part of all four spheres. The solid portion is a mixture of weathered rock debris (geosphere) and organic matter from decayed plant and animal life (biosphere). The decomposed and disintegrated rock debris is the product of weathering processes that require

air (atmosphere) and water (hydrosphere). Air and water also occupy the open spaces between the solid particles.

The Atmosphere. Earth is surrounded by a life-giving gaseous envelope called the **atmosphere.** When we view the atmosphere from the ground, it seems to be very deep (Figure 1–13). However, when compared to the thickness (radius) of the solid Earth (about 6400 kilometers or 4000 miles), the atmosphere is a very shallow layer. More than 99 percent of the atmosphere is within 30 kilometers (20 miles) of Earth's surface. This thin blanket of air is nevertheless an integral part of the planet. It not only provides the air that we breathe but also acts to protect us from the dangerous radiation emitted by the Sun. The energy exchanges that continually occur between the atmosphere and Earth's surface and between the atmosphere and space produce the effects we call *weather.* If, like the Moon, Earth had no atmosphere, our planet would not only be lifeless, but many of the processes and interactions that make the surface such a dynamic place could not operate.

The Hydrosphere. Earth is sometimes called the *blue planet.* Water more than anything else makes Earth unique. The **hydrosphere** is a dynamic mass that is continually on the move, evaporating from the oceans to the atmosphere, precipitating to the land, and running back to the ocean again. The global ocean is certainly the most prominent feature of the hydrosphere, blanketing nearly 71 percent of Earth's surface to an average depth of about 3800 meters (12,500 feet). It accounts for about 97 percent of Earth's water (Figure 1–14). However, the hydrosphere also includes the fresh water found in clouds, streams, lakes, and glaciers, as well as that found underground.

Although these latter sources constitute just a tiny fraction of the total, they are much more important than their meager percentage indicates. Clouds, of course, play a vital role in many weather and climate processes. In addition to providing the fresh water that is so vital to life on the land, streams, glaciers, and groundwater are responsible for sculpturing and creating many of our planet's varied landforms.

The Biosphere. The **biosphere** includes all life on Earth. Ocean life is concentrated in the sunlit surface waters of the sea. Most life on land is also concentrated near the surface, with tree roots and burrowing animals reaching a few meters underground and flying insects and birds reaching a kilometer or so above the surface. A surprising variety of life forms are also adapted to extreme environments. For example, on the ocean floor, where pressures are extreme and no light penetrates, there are places where vents spew hot, mineral-rich fluids that support communities of exotic life forms. On land, some bacteria thrive in rocks as deep as 4 kilometers (2.5 miles) and in boiling hot springs. Moreover, air currents can carry microorganisms many kilometers into the atmosphere. But even when we consider these extremes, life still must be thought of as being confined to a narrow band very near Earth's surface.

(a)   (b)

FIGURE 1–11 (a) View that greeted the *Apollo 8* astronauts as their spacecraft emerged from behind the Moon. (NASA Headquarters) (b) Africa and Arabia are prominent in this image of Earth taken from *Apollo 17*. The tan cloud-free zones over the land coincide with major desert regions. The band of clouds across central Africa is associated with a much wetter climate that in places sustains tropical rain forests. The dark blue of the oceans and the swirling cloud patterns remind us of the importance of the oceans and the atmosphere. Antarctica, a continent covered by glacial ice, is visible at the South Pole. *(Courtesy of NASA/Science Source/Photo Researchers, Inc.)*

FIGURE 1–12 The shoreline is one obvious example of an *interface*—a common boundary where different parts of a system interact. In this scene, ocean waves (*hydrosphere*) that were created by the force of moving air (*atmosphere*) break against California's rocky Big Sur shore (*geosphere*). *(Photo by Carr Clifton).*

FIGURE 1–13 This jet is flying high in the atmosphere at an altitude of more than 9000 meters (30,000 feet). More than two-thirds of the atmosphere is below this height. To someone on the ground, the atmosphere seems very deep. However, when compared to the thickness (radius) of the solid Earth, the atmosphere is a very shallow layer. *(Photo by Warren Faidley/Weatherstock.)*

Plants and animals depend on the physical environment for the basics of life. However, organisms do more than just respond to their physical environment. Through countless interactions, life forms help maintain and alter their physical environment. Without life, the makeup and nature of the geosphere, hydrosphere, and atmosphere would be very different.

Earth System Science

Anyone who studies Earth soon learns that our planet is a dynamic body with many separate but highly interactive parts or *spheres*. The atmosphere, hydrosphere, biosphere, and geosphere and all of their components can be studied separately. However, the parts are not isolated. Each is related in some way to the others to produce a complex and continuously interacting whole that we call the *Earth system*.

FIGURE 1–14 Distribution of Earth's water. Obviously most of Earth's water is in the oceans. Glacial ice represents about 85 percent of all the water *outside* the oceans. When only *liquid freshwater* is considered, more than 90 percent is groundwater.

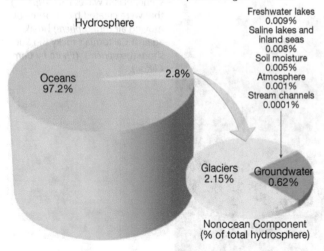

A simple example of the interactions among different parts of the Earth system occurs every winter as moisture evaporates from the Pacific Ocean and subsequently falls as rain in the hills of southern California, triggering destructive landslides such as the one pictured in Figure 1–1c. The processes that move water from the hydrosphere to the atmosphere and then to the solid Earth have a profound impact on the plants and animals (including humans) that inhabit the affected regions.

Scientists have recognized that in order to more fully understand our planet, they must learn how its individual components (land, water, air, and life forms) are interconnected. This endeavor, called *Earth system science*, aims to study Earth as a *system* composed of numerous interacting parts, or *subsystems*. Using an interdisciplinary approach, those who practice Earth system science attempt to achieve the level of understanding necessary to comprehend and solve many of our global environmental problems.

What Is a System?   Most of us hear and use the term *system* frequently. We may service our car's cooling *system*, make use of the city's transportation *system*, and be a participant in the political *system*. A news report might inform us of an approaching weather *system*. Further, we know that Earth is just a small part of a larger system known as the *solar system*, which in turn is a subsystem of an even larger system called the Milky Way Galaxy.

Loosely defined, a **system** can be any size group of interacting parts that form a complex whole. Most natural systems are driven by sources of energy that move matter and/or energy from one place to another. A simple analogy is a car's cooling system, which contains a liquid (usually water and antifreeze) that is driven from the engine to the radiator and back again. The role of this system is to transfer heat generated by combustion in the engine to the radiator, where moving air removes it from the system. Hence, the term cooling system.

Systems like a car's cooling system are self-contained with regard to matter and are called **closed systems.** Although energy moves freely in and out of a closed system, no matter (liquid in the case of our auto's cooling system) enters or leaves the system. (This assumes you don't get a leak in your radiator). By contrast, most natural systems are **open systems** and are far more complicated than the foregoing example. In an open system both energy and matter flow into and out of the system. In a weather system such as a hurricane, factors such as the quantity of water vapor available for cloud formation, the amount of heat released by condensing water vapor, and the flow of air into and out of the storm can fluctuate a great deal. At times the storm may strengthen; at other times it may remain stable or weaken.

Feedback Mechanisms.   Most natural systems have mechanisms that tend to enhance change, as well as other mechanisms that tend to resist change and thus stabilize the system. For example, when we get too hot, we perspire to cool down. This cooling phenomenon works to stabilize our body temperature and is referred to as a **negative**

feedback mechanism. Negative feedback mechanisms work to maintain the system as it is or, in other words, to maintain the status quo. By contrast, mechanisms that enhance or drive change are called **positive feedback mechanisms.**

Most of Earth's systems, particularly the climate system, contain a wide variety of negative and positive feedback mechanisms. For example, substantial scientific evidence indicates that Earth has entered a period of global warming. One consequence of global warming is that some of the world's glaciers and ice caps have begun to melt. Highly reflective snow- and ice-covered surfaces are gradually being replaced by brown soils, green trees, or blue oceans, all of which are darker, so they absorb more sunlight. The result is a positive feedback that contributes to the warming.

On the other hand, an increase in global temperature also causes greater evaporation of water from Earth's land-sea surface. One result of having more water vapor in the air is an increase in cloud cover. Because cloud tops are white and highly reflective, more sunlight is reflected back to space, which diminishes the amount of sunshine reaching Earth's surface and thus reduces global temperatures. Further, warmer temperatures tend to promote the growth of vegetation. Plants in turn remove carbon dioxide CO_2 from the air. Since carbon dioxide is one of the atmosphere's *greenhouse gases,* its removal has a negative impact on global warming.[*]

In addition to natural processes, we must also consider the human element. Extensive cutting and clearing of the tropical rain forests and the burning of fossil fuels (oil, natural gas, and coal) result in an increase in atmospheric CO_2. Such activity appears to have contributed to the increase in global temperature that our planet is experiencing. One of the daunting tasks of Earth system scientists is to predict what the climate will be like in the future by taking into account many variables, including technological changes, population trends, and the overall impact of the numerous competing positive and negative feedback mechanisms.

Earth As a System

The Earth system has a nearly endless array of subsystems in which matter is recycled over and over again. One familiar subsystem briefly considered earlier is the *hydrologic cycle* (Figure 1–15). It represents the unending circulation of Earth's water among the hydrosphere, atmosphere, biosphere, and geosphere. Water enters the atmosphere by evaporation from Earth's surface and by transpiration from plants. Water vapor condenses in the atmosphere to form clouds, which in turn produce precipitation that falls back to Earth's surface. Some of the rain that falls onto the land

[*]Greenhouse gases absorb heat energy emitted by Earth and thus help keep the atmosphere warm.

sinks in to be taken up by plants or becomes groundwater, and some flows across the surface toward the ocean.

Energy for the Earth System. The Earth system is powered by energy from two sources. The Sun drives external processes that occur in the atmosphere, hydrosphere, and at Earth's surface. Weather and climate, ocean circulation, and erosional processes are driven by energy from the Sun. Earth's interior is the second source of energy. Heat remaining from when our planet formed, and heat that is continuously generated by decay of radioactive elements powers the internal processes that produce volcanoes, earthquakes, and mountains.

The Parts are Linked. The parts of the Earth system are linked so that a change in one part can produce changes in any or all of the other parts. For example, when a volcano erupts, lava from Earth's interior may flow out at the surface and block a nearby valley. This new obstruction influences the region's drainage system by creating a lake or causing streams to change course. The large quantities of volcanic ash and gases that can be emitted during an eruption might be blown high into the atmosphere and influence the amount of solar energy that can reach Earth's surface. The result could be a drop in air temperatures over the entire hemisphere.

Where the surface is covered by lava flows or a thick layer of volcanic ash, existing soils are buried. This causes the soil-forming processes to begin anew to transform the new surface material into soil (Figure 1–16). The soil that eventually forms will reflect the interactions among many parts of the Earth system—the volcanic parent material, the climate, and the impact of biological activity. Of course, there would also be significant changes in the biosphere. Some organisms and their habitats would be eliminated by the lava and ash, whereas new settings for life, such as the lake, would be created. The potential climate change could also impact sensitive life forms.

The Earth system is characterized by processes that vary on spatial scales from fractions of millimeters to thousands of kilometers. Time scales for Earth's processes range from milliseconds to billions of years. As we learn about Earth, it becomes increasingly clear that despite significant separations in distance or time, many processes are connected, and a change in one component can influence the entire system.

Humans are *part of* the Earth system, a system in which the living and nonliving components are entwined and interconnected. Therefore, our actions produce changes in all of the other parts. When we burn gasoline and coal, dispose of our wastes, and clear the land, we cause other parts of the system to respond, often in unforeseen ways. Throughout this book you will learn about some of Earth's subsystems, including the hydrologic system and the climate system. Remember that these components *and we humans* are all part of the complex interacting whole we call the Earth system.

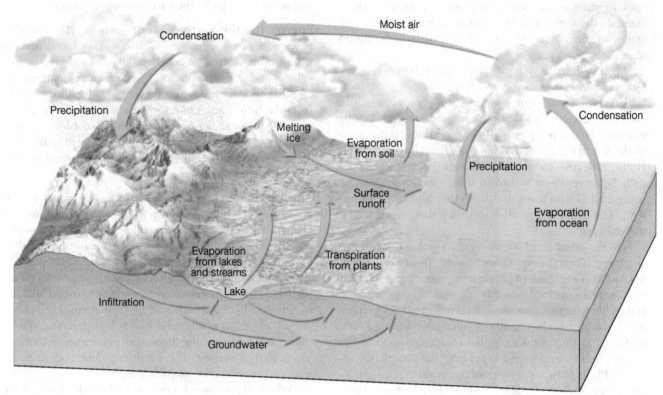

FIGURE 1–15 The hydrologic cycle is just one of Earth's many subsystems. Our planet's water is constantly cycled among all four of Earth's major spheres.

FIGURE 1–16 When Mount St. Helens erupted in May 1980, the area shown here was buried by a volcanic mudflow. Now, plants are reestablished and new soil is forming. *(Photo by Jack Dykinga)*

Composition of the Atmosphere

 Introduction to the Atmosphere
▶ A View of Earth

In the days of Aristotle, air was believed to be one of four fundamental substances that could not be further subdivided into constituent components. The other three substances were fire, earth (soil), and water. Even today the term **air** is sometimes used as if it were a specific gas, which of course it is not. The envelope of air that surrounds our planet is a *mixture* of many discrete gases, each with its own physical properties, in which varying quantities of tiny solid and liquid particles are suspended.

Major Components

The composition of air is not constant; it varies from time to time and from place to place (see Box 1–2). If the water vapor, dust, and other variable components were removed from the atmosphere, we would find that its makeup is very stable up to an altitude of about 80 kilometers (50 miles).

As you can see in Figure 1–17 and Table 1–2, two gases—nitrogen and oxygen—make up 99 percent of the volume of clean, dry air. Although these gases are the most

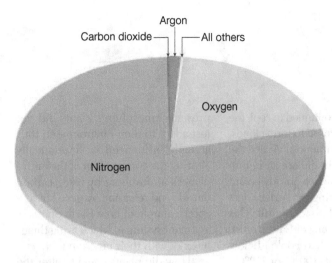

FIGURE 1–17 Proportional volume of gases composing dry air. Nitrogen and oxygen obviously dominate.

plentiful components of the atmosphere and are of great significance to life on Earth, they are of little or no importance in affecting weather phenomena. The remaining 1 percent of dry air is mostly the inert gas argon (0.93 percent) plus tiny quantities of a number of other gases.

Carbon Dioxide

Carbon dioxide, although present in only minute amounts (0.038 percent), is nevertheless a meteorologically important constituent of air. Carbon dioxide is of great interest to meteorologists because it is an efficient absorber of energy emitted by Earth and thus influences the heating of the atmosphere. Although the proportion of carbon dioxide in the atmosphere is relatively uniform, its percentage has been rising steadily for more than a century (Figure 1–18). This rise is attributed to the burning of ever increasing quantities of fossil fuels, such as coal and oil. Some of this additional carbon dioxide is absorbed by the waters of the ocean or is used by plants, but nearly half remains in the air. Estimates project that by sometime in the second half of

the twenty-first century, carbon dioxide levels will be twice as high as they were early in the twentieth century.

The precise impact of the increased carbon dioxide is difficult to predict, but most atmospheric scientists agree that it will bring about a warming of the lower atmosphere and thus trigger global climate change. The role of carbon dioxide in the atmosphere and its possible effect on climate are examined in more detail in Chapters 2 and 14.

Variable Components

Air includes many gases and particles that vary significantly from time to time and place to place. Important examples include water vapor, dust particles, and ozone. Although usually present in small percentages, they can have significant effects on weather and climate.

FIGURE 1–18 Changes in the atmosphere's carbon dioxide (CO_2) as measured at Hawaii's Mauna Loa Observatory. The oscillations reflect the seasonal variations in plant growth and decay in the Northern Hemisphere.

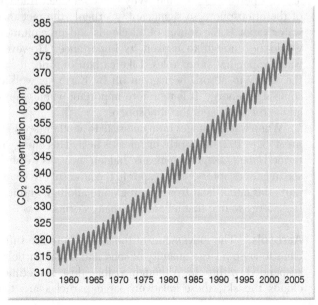

TABLE 1-2	Principal gases of dry air	
Constituent	**Percent by volume**	**Concentration in parts per million (PPM)**
Nitrogen (N_2)	78.084	780,840.0
Oxygen (O_2)	20.946	209,460.0
Argon (Ar)	0.934	9,340.0
Carbon dioxide (CO_2)	0.038	380.0
Neon (Ne)	0.00182	18.2
Helium (He)	0.000524	5.24
Methane (CH_4)	0.00015	1.5
Krypton (Kr)	0.000114	1.14
Hydrogen (H_2)	0.00005	0.5

BOX 1-2   Earth's Atmosphere Evolves

Earth's atmosphere is unlike that of any other body in the solar system. No other planet exhibits the same life-sustaining mixture of gases as Earth. Today the air you breathe is a stable mixture of 78 percent nitrogen, almost 21 percent oxygen, about 1 percent argon (an inert gas), and trace gases like carbon dioxide and water vapor. But our planet's original atmosphere, several billion years ago, was far different.

Earth's very earliest atmosphere probably was swept into space by the *solar wind*, a vast stream of particles emitted by the Sun. As Earth slowly cooled, a more enduring atmosphere formed. The molten surface solidified into a crust, and gases that had been dissolved in the molten rock were gradually released, a process called *outgassing*. Outgassing continues today from hundreds of active volcanoes worldwide. Thus, geologists hypothesize that Earth's original atmosphere was made up of gases similar to those released in volcanic emissions today: water vapor, carbon dioxide, nitrogen, and several trace gases.

As the planet continued to cool, the water vapor condensed to form clouds, and great rains commenced. At first the water evaporated in the hot air before reaching the ground, or quickly boiled away upon contacting the surface, just like water sprayed on a hot grill. This accelerated the cooling of Earth's crust. When the surface had cooled below water's boiling point (100°C, or 212°F), torrential rains slowly filled low areas, forming the oceans. This reduced not only the water vapor in the air but also the amount of carbon dioxide, for it became dissolved in the water. What remained was a nitrogen-rich atmosphere.

If Earth's primitive atmosphere resulted from volcanic outgassing, we have a quandary, because volcanoes do not emit free oxygen. Where did the very significant percentage of oxygen in our present atmosphere (nearly 21 percent) come from?

The major source of oxygen is green plants (Figure 1–C). Put another way, *life itself* has strongly influenced the composition of our present atmosphere. Plants did not just adapt to their environment; they actually influenced it, dramatically altering the composition of the entire planet's atmosphere by using carbon dioxide and releasing oxygen. This is a good example of how Earth operates as a giant system in which living things interact with their environment.

How did plants come to alter the atmosphere? The key is the way in which plants create their own food. They employ *photosynthesis*, in which they use light energy to synthesize food sugars from carbon dioxide and water. The process releases a waste gas—oxygen. Those of us in the animal kingdom rely on oxygen to metabolize our food, and we in turn exhale carbon dioxide as a waste gas. The plants use this carbon dioxide for more photosynthesis, and so on, in a continuing system.

The first life forms on Earth, probably bacteria, did not need oxygen. Their life processes were geared to the earlier, oxygenless atmosphere. Even today many *anaerobic* bacteria thrive in environments that lack free

Water Vapor. The amount of water vapor in the air varies considerably, from practically none at all up to about 4 percent by volume. Why is such a small fraction of the atmosphere so significant? Certainly the fact that water vapor is the source of all clouds and precipitation would be enough to explain its importance. However, water vapor has other roles. Like carbon dioxide, it has the ability to absorb heat given off by Earth, as well as some solar energy. It is therefore important when we examine the heating of the atmosphere.

When water changes from one state to another (see Figure 4–3, p. 102), it absorbs or releases heat. This energy is termed *latent heat,* which means "hidden" heat. As we shall see in later chapters, water vapor in the atmosphere transports this latent heat from one region to another, and it is the energy source that helps drive many storms.

Aerosols. The movements of the atmosphere are sufficient to keep a large quantity of solid and liquid particles suspended within it. Although visible dust sometimes clouds the sky, these relatively large particles are too heavy to stay in the air for very long. Still, many particles are microscopic and remain suspended for considerable periods of time. They may originate from many sources, both natural and human made, and include sea salts from breaking waves, fine soil blown into the air, smoke and soot from fires, pollen and microorganisms lifted by the wind, ash and dust from volcanic eruptions, and more (Figure 1–19a). Collectively, these tiny solid and liquid particles are called **aerosols.**

Aerosols are most numerous in the lower atmosphere near their primary source, Earth's surface. Nevertheless, the upper atmosphere is not free of them, because some dust is carried to great heights by rising currents of air, and other particles are contributed by meteoroids that disintegrate as they pass through the atmosphere.

From a meteorological standpoint, these tiny, often invisible particles can be significant. First, many act as surfaces on which water vapor may condense, an important function in the formation of clouds and fog. Second, aerosols can absorb or reflect incoming solar radiation. Thus, when an air-pollution episode is occurring or when ash fills the sky

FIGURE 1–C Life has strongly influenced the composition of our atmosphere. The primary source of the abundant oxygen in Earth's atmosphere is photosynthesis by green plants. *(Photo by Art Wolfe/Photo Researchers, Inc.)*

oxygen. Later, primitive plants evolved that used photosynthesis and released oxygen. Slowly the oxygen content of Earth's atmosphere increased. The geologic record of this ancient time suggests that much of the first free oxygen did not remain free, because it combined with (oxidized) other substances dissolved in water, especially iron. Iron has tremendous affinity for oxygen, and the two elements combine to form iron oxides (rust) at any opportunity.

Then, once the available iron satisfied its need for oxygen, substantial quantities of oxygen accumulated in the atmosphere. By the beginning of the Paleozoic era, about 4 billion years into Earth's existence (after seven-eighths of Earth's history had elapsed) the fossil record reveals abundant ocean-dwelling organisms that require oxygen to live. Hence, the composition of Earth's atmosphere has evolved together with its life forms, from an oxygenless envelope to today's oxygen-rich environment.

following a volcanic eruption, the amount of sunlight reaching Earth's surface can be measurably reduced. Finally, aerosols contribute to an optical phenomenon we have all observed—the varied hues of red and orange at sunrise and sunset (Figure 1–19b).

Ozone. Another important component of the atmosphere is **ozone.** It is a form of oxygen that combines three oxygen atoms into each molecule (O_3). Ozone is not the same as the oxygen we breathe, which has two atoms per molecule (O_2). There is very little ozone in the atmosphere. Overall, it represents just three out of every 10 million molecules. Moreover, its distribution is not uniform. In the lowest portion of the atmosphere, ozone represents less than one part in 100 million. It is concentrated well above the surface in a layer called the *stratosphere,* between 10 and 50 kilometers (6 and 31 miles).

In this altitude range, oxygen molecules (O_2) are split into single atoms of oxygen (O) when they absorb ultravio-

let radiation emitted by the Sun. Ozone is then created when a single atom of oxygen (O) and a molecule of oxygen (O_2) collide. This must happen in the presence of a third, neutral molecule that acts as *a catalyst* by allowing the reaction to take place without itself being consumed in the process. Ozone is concentrated in the 10- to 50-kilometer height range because a crucial balance exists there: The ultraviolet radiation from the Sun is sufficient to produce single atoms of oxygen, and there are enough gas molecules to bring about the required collisions (see Box 1–3).

The presence of the ozone layer in our atmosphere is crucial to those of us who dwell on Earth. The reason is that ozone absorbs the potentially harmful ultraviolet (UV) radiation from the Sun. If ozone did not filter a great deal of the ultraviolet radiation, and if the Sun's UV rays reached the surface of Earth undiminished, our planet would be uninhabitable for most life as we know it. Thus, anything that reduces the amount of ozone in the atmosphere could affect the well-being of life on Earth. Just such a problem exists and is described in the next section.

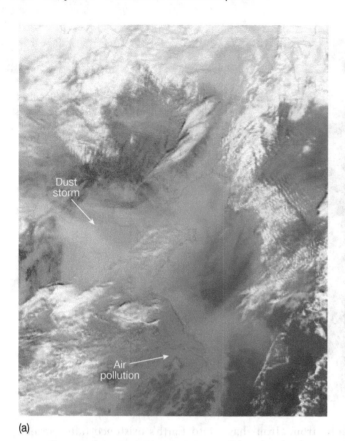

(a)

(b)

FIGURE 1–19 This satellite image (left) from November 11, 2002, shows two examples of aerosols. First, a large dust storm is blowing across northeastern China toward the Korean Peninsula. Second, a dense haze toward the south (bottom center) is human-generated air pollution. *(Image courtesy NASA)* Dust in the air (right) can cause sunsets to be especially colorful. *(Photo by Steve Elmore/CORBIS/The Stock Market)*

Students Sometimes Ask...

Isn't ozone some sort of pollutant?

Yes, you're right. Although the naturally occurring ozone in the stratosphere is critical to life on Earth, it is regarded as a pollutant when produced at ground level because it can damage vegetation and be harmful to human health. Ozone is a major component in a noxious mixture of gases and particles called photochemical smog. It forms as a result of reactions triggered by sunlight that occur among pollutants emitted by motor vehicles and industries.

Ozone Depletion—A Global Issue

The loss of ozone high in the atmosphere as a consequence of human activities is a serious global-scale environmental problem. For nearly a billion years Earth's ozone layer has protected life on the planet. However, over the past half century, people have unintentionally placed the ozone layer in jeopardy by polluting the atmosphere. The offending chemicals are known as chlorofluorocarbons (CFCs). They are versatile compounds that are chemically stable, odorless,

nontoxic, noncorrosive, and inexpensive to produce. Over the decades many uses were developed for CFCs, including as coolants for air-conditioning and refrigeration equipment, cleaning solvents for electronic components, propellants for aerosol sprays, and the production of certain plastic foams.

No one worried about how CFCs might affect the atmosphere until three scientists, Paul Crutzen, F. Sherwood Rowland, and Mario Molina, studied the relationship. In 1974 they alerted the world when they reported that CFCs were probably reducing the average concentration of ozone in the stratosphere. In 1995 these scientists were awarded the Nobel Prize in chemistry for their pioneering work.

They discovered that because CFCs are practically inert (that is, not chemically active) in the lower atmosphere, a portion of these gases gradually makes its way to the ozone layer, where sunlight separates the chemicals into their constituent atoms. The chlorine atoms released this way, through a complicated series of reactions, have the net effect of removing some of the ozone (see Box 1–3).

The Ozone Hole

Although ozone depletion by CFCs occurs worldwide, measurements have shown that ozone concentrations take an especially sharp drop over Antarctica during the Southern

BOX 1-3 Important Reactions Involving Ozone in the Stratosphere

Ozone (O_3) is found naturally in the atmosphere, where it is concentrated in the stratosphere, a layer between about 10 and 50 kilometers above Earth's surface. Here natural processes are continually creating and destroying ozone. These reactions account for the higher temperatures that occur in the stratosphere.

Natural Formation and Destruction of Ozone

Ozone is created in two steps. First, high-energy ultraviolet (UV) rays from the Sun strike ordinary oxygen molecules (O_2) and split them into two single oxygen atoms. Second, a freed oxygen atom (O) combines with an oxygen molecule (O_2) to form a molecule of ozone (O_3). Figure 1–D illustrates these steps.

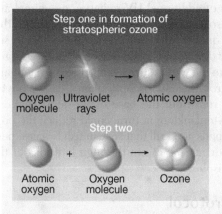

FIGURE 1–D Ozone in the stratosphere is created in two steps.

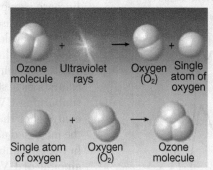

FIGURE 1–E The absorption of solar ultraviolet radiation by ozone during the two-step *ozone-oxygen cycle* causes temperatures in the stratosphere to rise.

When an ozone molecule (O_3) absorbs UV rays, it splits into an oxygen molecule (O_2) and a single atom of oxygen (O). Usually the single oxygen atom quickly collides with and rejoins an oxygen molecule to form another ozone molecule. These reactions, in which ozone is continually being broken down and re-created, are sometimes called the *ozone-oxygen cycle* and are depicted in Figure 1–E.

Ozone Destruction by CFCs

Scientists have learned that the use of certain chlorine-containing chemicals such as chlorofluorocarbons (CFCs) leads to a loss of ozone in the stratosphere. CFCs drift upward into the stratosphere, where they are

bombarded by solar ultraviolet rays. In response, CFC molecules break up by releasing chlorine (Cl) atoms. As shown in the top portion of Figure 1–F, these chlorine atoms react with ozone molecules by taking one oxygen atom to form chlorine monoxide (ClO) and leaving behind an oxygen molecule (O_2). Then whenever a molecule of chlorine monoxide encounters a single atom of oxygen (Figure 1–F, bottom), the oxygen "breaks up" the chlorine monoxide, stealing its oxygen atom and releasing chlorine back to the stratosphere to destroy more ozone. The reactions shown in Figure 1–F occur over and over again. In this manner, every chlorine atom that makes its way to the stratosphere is able to destroy *many* molecules of ozone

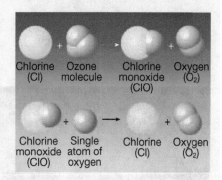

FIGURE 1–F Free chlorine atoms destroy ozone (top). Below, chlorine atoms are released back to the stratosphere where they destroy more ozone. These two reactions occur over and over again.

Hemisphere spring (September and October). Later, during November and December, the ozone concentration recovers to more normal levels (Figure 1–20). Between the early 1980s, when it was discovered, and the early 2000s, this well-publicized *ozone hole* intensified and grew larger until it covered an area roughly the size of North America (Figure 1–21).

The hole is caused in part by the relatively abundant ice particles in the south polar stratosphere. The ice boosts the

effectiveness of CFCs in destroying ozone, thus causing a greater decline than would otherwise occur. The zone of maximum depletion is confined to the Antarctic region by a swirling upper-level wind pattern. When this vortex weakens during the late spring, the ozone-depleted air is no longer restricted, and mixes freely with air from other latitudes where ozone levels are higher.

A few years after the Antarctic ozone hole was discovered, scientists detected a similar but smaller ozone thinning

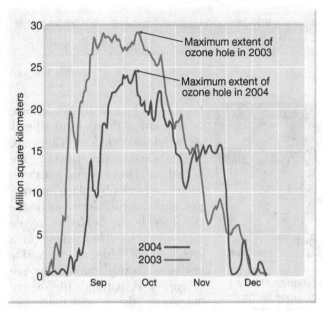

FIGURE 1–20 Changes in the size of the Antarctic ozone hole during 2003 and 2004. The ozone hole in both years began to form in late August and was well developed in September and October. As is typical, each year the ozone hole persisted through November and disappeared in December. At its maximum, the area of the ozone hole was about 29 million square kilometers in 2003, an area slightly larger than all of North America. A relatively warm Antarctic winter in 2004 reduced the thinning of the ozone layer and kept the extent of the hole slightly smaller than in 2003.

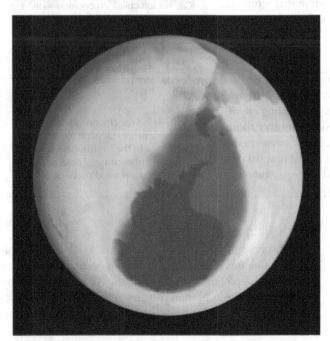

FIGURE 1–21 The Antarctic ozone hole on September 22, 2004. Dark blue colors correspond to the region with the sparsest ozone. Light blue, green, and yellow indicate progressively more ozone. *(Data from NOAA)*

in the vicinity of the North Pole during spring and early summer. When this pool breaks up, parcels of ozone-depleted air move southward over North America, Europe, and Asia.

Effects of Ozone Depletion

Because ozone filters out most of the UV radiation in sunlight, a decrease in its concentration permits more of these harmful wavelengths to reach Earth's surface. Scientists in New Zealand discovered that during the decade of the 1990s, damaging UV radiation gradually increased as concentrations of stratospheric ozone decreased. By 2000, peak sunburning UV levels in New Zealand were about 12 percent higher than 10 years earlier. What are the effects of the increased ultraviolet radiation? Each 1 percent decrease in the concentration of stratospheric ozone increases the amount of UV radiation that reaches Earth's surface by about 2 percent. Therefore, because ultraviolet radiation is known to induce skin cancer, ozone depletion seriously affects human health, especially among fair-skinned people and those who spend considerable time in the sun.

The fact that up to a half-million cases of these cancers occur in the United States annually means that ozone depletion could ultimately lead to many thousands of additional cases each year.[*] In addition to upping the risk of skin cancer, an increase in damaging UV radiation can negatively impact the human immune system, as well as promote cataracts, a clouding of the eye lens that reduces vision and may cause blindness if not treated.

The effects of additional UV radiation on animal and plant life are also important. There is serious concern that crop yields and quality will be adversely affected. Some scientists also fear that increased UV radiation in the Antarctic will penetrate the waters surrounding the continent and impair or destroy the microscopic plants, called phytoplankton, that represent the base of the food chain. A decrease in phytoplankton, in turn, could reduce the population of copepods and krill that sustain fish, whales, penguins, and other marine life in the high latitudes of the Southern Hemisphere.

Montreal Protocol

What has been done to protect the atmosphere's ozone layer? Realizing that the risks of not curbing CFC emissions were difficult to ignore, an international agreement known as the *Montreal Protocol on Substances that Deplete the Ozone Layer* was concluded under the auspices of the United Nations in late 1987. The protocol established legally binding controls on the production and consumption of gases known to cause ozone depletion. As the scientific understanding of ozone depletion improved after 1987 and substitutes and alternatives became available for the offending chemicals, the Montreal Protocol was strengthened several times. More than 180 nations eventually ratified the treaty.

[*]For more on this, see Box 2–3 "The Ultraviolet Index." p. 46

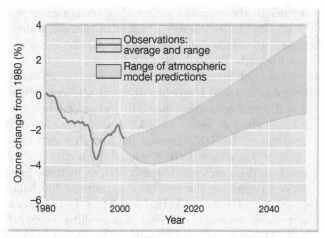

FIGURE 1–22 Global ozone recovery predictions. Observed values of global total ozone decreased beginning about 1980. As emissions of ozone-depleting gases decrease in the early twenty-first century, computer models indicate that ozone values will increase. Model results show that recovery is expected to be significant by 2050, or perhaps sooner.

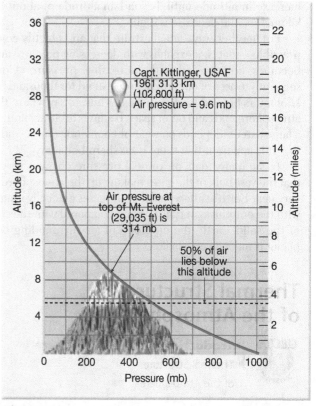

FIGURE 1–23 Atmospheric pressure changes with altitude. The rate of pressure decrease with an increase in altitude is not constant. Rather, pressure decreases rapidly near Earth's surface and more gradually at greater heights.

The Montreal Protocol represents a positive international response to a global environment problem. As a result of the action, the total abundance of ozone-depleting gases in the atmosphere has started to decrease in recent years. If the nations of the world continue to follow the provisions of the protocol, the decreases are expected to continue throughout the twenty-first century. Some offending chemicals are still increasing but will begin to decrease in coming decades. By mid-century, the abundance of ozone-depleting gases should fall to values that existed before the Antarctic ozone hole began to form in the 1980s. Figure 1–22 shows global ozone recovery predictions to the year 2050.

Extent of the Atmosphere

 Introduction to the Atmosphere

▶ Extent of the Atmosphere

To say that the atmosphere begins at Earth's surface and extends upward is obvious. However, where does the atmosphere end and outer space begin? There is no sharp boundary; the atmosphere rapidly thins as you travel away from Earth, until there are too few gas molecules to detect.

To understand the vertical extent of the atmosphere, let us examine the changes in atmospheric pressure with height. Atmospheric pressure is simply the weight of the air above. At sea level the average pressure is slightly more than 1000 millibars. This corresponds to a weight of slightly more than 1 kilogram per square centimeter (14.7 pounds per square inch). Obviously, the pressure at higher altitudes is less (Figure 1–23).

One half of the atmosphere lies below an altitude of 5.6 kilometers (3.5 miles). At about 16 kilometers (10 miles) 90 percent of the atmosphere has been traversed, and above

100 kilometers (62 miles) only 0.00003 percent of all the gases composing the atmosphere remain.

At an altitude of 100 kilometers the atmosphere is so thin that the density of air is less than could be found in the most perfect artificial vacuum at the surface. Nevertheless, the atmosphere continues to even greater heights. The truly rarefied nature of the outer atmosphere is described very well by Richard Craig:

> The earth's outermost atmosphere, the part above a few hundred kilometers, is a region of extremely low density. Near sea level, the number of atoms and molecules in a cubic centimeter of air is about 2×10^{19}; near 600 km, it is only about 2×10^7, which is the sea-level value divided by a million million. At sea level, an atom or molecule can be expected, on the average, to move about 7×10^{-6} cm before colliding with another particle; at the 600-km level, this distance, called the "mean free path," is about 10 km. Near sea level, an atom or molecule, on the average, undergoes about 7×10^9 such collisions each second; near 600 km, this number is reduced to about 1 each minute.[*]

The graphic portrayal of pressure data (Figure 1–23) shows that the rate of pressure decrease is not constant. Rather, pressure decreases at a decreasing rate with an

---

[*] Richard Craig. *The Edge of Space: Exploring the Upper Atmosphere* (New York: Doubleday & Company, Inc. 1968), p. 130.

increase in altitude until, beyond an altitude of about 35 kilometers, the decrease is slight.

Put another way, data illustrate that air is highly compressible—that is, it expands with decreasing pressure and becomes compressed with increasing pressure. Consequently, traces of our atmosphere extend for thousands of kilometers beyond Earth's surface. Thus, to say where the atmosphere ends and outer space begins is arbitrary and, to a large extent, depends on what phenomenon one is studying. It is apparent that there is no sharp boundary.

In summary, data on vertical pressure changes reveal that the vast bulk of the gases making up the atmosphere is very near Earth's surface and that the gases gradually merge with the emptiness of space. When compared with the size of the solid Earth, the envelope of air surrounding our planet is indeed very shallow.

Thermal Structure of the Atmosphere

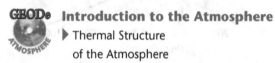

GEODe **Introduction to the Atmosphere**
▶ Thermal Structure
of the Atmosphere

By the early twentieth century much had been learned about the lower atmosphere. The upper atmosphere was partly known from indirect methods. Data from balloons and kites had revealed that the air temperature dropped with increas-

FIGURE 1–24 Temperatures drop with an increase in altitude in the troposphere. Therefore, it is possible to have snow on a mountaintop and warmer, snow-free lowlands below. San Juan Mountains, Colorado. *(Photo by Carr Clifton/Minden Pictures)*

ing height above Earth's surface. This phenomenon is felt by anyone who has climbed a high mountain, and is obvious in pictures of snow-capped mountaintops rising above snow-free lowlands (Figure 1–24).

Although measurements had not been taken above a height of about 10 kilometers (6 miles), scientists believed that the temperature continued to decline with height to a value of absolute zero ($-273°C$) at the outer edge of the atmosphere. In 1902, however, the French scientist Leon Philippe Teisserenc de Bort refuted the notion that temperature decreases continuously with an increase in altitude. In studying the results of more than 200 balloon launchings, Teisserenc de Bort found that the temperature stopped decreasing and leveled off at an altitude between 8 and 12 kilometers (5 and 7.5 miles). This surprising discovery was at first doubted, but subsequent data-gathering confirmed his findings. Later, through the use of radiosondes and rocket-sounding techniques, the temperature structure of the atmosphere up to great heights became clear. Today the atmosphere is divided vertically into four layers on the basis of temperature (Figure 1–25).

Troposphere

The bottom layer in which we live, where temperature decreases with an increase in altitude, is the **troposphere.** The term was coined in 1908 by Teisserrenc de Bort and literally means the region where air "turns over," a reference to the appreciable vertical mixing of air in this lowermost zone.

The temperature decrease in the troposphere is called the **environmental lapse rate.** Its average value is 6.5°C per kilometer (3.6°F per 1000 feet), a figure known as the *normal lapse rate.*[*] It needs to be emphasized, however, that the environmental lapse rate is not a constant but rather can be highly variable and must be regularly measured using radiosondes. It can vary during the course of a day with fluctuations of the weather, as well as seasonally and from place to place. Sometimes shallow layers where temperatures actually increase with height are observed in the troposphere. When such a reversal occurs, a *temperature inversion* is said to exist.[**]

The temperature decrease continues to an average height of about 12 kilometers (7.5 miles). Yet the thickness of the troposphere is not the same everywhere. It reaches heights in excess of 16 kilometers (10 miles) in the tropics, but in polar regions it is more subdued, extending to 9 kilometers (5.5 miles) or less (Figure 1–26). Warm surface temperatures and highly developed thermal mixing are responsible for the greater vertical extent of the troposphere near the equator. As a result, the environmental lapse rate extends to great heights; and despite relatively high surface temperatures below, the lowest tropospheric temperatures are found aloft in the tropics and not at the poles.

[*]For a more complete explanation of the term "normal," see Box 12-5, p. 368.
[**]Temperature inversions are described in greater detail in Chapter 13.

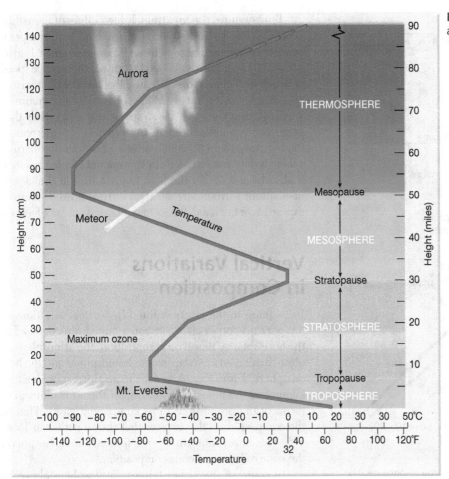

FIGURE 1–25 Thermal structure of the atmosphere.

The troposphere is the chief focus of meteorologists because it is in this layer that essentially all important weather phenomena occur. Almost all clouds and certainly all precipitation, as well as all our violent storms, are born in this lowermost layer of the atmosphere. There should be little wonder why the troposphere is often called the "weather sphere."

Stratosphere

Beyond the troposphere lies the **stratosphere;** the boundary between the troposphere and the stratosphere is known as the **tropopause.** Below the tropopause, atmospheric properties are readily transferred by large-scale turbulence and mixing, but above it, in the stratosphere, they are not. In the stratosphere, the temperature at first remains nearly constant to a height of about 20 kilometers (12 miles) before it begins a rather sharp increase that continues until the **stratopause** is encountered at a height of about 50 kilometers (30 miles) above Earth's surface. Higher temperatures occur in the stratosphere because it is in this layer that the atmosphere's ozone is concentrated. Recall that ozone absorbs ultraviolet radiation from the Sun. Consequently, the stratosphere is heated. Although the maximum ozone concentration exists between 15 and 30 kilometers (9 and 19 miles), the smaller amounts of ozone above this height range

absorb enough UV energy to cause the higher observed temperatures.

Mesosphere

In the third layer, the **mesosphere,** temperatures again decrease with height until at the **mesopause,** some 80 kilometers (50 miles) above the surface, the average temperature approaches −90°C (−130°F). The coldest temperatures anywhere in the atmosphere occur at the mesopause. Because accessibility is difficult, the mesosphere is one of the least explored regions of the atmosphere. The reason is that it cannot be reached by the highest research balloons nor is it accessible to the lowest orbiting satellites. Recent technical developments are just beginning to fill this knowledge gap.

Thermosphere

The fourth layer extends outward from the mesosphere and has no well-defined upper limit. It is the **thermosphere,** a layer that contains only a minute fraction of the atmosphere's mass. In the extremely rarefied air of this outermost layer, temperatures again increase, owing to the absorption of very shortwave, high-energy solar radiation by atoms of oxygen and nitrogen.

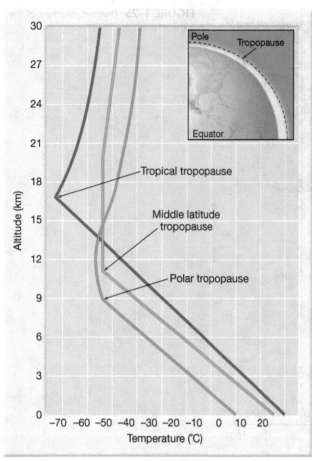

FIGURE 1–26 Differences in the height of the tropopause. The variation in the height of the tropopause, as shown on the small inset diagram, is greatly exaggerated.

Temperatures rise to extremely high values of more than 1000°C (1800°F) in the thermosphere. But such temperatures are not comparable to those experienced near Earth's surface. Temperature is defined in terms of the average speed at which molecules move. Because the gases of the thermosphere are moving at very high speeds, the temperature is very high. But the gases are so sparse that collectively they possess only an insignificant quantity of heat. For this reason, the temperature of a satellite orbiting Earth in the thermosphere is determined chiefly by the amount of solar radiation it absorbs and not by the high temperature of the almost nonexistent surrounding air. If an astronaut inside were to expose his or her hand, the air in this layer would not feel hot.

Vertical Variations in Composition

In addition to the layers defined by vertical variations in temperature, other layers, or zones, are also recognized in the atmosphere. Based on composition, the atmosphere is often divided into two layers: the homosphere and the heterosphere. From Earth's surface to an altitude of about 80 kilometers (50 miles), the makeup of the air is uniform in terms of the proportions of its component gases. That is, the composition is the same as that shown earlier in Table 1–2. This lower uniform layer is termed the *homosphere*, the zone of homogeneous composition.

In contrast, the rather tenuous atmosphere above 80 kilometers is not uniform. Because it has a heterogeneous composition, the term *heterosphere* is used. Here the gases

FIGURE 1–27 (a) Aurora borealis (northern lights) as seen from Alaska. The same phenomenon occurs toward the South Pole, where it is called the aurora australis (southern lights). (*Photo by Michio Hoshino/Minden Pictures*); (b) Aurora australis (southern lights) photographed from the Space Shuttle in May 1991. (*NASA*)

are arranged into four roughly spherical shells, each with a distinctive composition. The lowermost layer is dominated by molecular nitrogen (N_2); next, a layer of atomic oxygen (O) is encountered, followed by a layer dominated by helium (He) atoms; and finally a region consisting of hydrogen (H) atoms. The stratified nature of the gases making up the heterosphere varies according to their weights. Molecular nitrogen is the heaviest, and so it is lowest. The lightest gas, hydrogen, is outermost.

Ionosphere

Located in the altitude range between 80 to 400 kilometers (50 to 250 miles), and thus coinciding with the lower portions of the thermosphere and heterosphere, is an electrically charged layer known as the **ionosphere.** Here molecules of nitrogen and atoms of oxygen are readily ionized as they absorb high-energy shortwave solar energy. In this process, each affected molecule or atom loses one or more electrons and becomes a positively charged ion, and the electrons are set free to travel as electric currents.

Although ionization occurs at heights as great as 1000 kilometers (620 miles) and extends as low as perhaps 50 kilometers (30 miles), positively charged ions and negative electrons are most dense in the range of 80 to 400 kilometers (50 to 250 miles). The concentration of ions is not great below this zone because much of the short-wavelength radiation needed for ionization has already been depleted. In addition, the atmospheric density at this level results in a large percentage of free electrons being swiftly captured by positively charged ions. Beyond the 400-kilometer (250-mile) upward limit of the ionosphere, the concentration of ions is low because of the extremely low density of the air. Because so few molecules and atoms are present, relatively few ions and free electrons can be produced.

The electrical structure of the ionosphere is not uniform. It consists of three layers of varying ion density. From bottom to top, these layers are called the D, E, and F layers, respectively. Because the production of ions requires direct solar radiation, the concentration of charged particles changes from day to night, particularly in the D and E zones. That is, these layers weaken and disappear at night and reappear during the day. The uppermost, or F layer, on the other hand, is present both day and night. The density of the atmosphere in this layer is very low, and positive ions and electrons do not meet and recombine as rapidly as they do at lesser heights, where density is higher. Consequently, the concentration of ions and electrons in the F layer does not change rapidly, and the layer, although weak, remains through the night.

The Auroras

As best we can tell, the ionosphere has little impact on our daily weather. But this layer of the atmosphere is the site of one of nature's most interesting spectacles, the auroras (Figure 1–27). The **aurora borealis** (northern lights) and its Southern Hemisphere couterpart, the **aurora australis** (southern lights), appear in a wide variety of forms. Sometimes the displays consist of vertical streamers in which there can be considerable movement. At other times the auroras appear as a series of luminous expanding arcs or as a quiet glow that has an almost foglike quality.

The occurrence of auroral displays is closely correlated in time with solar-flare activity and, in geographic location, with Earth's magnetic poles. Solar flares are massive magnetic storms on the Sun that emit enormous amounts of energy and great quantities of fast-moving atomic particles. As the clouds of protons and electrons from the solar storm approach Earth, they are captured by its magnetic field, which in turn guides them toward the magnetic poles. Then, as the ions impinge on the ionosphere, they energize the atoms of oxygen and molecules of nitrogen and cause them to emit light—the glow of the auroras. Because the occurrence of solar flares is closely correlated with sunspot activity, auroral displays increase conspicuously at times when sunspots are most numerous.

Chapter Summary

• *Meteorology* is the scientific study of the atmosphere. *Weather* refers to the state of the atmosphere at a given time and place. It is constantly changing, sometimes from hour to hour and other times from day to day. *Climate* is an aggregate of weather conditions, the sum of all statistical weather information that helps describe a place or region. The nature of both weather and climate is expressed in terms of the same basic *elements*, those quantities or properties measured regularly. The most important elements are (1) air temperature, (2) humidity, (3) type and amount of cloudiness, (4) type and amount of precipitation, (5) air pressure, and (6) the speed and direction of the wind.

• All science is based on the assumption that the natural world behaves in a consistent and predictable manner. The process by which scientists gather facts through observation and careful measurement and formulate scientific *hypotheses* and *theories* is called the *scientific method*. To determine what is occurring in the natural world, scientists often (1) collect facts, (2) develop a scientific hypothesis, (3) construct experiments to validate the hypothesis, and (4) accept, modify, or reject the hypothesis on the basis of extensive testing. Other discoveries represent purely theoretical ideas that have stood up to extensive examination. Still other scientific advancements have been made when a totally unexpected event occurred during an experiment.

- *Balloons* play a significant role in the systematic investigation of the atmosphere by carrying *radiosondes* (lightweight packages of instruments that send back data on temperature, pressure, and relative humidity) into the lower atmosphere. Rockets, airplanes, satellites, and weather radar also play important roles in the study of the atmosphere.

- Earth's four spheres include the *atmosphere* (gaseous envelope), the *geosphere* (solid Earth), the *hydrosphere* (water portion), and the *biosphere* (life). Each sphere is composed of many interrelated parts and is intertwined with all other spheres.

- Although each of Earth's four spheres can be studied separately, they are all related in a complex and continuously interacting whole that we call the *Earth system. Earth system science* uses an interdisciplinary approach to integrate the knowledge of several academic fields in the study of our planet and its global environmental problems.

- A *system* is a group of interacting parts that form a complex whole. *Closed systems* are those in which energy moves freely in and out, but matter does not enter or leave the system. In an open system, both energy and matter flow into and out of the system.

- Most natural systems have mechanisms that tend to enhance change, called *positive feedback mechanisms,* and other mechanisms, called *negative feedback mechanisms,* that tend to resist change and thus stabilize the system.

- The two sources of energy that power the Earth system are (1) the Sun, which drives the external processes that occur in the atmosphere, hydrosphere, and at Earth's surface, and (2) heat from Earth's interior that powers the internal processes that produce volcanoes, earthquakes, and mountains.

- Air is a mixture of many discrete gases, and its composition varies from time to time and place to place. After water vapor, dust, and other variable components are removed, two gases, *nitrogen* and *oxygen*, make up 99 percent of the volume of the remaining clean, dry air. *Carbon dioxide,* although present in only minute amounts (0.038 percent), is an efficient absorber of energy emitted by Earth and thus influences the heating of the atmosphere. Due to the rising level of carbon dioxide in the atmosphere during the past century attributed to the burning of ever increasing quantities of fossil fuels, it is likely that a warming of the lower atmosphere is triggering global climate change.

- The variable components of air include *water vapor, dust particles,* and *ozone.* Like carbon dioxide, water vapor can absorb heat given off by Earth as well as some solar energy. When water vapor changes from one state to another, it absorbs or releases heat. In the atmosphere, water vapor transports this *latent* ("hidden") *heat* from one place to another, and it is the energy source that helps drive many storms. *Aerosols* (tiny solid and liquid particles) are meteorologically important because these often invisible particles act as surfaces on which water can condense and are also absorbers and reflectors of incoming solar radiation. *Ozone,* a form of oxygen that combines three oxygen atoms into each molecule (O_3), is a gas concentrated in the 10- to 50-kilometer height range in the atmosphere that absorbs the potentially harmful ultraviolet (UV) radiation from the Sun.

- Over the past half century, people have placed Earth's ozone layer in jeopardy by polluting the atmosphere with chlorofluorocarbons (CFCs), which remove some of the gas. Ozone concentrations take an especially sharp drop over Antarctica during the Southern Hemisphere spring (September and October). Furthermore, scientists have also discovered a similar but smaller ozone thinning near the North Pole during spring and early summer. Because ultraviolet radiation is known to produce skin cancer, ozone depletion seriously affects human health, especially among fair-skinned people and those who spend considerable time in the Sun. The *Montreal Protocol,* concluded under the auspices of the United Nations, represents a positive international response to the ozone problem.

- No sharp boundary to the upper atmosphere exists. The atmosphere simply thins as you travel away from Earth until there are too few gas molecules to detect. The change that occurs in atmospheric pressure (the weight of the air above) depicts the vertical extent of the atmosphere. One-half of the atmosphere lies below an altitude of 5.6 kilometers (3.5 miles), and 90 percent lies below 16 kilometers (10 miles). Traces of atmosphere extend for thousands of kilometers beyond Earth's surface.

- Using temperature as the basis, the atmosphere is divided into four layers. The temperature decrease in the *troposphere,* the bottom layer in which we live, is called the *environmental lapse rate.* Its average value is 6.5°C per kilometer, a figure known as the *normal lapse rate.* The environmental lapse rate is not a constant and must be regularly measured using radiosondes. A *temperature inversion,* in which temperatures increase with height, is sometimes observed in shallow layers in the troposphere. The thickness of the troposphere is generally greater in the tropics than in polar regions. Essentially all important weather phenomena occur in the troposphere. Beyond the troposphere lies the *stratosphere;* the boundary between the troposphere and stratosphere is known as the *tropopause.* In the stratosphere, the temperature at first remains constant to a height of about 20 kilometers (12 miles) before it begins a sharp increase due to the absorption of ultraviolet radiation from the Sun by ozone. The temperatures continue to increase until the *stratopause* is encountered at a height of about 50 kilometers (30 miles). In the *mesosphere*, the third layer, temperatures again decrease with height until the *mesopause*, some 80 kilometers (50 miles) above the surface. The fourth layer, the *thermosphere*, with no well-defined upper limit, consists of extremely rarefied air. Temperatures here increase with an increase in altitude.

- Besides layers defined by vertical variations in temperature, the atmosphere is often divided into two layers based on composition. The *homosphere* (zone of homogeneous composition), from Earth's surface to an altitude of about 80 kilometers (50 miles), consists of air that is uniform in terms of the proportions of its component gases. Above 80 kilometers, the *heterosphere* (zone of heterogenous composition) consists of gases arranged into four roughly spherical shells, each with a distinctive composition. The stratified nature of the gases in the heterosphere varies according to their weights.

- Occurring in the altitude range between 80 and 400 kilometers (50 and 250 miles) is an electrically charged layer known as the *ionosphere*. Here molecules of nitrogen and atoms of oxygen are readily ionized as they absorb high-energy, shortwave solar energy. Three layers of varying ion density make up the ionosphere. Auroras (the *aurora borealis*, northern lights, and its Southern Hemisphere counterpart the *aurora australis*, southern lights) occur within the ionosphere. Auroras form as clouds of protons and electrons ejected from the Sun during solar-flare activity enter the atmosphere near Earth's magnetic poles and energize the atoms of oxygen and molecules of nitrogen, causing them to emit light—the glow of the auroras.

Vocabulary Review

Review your understanding of important terms in this chapter by defining and explaining the importance of each term listed here. Terms are listed in alphabetical order. Page references indicate where the term is introduced and defined.

aerosols (p.18)
air (p. 16)
atmosphere (p. 12)
aurora australis (p. 27)
aurora borealis (p. 27)
biosphere (p. 12)
climate (p. 3)
closed system (p. 14)
elements of weather and climate (p. 4)
environmental lapse rate (p. 24)
geosphere (p. 12)

hydrosphere (p. 12)
hypothesis (p. 6)
ionosphere (p. 27)
mesopause (p. 25)
mesosphere (p. 25)
meteorology (p. 3)
model (p. 6)
negative feedback mechanism (p. 14)
open system (p. 14)
ozone (p. 19)

positive feedback mechanism (p. 15)
radiosonde (p. 9)
stratopause (p. 25)
stratosphere (p. 25)
system (p. 14)
theory (p. 6)
thermosphere (p. 25)
tropopause (p. 25)
troposphere (p. 24)
weather (p. 3)

Review Questions

1. Distinguish between the terms "weather" and "climate."
2. The following statements refer to either weather or climate. On the basis of your answer to Question 1, determine which statements refer to weather and which refer to climate. (*Note:* One statement includes aspects of both weather and climate.)
   a. The baseball game was rained out today.
   b. January is Peoria's coldest month.
   c. North Africa is a desert.
   d. The high this afternoon was 25°C.
   e. Last evening a tornado ripped through Canton.
   f. I am moving to southern Arizona because it is warm and sunny.

   g. The highest temperature ever recorded at this station is 43°C.
   h. Thursday's low of −20°C is the coldest temperature ever recorded for that city.
   i. It is partly cloudy.
3. What are the basic elements of weather and climate?
4. How is a scientific hypothesis different from a scientific theory?
5. What is a radiosonde?
6. List and briefly describe the four "spheres" that constitute our environment.
7. How is an open system different from a closed system?

8. Contrast positive feedback mechanisms and negative feedback mechanisms.

9. What are the two sources of energy for the Earth system?

10. What are the major components of clean, dry air?

11. Outline the stages in the formation of Earth's atmosphere. (See Box 1–2)

12. What is responsible for the increasing carbon dioxide content of the air? What is one possible effect of increased carbon dioxide in the atmosphere?

13. Why are water vapor and dust important constituents of our atmosphere?

14. a. Why is ozone important to life on Earth?
    b. What are CFCs, and what is their connection to the ozone problem?

c. What are the effects on human health of a decrease in the stratosphere's ozone?

15. The atmosphere is divided vertically into four layers on the basis of temperature. List the names of these layers and their boundaries in order (from lowest to highest), and list as many characteristics of each as you can.

16. Why does the temperature increase in the stratosphere?

17. Why are temperatures in the thermosphere not strictly comparable to those experienced near Earth's surface?

18. Distinguish between the homosphere and the heterosphere.

19. What is the primary cause of auroral displays?

Problems

1. Refer to the newspaper-type weather map in Figure 1–2 to answer the following:
   a. Estimate the predicted high temperatures in central New York State and the northwest corner of Arizona.
   b. Where is the coldest area on the weather map? Where is the warmest?
   c. On this weather map, H stands for the center of a region of high pressure. Does it appear as though high pressure is associated with precipitation or fair weather?
   d. Which is warmer—central Texas or central Maine? Would you normally expect this to be the case?

2. Refer to the graph in Figure 1–4 to answer the following questions about temperatures in New York City:
   a. What is the approximate average daily high temperature in January? In July?
   b. Approximately what are the highest and lowest temperatures ever recorded?

3. Refer to the graph in Figure 1–6. Which year had the greatest number of billion-dollar weather disasters? How many events occurred that year? In which year was the damage amount greatest?

4. Refer to the graph in Figure 1–23 to answer the following:
   a. Approximately how much does the air pressure drop (in millibars) between the surface and 4 kilometers? (Use a surface pressure of 1000 mb.)
   b. How much does the pressure drop between 4 and 8 kilometers?
   c. Based on your answers to parts a and b, with an increase in altitude, air pressure decreases at a(n) (constant, increasing, decreasing) rate. Underline the correct answer.

5. If the temperature at sea level were 23°C, what would the air temperature be at a height of 2 kilometers under average conditions?

6. Use the graph of the atmosphere's thermal structure (Figure 1–25) to answer the following:
   a. What is the approximate height and temperature of the stratopause?
   b. At what altitude is the temperature lowest? What is the temperature at that height?

7. Answer the following questions by examining the graph in Figure 1–26.
   a. In which one of the three regions (tropics, middle latitudes, poles) is the *surface* temperature lowest?
   b. In which region is the tropopause encountered at the lowest altitude? The highest? What are the altitudes and temperatures of the tropopause in those regions?

8. a. On a spring day a middle-latitude city (about 40° north latitude) has a surface (sea-level) temperature of 10°C. If vertical soundings reveal a nearly constant environmental lapse rate of 6.5°C per kilometer and a temperature at the tropopause of −55°C, what is the height of the tropopause?
   b. On the same spring day a station near the equator has a surface temperature of 25°C, 15°C higher than the middle-latitude city mentioned in part a. Vertical soundings reveal an environmental lapse rate of 6.5°C per kilometer and indicate that the tropopause is encountered at 16 kilometers. What is the air temperature at the tropopause?

Atmospheric Science Online

The Atmosphere 10e web site uses the resources and flexibility of the Internet to aid in your study of the topics in this chapter. Written and developed by meteorology instructors, this site will help improve your understanding of meteorology. Visit **http://www .prenhall.com/lutgens** and click on the cover of *The Atmosphere 10e* to find:

- **Online review quizzes**
- **Critical thinking exercises**
- **Links to chapter-specific web resources**
- **Internet-wide key term searches**

http://www.prenhall.com/lutgens

HEATING EARTH'S
SURFACE *and*
ATMOSPHERE

CHAPTER

2

Solar radiation provides more than 99.9 percent of the energy that heats Earth's surface. *(Photo by Shin Yoshino/Minden Pictures)*

From our everyday experiences, we know that the Sun's rays feel hotter on a clear day than on an overcast day. After taking a barefoot walk on a sunny day, we realize that city pavement becomes much hotter than a grassy boulevard. A picture of a snowcapped mountain reminds us that temperature decreases with altitude. And we know that the fury of winter is always replaced by the newness of spring. You may not know, however, that these occurrences are manifestations of the same phenomenon that causes the blue color of the sky and the red color of a brilliant sunset. All such common occurrences are a result of the interaction of solar radiation with Earth's atmosphere and its land–sea surface (Figure 2–1). That is the essence of this chapter.

Earth–Sun Relationships

Heating Earth's Surface and Atmosphere
▶ Understanding Seasons

Earth intercepts only a minute percentage of the energy given off by the Sun—less than one two-billionth. This may seem an insignificant amount until we realize that it is several hundred thousand times the electrical generating capacity of the United States. Solar radiation, in fact, represents more than 99.9 percent of the energy that heats our planet.

Solar energy is not distributed equally over Earth's land–sea surface. The amount of energy received varies with latitude, time of day, and season of the year. Contrasting images of polar bears on ice rafts and palm trees along a remote tropical beach serve to illustrate the extremes. It is the unequal heating of Earth that creates winds and drives the ocean's currents. These movements in turn transport heat from the tropics toward the poles in an unending attempt to balance energy inequalities. The consequences of these processes are the phenomena we call weather. If the Sun were "turned off," global winds and ocean currents would quickly cease. Yet as long as the Sun shines, the winds *will* blow and weather *will* persist. So to understand how the atmosphere's dynamic weather machine works, we must first know why different latitudes receive varying quantities of solar energy and why the amount of solar energy changes to produce the seasons. As we shall see, the variations in solar heating are caused by the motions of Earth relative to the Sun and by variations in Earth's land–sea surface.

Earth's Motions

Earth has two principal motions—rotation and revolution. **Rotation** is the spinning of Earth about its axis that produces the daily cycle of daylight and darkness. In the following chapter, we will examine the effects that this daily variation in solar heating has on the atmosphere.

The other motion of Earth, **revolution,** refers to its movement in orbit around the Sun. Hundreds of years ago most people believed that Earth was stationary in space. The reasoning was that if Earth was moving, people would

FIGURE 2-1 The Sun over a snow-covered Norwegian landscape. *(Photo by Per Breiehagen/Getty Images)*

feel the movement of the wind rushing past them. Today we know that Earth is traveling at nearly 113,000 kilometers (70,000 miles) per hour in a slightly elliptical orbit about the Sun. Why don't we feel the air rushing past us? The answer is that the atmosphere, bound by gravity to Earth, is carried along at the same speed as Earth.

The distance between Earth and Sun averages about 150 million kilometers (93 million miles). Because Earth's orbit is not perfectly circular, however, the distance varies during the course of a year. Each year, on about January 3, our planet is about 147.3 million kilometers (91.5 million miles) from the Sun, closer than at any other time. This position is called the **perihelion.** About six months later, on July 4, Earth is about 152.1 million kilometers (94.5 million miles) from the Sun, farther away than at any other time. This position is called the **aphelion.** Although Earth is closest to the Sun and thus receives more energy in January than in July, this difference plays only a minor role in producing seasonal temperature variations. As proof, consider that Earth is closest to the Sun during the Northern Hemisphere winter.

The Seasons

We know that it is colder in winter than in summer, but if variations in the distance between the Sun and Earth do not cause this seasonal temperature change, what does? We adjust to the continuous changes in the duration of daylight that occur throughout the year by planning our outdoor activities accordingly. The gradual but significant *change in day length* certainly accounts for some of the difference we notice between summer and winter. Furthermore, a gradual change in the angle of the noon Sun above the horizon is quite noticeable (Figure 2–2). At midsummer the noon Sun is seen high above the horizon. But as summer gives way to autumn, the noon Sun appears lower in the sky, and sunset occurs earlier each evening.

The seasonal variation in the angle of the Sun above the horizon affects the amount of energy received at Earth's surface in two ways. First, when the Sun is directly overhead (at a 90° angle), the solar rays are most concentrated. The lower the angle, the more spread out and less intense is the solar radiation that reaches the surface. This idea is illustrated in Figure 2–3. You have probably experienced this when using a flashlight. If the beam strikes a surface perpendicularly, a small intense spot is produced. When the flashlight beam strikes the object at an oblique angle, however, the area illuminated is larger—and dimmer.

Second, and of less importance, the angle of the Sun determines the thickness of atmosphere that the rays must penetrate (Figure 2–4). When the Sun is directly overhead, the rays pass through a thickness of only 1 atmosphere. But rays entering at a 30° angle travel through twice this amount, and 5° rays travel through a thickness roughly equal to 11 atmospheres (Table 2–1). The longer the path, the greater is the chance that sunlight will be absorbed, reflected, or scattered by the atmosphere, all of which reduce the intensity at the surface. These same effects account for the fact

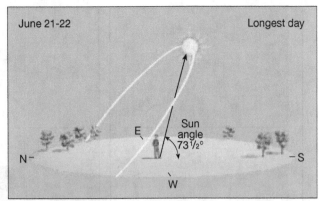

(a) Summer solstice

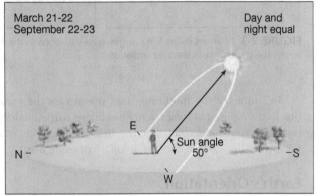

(b) Spring or fall equinox

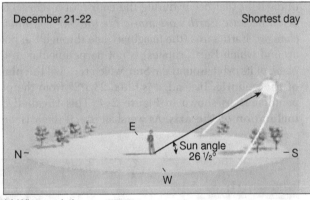

(c) Winter solstice

FIGURE 2-2 Daily paths of the Sun for a place located at 40°N latitude for: (a) summer solstice; (b) spring or fall equinox, and (c) winter solstice. As we move from summer to winter, the angle of the noon Sun decreases from 73½ to 26½ degrees—a difference of 47 degrees (see Figure 2-6). Notice also how the location of sunrise (east) and sunset (west) changes during a year.

that we cannot look directly at the midday Sun but we can enjoy gazing at a sunset.

It is important to remember that Earth has a spherical shape. Hence, on any given day, only places located along a particular latitude will receive vertical (90°) rays from the Sun. As we move either north or south of this location, the Sun's rays strike at an ever decreasing angle. Thus, the nearer a place is situated to the latitude receiving the vertical rays of the Sun, the higher will be its noon Sun, and the more concentrated will be the radiation it receives.

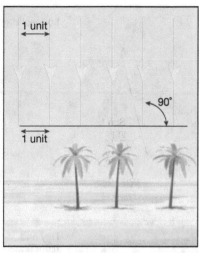
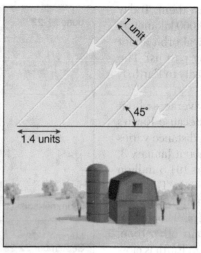
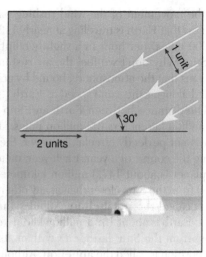

FIGURE 2-3 Changes in the Sun's angle cause variations in the amount of solar energy reaching Earth's surface. The higher the angle, the more intense the solar radiation.

In summary, the most important reasons for the variation in the amount of solar energy reaching a particular location are the seasonal changes in the angle at which the Sun's rays strike the surface and in the length of daylight.

Earth's Orientation

What causes the fluctuations in the Sun's angle and length of daylight that occur during the course of a year? They occur *because Earth's orientation to the Sun continually changes.* Earth's axis (the imaginary line through the poles around which Earth rotates) is not perpendicular to the plane of its orbit around the Sun, which is called the **plane of the ecliptic.** Instead, it is tilted 23 1/2° from the perpendicular, as shown in Figure 2–4. This is called the **inclination of the axis.** As we shall see, if the axis were

not so inclined, we would have no seasonal changes. In addition, because the axis remains pointed in the same direction (toward the North Star) as Earth journeys around the Sun, the orientation of Earth's axis to the Sun's rays is constantly changing (Figure 2–5).

For example, on one day in June each year, Earth's position in orbit is such that the Northern Hemisphere is "leaning" 23 1/2° *toward* the Sun (left in Figure 2–5). Six months later, in December, when Earth has moved to the opposite side of its orbit, the Northern Hemisphere "leans" 23 1/2° *away* from the Sun (Figure 2–5, right). On days between these extremes, Earth's axis is leaning at amounts less than 23 1/2° to the rays of the Sun. This change in orientation causes the spot where the Sun's rays are vertical to make an annual migration from 23 1/2° north of the equator to 23 1/2° south of the equator. In turn, this migration causes the angle of the noon Sun to vary by up to 47° (23 1/2 + 23 1/2) for many locations during a year. A mid-

FIGURE 2-4 Rays striking Earth at a low angle (toward the poles) must traverse more of the atmosphere than rays striking at a high angle (around the equator) and thus are subject to greater depletion by reflection and absorption.

TABLE 2-1 Distance radiation must travel through the atmosphere	
Angle of Sun above horizon	**Equivalent number of atmospheres sunlight must pass through**
90° (Directly overhead)	1.00
80°	1.02
70°	1.06
60°	1.15
50°	1.31
40°	1.56
30°	2.00
20°	2.92
10°	5.70
5°	10.80
0° (At horizon)	45.00

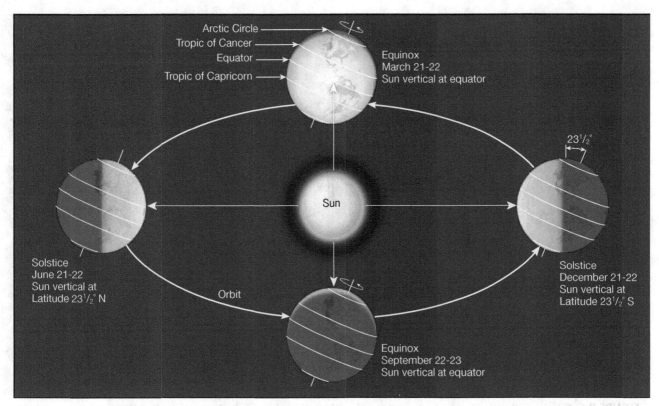

Arctic Circle
Tropic of Cancer
Equator
Tropic of Capricorn

Equinox
March 21–22
Sun vertical at equator

Sun

$23\frac{1}{2}°$

Solstice
June 21–22
Sun vertical at
Latitude $23\frac{1}{2}°$ N

Orbit

Solstice
December 21–22
Sun vertical at
Latitude $23\frac{1}{2}°$ S

Equinox
September 22–23
Sun vertical at equator

FIGURE 2-5 Earth–Sun relationships.

latitude city like New York, for instance, has a maximum noon Sun angle of 73 1/2° when the Sun's vertical rays have reached their farthest northward location in June and a minimum noon Sun angle of 26 1/2° six months later (Figure 2–6).

Solstices and Equinoxes

Historically, four days each year have been given special significance based on the annual migration of the direct rays of the Sun and its importance to the yearly cycle of weather. On June 21 or 22, Earth is in a position where the axis in the Northern Hemisphere is tilted 23 1/2° toward the Sun (Figure 2–5). At this time the vertical rays of the Sun are striking 23 1/2° north latitude (23 1/2° north of the equator), a line of latitude known as the **Tropic of Cancer.** For peo-

ple living in the Northern Hemisphere, June 21 or 22 is known as the **summer solstice,** the first "official" day of summer (see Box 2–1).

Six months later, on about December 21 or 22, Earth is in an opposite position, where the Sun's vertical rays are striking at 23 1/2° south latitude. This line is known as the **Tropic of Capricorn.** For those of us in the Northern Hemisphere, December 21 or 22 is the **winter solstice,** the first day of winter. However, at the same time in the Southern Hemisphere, people are experiencing just the opposite—the summer solstice.

The *equinoxes* occur midway between the solstices. September 22 or 23 is the date of the **autumnal equinox** in the Northern Hemisphere, and March 21 or 22 is the date of the **spring equinox** (also called the *vernal equinox*). On these dates the vertical rays of the Sun strike along the equator (0° latitude), for Earth is in such a position in its orbit that the axis is tilted neither toward nor away from the Sun.

The length of daylight versus darkness is also determined by the position of Earth in its orbit. The length of daylight on June 21, the summer solstice in the Northern Hemisphere, is greater than the length of night. This fact can be established by examining Figure 2–7, which illustrates the **circle of illumination**—that is, the boundary separating the dark half of Earth from the lighted half. The length of daylight is established by comparing the fraction of a line of latitude that is on the "day" side of the circle of illumination with the fraction on the "night" side. Notice that on June 21 all locations in the Northern Hemisphere experience longer periods

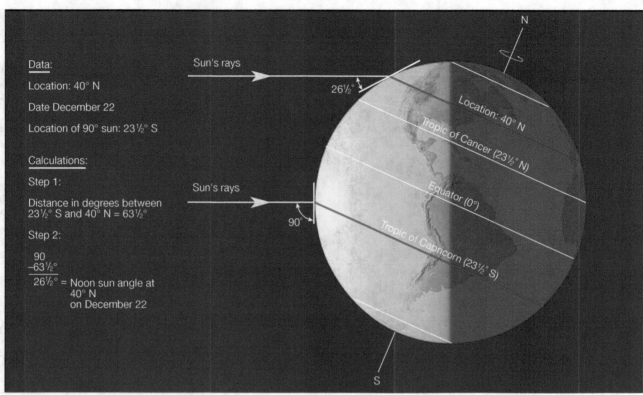

Data:

Location: 40° N

Date December 22

Location of 90° sun: 23½° S

Calculations:

Step 1:

Distance in degrees between
23½° S and 40° N = 63½°

Step 2:

$$\begin{array}{r} 90 \\ -63\frac{1}{2}° \\ \hline 26\frac{1}{2}° \end{array}$$ = Noon sun angle at
40° N
on December 22

FIGURE 2-6 Calculating the noon Sun angle. Recall that on any given day, only one latitude receives vertical (90°) rays of the Sun. A place located 1° away (either north or south) receives an 89° angle; a place 2° away, an 88° angle, and so forth. To calculate the noon Sun angle, simply find the number of degrees of latitude separating the location you want to know about from the latitude that is receiving the vertical rays of the Sun. Then subtract that value from 90°. The example in this figure illustrates how to calculate the noon Sun angle for a city located at 40° north latitude on December 22 (winter solstice).

of daylight than darkness (Figure 2–7). The opposite is true for the December solstice, when the length of darkness exceeds the length of daylight at all locations in the Northern Hemisphere. Again, for comparison, let us consider New York City (about 40°N). It has 15 hours of daylight on June 21 and only nine hours on December 21.

Also note, from Table 2–2, that the farther north you are of the equator on June 21, the longer the period of daylight. When you reach the Arctic Circle (66 1/2°N), the length of daylight is 24 hours. This is the "midnight Sun,"

which does not set for about six months at the North Pole (Figure 2–8).

As a review of the characteristics of the summer solstice for the Northern Hemisphere, examine Figure 2–7 and Table 2–2 and consider the following facts:

1. The date of occurrence is June 21 or 22.
2. The vertical rays of the Sun are striking the Tropic of Cancer (23 1/2° north latitude).
3. Locations in the Northern Hemisphere are experiencing their longest length of daylight and highest Sun angle (opposite for the Southern Hemisphere).
4. The farther north you are of the equator, the longer the period of daylight until the Arctic Circle is reached, where the length of daylight becomes 24 hours long (opposite for the Southern Hemisphere).

The facts about the winter solstice are just the opposite. It should now be apparent why a midlatitude location is warmest in the summer. It is then that the days are longest and the angle of the Sun is highest (see Box 2–2).

During an equinox (meaning "equal night"), the length of daylight is 12 hours everywhere on Earth because the circle of illumination passes directly through the poles, thus dividing the latitudes in half.

TABLE 2-2 Length of daylight

Latitude (degrees)	Summer solstice	Winter solstice	Equinoxes
0	12 hr	12 hr	12 hr
10	12 hr 35 min	11 hr 25 min	12 hr
20	13 hr 12 min	10 hr 48 min	12 hr
30	13 hr 56 min	10 hr 04 min	12 hr
40	14 hr 52 min	9 hr 08 min	12 hr
50	16 hr 18 min	7 hr 42 min	12 hr
60	18 hr 27 min	5 hr 33 min	12 hr
70	2 mo	0 hr 00 min	12 hr
80	4 mo	0 hr 00 min	12 hr
90	6 mo	0 hr 00 min	12 hr

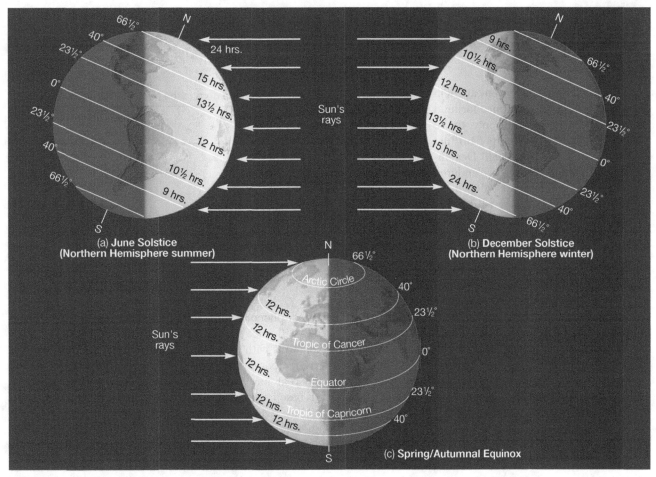

FIGURE 2-7 Characteristics of the solstices and equinoxes.

FIGURE 2-8 Multiple exposures of the midnight Sun in late June or July in high northern latitudes—Alaska, Scandinavia, Northern Canada, etc. *(Photo by Brian Stablyk/Getty Images, Inc./Stone Allstock)*

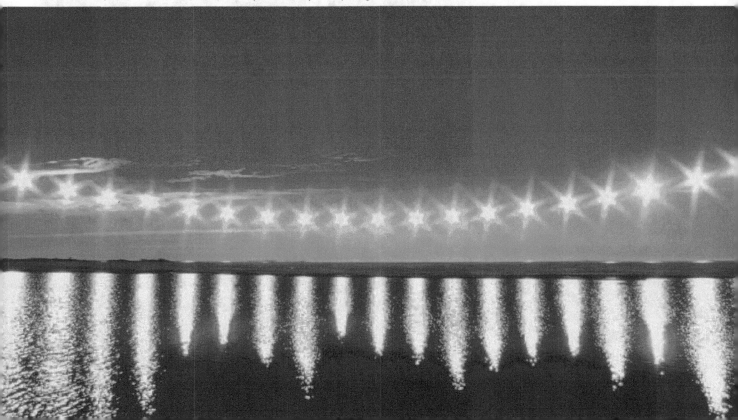

BOX 2-1   When Are the Seasons?

Have you ever been caught in a snowstorm around Thanksgiving, only to be told by the TV weatherperson that winter does not begin until December 21? Or perhaps you have endured several consecutive days of 100° temperatures only to discover that summer has not "officially" started? The idea of dividing the year into four seasons clearly originated from the Earth–Sun relationships discussed in this chapter (Table 2–A). This astronomical definition of the seasons defines winter (Northern Hemisphere) as the period from the winter solstice (December 21–22) to the spring equinox (March 21–22) and so forth. This is also the definition used most widely by the news media, yet it is not unusual for portions of the United States and Canada to have significant snowfalls weeks before the "official" start of winter (Figure 2–A).

TABLE 2-A Occurrence of the seasons in the Northern Hemisphere

Season	Astronomical season	Climatological season
Spring	March 21 or 22 to June 21 or 22	March, April, May
Summer	June 21 or 22 to September 22 or 23	June, July, August
Autumn	September 22 or 23 to December 21 or 22	September, October, November
Winter	December 21 or 22 to March 21 or 22	December, January, February

Because the weather phenomena we normally associate with each season do not coincide well with the astronomical seasons, meteorologists prefer to divide the year into four three-month periods based primarily on temperature. Thus, winter is defined as December, January, and February, the three coldest months of the year in the Northern Hemisphere.

Summer is defined as the three warmest months, June, July, and August. Spring and autumn are the transition periods between these two seasons. Inasmuch as these four three-month periods better reflect the temperatures and weather that we associate with the respective seasons, this definition of the seasons is more useful for meteorological discussions.

FIGURE 2-A Fall scene in the Adirondacks of upstate New York. *(Photo by Kim Heacox Photography/DRK Photo)*

In summary, *seasonal fluctuations in the amount of solar energy reaching various places on Earth's surface are caused by the migrating vertical rays of the Sun and the resulting variations in Sun angle and length of daylight.* These changes in turn cause the month-to-month variations in temperature observed at most locations outside the tropics. Figure 2–9 shows mean monthly temperatures for selected cities at different latitudes. Notice that the cities located at more poleward latitudes experience larger temperature differences from summer to winter than do cities located nearer the equator. Also notice that temperature minimums for Southern Hemisphere locations occur in July, whereas they occur in January for most places in the Northern Hemisphere.

All places situated at the same latitude have identical Sun angles and lengths of daylight. If the Earth–Sun relationships just described were the only controls of temperature, we would expect these places to have identical temperatures as well. Obviously, such is not the case. Although the angle of the Sun above the horizon and the length of daylight are the main controls of temperature, they are not the only controls, as we shall see in Chapter 3.

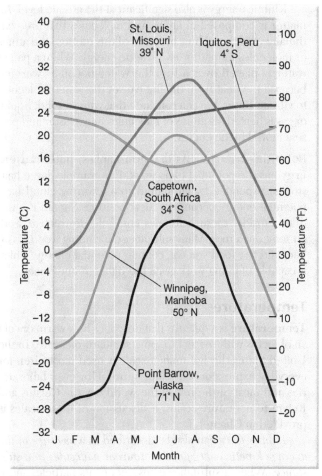

FIGURE 2-9 Mean monthly temperatures for six cities located at different latitudes. Note that Capetown, South Africa, experiences winter in June, July, and August.

Energy, Heat, and Temperature

The universe is made up of a combination of matter and energy. The concept of matter is easy to grasp because it is the "stuff" we can see, smell, and touch. Energy, on the other hand, is abstract and therefore more difficult to describe. Energy comes to Earth from the Sun in the form of electromagnetic radiation, which we see as light and feel as heat. There are countless places and situations where energy is present. We find it in the food we eat, the water located at the top of a falls, and the waves that break along the shore.

For our purposes we will define **energy** simply as *the capacity to do work.* We can think of work as being done whenever matter is moved. Everyday examples include the chemical energy from gasoline that powers an automobile, the heat energy from a stove that excites water molecules (boils water), and the gravitational energy that has the capacity to move snow down a mountain slope in the form of an avalanche. These examples illustrate that energy takes many forms. Moreover, energy can change from one form to another. For example, the chemical energy in gasoline is first converted to heat in the engine of an automobile, which is then converted to mechanical energy that moves the automobile along.

Forms of Energy

You are undoubtedly familiar with some of the common forms of energy, such as heat, chemical, nuclear, radiant (light), and gravitational energy. In addition, some forms of energy are classified into two major categories: *kinetic energy* and *potential energy.*

Kinetic Energy. *Energy associated with an object by virtue of its motion* is described as **kinetic energy.** A simple example of kinetic energy is the motion of a hammer when driving a nail. Because of its motion, the hammer is able to move another object (do work). The faster the hammer is swung, the greater its kinetic energy (energy of motion). Similarly, a larger (more massive) hammer will possess more kinetic energy than a smaller one, provided both are swung at the same velocity. Likewise, the winds associated with a hurricane possess much more kinetic energy than do light, localized breezes. Hurricane-force winds are both larger in scale (more massive) and travel at higher velocities.

Kinetic energy is also significant at the atomic level. All matter is composed of atoms and molecules that are continually vibrating. Thus, by virtue of this motion, the atoms or molecules in matter have kinetic energy. When a pan of water is placed over a fire, the water becomes warmer, because the heat from the fire causes the water molecules to vibrate faster. We can conclude that when a solid, liquid, or gas is heated, its atoms or molecules move faster and possess more kinetic energy.

Potential Energy. As the term implies, **potential energy** has the potential to do work. For example, large hailstones suspended by an updraft in a towering cloud have potential energy because of their position. Should the updraft subside, these hailstones could do destructive work on someone's roof. Many substances, including wood, gasoline, and the food you eat, contain potential energy, which is capable of doing work given the right circumstances.

Temperature

Temperature is a quantity that describes how warm or cold an object is with respect to some standard measure. In the United States the Fahrenheit scale is used most often for everyday expressions of temperature. However, laboratories and most of the rest of the world use the Celsius and Kelvin temperature scales. A discussion of these scales is provided in Chapter 3.

Temperature can also be described as a *measure of the average kinetic energy of the atoms or molecules in a substance*. When a substance gains energy, its particles move faster and its temperature rises. By contrast, when energy is lost, the atoms and molecules vibrate more slowly and its temperature drops.

It is important to note that temperature is *not* a measure of the total kinetic energy of the particles within a substance. For example, a cup of boiling water has a higher temperature than a tub of lukewarm water. However, the quantity of water in the cup is small, so it contains far less kinetic energy than the water in the tub. Much more ice would melt in the tub of lukewarm water than in the cup of boiling water. The temperature of the water in the cup is higher because the atoms and molecules are vibrating faster, but the total amount of kinetic energy is much smaller because there are many fewer particles.

Heat

When you touch a hot stove, heat enters your hand because the stove is warmer than your hand. By contrast, when you hold an ice cube, heat is transferred from your hand to the ice cube. The transfer of energy into or out of an object because of temperature differences between that object and its surroundings is called **heat.** Heat flows from a region of higher temperature to one of lower temperature. Once the temperatures become equal, heat flow stops.

When an object absorbs heat, it appears as an increase in internal energy, often in the form of increased molecular motion. (Sometimes, as when ice melts, a substance absorbs heat without an increase in kinetic energy, a topic we shall consider in Chapter 4.) However, we do not say that a substance has heat, because heat describes energy that is flowing or being transferred. We can examine the flow of energy between substances of different temperatures by imagining a warm bottle of wine placed in a bucket of chilled water. According to the concept of kinetic energy, the average speed of the molecules in the bottle of wine is greater than those in the cold water. As the molecules collide with the sides of the wine bottle, the faster molecules (warm wine) tend to slow down, while the slower molecules (cold water) tend to speed up. Assuming no other source of energy, the average speed of the molecules in these liquids (and therefore their temperatures) eventually becomes equal. The net result is that energy has flowed from the warm wine to the cold water. So heat can be thought of as internal energy of matter that transfers from one thing to another by virtue of a temperature difference.

Mechanisms of Heat Transfer

GEODe **Heating Earth's Surface and Atmosphere**
▶ Solar Radiation

As we consider heat-transfer mechanisms, recall that heat flows from warmer substances to cooler substances. If two objects are in contact, the one that is warmer will become cooler and the cooler one will become warmer, until they reach a common temperature. This flow of energy called *heat* can occur in three ways: *conduction, convection,* and *radiation* (Figure 2-10). Although they are presented separately, all three mechanisms of heat transfer can operate simultaneously. In addition, these processes transfer heat between the Sun and Earth and between Earth's surface, the atmosphere, and outer space.

Conduction

Conduction is familiar to most of us through our everyday experiences. Anyone who has attempted to pick up a metal spoon that was left in a boiling pot of soup realized that heat was transmitted along the entire length of the spoon. The transfer of heat in this manner is called conduction. The hot soup caused the molecules at the lower end of the spoon to

BOX 2-2   The Analemma

The analemma is a graph resembling a figure 8 that can be used as a reference when calculating the angle of noon Sun for any location on the globe, for any day of the year. An analemma shows the latitude where the noon Sun is directly overhead (90-degree angle) for each day of the year. Notice that on March 21–22 and September 21–22 the Sun is directly overhead at the equator, a fact we considered earlier (Figure 2-B).

By knowing where the noon Sun is overhead, you can readily calculate the angle of the noon Sun at any other latitude for any date. For each degree of latitude that a particular location is from the latitude where the Sun is overhead, the angle of the noon Sun at that location is one degree less than 90 degrees. For example, if you want to know the angle of the noon Sun at New York City (40°N) on May 14, you first find that date on the analemma to establish the latitude where the noon Sun is directly overhead. In this case it is 18 degrees north latitude. *It is important to note whether the location is north or south of the equator.* Thus, New York City is 22 degrees (40° N − 18° N = 22°) from the location where the Sun is directly overhead on May 14. Consequently, the angle of the noon Sun at New York City on May 14 is 68 degrees above the horizon. (Note that New York is 22 degrees from the location where the Sun is directly overhead. Subtracting that figure from 90 degrees yields 68 degrees [90 − 22 = 68]). Can you calculate the noon Sun angle for a place located at 40°S latitude on May 14? (*Hint:* See Figure 2-6.)

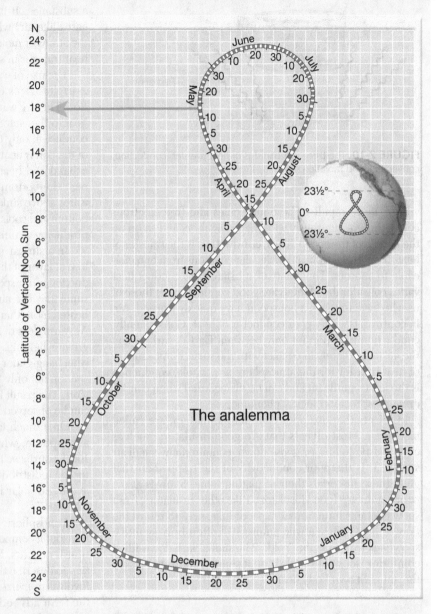

FIGURE 2-B The analemma, a graph showing the latitude of the overhead (vertical) noon Sun throughout the year.

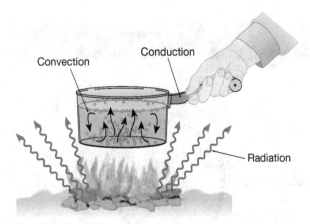

FIGURE 2-10 The three mechanisms of heat transfer: conduction, convection, and radiation.

vibrate more rapidly. These molecules and free electrons collided more vigorously with their neighbors and so on up the handle of the spoon. Thus, **conduction** is the transfer of heat through electron and molecular collisions from one molecule to another. The ability of substances to conduct heat varies considerably. Metals are good conductors, as those of us who have touched a hot spoon have quickly learned. Air, in contrast, is a very poor conductor of heat. Consequently, conduction is important only between Earth's surface and the air immediately in contact with the surface. As a means of heat transfer for the atmosphere as a whole, conduction is the least significant and can be disregarded when considering most meteorological phenomena.

Objects that are poor conductors, like air, are called *insulators*. Most objects that are good insulators, such as cork, plastic foams, or goose down, contain many small air spaces. It is the poor conductivity of the trapped air that gives these materials their insulating value. Snow is also a poor conductor (good insulator). Like other insulators, fresh snow contains numerous air spaces that serve to retard the flow of heat. Thus, a wild animal will often burrow into a snowbank to escape the "cold." The snow, like a down-filled comforter, does not supply heat; it simply retards the loss of the animal's own body heat.

Students Sometimes Ask...

In the morning when I get out of bed, why does the tile flooring in the bathroom feel much colder than the carpeted area, even though both materials are the same temperature?

The difference you feel is due mainly to the fact that floor tile is a much better conductor of heat than carpet. Hence, heat is more rapidly conducted from your bare feet when you are standing on the tile floor than when you are on the carpeted floor. Even at room temperature (20°C or 68°F), objects that are good conductors can feel chilly to the touch. (Remember, body temperature is about 98.6°F.)

Convection

Much of the heat transport that occurs in the atmosphere and ocean is carried on by convection. **Convection** is heat transfer that involves the actual movement or circulation of a substance. It takes place in fluids (liquids like water and gases like air) where the material is able to flow. Because the atoms or molecules in solids vibrate around a fixed point, heat transfer in solids takes place by conduction.

The pan of water being heated over a campfire in Figure 2-10 illustrates the nature of a simple convective circulation. The fire warms the bottom of the pan, which conducts heat to the water inside. Because water is a relatively poor conductor, only the water in close proximity to the bottom of the pan is heated by conduction. Heating causes water to expand and become less dense. Thus, the buoyant water near the bottom of the pan rises while the cooler, denser water above sinks. As long as the water is heated from the bottom and cools near the top, it will continue to "turn over," producing a *convective circulation*.

In a similar manner, much of the heat acquired in the lowest layer of the atmosphere by way of radiation and conduction is transported by convection. For example, on a hot, sunny day the air above a large asphalt parking lot will be heated more than the air above the surrounding woodlands. As warm, less dense air buoys upward, it transports heat to greater heights. These movements, called **thermals,** are what hang-glider pilots use to keep their crafts soaring. Convection not only transfers heat but also transports moisture aloft. The result is an increase in cloudiness that frequently can be observed on warm summer afternoons.

On a much larger scale is the global circulation of the atmosphere, which is driven by the unequal heating of Earth's surface. These complex movements are responsible for the redistribution of heat between hot equatorial regions and frigid polar latitudes and will be discussed in detail in Chapter 7.

Atmospheric circulation consists of vertical as well as horizontal components, so both vertical and horizontal heat transfer occurs. Meteorologists often use the term *convection* to describe that part of the atmospheric circulation that involves *upward and downward* heat transfer. By contrast, the term **advection** is used to denote the horizontal component of convective flow. (The common term for advection is "wind," a phenomenon we will examine closely in later chapters.) Those who reside in the midlatitudes often experience the effects of heat transfer by advection. For example, when frigid Canadian air invades the Midwest in January, it brings bitterly cold winter weather. By contrast, the northward flow of air from the Gulf of Mexico is associated with warm temperatures.

Radiation

The third mechanism of heat transfer is radiation. Unlike conduction and convection, which need a medium in which to travel, radiant energy does not. Radiation is the only mechanism of heat transfer that travels through the vacuum of space. Therefore, it is the heat-transfer mechanism by which solar energy reaches our planet.

Solar Radiation.   As noted earlier, the Sun is the ultimate source of energy that drives the weather machine. For this reason, we consider the nature of solar radiation in more detail. From our everyday experience, we know that the Sun emits light and heat as well as the rays that give us a suntan. Although these forms of energy constitute a major portion of the total energy that radiates from the Sun, they are only a part of a large array of energy called **radiation** or **electromagnetic radiation.** This array or spectrum of electromagnetic energy is shown in Figure 2-11.

All types of radiation, whether X rays, radio waves or heat waves, travel through the vacuum of space at 300,000 kilometers (186,000 miles) per second, a value known as the *speed of light.* To help visualize radiant energy, imagine ripples made in a calm pond when a pebble is tossed in. Like the waves produced in the pond, electromagnetic waves come in various sizes or **wavelengths**—the distance from one crest to the next (Figure 2-11). Radio waves have the longest wavelengths, up to tens of kilometers in length. Gamma waves are the shortest, being less than a billionth of a centimeter long. Visible light is roughly in the middle of this range.

Radiation is often identified by the effect that it produces when it interacts with an object. The retinas of our eyes, for instance, are sensitive to a range of wavelengths that we call **visible light.** We often refer to visible light as white light, for it appears "white" in color. It is easy to show, however, that white light is really an array of colors, each color corresponding to a specific range of wavelengths. By using a prism, white light can be divided into the colors of

the rainbow, from violet with the shortest wavelength, 0.4 micrometer (1 micrometer is 0.001 centimeter), to red with the longest wavelength, 0.7 micrometer.

Located adjacent to the color red, and having a longer wavelength, is **infrared radiation,** which we cannot see but our skin detects as heat. (Only the infrared energy that is nearest the visible part of the spectrum is intense enough to be felt as heat.) The invisible waves located next to violet are called **ultraviolet radiation.** These are the wavelengths that are responsible for sunburn (see Box 2-3).

Although we divide radiant energy into categories based on our ability to perceive them, all wavelengths of radiation behave in a similar manner. When an object absorbs any form of electromagnetic energy, the waves excite subatomic particles (electrons), which results in an increase in molecular motion and a corresponding increase in temperature. Thus, the rapid vibrations of extremely hot molecules on the Sun create electromagnetic waves that travel through space and, upon being absorbed, increase the molecular motion of other groups of molecules—including those that make up the atmosphere, Earth's land-sea surface, and even our bodies.

One important difference among the various wavelengths of radiant energy is that shorter wavelengths are more energetic. This accounts for the fact that relatively short (high-energy) ultraviolet waves can damage human tissue more readily than similar exposures to longer wavelength radiation. The damage can result in skin cancer and cataracts.

It is important to note that the Sun emits all forms of radiation, as shown in Figure 2-11, but in varying quantities. Over 95 percent of all solar radiation is emitted in wavelengths between 0.1 and 2.5 micrometers, with much of this energy concentrated in the visible and near-visible parts of the electromagnetic spectrum (Figure 2-12). The narrow band of visible light, between 0.4 and 0.7 micrometer, represents over

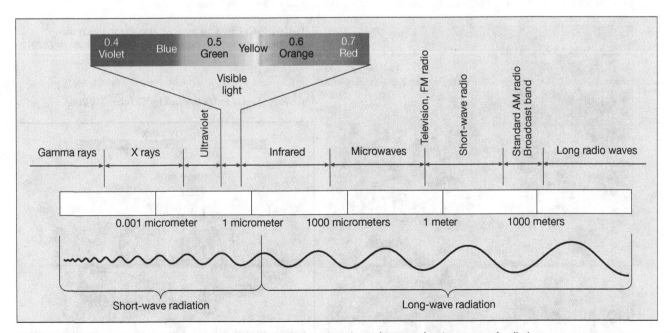

FIGURE 2-11 The electromagnetic spectrum, illustrating the wavelengths and names of various types of radiation.

BOX 2-3 The Ultraviolet Index

Gong-Yuh Lin*

Most people welcome sunny weather. On warm days, when the sky is cloudless and bright, many spend a great deal of time outdoors "soaking up" the sunshine (Figure 2-C). The goal is to develop a dark tan, one that sunbathers often describe as "healthy-looking." Ironically, there is strong evidence that too much sunshine (specifically, too much ultraviolet radiation) can lead to serious health problems, mainly skin cancer and cataracts.

Since June 1994 the National Weather Service (NWS) has issued the next-day ultraviolet index (UVI) for the United States to warn the public of potential health risks of exposure to sunlight (Figure 2-D). The UV index is determined by taking into account the predicted cloud cover and reflectivity of the surface, as well as the Sun angle and atmospheric depth for each forecast location. Because atmospheric ozone strongly absorbs ultraviolet radiation, the extent of the ozone layer is also considered. The UVI values lie on a scale from 0 to 11 and higher, with larger values representing greatest risk.

The U.S. Environmental Protection Agency has established five exposure categories based on UVI values—Low, Moderate, High, Very High, and

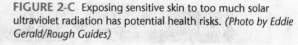

UVI value	Exposure category	Description	Minutes to burn
0–2	Low	Low danger from the Sun's UV rays for the average person.	> 60
3–5	Moderate	Moderate risk from unprotected Sun exposure. Take precautions during the mid-day when Sun is strongest.	40–60
6–7	High	Protection against sunburn is needed. Cover up, wear a hat and sunglasses, and use sunscreen.	25–40
8–10	Very High	Try to avoid the Sun between 11 AM and 4 PM. Otherwise, cover up and use sunscreen.	10–25
11–12	Extreme	Take all precautions. Unprotected skin will burn in minutes. Do not pursue outdoor activities if possible. If out of doors, apply sunscreen liberally every 2 hours.	< 10

TABLE 2-B The UV Index: Minutes to burn for the most susceptible skin type.

Extreme (Table 2-B). Precautionary measures have been developed for each category. The public is advised to minimize outdoor activities when the UVI is Very High or Extreme. Sunscreen with a sun-protection factor (SPF) of 15 or higher is recommended for all exposed skin. This is especially important after swimming or while sunbathing, even on cloudy days with the UVI in the Low category.

Table 2-B shows the range of minutes to burn for the most susceptible skin type (pale or milky white) for each exposure category. Note that the exposure that results in sunburn varies from over 60 minutes for the Low category to less than 10 minutes for the Extreme category. It takes approximately five times longer to cause sunburn of the least susceptible skin type, brown to dark. The most susceptible skin type develops red sunburn, painful swelling, and skin peeling when exposed to excessive sunlight. By contrast, the least susceptible skin type rarely burns and shows very rapid tanning response.

*Professor Lin is a faculty member in the Department of Geography at California State University, Northridge.

FIGURE 2-C Exposing sensitive skin to too much solar ultraviolet radiation has potential health risks. *(Photo by Eddie Gerald/Rough Guides)*

FIGURE 2-D UV Index forecast for October 10, 2005.

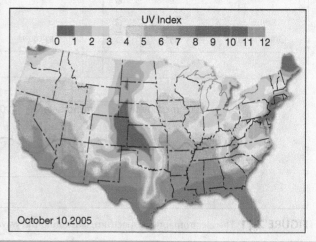

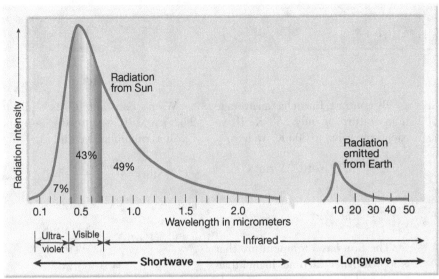

FIGURE 2-12 Comparison of the intensity of solar radiation and radiation emitted by Earth. Because of the Sun's high surface temperature, most of its energy is radiated at wavelengths shorter than 4 micrometers, with the greatest intensity in the visible range of the electromagnetic spectrum. Earth, in contrast, radiates most of its energy in wavelengths longer than 4 micrometers, primarily in the infrared band. Thus, we call the Sun's radiation *shortwave* and Earth's radiation *longwave*. (*After Tom L. McKnight,* Physical Geography, © *1990, Prentice Hall, Inc.*)

43 percent of the total energy emitted. The bulk of the remainder lies in the infrared zone (49 percent) and ultraviolet (UV) section (7 percent). Less than 1 percent of solar radiation is emitted as X rays, gamma rays, and radio waves.

Laws of Radiation. To obtain a better appreciation of how the Sun's radiant energy interacts with Earth's atmosphere and land–sea surface, it is helpful to have a general understanding of the basic radiation laws. The principles that follow were set forth by physicists during the late 1800s and early 1900s. Although the mathematics of these laws is beyond the scope of this book, the concepts themselves are easy to grasp:

1. **All objects continually emit radiant energy over a range of wavelengths.**° Thus, not only do hot objects like the Sun continually emit energy, but Earth does as well, even its polar ice caps.
2. **Hotter objects radiate more total energy per unit area than do colder objects.** The Sun, which has a surface temperature of 6000 K (10,000°F), emits about 160,000 times more energy per unit area than does Earth, which has an average surface temperature of 288 K (59°F). This concept is called the *Stefan–Boltzman law* and is expressed mathematically in Box 2-4.
3. **The hotter the radiating body, the shorter is the wavelength of maximum radiation.** We can visualize this law by imagining a piece of metal that, when heated sufficiently (as occurs in a blacksmith's shop), produces a white glow. As it cools, the metal emits more of its energy in longer wavelengths and glows a reddish color. Eventually, no light is given off, but if you place your hand near the metal, the still longer

infrared radiation will be detectable as heat. The Sun radiates maximum energy at 0.5 micrometer, which is in the visible range (Figure 2-12). The maximum radiation emitted from Earth occurs at a wavelength of 10 micrometers, well within the infrared (heat) range. Because the maximum Earth radiation is roughly 20 times longer than the maximum solar radiation, it is often referred to as **longwave radiation,** whereas solar radiation is called **shortwave radiation.** This concept is known as *Wien's displacement law* and is expressed mathematically in Box 2-4.

4. **Objects that are good absorbers of radiation are also good emitters.** The perfect absorber (and emitter) is a theoretical object called a **blackbody.** In the visible wavelengths, black coal dust is an excellent absorber (reflects very little light), hence the name blackbody. However, blackbodies do not have to be black in color, they simply must absorb and emit all possible radiation for their respective temperatures. Earth's surface and the Sun approach being blackbodies because they absorb and radiate with nearly 100 percent efficiency. By contrast, the gases that compose our atmosphere are *selective* absorbers and emitters of radiation. For some wavelengths the atmosphere is nearly transparent (little radiation absorbed). For others, however, it is nearly opaque (absorbs most of the radiation that strikes it). Experience tells us that the atmosphere is quite transparent to visible light emitted by the Sun because it readily reaches Earth's surface.

To summarize, although the Sun is the ultimate source of radiant energy, all objects continually radiate energy over a range of wavelengths. Hot objects, like the Sun, emit mostly shortwave radiation. By contrast, most objects at everyday temperatures (Earth's surface and atmosphere) emit mostly longwave (low-energy) radiation. Objects that

°The temperature of the object must be above a theoretical value called *absolute zero* (−273°C) for it to emit radiant energy. The letter K is used for values on the Kelvin temperature scale. For more explanation, see the section on "Temperature Scales" in Chapter 3.

BOX 2-4 Radiation Laws

*Gregory J. Carbone**

All bodies radiate energy. Both the rate and the wavelength of radiation emission depend on the temperature of the radiating body.

Stefan–Boltzman Law

This law mathematically expresses the rate of radiation emission per unit area:

$$E = \sigma T^4$$

E, the rate of radiation emitted by a body, is proportional to the fourth power of the body's temperature (T). The Stefan–Boltzmann constant (σ) is equal to 5.67×10^{-8} W/m² K⁴. Compare the difference between the radiation emission from the Sun and Earth. The Sun, with an average temperature of 6000 K, emits 73,483,200 watts per square meter (Wm⁻²):

$$E = (5.67 \times 10^{-8} \text{ W/m}^2 \text{ K}^4)$$
$$(6000 \text{ K})^4$$

$$= 73,483,200 \text{ W/m}^2$$

By contrast, Earth has an average temperature of only 288 K. If we round the value to 300 K, we have

$$E = (5.67 \times 10^{-8} \text{ W/m}^2\text{K}^4)$$
$$(300 \text{ K})^4$$

$$= 459 \text{ W/m}^2$$

The Sun has a temperature that is approximately 20 times higher than Earth and thus emits approximately 160,000 times more radiation per unit area. This makes sense because $20^4 = 160,000$.

Wien's Displacement Law

This law describes mathematically the relationship between the temperature (T) of a radiating body and its wavelength of maximum emission (λ_{max}):

$$\lambda_{max} = C/T$$

Wien's constant (C) is equal to $2898 \ \mu mK$. If we use the Sun and Earth as examples, we find

$$\lambda_{max}(\text{Sun}) = \frac{2898 \ \mu mK}{6000 \text{ K}} = 0.483 \ \mu m$$

and

$$\lambda_{max}(\text{Earth}) = \frac{2898 \ \mu mK}{300 \text{ K}}$$

$$= 9.66 \ \mu m$$

Note that the Sun radiates its maximum energy within the visible portion of the electromagnetic spectrum. The cooler Earth radiates its maximum energy in the infrared portion of the electromagnetic spectrum.

*Professor Carbone is a faculty member in the Department of Geography at the University of South Carolina.

---

are good absorbers of radiation, like Earth's surface, are also good emitters. By contrast, most gases are only good absorbers (emitters) in certain wavelengths but poor absorbers in other wavelengths.

What Happens to Incoming Solar Radiation?

GEODe **Heating Earth's Surface and Atmosphere**

▶ What Happens to Incoming Solar Radiation?

When radiation strikes an object, there are usually three different results. First, some of the energy is *absorbed* by the object. Recall that when radiant energy is absorbed, the molecules begin to vibrate faster, which causes an increase in temperature. Second, substances such as water and air are transparent to certain wavelengths of radiation. Such materials simply *transmit* this energy. Radiation that is transmitted does not contribute energy to the object. Third, some radiation may "bounce off" the object without being absorbed or transmitted. *Reflection* and *scattering* are responsible for

redirecting incoming solar radiation. In summary, *radiation may be absorbed, transmitted, or redirected (reflected or scattered).*

Figure 2-13 shows the fate of incoming solar radiation averaged for the entire globe. Notice that the atmosphere is quite transparent to incoming solar radiation. On average, about 50 percent of the energy reaching the top of the atmosphere is absorbed at Earth's surface. Another 30 percent is reflected back to space by the atmosphere, clouds, and reflective surfaces such as snow and water. The remaining 20 percent is absorbed by clouds and the atmosphere's gases.

What determines whether solar radiation will be transmitted to the surface, scattered, reflected back to space, or absorbed by the atmosphere? As we shall see, it depends greatly upon the *wavelength* of the energy being transmitted, as well as upon the size and nature of the absorbing or reflecting substance.

Reflection and Scattering

Reflection is the process whereby light bounces back from an object at the same angle at which it encounters a surface and with the same intensity (Figure 2-14a). By contrast,

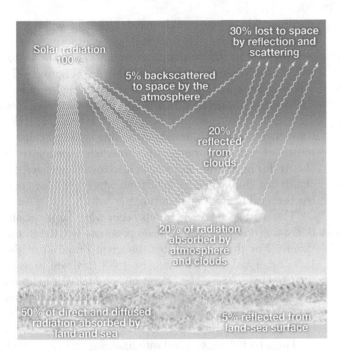

FIGURE 2-13 Average distribution of incoming solar radiation by percentage. More solar energy is absorbed by Earth's surface than by the atmosphere. Consequently, the air is not heated directly by the Sun, but is heated indirectly from Earth's surface.

scattering produces a larger number of weaker rays, traveling in different directions. Although scattering disperses light both forward and backward (**backscattering**), more energy is dispersed in the forward direction (Figure 2-14b).

Reflection and Earth's Albedo. Energy is returned to space from Earth in two ways: reflection and emission of radiant energy. The portion of solar energy that is reflected back to space leaves in the same short wavelengths in which

it came to Earth. About 30 percent of the solar energy reaching the outer atmosphere is reflected back to space (Figure 2-13). Included in this figure is the amount sent skyward by backscattering. This energy is lost to Earth and does not play a role in heating the atmosphere.

The fraction of radiation that is reflected by a surface is called its **albedo.** The albedo from place to place as well as from time to time varies considerably, depending on the amount of cloud cover and particulate matter in the air, plus the angle of the Sun's rays and the nature of the surface. Figure 2-15 gives the albedo for various surfaces. Fresh snow and thick clouds have high albedos (good reflectors). By contrast, dark soil is not very reflective and thus absorbs much of the radiation it receives. In the case of a lake or the ocean, note that the angle at which the Sun's rays strike the water surface greatly affects its albedo.

The albedo for Earth as a whole (planetary albedo) is 30 percent. The amount of light reflected from Earth's land–sea surface represents only about 5 percent of the total planetary albedo (Figure 2-13). Clouds are largely responsible for most of Earth's "brightness" as seen from space. This high reflectivity of clouds should not surprise anyone who has tried to drive on a foggy night with bright lights.

In comparison to Earth, the Moon, which is without clouds or an atmosphere, has an average albedo of only 7 percent. Even though a full Moon gives us a good bit of light on a clear night, the much brighter Earth would provide an astronaut on the Moon with far more light for an "Earth-lit" walk at night.

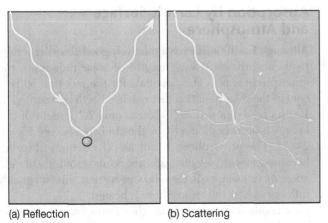

(a) Reflection (b) Scattering

FIGURE 2-14 Reflection and scattering. (a) Reflected light bounces back from a surface at the same angle at which it strikes that surface and with the same intensity. (b) When a beam of light is scattered, it results in a larger number of weaker rays, traveling in all different directions. Usually more energy is scattered in the forward direction than is backscattered.

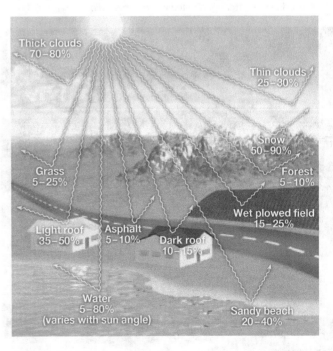

FIGURE 2-15 Albedo (reflectivity) of various surfaces. In general, light-colored surfaces tend to be more reflective than dark-colored surfaces and thus have higher albedos.

Blue Skies and Red Sunsets. Although incoming solar radiation travels in a straight line, small dust particles and gas molecules in the atmosphere scatter some of this energy in all directions. The result, called **diffused light,** explains how light reaches into the area beneath a shade tree, and how a room is lit in the absence of direct sunlight. Further, scattering accounts for the brightness and even the blue color of the daytime sky. In contrast, bodies like the Moon and Mercury, which are without atmospheres, have dark skies and "pitch-black" shadows, even during daylight hours. Overall, about one-half of solar radiation that is absorbed at Earth's surface arrives as scattered light.

To a large extent, the degree of scattering is determined by the size of the intervening gas molecules and dust particles. When light is scattered by very small particles, primarily gas molecules, it is distributed in all directions; however, more energy is scattered in the forward direction. The light that is lost to space is said to be *backscattered.*

Gas molecules more effectively scatter the shorter wavelengths (blue and violet) of visible light than the longer wavelengths (red and orange). This fact, in turn, explains the blue color of the sky and the orange and red colors seen at sunrise and sunset (Figure 2–16). Remember, sunlight appears white, but it is composed of all colors. When the Sun is overhead, you can look in any direction away from

the direct Sun and see predominantly blue light, which is the wavelength more readily scattered by the atmosphere.

Conversely, the Sun appears to have an orangish-to-reddish tint when viewed near the horizon (Figure 2–17). This is because solar radiation must travel through a greater thickness of atmosphere before it reaches your eyes (see Table 2–1). As a consequence, most of the blue and violet wavelengths will be scattered out, leaving light that consists mostly of reds and oranges. The reddish appearance of clouds during sunrise and sunset also results because the clouds are illuminated by light from which the blue color has been subtracted by scattering.

The most spectacular sunsets occur when large quantities of fine dust or smoke particles penetrate into the stratosphere. For three years after the great eruption of the Indonesian volcano Krakatau in 1883, brilliant sunsets occurred worldwide. The European summer that followed this colossal explosion was cooler than normal, a fact that has been attributed to the greater loss of radiation caused by backscattering.

Large particles associated with haze, fog, or smog scatter light more equally in all wavelengths. Because no color is predominant over any other, the sky appears white or gray on days when large particles are abundant. Scattering of sunlight by haze, water droplets, or dust particles makes it possible for us to observe bands (or rays) of sunlight called *crepuscular rays*. These bright fan-shaped bands are most commonly seen when the Sun shines through a break in the clouds, as shown in Figure 2–18. Crepuscular rays can also be observed around twilight when towering clouds cause alternating lighter and darker bands (light rays and shadows) to streak across the sky.

In summary, the color of the sky gives an indication of the number of large or small particles present. Lots of small particles produce red sunsets, whereas large particles produce a white sky. Furthermore, the bluer the sky, the cleaner the air.

FIGURE 2-16 At sunset, clouds often appear red because they are illuminated by sunlight in which most of the blue light has been lost due to scattering. *(Photo by Carr Clifton/Minden Pictures)*

Absorption by Earth's Surface and Atmosphere

Although Earth's surface is a relatively good absorber (effectively absorbs most wavelengths of solar radiation), the atmosphere is not. This accounts for the fact that 50 percent of the solar radiation that reaches Earth is absorbed by Earth's land–sea surface, whereas only 20 percent of this energy is absorbed directly by the atmosphere (see Figure 2–13). The atmosphere is not as effective an absorber because gases are selective absorbers (and emitters) of radiation. As you will see in the following section, this fact greatly influences how the atmosphere is heated.

Freshly fallen snow is another example of a selective absorber. Anyone who has experienced the blinding reflection of sunlight from snow is aware that fresh snow is a poor absorber of visible light (reflects up to 85 percent). Because of this, the temperature directly above a snow-covered surface is colder than it would otherwise be because much of

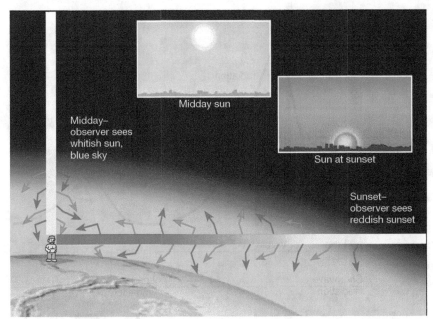

Midday sun

Midday–
observer sees
whitish sun,
blue sky

Sun at sunset

Sunset–
observer sees
reddish sunset

FIGURE 2-17 Short wavelengths (blue and violet) of visible light are scattered more effectively than are longer wavelengths (red, orange). Therefore, when the Sun is overhead, an observer can look in any direction and see predominantly blue light that was selectively scattered by the gases in the atmosphere. By contrast, at sunset, the path that light must take through the atmosphere is much longer. Consequently, most of the blue light is scattered before it reaches an observer. Thus, the Sun appears reddish in color.

the incoming radiation is reflected away. However, snow is a very good absorber (absorbs up to 95 percent) of the infrared (heat) radiation that is emitted from Earth's surface. As the ground radiates heat upward, the lowest layer of snow absorbs this energy and reradiates most of it downward. Thus, the depth at which a winter's frost can penetrate into the ground is much less when the ground has a snow cover than in an equally cold region without snow. The statement "The ground is blanketed with snow" can be taken literally. Farmers who plant winter wheat desire a deep snow cover because it insulates their crops from bitter midwinter temperatures.

FIGURE 2-18 Crepuscular rays are produced when haze scatters light. Crepuscular rays are most commonly seen when the Sun shines through a break in the clouds. *(Photo by Adam Jones/Visuals Unlimited, Inc.)*

Radiation Emitted by Earth

GEODe   **Heating Earth's Surface and Atmosphere**
▶ The Greenhouse Effect

Although we often talk about radiation in terms of the Sun, recall that *all* objects continuously emit radiation. Because Earth is much cooler than the Sun, it emits considerably less radiant energy. Furthermore, radiation emanating from Earth's surface and atmosphere is emitted at longer wavelengths than most solar radiation. Over 95 percent of Earth's radiation has wavelengths between 2.5 and 30 micrometers, placing it in the long end of the infrared band of the electromagnetic spectrum (Figure 2–19). Recall that the bulk of solar radiation is emitted in wavelengths shorter than 2.5 micrometers (shortwave radiation). This difference between incoming solar radiation and radiation emitted by Earth is very important to our understanding of how our atmosphere is heated.

Heating the Atmosphere

As stated earlier, gases are selective absorbers, meaning that they absorb strongly in some wavelengths, moderately in others, and only slightly in still others. When a gas molecule absorbs radiation, this energy is transformed into internal molecular motion, which is detectable as a rise in temperature. *Thus, it is the gases that are the most effective absorbers of radiation that play the primary role in heating the atmosphere.*

At first glance Figure 2–19 appears complicated; nevertheless, it is a useful aid to understanding how the atmosphere is heated. The upper portion shows that most (95 percent) incoming solar radiation has wavelengths between 0.1 and 2.5 micrometers (abbreviated μm) and includes the

FIGURE 2-19 The absorptivity of selected gases of the atmosphere and the atmosphere as a whole. The atmosphere as a whole is quite transparent to solar radiation between 0.3 and 0.7 micrometer, which includes the band of visible light. Most solar radiation falls in this range, explaining why a large amount of solar radiation penetrates the atmosphere and heats Earth's surface. Also, note that longwave infrared radiation in the zone between 8 and 12 micrometers can escape the atmosphere most readily. This zone is called the atmospheric window. *(Data after R. G. Fleagle and J. A. Businger,* An Introduction to Atmospheric Physics. *1963 by Academic Press)*

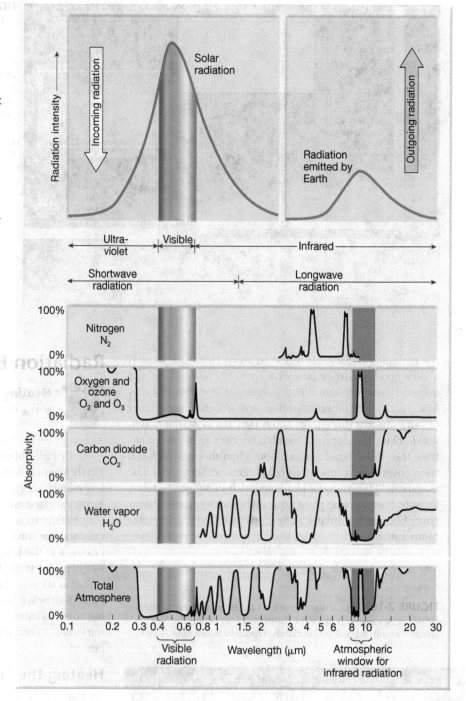

band of visible light (shown as the colors of the rainbow). The lower half of Figure 2–19 gives the absorptivity of the principal atmospheric gases. Note that nitrogen, the most abundant constituent in the atmosphere (78 percent), is a relatively poor absorber of incoming solar radiation because it absorbs best in that part of the electromagnetic spectrum, with wavelengths greater than 2.5 micrometers.

The only significant absorbers of incoming solar radiation are water vapor, oxygen, and ozone, which together accounts

for most of the solar energy absorbed directly by the atmosphere. Oxygen and ozone are efficient absorbers of high-energy, shortwave radiation. Oxygen removes most of the shorter-wavelength UV radiation high in the atmosphere, and ozone absorbs UV rays in the stratosphere between 10 and 50 kilometers (6 and 30 miles). The absorption of UV energy in the stratosphere accounts for the high temperatures experienced there. More important, without the removal of UV radiation, human life would not be possible because UV energy disrupts the genetic code (see Chapter 1).

Looking at the bottom of Figure 2–19, you can see that for the atmosphere as a whole, none of the gases are effective absorbers of radiation that has wavelengths between 0.3 and 0.7 micrometers. This region of the spectrum corresponds to the visible light band, which constitutes about 43 percent of the energy radiated by the Sun. Because the atmosphere is a poor absorber of visible radiation, most of this energy is transmitted to Earth's surface. Thus, we say that *the atmosphere is nearly transparent to incoming solar radiation and that direct solar energy is not an effective "heater" of Earth's atmosphere.*

We can also see in Figure 2–19 that the atmosphere as a whole is a relatively efficient absorber of longwave (infrared) radiation emitted by Earth (see bottom right of Figure 2–19). Water vapor and carbon dioxide are the principal absorbing gases, with water vapor absorbing about 60 percent of the radiation emitted by Earth. Therefore, water vapor accounts (more than any other gas) for the warm temperatures of the lower troposphere, where it is most highly concentrated.

Although the atmosphere is an effective absorber of radiation emitted by Earth's surface, it is nevertheless quite transparent to the band of radiation between 8 and 12 micrometers. Notice in Figure 2-19 (lower right) that the gases in the atmosphere absorb very little energy in these wavelengths. Because the atmosphere is transparent to radiation between 8 and 12 micrometers, much like window glass is transparent to visible light, this band is called the **atmospheric window.** Although other "atmospheric windows" exist, the one located between 8 and 12 micrometers is the most significant because this happens to be located where Earth's radiation is most intense.

By contrast, clouds that are composed of tiny liquid droplets are excellent absorbers of this energy. This explains why nighttime temperatures remain higher on cloudy nights than on clear nights. Clouds absorb outgoing radiation and reradiate much of this energy back to Earth's surface. Thus, clouds serve a purpose similar to window blinds because they effectively shut the atmospheric window. As a result, clouds lower the rate at which the surface cools.

Because the atmosphere is largely transparent to solar (shortwave) radiation but more absorptive of the longwave radiation emitted by Earth, the atmosphere is heated from the ground up, instead of vice versa. This explains the general drop in temperature with increased altitude in the troposphere. The farther from the "radiator" (Earth's surface), the colder it gets. On average, the temperature drops 6.5°C for each kilometer increase in altitude, a figure known as the *normal lapse rate.* The fact that the atmosphere does not acquire the bulk of its energy directly from the Sun, but is heated by Earth's surface, is of utmost importance to the dynamics of the weather machine.

The Greenhouse Effect

If Earth had no atmosphere, it would experience an average surface temperature far below freezing. But the atmosphere warms the planet and makes Earth livable. The extremely important role the atmosphere plays in heating Earth's surface has been named the **greenhouse effect.**

As you saw earlier, cloudless air is largely transparent to incoming shortwave solar radiation and, hence, transmits it to Earth's surface. By contrast, a significant fraction of the longwave radiation emitted by Earth's land–sea surface is absorbed by water vapor, carbon dioxide, and other trace gases in the atmosphere. This energy heats the air and increases the rate at which it radiates energy, both out to space and back toward Earth's surface. The energy that is emitted back to the surface causes it to heat up more, which then results in greater emissions from the surface. This complicated game of "pass the hot potato" keeps Earth's average temperature 33°C (59°F) warmer than it would otherwise be (Figure 2–20). Without these absorptive gases in our atmosphere, Earth would not provide a suitable habitat for humans and other life forms.

This natural phenomenon was named the greenhouse effect because it was once thought that greenhouses were heated in a similar manner. The glass in a greenhouse allows shortwave solar radiation to enter and be absorbed by the objects inside. These objects, in turn, radiate energy but at longer wavelengths, to which glass is nearly opaque. The heat, therefore, is "trapped" in the greenhouse. It has been shown, however, that air inside greenhouses attains higher temperatures than outside air mainly because greenhouses restrict the exchange of air between the inside and outside. Nevertheless, the term "greenhouse effect" remains.

The popular press frequently points to the greenhouse effect as the "villain" of the global warming problem. It is important to note that the greenhouse effect and global warming *are not* the same thing. Without the greenhouse

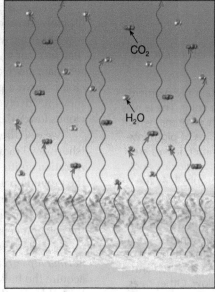
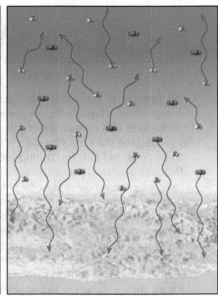

1. Short-wave solar radiation is absorbed by Earth's surface.

2. Earth's surface radiates long-wave radiation which is absorbed by greenhouse gasses.

3. Greenhouse gasses reradiate some energy Earthward, thus trapping heat in the lower atmosphere.

FIGURE 2-20 The heating of the atmosphere. Most of the short-wavelength radiation from the Sun passes through the atmosphere and is absorbed by Earth's land–sea surface. This energy is then emitted from the surface as longer-wavelength radiation, much of which is absorbed by certain gases in the atmosphere. Some of the energy absorbed by the atmosphere will be reradiated Earthward. This so-called greenhouse effect is responsible for keeping Earth's surface much warmer than it would be otherwise.

effect Earth would be uninhabitable. We do have mounting evidence that human activity (particularly the release of carbon dioxide into the atmosphere) is responsible for a rise in global temperature (see Chapter 14). Thus, human activity seems to be enhancing an otherwise natural process (the greenhouse effect) to increase Earth's temperature. Nevertheless, it is wrong to equate the greenhouse phenomenon, which makes life possible, with undesirable changes to our atmosphere caused by human activities.

Students Sometimes Ask...

Is Venus so much hotter than Earth because it is closer to the Sun?

Proximity to the Sun is actually not the primary factor. On Earth, water vapor and carbon dioxide are the primary greenhouse gases and are responsible for elevating Earth's average surface temperature by 33°C (59°F). However, greenhouse gases make up less than 1 percent of Earth's atmosphere. By contrast, the Venusian atmosphere is much denser and consists of 97 percent carbon dioxide. Thus, the Venusian atmosphere experiences extraordinary greenhouse warming, which is estimated to raise its surface temperature by 523°C (941°F).

Role of Clouds in Heating Earth

Clouds, like water vapor and carbon dioxide, are good absorbers of infrared radiation emitted by Earth (see Box 2–5). Thus, at night clouds play a key role in keeping the surface warm. A thick cloud cover will absorb most outward directed radiation and radiate much of that energy back to the surface. This explains why on clear, dry nights the surface cools considerably more than on cloudy or humid evenings. Furthermore, although desert areas often experience high daytime temperatures, they are also likely to experience cold nights, for they generally have cloudless skies.

During daylight hours the effect of clouds on heating Earth's surface depends on the type of clouds present. High, thin clouds primarily transmit incoming solar radiation. At the same time these clouds absorb a portion of the outgoing infrared radiation emitted by Earth and radiate some of that energy back to the surface. The net effect is that high thin clouds tend to warm the surface.

The impact of low, thick clouds is opposite that of high clouds. Thick, low clouds have a high albedo and therefore reflect a significant portion of incoming solar radiation back to space. Because less solar radiation is transmitted, Earth's surface is cooler than it would otherwise be.

Whether a given cloud will cause the surface temperature to be higher or lower than when the sky is clear depends on several factors, including the time of day, the cloud's thickness, its height, and the nature of the particles that compose it. The balance between the cooling and warming effects of

BOX 2-5   Infrared Imaging

I t is worth noting that our eyes have evolved to be sensitive to the wavelengths of solar radiation having the greatest intensities (visible radiation). If early humans had been solely dependent upon hunting nocturnal mammals (warm-blooded), evolutionary changes might have resulted in "eyes" sensitive to infrared radiation (heat), just like those of some reptiles. Despite our inability to naturally see infrared energy, we have developed artificial detectors (including infrared film) capable of extending our vision into the long-wavelength part of the electromagnetic spectrum.

One type of infrared imaging employs satellites to detect infrared radiation emitted by Earth's surface and atmosphere. From these images the temperatures of objects emitting radiation, such as clouds, large bodies of water, and various landforms, can be established. Recall that the wavelengths of radiation emitted by an object are temperature-dependent. When more of the energy is emitted in shorter wavelengths, it translates to objects at higher temperatures, whereas longer wavelengths indicate surfaces at lower temperatures.

One technique uses infrared images to determine which clouds are the most probable precipitation producers. The high tops of towering thunderstorms are colder than the tops of clouds at lower altitudes (less vertically developed clouds). In the image shown in Figure 2–E the highest (coldest) cloud tops are associated with towering storm clouds that are part of Hurricane Isidore in the Gulf of Mexico. The tallest clouds and thus the heaviest rain are in the areas shaded in red and yellow.

Unlike photos produced by exposing film to visible light, infrared images can be made at any time of the day or night. The military uses infrared imaging in their "night vision" technology to detect such things as troop movements made under the cover of darkness.

FIGURE 2-E This infrared image shows the tops of the towering storm clouds (red and yellow) that were part of Hurricane Isidore as it crossed the Gulf of Mexico in late September 2002. *(Image courtesy of NASA)*

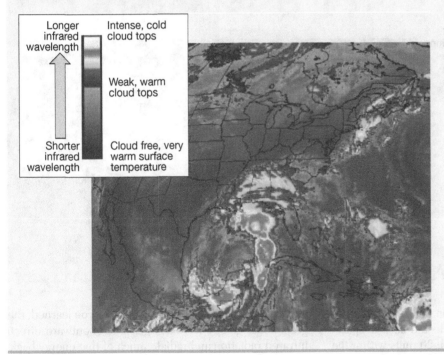

clouds is quite close; however, averaging the influence of all the clouds around the globe, cooling predominates.

Heat Budget

Worldwide, Earth's average temperature remains relatively constant, despite seasonal cold spells and heat waves. This stability indicates that a balance exists between the amount of incoming solar radiation and the amount of radiation emitted back to space; otherwise, Earth would be getting progressively colder or progressively warmer. The annual balance of incoming and outgoing radiation is called Earth's **heat budget.** The following examination of this budget provides a good review of the process just discussed.

Figure 2–21 illustrates Earth's heat budget. For simplicity we will use 100 units to represent the solar radiation intercepted at the outer edge of the atmosphere. You have

BOX 2-6   Solar Power

Nearly 95 percent of the world's energy needs are derived from fossil fuels, primarily oil, coal, and natural gas. Present estimates indicate that the amount of recoverable fossil fuels may equal 10 trillion barrels of oil, which at the present rate of consumption is enough to last 170 years. Of course, as world population increases, the rate of consumption will climb. Thus, reserves will eventually be in short supply. In the meantime, the adverse environmental impacts associated with burning huge quantities of fossil fuels will likely grow more severe. How can a growing demand for energy be met without radically altering the planet we inhabit? Although no clear answer has yet emerged, we must con-

sider greater use of alternate energy sources, such as solar power.

The term *solar energy* generally refers to the direct use of the Sun's rays to supply energy for the needs of people. The simplest, and perhaps most widely used, *passive solar collectors* are south-facing windows. As shortwave sunlight passes through the glass, its energy is absorbed by objects in the room. These objects, in turn, radiate longwave heat that warms the air in the room. In the United States we often use south-facing windows, along with better insulated and more airtight construction, to reduce heating costs substantially.

More elaborate systems used for home heating involve an *active solar*

collector. These roof-mounted devices are normally large blackened boxes that are covered with glass. The heat they collect can be transferred to where it is needed by circulating air or fluids through pipes. Solar collectors are also used successfully to heat water for domestic and commercial needs. In Israel, for example, about 80 percent of all homes are equipped with solar collectors that provide hot water.

Although solar energy is free, the necessary equipment and its installation are not. The initial cost of setting up a system, including a supplemental heating unit for times when solar energy is diminished (cloudy days and winter) or unavailable (nighttime),

FIGURE 2-F Solar One, a solar installation used to generate electricity in the Mojave Desert near Barstow, California. *(Photo by Thomas Braise/Corbis/Stock Market)*

already seen that, of the total radiation that reaches Earth, roughly 30 units (30 percent) are reflected back to space. The remaining 70 units are absorbed, 20 units within the atmosphere and 50 units by Earth's land–sea surface. How does Earth transfer this energy back to space?

If all of the energy absorbed by our atmosphere, land, and water were reradiated directly and immediately back to space, Earth's heat budget would be simple—100 units of radiation received and 100 units returned to space. In fact, this does happen *over time* (minus small quantities of energy that become locked up in biomass that may eventually become fossil fuel). What makes the heat budget complicated is the behavior of certain greenhouse gases, particu-

larly water vapor and carbon dioxide. As you learned, these greenhouse gases absorb a large share of outward-directed infrared radiation and radiate much of that energy back to Earth. This "recycled" energy significantly increases the radiation received by Earth's surface. In addition to the 50 units received directly from the Sun, Earth's surface receives another 94 units from the atmosphere, bringing the total absorbed to 144 units. A balance is maintained, however, because all 144 units are returned to the atmosphere and eventually lost to space.

Earth's surface loses the 144 units mainly by emitting longwave radiation skyward. As Figure 2–21 illustrates, 102 units are emitted from Earth's surface and absorbed by the

FIGURE 2-G A proposed solar facility near Los Angeles will consist of a 20,000-dish array using Stirling dish technology. *(Photo by Randy J. Montoya/ Sandia National Laboratories)*

can be substantial. Nevertheless, over the long term, solar energy is economical in most parts of the United States and will become even more cost-efficient as the price of other fuels increases.

Research is currently underway to improve the technologies for concentrating sunlight. One method being examined uses mirrors that track the Sun and keep its rays focused on a receiving tower. A facility, with an array of 2000 mirrors, has been constructed near Barstow, California (Figure 2-F). Solar energy focused on the tower heats water in pressurized pan-

els to over 500°C. The superheated water is then transferred to turbines, which turn electrical generators.

Another type of collector uses photovoltaic (solar) cells that convert the Sun's energy directly into electricity. A large experimental facility using photovoltaic cells is located near Hesperia, California, and supplies electricity to customers of Southern California Edison.

In late 2005, Southern California Edison announced an agreement that could result in construction of a massive 4,500-acre solar-generating facility located 70 miles northeast of Los Ange-

les. The technology being employed, called the *Stirling dish,* converts thermal energy to electricity by using a mirror array to focus the Sun's rays on the receiver end of a Stirling engine (Figure 2-G). The internal side of a receiver then heats hydrogen gas, causing it to expand. The pressure created by the expanding gas drives a piston, which turns a small electric generator. When completed, this facility is expected to consist of a 20,000-dish array that will produce 500 megawatts of electricity, enough to serve 278,000 homes.

---

atmosphere. In addition, 12 units are transmitted through the atmosphere without being absorbed. (Recall that radiation between 8 and 12 micrometers escapes the troposphere most readily because water vapor and carbon dioxide do not absorb these wavelengths.) In addition, energy is carried from Earth's land–sea surface to the atmosphere by water molecules during the process of evaporation (23 units) and by conduction and convection (7 units).

The energy transferred to the atmosphere is reradiated skyward as well as toward the surface. However, a balance has been established, so that on average the atmosphere radiates back to space the same amount of energy as it receives. A careful examination of Figure 2–21 confirms that

incoming shortwave radiation is in fact balanced by outgoing longwave radiation.

Latitudinal Heat Balance

Because the amount of incoming solar radiation is nearly equal to the amount of outgoing radiation for Earth as a whole, the average worldwide temperature remains constant. However, the balance of incoming and outgoing radiation that holds for the entire planet obviously is not maintained at each latitude. Averaged over the entire year, a zone around Earth between 38°N and 38°S *receives more solar radiation than is lost to space* (Figure 2–22). Not surprisingly, this zone,

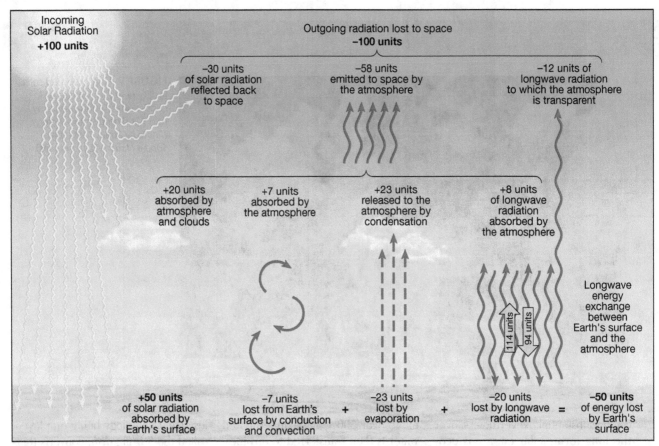

FIGURE 2-21 Heat budget of Earth and atmosphere. These estimates of the average global energy budget come from satellite obser vations and radiation studies. As more data are accumulated these numbers will be modified. (*Data from Kiehl, Trenberth, Liou, and others.*)

centered on the equator, includes the southern United States and the warm tropical areas of Earth. The opposite is true for higher latitudes, where *more heat is lost through longwave terrestrial radiation than is received.*

A conclusion that might be drawn is that the tropics should be getting hotter and the poles should be getting colder. But

we know that is not happening. Instead, the atmosphere and the oceans act as giant thermal engines transferring surplus heat from the tropics poleward. In effect, it is this energy imbalance that drives the winds and the ocean currents.

The amount of solar radiation received at a given location fluctuates with changes in cloud cover and atmos-

FIGURE 2-22 Latitudinal heat balance averaged over the entire year. We see that in a zone extending 38 degrees on both sides of the equator, the amount of incoming solar radiation exceeds the loss from outgoing Earth radiation. The reverse is true for the middle and high (polar) latitudes, where losses from outgoing Earth radiation exceed gains from incoming solar radiation.

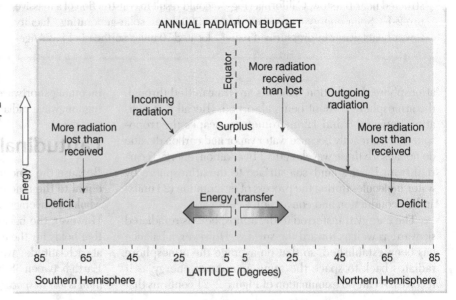

pheric composition. For example, the tropics often experience thick cloud cover, which reduces incoming radiation. Events such as forest fires, dust storms, and volcanic eruptions can also reduce the amount of incoming solar radiation. More important, however, are seasonal changes in Sun angle and length of daylight, which determine, to a large degree,

the amount of radiation reaching the ground at any given latitude.

Notice in December (Figure 2-23) that the zone of maximum heating is centered roughly over the Tropic of Capricorn, because this is the latitude that experiences the direct rays of the Sun. By contrast, short days and low

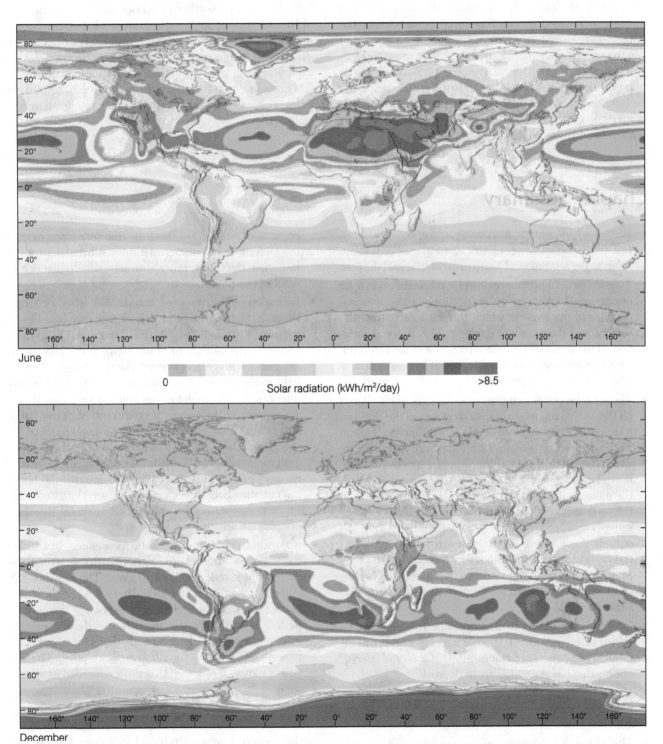

June

Solar radiation (kWh/m²/day)

0   >8.5

December

FIGURE 2-23 These false-color images show the average rate of incoming solar radiation at Earth's surface for the months of June and December. The colors correspond to values (kilowatt hours per square meter per day) measured by a variety of Earth-observing satellites and averaged over a 10-year period. Because the measurements are taken at Earth's surface, cloud cover reduces the radiation reaching the ground. This effect is apparent in some tropical regions where cloud cover is extensive.

Sun angles are mainly responsible for the relatively small amounts of solar radiation reaching the middle and high latitudes in the Northern Hemisphere. Also notice that Antarctica receives what might appear to be an unusually large amount of solar radiation in December. This occurs because in December much of Antarctica experiences nearly continuous daylight. Despite the abundance of energy received during the Antarctic summer, it is not enough to balance the outflows that occur during the long winter. Moreover, much of the summer sunshine in Antarctica is reflected back to space by its snow-and-ice-covered surface. The top part of Figure 2-23 shows the opposite situation, summer in the Northern Hemisphere. In June the incoming solar radiation is most intense near the Tropic of Cancer, and the Northern Hemisphere is bathed in sunshine.

The shift in incoming solar radiation from the Southern to Northern Hemisphere and back again can be clearly seen by comparing the June and December maps in Figure 2-22. Because energy imbalances drive Earth's general circulation, the regions of greatest energy transfer also migrate seasonally.

It should be of interest to those who live in the middle latitudes—in the Northern Hemisphere, from the latitude of New Orleans at 30°N to the latitude of Winnipeg, Manitoba, at 50°N—that most heat transfer takes place across this region. Consequently, much of the stormy weather experienced in the middle latitudes can be attributed to this unending transfer of heat from the tropics toward the poles. These processes are discussed in more detail in later chapters.

Chapter Summary

- Earth has two principal motions—*rotation* and *revolution*. Rotation is the spinning of Earth about its axis. Revolution refers to the movement of Earth in its orbit around the Sun.

- The two most important reasons for the variation in solar energy reaching a particular location are the seasonal changes in the angle at which the Sun's rays strike the surface and the length of daylight. The seasonal variation in the angle of the Sun affects where on Earth the solar rays are most concerned and the thickness of atmosphere the rays must penetrate.

- The four days each year given special significance based on the annual migration of the direct rays of the Sun and its importance to the yearly cycle of weather are (1) June 21/22, the *summer solstice* in the Northern Hemisphere, when the vertical rays of the Sun are striking 23 1/2° north latitude (*Tropic of Cancer*), (2) December 21/22, the *winter solstice* in the Northern Hemisphere, when the vertical rays of the Sun are striking 23 1/2° south latitude (*Tropic of Capricorn*), (3) September 22/23, the *autumnal equinox* in the Northern Hemisphere, when the vertical rays of the Sun strike the equator, and (4) March 21/22, the *spring*, or *vernal*, *equinox* in the Northern Hemisphere, when the vertical rays of the Sun also strike the equator.

- *Energy* is the ability to do work. The two major categories of energy are (1) *kinetic energy*, which can be thought of as energy of motion, and (2) *potential energy*, energy that has the capability to do work.

- *Heat* is the transfer of energy into or out of an object because of temperature differences between that object and its surroundings.

- The three mechanisms of energy transfer are (1) *conduction*, the transfer of heat through matter by molecular activity, (2) *convection*, the transfer of heat by mass movement or circulation within a substance, and (3) *radiation*, the transfer mechanism by which solar energy reaches our planet.

- *Radiation* or *electromagnetic radiation*, whether X rays, visible light, heat waves, or radio waves, travels as various size waves through the vacuum of space at 300,000 kilometers per second. Shorter wavelengths of radiation are associated with greater energy. The wavelength of visible light ranges from 0.4 micrometer (violet) to 0.7 micrometer (red). Although the Sun emits many forms of radiation, most of the energy is concentrated in the visible and near visible (infrared and ultraviolet) parts of the spectrum. The basic laws of radiation are (1) all objects emit radiant energy, (2) hotter objects radiate more total energy per unit area than colder objects, (3) the hotter the radiating body, the shorter is the wavelength of maximum radiation, and (4) objects that are good absorbers of radiation are also good emitters.

- Approximately 50 percent of the solar energy that strikes the top of the atmosphere reaches Earth's surface. About 30 percent is reflected back to space. The remaining 20 percent of the energy is absorbed by clouds and the atmosphere's gases. The wavelength of the energy being transmitted, as well as the size and nature of the absorbing or reflecting substance, determine whether solar radiation will be scattered, reflected back to space, or absorbed. The fraction of radiation reflected by a surface is called its *albedo*.

- Radiant energy that is absorbed heats Earth and eventually is reradiated skyward. Because Earth has a much lower surface temperature than the Sun, its radiation is in the form of longwave infrared radiation. Because the atmospheric gases, primarily water vapor and carbon dioxide, are more efficient absorbers of terrestrial (longwave) radiation, the atmosphere is heated from the ground up. The general drop in temperature with increased altitude in the troposphere (about 6.5°C/kilometer, a figure called the *normal lapse rate*) supports the fact that the atmosphere is heated from below. The transmission of shortwave solar radiation by the atmosphere, coupled with the selective absorption of Earth radiation by atmospheric gases that results in the warming of the atmosphere, is referred to as the *greenhouse effect*.

- Because of the annual balance that exists between incoming and outgoing radiation, called the *heat budget,* Earth's average temperature remains relatively constant despite seasonal cold spells and heat waves.

- Although the balance of incoming and outgoing radiation holds for the entire planet, it is not maintained at

each latitude. Averaged over the entire year, a zone around Earth between 38°N and 38°S receives more solar radiation than is lost to space. The opposite is true for higher latitudes, where more heat is lost through outgoing longwave radiation than is received. It is this energy imbalance between the low and high latitudes that drives the global winds and ocean currents, which in turn transfer surplus heat from the tropics poleward. Furthermore, the radiation balance of a given place fluctuates with changes in cloud cover, atmospheric composition, and most important, Sun angle and length of daylight. Thus, areas of radiation surplus and deficit migrate seasonally as the Sun angle and length of daylight change.

Vocabulary Review

advection (p. 42)
albedo (p. 47)
aphelion (p. 33)
atmospheric window (p. 51)
autumnal equinox (p. 35)
backscattered (p. 47)
blackbody (p. 45)
circle of illumination (p. 35)
conduction (p. 42)
convection (p. 42)
diffused light (p. 48)
energy (p. 40)
greenhouse effect (p. 51)

heat (p. 41)
heat budget (p. 53)
inclination of the axis (p. 34)
infrared radiation (p. 43)
kinetic energy (p. 40)
longwave radiation (p. 45)
perihelion (p. 33)
plane of the ecliptic (p. 34)
potential energy (p. 41)
radiation or electromagnetic
   radiation (p. 43)
reflection (p. 46)
revolution (p. 32)

rotation (p. 32)
scattering (p. 47)
shortwave radiation (p. 45)
spring equinox (p. 35)
summer solstice (p. 35)
temperature (p. 41)
thermal (p. 42)
Tropic of Cancer (p. 35)
Tropic of Capricorn (p. 35)
ultraviolet radiation (p. 43)
visible light (p. 43)
wavelength (p. 43)
winter solstice (p. 35)

Review Questions

1. Can the annual variations in Earth–Sun distance adequately account for seasonal temperature changes? Explain.

2. Why does the amount of solar energy received at Earth's surface change when the angle of the Sun changes?

3. List four characteristics of the summer solstice for the Northern Hemisphere. For the Southern Hemisphere.

4. What is meant by temperature? Heat?

5. Describe the three basic mechanisms of energy transfer. Which mechanism is least important meteorologically?

6. What is the difference between convection and advection?

7. Compare visible, infrared, and ultraviolet radiation. For each, indicate whether it is considered short wavelength or long wavelength.

8. In what part of the electromagnetic spectrum does solar radiation have the highest intensity?

9. Describe the relationship between the temperature of a radiating body and the wavelengths it emits.

10. Why does the daytime sky usually appear blue?

11. Why may the sky appear to have a red or orange tint near sunrise or sunset?

12. What factors influence albedo from time to time and from place to place?

13. Explain why the atmosphere is heated chiefly by radiation from Earth's surface rather than by direct solar radiation.

14. Which gases are the primary heat absorbers in the lower atmosphere? Which one is most influential in weather?

15. How does Earth's atmosphere act as a "greenhouse"?

16. What is responsible for absorbing the largest portion of incoming solar radiation?

17. What is the atmospheric window? How is it "closed"?

18. What two phenomena are driven by the imbalance of heating that exists between the tropics and poles?

Problems

1. Refer to Figure 2–6 and calculate the noon Sun angle on June 21 and December 21 at 50° north latitude, 0° latitude (the equator), and 20° south latitude. Which of these latitudes has the greatest variation in noon Sun angle between summer and winter?

2. For the latitudes listed in Problem 1, determine the length of daylight and darkness on June 21 and December 21 (refer to Table 2–2). Which of these latitudes has the largest seasonal variation in length of daylight? Which latitude has the smallest variation?

3. How would our seasons be affected if Earth's axis were not inclined 23 1/2° to the plane of its orbit but were instead perpendicular?

4. Describe the seasons if Earth's axis were inclined 40°. Where would the tropics of Cancer and Capricorn be located? How about the Arctic and Antarctic circles?

5. Calculate the noon Sun angle at your location for the equinoxes and solstices.

6. Calculate the noon Sun angle for a city located at 52°N latitude on August 5. What about the same location on January 17? (*Hint:* See Box 2-2.)

7. If Earth had no atmosphere, its longwave radiation emission would be lost quickly to space, making the planet approximately 33 K cooler. Calculate the rate of radiation emitted (E), and the wavelength of maximum radiation emission (λ_{max}) for Earth at 255 K.

8. The intensity of solar radiation can be calculated using trigonometry, as shown in Figure 2-24. For simplicity, consider a solar beam of 1 unit width. The surface area over which the beam would be spread changes with Sun angle, such that

$$\text{Surface area} = \frac{1 \text{ unit}}{\sin\,(\text{Sun angle})}$$

Therefore, if the Sun angle at solar noon is 56°:

$$\text{Surface area} = \frac{1 \text{ unit}}{\sin 56°} = \frac{1 \text{ unit}}{0.829} = 1.206 \text{ units}$$

Using this method and your answers to Problem 5, calculate the intensity of solar radiation (surface area) for your location at noon during the summer and winter solstices.

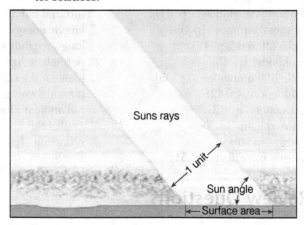

FIGURE 2-24 Calculating solar intensity.

Atmospheric Science Online

The Atmosphere 10e web site uses the resources and flexibility of the Internet to aid in your study of the topics in this chapter. Written and developed by meteorology instructors, this site will help improve your understanding of meteorology. Visit **http://www .prenhall.com/lutgens** and click on the cover of *The Atmosphere 10e* to find:

- **Online review quizzes**
- **Critical thinking exercises**
- **Links to chapter-specific web resources**
- **Internet-wide key term searches**

http://www.prenhall.com/lutgens

TEMPERATURE

CHAPTER

3

The highest temperature ever recorded in the Western Hemisphere occurred in Califormia's Death Valley. *(Tim Fitzharris/ Minden Pictures)*

Temperature is one of the basic elements of weather and climate. When someone asks what the weather is like outside, air temperature is often the first element we mention (Figure 3–1). From everyday experience, we know that temperatures vary on different time scales: seasonally, daily, sometimes even hourly. Moreover, we all realize that substantial temperature differences exist from one place to another. In Chapter 2 we learned how air is heated, and we examined the role of Earth–Sun relationships in causing temperature variations from season to season and from latitude to latitude. In Chapter 3 we will focus on several other aspects of this very important atmospheric property, including factors other than Earth–Sun relationships that act as temperature controls. We will also look at how temperature is measured and expressed and see that temperature data can be of very practical value to us all. Applications include calculations that are useful in evaluating energy consumption, crop maturity, and human comfort.

For the Record: Air-Temperature Data

Temperature Data and the Controls of Temperature

▶ Basic Temperature Data

Temperatures recorded daily at thousands of weather stations worldwide provide much of the temperature data compiled by meteorologists and climatologists (see Box 3–1). Hourly temperatures may be recorded by an observer or obtained from automated observing systems that continually monitor the atmosphere. At many locations only the maximum and minimum temperatures are obtained. The **daily mean temperature** is determined by averaging the 24 hourly readings or more frequently by adding the maximum and minimum temperatures for a 24-hour period and dividing by 2. From the maximum and minimum, the **daily temperature range** is computed by finding the difference between these figures. Other data involving longer periods are also compiled:

1. The **monthly mean temperature** is calculated by adding together the daily means for each day of the month and dividing by the number of days in the month.
2. The **annual mean temperature** is an average of the 12 monthly means.
3. The **annual temperature range** is computed by finding the difference between the warmest and coldest monthly mean temperatures.

Mean temperatures are especially useful for making daily, monthly, or annual comparisons. It is common to hear a weather reporter state, "Last month was the warmest

FIGURE 3-1 At 1886 meters (6288 feet), Mount Washington is the highest peak in the White Mountains and in fact the entire Northeast. It is a popular destination for hikers and is considered by some to be "the Home of the World's Worst Weather" due to its extreme cold, heavy snows, high winds, frequent icing, and dense fog. The observatory at its summit keeps detailed weather records. *(Photo by Jim Salge)*

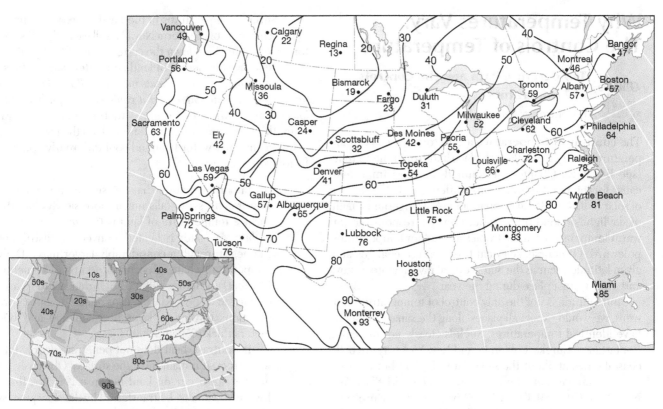

FIGURE 3-2 Isothermal map for a spring day. Isotherms are lines that connect points of equal temperature. Showing temperature distribution in this way makes patterns easier to see. On television and in many newspapers, temperature maps are in color. Rather than labeling isotherms, the area *between* isotherms is labeled. For example, the zone between the 60° and 70° isotherms is labeled "60s."

February on record" or "Today Omaha was 10 degrees warmer than Chicago." Temperature ranges are also useful statistics because they give an indication of extremes, a necessary part of understanding the weather and climate of a place or an area.

To examine the distribution of air temperatures over large areas, isotherms are commonly used. An **isotherm** is a line that connects points on a map that have the same temperature (*iso* = equal, *therm* = temperature). Therefore, all points through which an isotherm passes have identical temperatures for the time period indicated. Generally, isotherms representing 5° or 10° temperature differences are used, but any interval may be chosen. Figure 3–2 illustrates how isotherms are drawn on a map. Notice that most isotherms do not pass directly through the observing stations, because the station readings may not coincide with the values chosen for the isotherms. Only an occasional station temperature will be exactly the same as the value of the isotherm, so it is usually necessary to draw the lines by estimating the proper position between stations.

Isothermal maps are valuable tools because they clearly make temperature distribution visible at a glance. Areas of low and high temperatures are easy to pick out. In addition, the amount of temperature change per unit of distance, called the **temperature gradient,** is easy to visualize. Closely spaced isotherms indicate a rapid rate of tempera-

ture change, whereas more widely spaced lines indicate a more gradual rate of change. For example, notice in Figure 3–2 that the isotherms are closer in Colorado and Utah (steeper temperature gradient), whereas the isotherms are spread farther in Texas (gentler temperature gradient). Without isotherms a map would be covered with numbers representing temperatures at tens or hundreds of places, which would make patterns difficult to see.

Students Sometimes Ask...

What's the hottest city in the United States?

It depends on how you want to define "hottest." If average annual temperature is used, then Key West, Florida, is the hottest, with an annual mean of 25.6°C (78°F) for the 30-year span 1971–2000. However, if we look at cities with the highest July maximums during the 1971–2000 span, then the desert community of Palm Springs, California, has the distinction of being hottest. Its average daily high in July is a blistering 42.4°C (108.3°F)! Yuma, Arizona (41.7°C/107°F), Phoenix, Arizona (41.4°C/106°F), and Las Vegas, Nevada (40°C/104.1°F), aren't far behind.

Why Temperatures Vary: The Controls of Temperature

Temperature Data and the Controls of Temperature

▶ Controls of Temperature

The **controls of temperature** are factors that cause temperature to vary from place to place and from time to time (see Box 3–2). Chapter 2 examined the most important cause for temperature variation—differences in the receipt of solar radiation. Because variations in Sun angle and length of daylight depend on latitude, they are responsible for warm temperatures in the tropics and colder temperatures poleward. Of course, seasonal temperature changes at a given latitude occur as the Sun's vertical rays migrate toward and away from a place during the year.

But latitude is not the only control of temperature. If it were, we would expect all places along the same parallel to have identical temperatures. Such is clearly not the case. For instance, Eureka, California, and New York City are both coastal cities at about the same latitude, and both places have an annual mean temperature of 11°C (51.8°F). Yet New York City is 9.4°C (16.9°F) warmer than Eureka in July and 9.4°C (16.9°F) colder than Eureka in January. In another example, two cities in Ecuador—Quito and Guayaquil—are relatively close to one another, but the mean annual temperatures at these two cities differ by 12.2°C (22°F). To explain these situations and countless others, we must realize that factors other than latitude also exert a strong influence on temperature. In the next sections we examine these other controls, which include:

1. differential heating of land and water
2. ocean currents
3. altitude
4. geographic position
5. cloud cover and albedo

Land and Water

In Chapter 2 we saw that the heating of Earth's surface controls the heating of the air above it. Therefore, to understand variations in air temperature, we must understand the variations in heating properties of the different surfaces that Earth presents to the Sun—soil, water, trees, ice, and so on. Different land surfaces reflect and absorb varying amounts of incoming solar energy, which in turn cause variations in the temperature of the air above. The greatest contrast, however, is not between different land surfaces but between land and water. Figure 3–3 illustrates this idea nicely. This satellite image shows surface temperatures in portions of Nevada, California, and the adjacent Pacific Ocean on the afternoon of May 2, 2004, during a spring heat wave. Land-surface temperatures are clearly much higher than water-surface temperatures. The image shows the extreme high surface temperatures in southern California and Nevada in dark

red.[*] Surface temperatures in the Pacific Ocean are much lower. The peaks of the Sierra Nevada, still capped with snow, form a cool blue line down the eastern side of California.

In side-by-side bodies of land and water, such as those shown in Figure 3–3, *land heats more rapidly and to higher temperatures than water, and it cools more rapidly and to lower temperatures than water.* Variations in air temperatures, therefore, are much greater over land than over water. Why do land and water heat and cool differently? Several factors are responsible.

1. An important reason that the surface temperature of water rises and falls much more slowly than the surface temperature of land is that *water is highly mobile.* As water is heated, convection distributes the heat through a considerably larger mass. Daily temperature changes occur to depths of 6 meters (20 feet) or more below the surface, and yearly, oceans and deep lakes experience temperature variations through a layer between 200 and 600 meters thick (650 and 2000 feet).

   In contrast, heat does not penetrate deeply into soil or rock; it remains near the surface. Obviously, no mixing can occur on land because it is not fluid. Instead, heat must be transferred by the slow process of conduction. Consequently, daily temperature changes are small below a depth of 10 centimeters (4 inches), although some change can occur to a depth of perhaps 1 meter (3 feet). Annual temperature variations usually reach depths of 15 meters (50 feet) or less. Thus, as a result of the mobility of water and the lack of mobility in the solid Earth, a relatively thick layer of water is heated to moderate temperatures during the summer. On land only a thin layer is heated but to much higher temperatures.

   During winter the shallow layer of rock and soil that was heated in summer cools rapidly. Water bodies, in contrast, cool slowly as they draw on the reserve of heat stored within. As the water surface cools, vertical motions are established. The chilled surface water, which is dense, sinks and is replaced by warmer water from below, which is less dense. Consequently, a larger mass of water must cool before the temperature at the surface will drop appreciably.

2. Because land surfaces are opaque, heat is absorbed only at the surface. This fact is easily demonstrated at a beach on a hot summer afternoon by comparing the surface temperature of the sand to the temperature just a few centimeters beneath the surface. Water, being more transparent, allows some solar radiation to penetrate to a depth of several meters.

3. The **specific heat** (the amount of heat needed to raise the temperature of 1 gram of a substance 1°C) is more than three times greater for water than for

---

[*]Realize that air temperatures are cooler than surface temperatures. For example, the surface of a sandy beach can be painfully hot even though the air temperature is comfortable.

BOX 3-1 | North America's Hottest and Coldest Places

Most people living in the United States have experienced temperatures of 38°C (100°F) or more. When statistics for the 50 states are examined for the past century or longer, we find that every state has a maximum temperature record of 38°C or higher. Even Alaska has recorded a temperature this high. Its record was set June 27, 1915, at Fort Yukon, a town along the Arctic Circle in the interior of the state.

Maximum Temperature Records

Surprisingly, the state that ties Alaska for the "lowest high" is Hawaii. Panala, on the south coast of the big island, recorded 38°C on April 27, 1931. Although humid tropical and subtropical places like Hawaii are known for being warm throughout the year, they seldom experience maximum temperatures that surpass the low to mid-30s Celsius (90s Fahrenheit) (Figure 3–A).

The highest accepted temperature record for the United States as well as the entire Western Hemisphere is 57°C (134°F). This long-standing record was set at Death Valley, California, on July 10, 1913. Summer temperatures at Death Valley are consistently among the highest in the Western Hemisphere. During June, July, and August, temperatures exceeding 49°C (120°F) are to be expected. Fortunately, Death Valley has few human summertime residents.

Why are summer temperatures at Death Valley so high? In addition to having the lowest elevation in the Western Hemisphere (53 meters/174 feet below sea level), Death Valley is a desert. Although it is only about 300 kilometers (less than 200 miles) from the Pacific Ocean, mountains cut off the valley from the ocean's moderating influence and moisture. Clear skies allow a maximum of sunshine to strike the dry, barren surface. Because no energy is used to evaporate moisture as occurs in humid regions, all of the energy is available to heat the ground. In addition, subsiding air that warms by compression as it descends is also common to the region and contributes to its high maximum temperatures.

Minimum Temperature Records

The temperature controls that produce truly frigid temperatures are predictable, and they should come as no surprise. We should expect extremely cold temperatures during winter in high-latitude places that lack the moderating influence of the ocean. Moreover, stations located on ice sheets and glaciers should be especially cold, as should stations positioned high in the mountains. *All* of these criteria apply to Greenland's Northice station (elevation 2307 meters/7567 feet). Here on January 9, 1954, the temperature plunged to −66°C (−87°F). If we exclude Greenland from consideration, Snag, in Canada's Yukon Territory, holds the record for North America. This remote outpost experienced a temperature of −63°C (−81°F) on February 3, 1947. When only locations in the United States are considered, Prospect Creek, located north of the Arctic Circle in the Endicott Mountains of Alaska, came close to the North American record on January 23, 1971, when the temperature plunged to −62°C (−80°F). In the lower 48 states the record of −57°C (−70°F) was set in the mountains at Rogers Pass, Montana, on January 20, 1954. Remember that many other places have no doubt experienced equally low or even lower temperatures; they just were not recorded.

FIGURE 3-A Surprisingly, the highest temperature recorded for Hawaii is 38°C (100°F). It ties Alaska for the "lowest high." *(Photo by Mark Muench)*

BOX 3-2 Atmospheric Hazard: Heat Waves—Deadly Events*

A *heat wave* is a prolonged period of abnormally hot and usually humid weather that typically lasts from a few days to several weeks (Figure 3–B). The impact of heat waves on individuals varies greatly. The elderly are the most vulnerable because heat puts more stress on weak hearts and bodies. The poor, who often cannot afford air-conditioning, also suffer disproportionally. Studies also show that the temperatures at which death rates increase varys from city to city. In Dallas, Texas, a temperature of 39°C (103°F)

is required before the death rate climbs. In San Francisco the key temperature is just 29°C (84°F).

Heat waves are deadly events.

Heat is the deadliest of all atmospheric phenomena. From 1979 to 1999, the deaths of 8,015 Americans were directly associated with excessive heat exposure. This toll underestimates heat's true impact, however, as there is no consensus on what constitutes a "heat-related death," and death certificates often do not identify when heat has acted as a catalyst

in exacerbating preexisting cardiovascular, respiratory, and other conditions. Indeed, during the hot summer of 1980, across the United States some 10,000 deaths may have been associated with the oppressive heat, and the hot summer of 2003 in Europe may have claimed nearly 15,000 lives in France. **

The dangerous impact of summer heat is reinforced when examining Figure 3–C, which shows average annual weather-related deaths for the 10-year period 1994–2003. A com-

FIGURE 3-B Getting some relief during a heat wave in Washington, D.C. *(Photo by Mark Reinstein/The Image Works)*

*For a related discussion, see Box 4–4, "Humidity and Heat Stress," p. 112
**Scott C. Sheridan and Laurence S. Kalkstein, "Progress in Heat Watch-Warning System Technology," *Bulletin of the American Meteorological Society*, Vol. 85, No. 12, December 2004, p. 1931.

land. Thus, water requires considerably more heat to raise its temperature the same amount as an equal quantity of land.

4. Evaporation (a cooling process) from water bodies is greater than from land surfaces. Energy is required to evaporate water. When energy is used for evaporation, it is not available for heating.*

*Evaporation is an important process that is discussed more thoroughly in the section on "Water's Changes of State" in Chapter 4.

All these factors collectively cause water to warm more slowly, store greater quantities of heat energy, and cool more slowly than land.

Monthly temperature data for two cities will demonstrate the moderating influence of a large water body and the extremes associated with land (Figure 3–4). Vancouver, British Columbia, is located along the windward Pacific coast, whereas Winnipeg, Manitoba, is in a continental position far from the influence of water. Both cities are at about the same latitude and thus experience similar sun angles and lengths

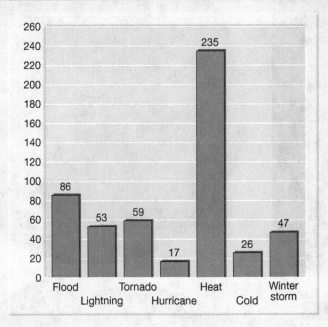

FIGURE 3-C Average annual weather-related fatalities for the 10-year period 1994–2003. *(After NOAA)*

many other impacts, including the following:

- Energy use vastly increased. This resulted in some power failures during peak stress hours and, of course, in substantially higher electric bills.

- Highways and railroads were damaged due to heat-induced heaving and buckling of roadway joints and rails.

- Many companies reported a substantial reduction in employee work efficiency.

- Shopping declined dramatically.

- In rural areas, livestock were affected. For example, on July 14 the *Wisconsin Journal* reported that 850 dairy cattle had died, major flocks of poultry were killed, and milk production was off by 25 percent.

parison of values reveals that the number of heat deaths far surpasses those of any other weather condition.

In July 1995 a brief but intense heat wave developed in the central United States. A total of 830 deaths were attributed to this severe five-day event, the worst in 50 years in the northern Midwest. The greatest loss of life occurred in Chicago, where there were 525 fatalities. The *Chicago Tribune* appropriately labeled the event "a citywide tragedy."

The severity of heat waves is usually greater in cities because of the *urban heat island* (see Box 3–4). Large cities do not cool off as much at night during heat waves as rural areas do, and this can be a critical difference in the amount of heat stress within the inner city. In addition, the stagnant atmospheric conditions usually associated with heat waves trap pollutants in urban areas and add the stresses of severe air pollution to the already dangerous stresses caused by the high temperatures.

In addition to the tragic loss of life, the 1995 Midwest heat wave had

Not everyone is adversely affected by a heat wave. In response to the 1995 event, tourism from Chicago to nearby (and cooler) Wisconsin increased 10 percent. As we would expect, sales of air conditioners in the Midwest rose as well—more than 50 percent over the previous year.

The 1995 heat wave in the upper Midwest was the most intense in half a century. It provided a sobering lesson by focusing attention on the need for more effective warning and response plans, especially in major urban areas where heat stress is greatest.

of daylight. Winnipeg, however, has a mean January temperature that is 20°C lower than Vancouver's. Conversely, Winnipeg's July mean is 2.6°C higher than Vancouver's. Although their latitudes are nearly the same, Winnipeg, which has no water influence, experiences much greater temperature extremes than does Vancouver. The key to Vancouver's moderate year-round climate is the Pacific Ocean.

On a different scale, the moderating influence of water may also be demonstrated when temperature variations in the Northern and Southern hemispheres are compared. The views of Earth in Figure 3–5 show the uneven distribution of land and water over the globe. Water covers 61 percent of the Northern Hemisphere; land represents the remaining 39 percent. However, the figures for the Southern Hemisphere (81 percent water, 19 percent land) reveal why it is correctly called the *water hemisphere*. Between 45° north and 79° north latitude there is actually more land than water, whereas between 40° south and 65° south latitude there is almost no land to interrupt the oceanic and atmospheric circulation. Table 3–1 portrays the considerably smaller annual temperature ranges in the water-dominated Southern Hemisphere compared with the Northern Hemisphere.

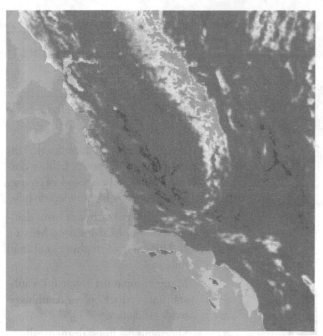

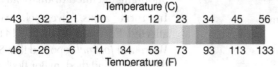

Temperature (C)
-43 -32 -21 -10 1 12 23 34 45 56

-46 -26 -6 14 34 53 73 93 113 133
Temperature (F)

FIGURE 3-3 The differential heating of land and water is an important control of air temperatures. In this satellite image from the afternoon of May 2, 2004, water-surface temperatures in the Pacific Ocean are much lower than land-surface temperatures in California and Nevada. *(NASA image)*

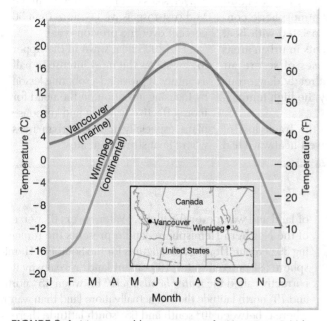

FIGURE 3-4 Mean monthly temperatures for Vancouver, British Columbia, and Winnipeg, Manitoba. Vancouver has a much smaller annual temperature range owing to the strong marine influence of the Pacific Ocean. Winnipeg illustrates the greater extremes associated with an interior location.

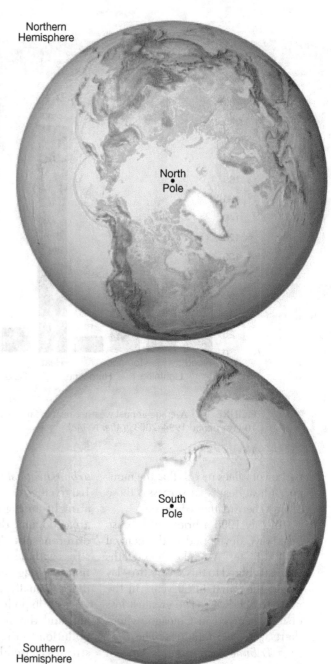

FIGURE 3-5 The uneven distribution of land and water between the Northern and Southern hemispheres. Almost 81 percent of the Southern Hemisphere is covered by the oceans—20 percent more than the Northern Hemisphere.

TABLE 3-1 Variation in mean annual temperature range (°C) with latitude.

Latitude	Northern Hemisphere	Southern Hemisphere
0	0	0
15	3	4
30	13	7
45	23	6
60	30	11
75	32	26
90	40	31

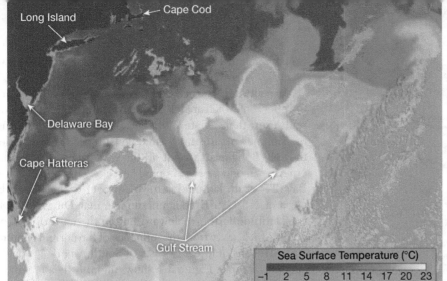

FIGURE 3-6 This satellite image shows sea-surface temperatures off the East Coast of the United States on April 18, 2005. The warm waters of the Gulf Stream (lighter shades) extend diagonally from bottom left to top right. The current transports heat from the tropics far into the North Atlantic. This image shows several deep bends in the path of the Gulf Stream. In fact, the northernmost of the two deep bends actually loops back on itself, creating a closed-off eddy. On the northern side of the current, cold waters (blue) dip southward into the Gulf Stream's warmth. Gray areas indicate clouds. *(NASA image)*

Ocean Currents

You probably have heard of the Gulf Stream, an important surface current in the Atlantic Ocean that flows northward along the East Coast of the United States (Figure 3–6). Surface currents like this one are set in motion by the wind. At the water surface, where the atmosphere and ocean meet, energy is passed from moving air to the water through friction. As a consequence, the drag exerted by winds blowing steadily across the ocean causes the surface layer of water to move. Thus, major horizontal movements of surface waters are closely related to the circulation of the atmosphere, which in turn is driven by the unequal heating of Earth by the Sun (Figure 3–7).*

Surface ocean currents have an important effect on climate. It is known that for Earth as a whole, the gains in solar energy equal the losses to space of heat radiated from the surface. When most latitudes are considered individually, however, this is not the case. There is a net gain of energy in lower latitudes and a net loss at higher latitudes. Because the tropics are not becoming progressively warmer, nor the polar regions colder, there must be a large-scale transfer of heat from areas of excess to areas of deficit. This is indeed the case. *The transfer of heat by winds and ocean currents equalizes these latitudinal energy imbalances.* Ocean water movements account for about a quarter of this total heat transport, and winds the remaining three-quarters.

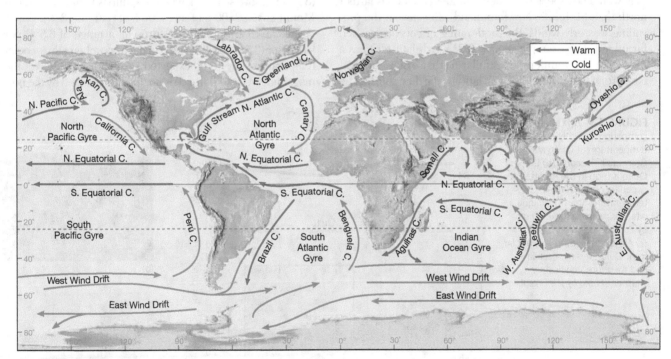

FIGURE 3-7 Major surface ocean currents. Poleward-moving currents are warm, and equatorward-moving currents are cold. Surface ocean currents are driven by global winds and play an important role in redistributing heat around the globe. Note that cities mentioned in the text discussion are shown on this map.

*The relationship between global winds and surface ocean currents is examined in Chapter 7.

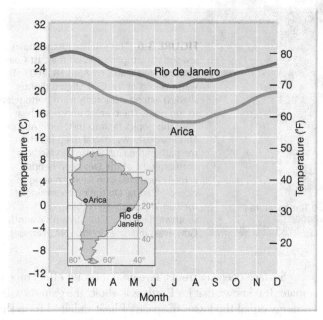

FIGURE 3-8 Monthly mean temperatures for Rio de Janeiro, Brazil, and Arica, Chile. Both are coastal cities near sea level. Even though Arica is closer to the equator than Rio de Janeiro, its temperatures are cooler. Arica is influenced by the cold Peruvian Current, whereas Rio de Janeiro is adjacent to the warm Brazilian Current.

The moderating effect of poleward-moving warm ocean currents is well known. The North Atlantic Drift, an extension of the warm Gulf Stream, keeps wintertime temperatures in Great Britain and much of Western Europe warmer than would be expected for their latitudes (London is farther north than St. John's, Newfoundland). Because of the prevailing westerly winds, the moderating effects are carried far inland. For example, Berlin (52° north latitude) has a mean January temperature similar to that experienced at New York City, which lies 12° latitude farther south. The January mean at London (51° north latitude) is 4.5°C (8.1°F) higher than at New York City.

In contrast to warm ocean currents like the Gulf Stream, the effects of which are felt most during the winter, cold currents exert their greatest influence in the tropics or during the summer months in the middle latitudes. For example, the cool Benguela Current off the western coast of southern Africa moderates the tropical heat along this coast. Walvis Bay (23° south latitude), a town adjacent to the Benguela Current, is 5°C (9°F) cooler in summer than Durban, which is 6° latitude farther poleward but on the eastern side of South Africa, away from the influence of the current (Figure 3–7). The east and west coasts of South America provide another example. Figure 3–8 shows monthly mean temperatures for Rio de Janeiro, Brazil, which is influenced by the warm Brazilian Current and Arica, Chile, which is adjacent to the cold Peruvian Current. Closer to home, because of the cold California current, summer temperatures in subtropical coastal southern California are lower by 6°C (10.8°F) or more compared to East Coast stations.

Altitude

The two cities in Ecuador mentioned earlier, Quito and Guayaquil, demonstrate the influence of altitude on mean temperature. Both cities are near the equator and relatively close to one another, but the annual mean temperature at Guayaquil is 25.5°C (77.9°F) compared with Quito's mean of 13.3°C (55.9°F). The difference may be understood when the cities' elevations are noted. Guayaquil is only 12 meters (39 feet) above sea level, whereas Quito is high in the Andes Mountains at 2800 meters (9200 feet) (Figure 3–9).

Recall that temperatures drop an average of 6.5°C per kilometer (3.5°F per 1000 feet) in the troposphere; thus, cooler temperatures are to be expected at greater heights. Yet the magnitude of the difference is not totally explained by the nor-

FIGURE 3-9 (a) Graph comparing monthly mean temperatures at Quito and Guayaquil, Ecuador. (b) Because Quito is high in the Andes, it experiences much cooler temperatures than Guayaquil, which is near sea level. (Photo by Pablo Corral Vega/CORBIS) (c) Although Guayaquil is not far from Quito, it is near sea level and therefore significantly warmer. (Photo by Jeff Greenberg)

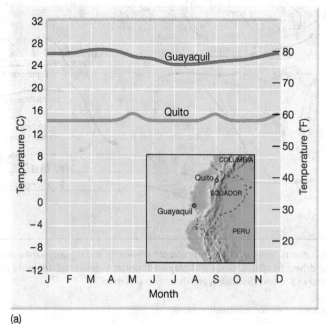

(a)

(b)

(c)

mal lapse rate. If this figure were used, we would expect Quito to be about 18.2°C (32.7°F) cooler than Guayaquil, but the difference is only 12.2°C (22°F). The fact that high-altitude places, such as Quito, are warmer than the value calculated using the normal lapse rate results from the absorption and reradiation of solar energy by the ground surface.

In addition to the effect of altitude on mean temperatures, the daily temperature range also changes with variations in height. Not only do temperatures drop with an increase in altitude but atmospheric pressure and density also diminish. Because of the reduced density at high altitudes, the overlying atmosphere absorbs and reflects a smaller portion of the incoming solar radiation. Consequently, with an increase in altitude, the intensity of solar radiation increases, resulting in relatively rapid and intense daytime heating. Conversely, rapid nighttime cooling is also the rule in high mountain locations. Therefore, stations located high in the mountains generally have a greater daily temperature range than do stations at lower elevations.

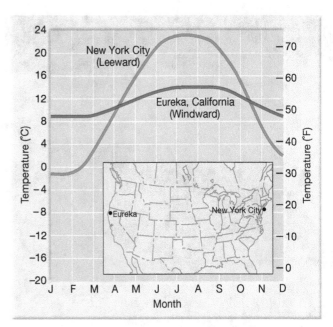

FIGURE 3-10 Monthly mean temperatures for Eureka, California, and New York City. Both cities are coastal and located at about the same latitude. Because Eureka is strongly influenced by prevailing winds from the ocean and New York City is not, the annual temperature range at Eureka is much smaller.

Students Sometimes Ask...

Can high mountain areas in the tropics be cold enough for glaciers?

Yes. Glaciers do indeed occur in the tropics at high elevations. Near the equator, glaciers sometimes form above about 5000 meters (16,400 feet). Examples of equatorial glaciers include those atop Mount Kenya and Mount Kilimanjaro in East Africa and those in the tall mountains of New Guinea.

Geographic Position

The geographic setting can greatly influence the temperatures experienced at a specific location. A coastal location where prevailing winds blow from the ocean onto the shore (a *windward* coast) experiences considerably different temperatures than does a coastal location where prevailing winds blow from the land toward the ocean (a *leeward* coast). In the first situation the windward coast will experience the full moderating influence of the ocean—cool summers and mild winters—compared to an inland station at the same latitude.

A leeward coastal situation, however, will have a more continental temperature regime because the winds do not carry the ocean's influence onshore. Eureka, California, and New York City, the two cities mentioned earlier, illustrate this aspect of geographic position (Figure 3–10). The annual temperature range at New York City is 19°C (34°F) greater than Eureka's.

Seattle and Spokane, both in the state of Washington, illustrate a second aspect of geographic position: mountains acting as barriers. Although Spokane is only about 360 kilometers (225 miles) east of Seattle, the towering Cascade Range separates the cities. Consequently, Seattle's temperatures show a marked marine influence, but Spokane's are more typically continental (Figure 3–11). Spokane is 7°C (12.6°F) cooler than Seattle in January and 4°C (7.2°F)

warmer than Seattle in July. The annual range at Spokane is 11°C (nearly 20°F) greater than at Seattle. The Cascade Range effectively cuts off Spokane from the moderating influence of the Pacific Ocean.

Cloud Cover and Albedo

You may have noticed that clear days are often warmer than cloudy ones and that clear nights usually are cooler than cloudy ones. This demonstrates that cloud cover is another

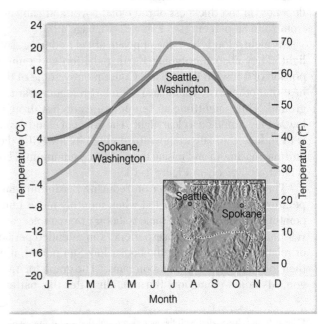

FIGURE 3-11 Monthly mean temperatures for Seattle and Spokane, Washington. Because the Cascade Mountains cut off Spokane from the moderating influence of the Pacific Ocean, its annual temperature range is greater than Seattle's.

(a)

(b)

FIGURE 3-12 (a) It is obvious when you are above thick, dense clouds that a great deal of light is reflected that otherwise would reach Earth's surface. (b) When there is a dense overcast, maximum temperatures at the surface are lower than they would be if the sky was clear. *(Photo (a) by Detlev Ravenswaay/Photo Researchers, Inc.; photo (b) by David Muench)*

factor that influences temperature in the lower atmosphere. Studies using satellite images show that at any particular time about half of our planet is covered by clouds. Cloud cover is important because many clouds have a high albedo and therefore reflect a significant proportion of the sunlight that strikes them back to space. By reducing the amount of incoming solar radiation, daytime temperatures will be lower than if the clouds were absent and the sky were clear (Figure 3–12). As was noted in Chapter 2, the albedo of clouds depends on the thickness of the cloud cover and can vary from 25 to 80 percent (see Figure 2–15, page 49).

At night, clouds have the opposite effect as during daylight. They absorb outgoing Earth radiation and emit a portion of it toward the surface. Consequently, some of the heat that otherwise would have been lost remains near the ground. Thus, nighttime air temperatures do not drop as low as they would on a clear night. The effect of cloud cover is to reduce the daily temperature range by lowering the daytime maximum and raising the nighttime minimum. This is illustrated nicely in Figure 3–13.

The effect of cloud cover on reducing maximum temperatures can also be detected when monthly mean temperatures are examined for some stations. For example, each year much of southern Asia experiences an extended period of relative drought during the cooler low-Sun period; it is then followed by heavy monsoon rains.° The graph for Yangon, Myanmar (Rangoon, Burma), illustrates this pattern

°This pattern is associated with the monsoon circulation and is discussed in Chapter 7.

(Figure 3–14). Notice that the highest monthly mean temperatures occur in April and May, before the summer solstice, rather than in July and August, as normally occurs at most stations in the Northern Hemisphere. Why?

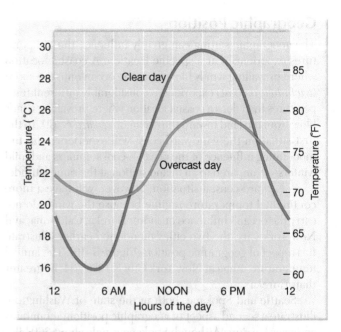

FIGURE 3-13 The daily cycle of temperature at Peoria, Illinois, for two July days. On the clear day the maximum temperature was higher, and the minimum temperature was lower than on the cloudy day.

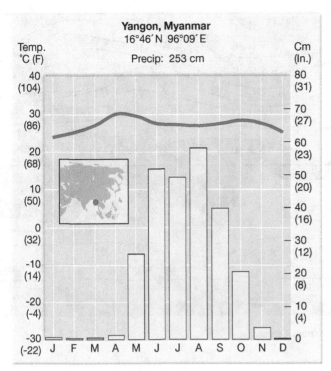

FIGURE 3-14 Monthly mean temperatures (curve) and monthly mean precipitation (bar graph) for Yangon, Myanmar. The highest mean temperature occurs in April, just before the onset of heavy summer rains. The abundant cloud cover associated with the rainy period reflects back into space the solar energy that otherwise would strike the ground and raise summer temperatures.

The reason is that during the summer months when we would usually expect temperatures to climb, the extensive cloud cover increases the albedo of the region, which reduces incoming solar radiation. As a result, the highest monthly mean temperatures occur in late spring when the skies are still relatively clear.

Cloudiness is not the only phenomenon that increases albedo and thereby reduces air temperature. We also recognize that snow- and ice-covered surfaces have high albedos. This is one reason why mountain glaciers do not melt away in the summer and why snow may still be present on a mild spring day. In addition, during the winter when snow covers the ground, daytime maximums on a sunny day are cooler than they otherwise would be, because energy that the land would have absorbed and used to heat the air is reflected and lost.

World Distribution of Temperatures

Take a moment to study the two world isothermal maps (Figures 3–15 and 3–16). From hot colors near the equator to cool colors toward the poles, these maps portray sea-level temperatures in the seasonally extreme months of January and July. On these maps you can study global temperature

patterns and the effects of the controls of temperature, especially latitude, the distribution of land and water, and ocean currents (see Box 3–3). Like most isothermal maps of large regions, all temperatures on these world maps have been reduced to sea level to eliminate the complications caused by differences in altitude.

On both maps the isotherms generally trend east and west and show a decrease in temperatures poleward from the tropics. They illustrate one of the most fundamental aspects of world temperature distribution: that the effectiveness of incoming solar radiation in heating Earth's surface and the atmosphere above it is largely a function of latitude.

Moreover, there is a latitudinal shifting of temperatures caused by the seasonal migration of the Sun's vertical rays. To see this, compare the color bands by latitude on the two maps. For example, on the January map the "hot spots" of 30°C are *south* of the equator, but in July they have shifted *north* of the equator.

If latitude were the only control of temperature distribution, our analysis could end here, but this is not the case. The added effect of the differential heating of land and water is clearly reflected on the January and July temperature maps. The warmest and coldest temperatures are found over land—note the coldest area, a purple oval in Siberia, and the hottest areas, the deep orange ovals—all over land. Consequently, because temperatures do not fluctuate as much over water as over land, the north–south migration of isotherms is greater over the continents than over the oceans. In addition, it is clear that the isotherms in the Southern Hemisphere, where there is little land and where the oceans predominate, are much more regular than in the Northern Hemisphere, where they bend sharply northward in July and southward in January over the continents.

Isotherms also reveal the presence of ocean currents. Warm currents cause isotherms to be deflected toward the poles, whereas cold currents cause an equatorward bending. The horizontal transport of water poleward warms the overlying air and results in air temperatures that are higher than would otherwise be expected for the latitude. Conversely, currents moving toward the equator produce cooler-than-expected air temperatures.

Figures 3–15 and 3–16 show the seasonal extremes of temperature, so comparing them enables us to see the annual range of temperature from place to place. Comparing the two maps shows that a station near the equator has a very small annual range because it experiences little variation in the length of daylight and it always has a relatively high Sun angle. A station in the middle latitudes, however, experiences wide variations in Sun angle and length of daylight and hence large variations in temperature. Therefore, we can state that the annual temperature range increases with an increase in latitude (see Box 3–30).

Moreover, land and water also affect seasonal temperature variations, especially outside the tropics. A continental location must endure hotter summers and colder winters

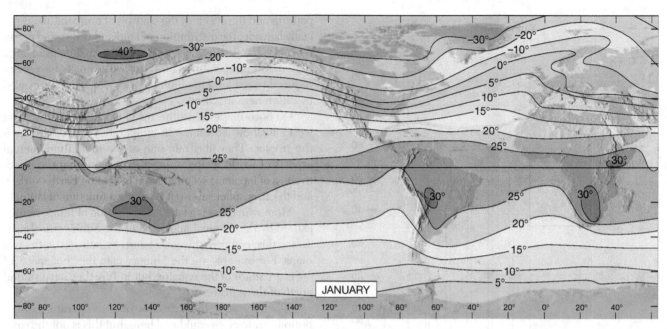

FIGURE 3-15 World mean sea-level temperatures in January in degrees Celsius.

than a coastal location. Consequently, outside the tropics the annual range will increase with an increase in continentality.

Figure 3–17, which shows the global distribution of annual temperature ranges, serves to summarize the preceding two paragraphs. By examining this map, it is easy to see the influence of latitude and continentality on this temperature statistic. The tropics clearly experience small annual temperature variations. As expected, the highest values occur in the middle of large landmasses in the subpolar latitudes. It is also obvious that annual temperature ranges in the ocean-dominated Southern Hemisphere are much smaller than in the Northern Hemisphere with its large continents.

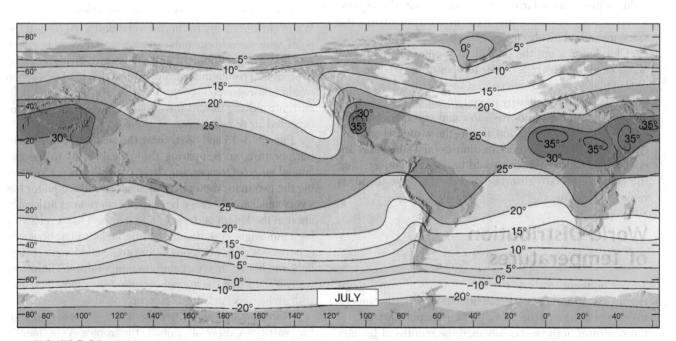

FIGURE 3-16 World mean sea-level temperatures in July in degrees Celsius.

BOX 3-3   Latitude and Temperature Range

Gregory J. Carbone°

Latitude, because of its influence on Sun angle, is the most important temperature control. Figures 3–15 and 3–16 clearly show higher temperatures in tropical loca- tions and lower temperatures in polar regions. The maps also show that higher latitudes experience a greater range of temperatures during the year than do lower latitudes. Notice also that the temperature gradient between the subtropics and the poles is greatest during the winter season. A look at two cities—San Antonio, Texas, and Winnipeg, Manitoba—illustrates how seasonal differences in Sun angle and day length account for these tem- perature patterns. Figure 3–D shows the annual march of temperature for the two cities, whereas Figure 3–E illustrates the Sun angles for the June and December solstices.

San Antonio and Winnipeg are a fixed distance apart (approximately 20.5° latitude), so the difference in Sun angles between the two cities is the same throughout the year. How- ever, in December, when the Sun's rays are least direct, this difference more strongly affects the intensity of solar radiation received at Earth's sur- face. Therefore, we expect a greater difference in temperatures between the two stations in winter than in summer. Moreover, the seasonal dif- ference in intensity (spreading out of the light beam) at Winnipeg is con- siderably greater than at San Antonio. This helps to explain the greater annual temperature range at the more northerly station. Table 2–2, Chapter 2, shows that seasonal con- trasts in day length also contribute to different temperature patterns at the two cities.

FIGURE 3-D The annual temperature range at Winnipeg is much greater than at San Antonio.

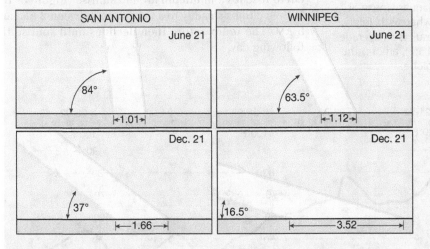

FIGURE 3-E A comparison of Sun angles (solar noon) for summer and winter solstices at San Antonio and Winnipeg. The space covered by a 90° angle = 1.00.

°Professor Carbone is a faculty member in the Department of Geography at the University of South Carolina.

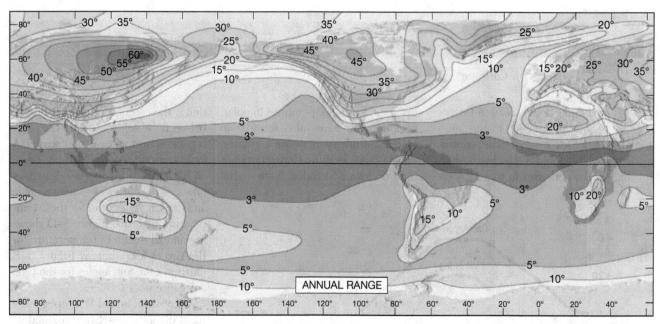

FIGURE 3-17 Global annual temperature ranges in degrees Celsius. Annual ranges are small near the equator and increase toward the poles. Outside the tropics, annual temperature ranges increase as we move away from the ocean toward the interior of large landmasses. *(After Robert W. Christopherson,* Geosystems: An Introduction to Physical Geography, *Fifth Edition, Prentice Hall, 2003)*

Students Sometimes Ask...

Where in the world would I experience the greatest contrast between summer and winter temperatures?

Among places for which records exist, it appears as though Yakutsk, a station in the heart of Siberia, is the best candidate. The latitude of Yakutsk is 62° north, just a few degrees south of the Arctic Circle. Moreover, it is far from the influence of water. The January mean at Yakutsk is a frigid −43°C (−45°F), whereas its July mean is a pleasant 20°C (68°F). The result is an average annual temperature range of 63°C (113°F), among the highest anywhere on the globe.

Cycles of Air Temperature

You know from experience that a rhythmic rise and fall of air temperature occurs almost every day. Your experience is confirmed by thermograph records like the one in Figure 3–18 (a thermograph is an instrument that continuously records temperature). The temperature curve reaches a minimum around sunrise (Figure 3–19). It then climbs steadily to a maximum between 2 P.M. and 5 P.M. The temperature then declines until sunrise the following day.

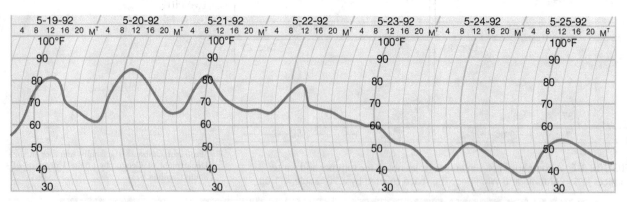

FIGURE 3-18 Thermograph of temperatures in Peoria, Illinois, during a seven-day span in May 1992. The typical daily rhythm, with minimums around sunrise and maximums in mid- to late afternoon, occurred on most days. The obvious exception occurred on May 23, when the maximum was reached at midnight and temperatures dropped throughout the day.

(a)

(b)

FIGURE 3-19 The minimum daily temperature usually occurs near the time of sunrise. As the ground and air cool during the nighttime hours, familiar early morning phenomena such as the frost in photo (a) and the ground fog in photo (b) may form. *(Photo (a) by AP Photo/Daily Telegram/Jed Carlson. Photo (b) by Michael Collier)*

Daily Temperature Variations

The primary control of the daily cycle of air temperature is as obvious as the cycle itself: It is Earth's daily rotation, which causes a location to move into daylight for part of each day and then into darkness. As the Sun's angle increases

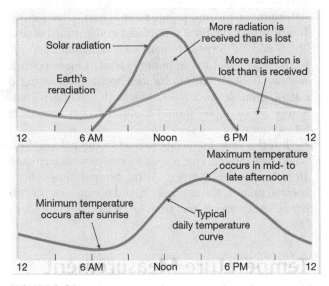

FIGURE 3-20 The daily cycle of incoming solar radiation, Earth's radiation, and the resulting temperature cycle. This example is for a midlatitude site around the time of an equinox. As long as solar energy gained exceeds outgoing energy emitted by Earth, the temperature rises. When outgoing energy from Earth exceeds the input of solar energy, temperature falls. Note that the daily temperature cycle *lags* behind the solar radiation input by a couple of hours.

throughout the morning, the intensity of sunlight also rises, reaching a peak at local noon and gradually diminishing in the afternoon.

Figure 3–20 shows the daily variation of incoming solar energy versus outgoing Earth radiation and the resulting temperature curve for a typical middle-latitude location at the time of an equinox. During the night the atmosphere and the surface of Earth cool as they radiate heat away that is not replaced by incoming solar energy. The minimum temperature, therefore, occurs about the time of sunrise, after which the Sun again heats the ground, which in turn heats the air.

It is apparent that the time of highest temperature does not generally coincide with the time of maximum radiation. By comparing Figures 3–18 and 3–20, you can see that the curve for incoming solar energy is symmetrical with respect to noon, but the daily air temperature curves are not. The delay in the occurrence of the maximum until mid- to late afternoon is termed the *lag of the maximum*.

Although the intensity of solar radiation drops in the afternoon, it still exceeds outgoing energy from Earth's surface for a period of time. This produces an energy surplus for up to several hours in the afternoon and contributes substantially to the lag of the maximum. In other words, as long as the solar energy gained exceeds the rate of Earth radiation lost, the air temperature continues to rise. When the input of solar energy no longer exceeds the rate of energy lost by Earth, the temperature falls.

The lag of the daily maximum is also a result of the process by which the atmosphere is heated. Recall that air is a poor absorber of most solar radiation; consequently, it is heated primarily by energy reradiated from Earth's surface. The rate at which Earth supplies heat to the atmosphere through radiation, conduction, and other means, however, is not in balance with the rate at which the atmosphere radiates heat away. Generally, for a few hours after the period of maximum solar radiation, more heat is supplied to the atmosphere by Earth's surface than is emitted by the atmosphere to space. As a result, most locations experience an increase in air temperature during the afternoon.

In dry regions, particularly on cloud-free days, the amount of radiation absorbed by the surface will generally be high. Therefore, the time of the maximum temperature at these locales will often occur quite late in the afternoon. Humid locations, in contrast, will frequently experience a shorter time lag in the occurrence of their temperature maximum.

Magnitude of Daily Temperature Changes

The magnitude of daily temperature changes is variable and may be influenced by locational factors, or local weather conditions, or both (see Box 3–4). Four common examples illustrate this point. The first two relate to location, and the second two pertain to local weather conditions.

1. Variations in Sun angle are relatively great during the day in the middle and low latitudes. However, points near the poles experience a low Sun angle all day. Consequently, the temperature change experienced during a day in the high latitudes is small.

2. A windward coast is likely to experience only modest variations in the daily cycle. During a typical 24-hour period the ocean warms less than 1°C. As a result, the air above it shows a correspondingly slight change in temperature. For example, Eureka, California, a windward coastal station, consistently has a lower daily temperature range than Des Moines, Iowa, an inland city at about the same latitude. Annually the daily range at Des Moines averages 10.9°C (19.6°F) compared with 6.1°C (11°F) at Eureka, a difference of 4.8°C (8.6°F).

3. As mentioned earlier, an overcast day is responsible for a flattened daily temperature curve (see Figure 3–13). By day, clouds block incoming solar radiation and so reduce daytime heating. At night the clouds retard the loss of radiation by the ground and air. Therefore, nighttime temperatures are warmer than they otherwise would have been.

4. The amount of water vapor in the air influences daily temperature range because water vapor is one of the atmosphere's important heat-absorbing gases. When the air is clear and dry, heat rapidly escapes at night, and the temperature falls rapidly. When the air is humid, absorption of outgoing long-wavelength radiation by water vapor slows nighttime cooling, and the temperature does not fall to as low a value. Thus, dry conditions are associated with a higher daily temperature range because of greater nighttime cooling.

Although the rise and fall of daily temperatures usually reflects the general rise and fall of incoming solar radiation, such is not always the case. For example, a glance back at Figure 3–18 reveals that on May 23 the maximum temperature occurred at midnight, after which temperatures fell throughout the day. If records for a station are examined for a period of several weeks, apparently random variations are seen. Obviously these are not Sun-controlled. Such irregularities are caused primarily by the passage of atmospheric disturbances (weather systems) that are often accompanied by variable cloudiness and winds that bring air having contrasting temperatures. Under these circumstances, the maximum and minimum temperatures may occur at any time of the day or night.

Annual Temperature Variations

In most years the months with the highest and lowest mean temperatures do not coincide with the periods of maximum and minimum incoming solar radiation. Poleward of the tropics the greatest intensity of solar radiation occurs at the time of the summer solstice in June, yet the months of July and August are generally the warmest of the year in the Northern Hemisphere. Conversely, a minimum of solar energy is received in December at the time of the winter solstice, but January and February are usually colder.

The fact that the occurrence of annual maximum and minimum radiation does not coincide with the times of temperature maximums and minimums indicates that the amount of solar radiation received is not the only factor determining the temperature at a particular location. Recall from Chapter 2 that places equatorward of about 38° N and 38° S receive more solar radiation than is lost to space and that the opposite is true of more poleward regions. Based on this imbalance between incoming and outgoing radiation, any location in the southern United States, for example, should continue to get warmer late into autumn.

But this does not occur, because more poleward locations begin experiencing a negative radiation balance shortly after the summer solstice. As the temperature contrasts become greater, the atmosphere and ocean currents "work harder" to transport heat from lower latitudes poleward.

Temperature Measurement

Temperature Data and the Controls of Temperature

▶ Basic Temperature Data

Thermometers are "meters of therms": They measure temperature. Thermometers measure temperature either mechanically or electrically.

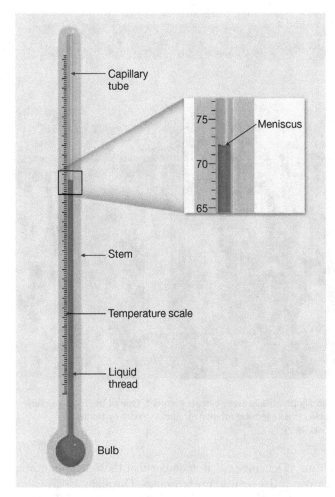

FIGURE 3-21 The main components of a liquid-in-glass thermometer.

Mechanical Thermometers

Most substances expand when heated and contract when cooled, so many common thermometers are based on this property. More precisely, they rely on the fact that different substances react to temperature changes differently.

The **liquid-in-glass thermometer** shown in Figure 3–21 is a simple instrument that provides relatively accurate readings over a wide temperature range. Its design has remained essentially unchanged ever since it was developed in the late 1600s. When temperature rises, the molecules of fluid grow more active and spread out (the fluid expands). Expansion of the fluid in the bulb is much greater than the expansion of the enclosing glass. As a consequence, a thin "thread" of fluid is forced up the capillary tube. Conversely, when temperature falls, the liquid contracts and the thread of fluid moves back down the tube toward the bulb. The movement of the end of this thread (known as the *meniscus*) is calibrated against an established scale to indicate the temperature.

The highest and lowest temperatures that occur each day are of considerable importance and are often obtained by using specially designed liquid-in-glass thermometers. Mercury is the liquid used in the **maximum thermometer,** which has a narrowed passage called a *constriction* in the bore of the glass tube just above the bulb (Figure 3–22a). As the temperature rises, the mercury expands and is forced through the constriction. When the temperature falls, the constriction prevents a return of mercury to the bulb. As a result, the top of the mercury column remains at the highest point (maximum temperature attained during the measurement period). The instrument is reset by shaking or by whirling it to force the mercury through the constriction back into the bulb. Once the thermometer is reset, it indicates the current air temperature.

In contrast to a maximum thermometer that contains mercury, a **minimum thermometer** contains a liquid of low density, such as alcohol. Within the alcohol, and resting

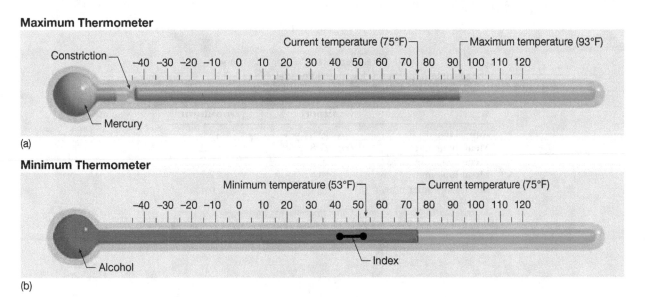

FIGURE 3-22 (a) Maximum thermometer and (b) minimum thermometer.

BOX 3-4   How Cities Influence Temperature: The Urban Heat Island

The most apparent human impact on climate is the modification of the atmospheric environment by the building of cities. The construction of every factory, road, office building, and house destroys microclimates and creates new ones of great complexity (Figure 3–F).

The most studied and well-documented urban climatic effect is the *urban heat island*. The term refers to the fact that temperatures within cities are generally higher than in rural areas. The heat island is evident when temperature data such as that which appears in Table 3–A are examined. As is typical, the data for Philadelphia show the heat island is most pronounced when minimum temperatures are examined. The magnitude of the temperature differences shown by Table 3–A is probably even greater than the figures indicate, because temperatures observed at suburban airports are usually higher than those in truly rural environments.

Figure 3–G, which shows the distribution of average minimum temperatures in the Washington, D.C., metropolitan area for the three-

FIGURE 3-F Cities modify practically every climate element. One of the most studied and best documented effects is called the *urban heat island. (Photo by Daniel Philippe/Photo Researchers, Inc.)*

month winter period (December through February) over a five-year span, also illustrates a well-developed heat island. The warmest winter temperatures occurred in the heart of the city, whereas the suburbs and surrounding countryside experienced average minimum temperatures that were as much as 3.3°C (6°F) lower.

Remember that these temperatures are averages. On many clear, calm nights the temperature difference between the city center and the countryside was considerably greater, often 11°C (20°F) or more. Conversely, on many overcast or windy nights the temperature differential approached zero degrees.

TABLE 3-A Average temperatures (°C) for suburban Philadelphia Airport and downtown Philadelphia (10-year averages)

	Airport	Downtown
Annual mean	12.8	13.6
Mean June max	27.8	28.2
Mean December max	6.4	6.7
Mean June min	16.5	17.7
Mean December min	−2.1	−0.4

Source: After H. Neuberger and J. Cahir, Principles of Climatology *(New York: Holt, Rinehart and Winston, 1969), 128.*

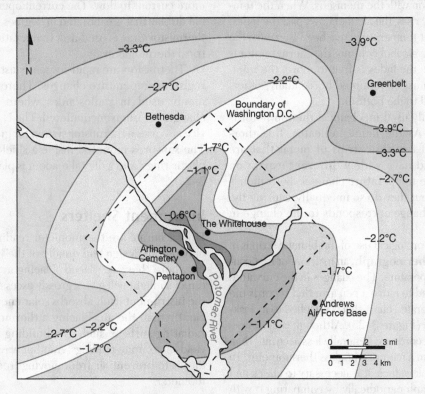

FIGURE 3-G The heat island of Washington, D.C., as shown by the average minimum temperatures (°C) during the winter season (December through February). The city center had an average minimum that was nearly 4°C higher than some outlying areas. *(After Clarence A. Woolum, "Notes from the Study of the Microclimatology of the Washington, D.C. Area for the Winter and Spring Seasons," Weatherwise, 17, no. 6 (1964), 264, 267.)*

A recent study indicates that one effect of the urban heat island is to influence the biosphere by extending the plant cycle.* After examining data for 70 cities in eastern North America, researchers found that the growing cycle in cities was about 15 days longer than surrounding rural areas. Plants began the growth cycle an average of about seven days earlier in spring and continued growing an average of eight days longer in fall.

Why are cities warmer? The radical change in the surface that re-

*Reported in *Weatherwise*, Vol. 57, No. 6, Nov/Dec 2004, p. 20.

sults when rural areas are transformed into cities is a significant cause of the urban heat island. First, the tall buildings and the concrete and asphalt of the city absorb and store greater quantities of solar radiation than do the vegetation and soil typical of rural areas. In addition, because the city surface is impermeable, the runoff of water following a rain is rapid, resulting in a significant reduction in the evaporation rate. Hence, heat that once would have been used to convert liquid water to a gas now goes to increase further the surface temperature. At night, as both the city

and countryside cool by radiative losses, the stonelike surface of the city gradually releases the additional heat accumulated during the day, keeping the urban air warmer than that of the outlying areas.

A portion of the urban temperature rise is also attributed to waste heat from sources such as home heating and air-conditioning, power generation, industry, and transportation. In addition, the "blanket" of pollutants over a city contributes to the heat island by absorbing a portion of the upward-directed long-wave radiation emitted by the surface and reemitting some of it back to the ground.

at the top of the column, is a small dumbbell-shaped index (Figure 3–22b). As the air temperature drops, the column shortens and the index is pulled toward the bulb by the effect of surface tension with the meniscus. When the temperature subsequently rises, the alcohol flows past the index, leaving it at the lowest temperature reached. To return the index to the top of the alcohol column, the thermometer is simply tilted. Because the index is free to move, the minimum thermometer must be mounted horizontally; otherwise the index will fall to the bottom.

Another commonly used mechanical thermometer is the **bimetal strip.** As the name indicates, this thermometer consists of two thin strips of metal that are bonded together and have widely different expansion properties. When the temperature changes, both metals expand or contract, but they do so unequally, causing the strips to curl. This change corresponds to the change in temperature.

The primary meteorological use of the bimetal strip is in the construction of a **thermograph,** an instrument that continuously records temperature. The changes in the curvature of the strip can be used to move a pen arm that records the temperature on a calibrated chart that is attached to a clock-driven, rotating drum (Figure 3–23). Although very convenient, thermograph records are generally less accurate than readings obtained from a mercury-in-glass thermometer. To obtain the most reliable values, it is necessary to check and correct the thermograph periodically by comparing it with an accurate, similarly exposed thermometer.

Electrical Thermometers

Some thermometers do not rely on differential expansion but instead measure temperature electrically.

A resistor is a small electronic part that resists the flow of electrical current. A **thermistor** (thermal resistor) is similar, but its resistance to current flow varies with tempera-
ture. As temperature increases, so does the resistance of the thermistor, reducing the flow of current. As temperature drops, so does the resistance of the thermistor, allowing more current to flow. The current operates a meter or digital display that is calibrated in degrees of temperature. The thermistor thus is used as a temperature sensor—an electrical thermometer.

Thermistors are rapid-response instruments that quickly register temperature changes. Therefore, they are commonly used in radiosondes where rapid temperature changes are often encountered. The National Weather Service also uses a thermistor system for ground-level readings. The sensor is mounted inside a shield made of louvered plastic rings, and a digital readout is placed indoors (Figure 3–24).

Instrument Shelters

How accurate are thermometer readings? It depends not only on the design and quality of the instruments but also on where they are placed. Placing a thermometer in the direct sunlight will give a grossly excessive reading, because the instrument itself absorbs solar energy much more efficiently than the air. Placing a thermometer near a heat-radiating surface, such as a building or the ground, also yields inaccurate readings. Another way to assure false readings is to prevent air from moving freely around the thermometer.

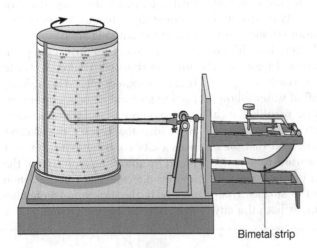

Bimetal strip

FIGURE 3-23 A common use of the bimetal strip is in the construction of a thermograph, an instrument that continuously records temperatures.

FIGURE 3-24 This modern shelter contains an electrical thermometer called a *thermistor. (Photo by Bobbé Christopherson)*

FIGURE 3-25 This traditional standard instrument shelter is white (for high albedo) and louvered (for ventilation). It protects instruments from direct sunlight and allows for the free flow of air. *(Courtesy of Qualimetrics, Inc.)*

So where should a thermometer be placed to read air temperature accurately? The ideal location is an instrument shelter (Figure 3–25). The shelter is a white box that has louvered sides to permit the free movement of air through it, while shielding the instruments from direct sunshine, heat from the ground, and precipitation. Furthermore, the shelter is placed over grass whenever possible and as far away from buildings as circumstances permit. Finally, the shelter must conform to a standardized height so that the thermometers will be mounted at 1.5 meters (5 feet) above the ground.

Students Sometimes Ask...
What are the highest and lowest temperatures ever recorded at Earth's surface?

The world's record-high temperature is nearly 59°C (136°F)! It was recorded on September 13, 1922, at Azizia, Libya, in North Africa's Sahara Desert. The lowest recorded temperature is $-89°C$ $(-129°F)$. It should come as no surprise that this incredibly frigid temperature was recorded in Antarctica, at the Russian Vostok Station, on July 21, 1983.

Temperature Scales

In the United States, TV weather reporters give temperatures in degrees Fahrenheit. But scientists as well as most people outside of the United States use degrees Celsius. Scientists sometimes also use the Kelvin or absolute scale. What are the differences among these three temperature scales? To make quantitative measurement of temperature possible, it was necessary to establish scales. Such temperature scales are based on the use of reference points, sometimes called **fixed points.** In 1714, Gabriel Daniel **Fahrenheit,** a German physicist, devised the temperature scale that bears his name. He constructed a mercury-in-glass thermometer in which the zero point was the lowest temperature he could attain with a mixture of ice, water, and common salt. For his second fixed point he chose human body temperature, which he arbitrarily set at 96°.

On this scale, he determined that the melting point of ice (the **ice point**) was 32° and the boiling point of water (the **steam point**) was 212°. Because Fahrenheit's original reference points were difficult to reproduce accurately, his scale is now defined by using the ice point and the steam point. As thermometers improved, average human body temperature was later changed to 98.6°F.*

In 1742, 28 years after Fahrenheit invented his scale, Anders Celsius, a Swedish astronomer, devised a decimal scale on which the melting point of ice was set at 0° and the boiling point of water at 100°.** For many years it was called the *centigrade scale*, but it is now known as the **Celsius scale,** after its inventor.

Because the interval between the melting point of ice and the boiling point of water is 100° on the Celsius scale and 180° on the Fahrenheit scale, a Celsius degree (°C) is larger than a Fahrenheit degree (°F) by a factor of 180/100, or 1.8. So, to convert from one system to the other, allowance must be made for this difference in the size of the degrees. Also, conversions must be adjusted because the ice point on the Celsius scale is at 0° rather than at 32°. This relationship is shown graphically in Figure 3–26.

The Celsius–Fahrenheit relationship also is shown by the following formulas:

$$°F = (1.8 \times °C) + 32$$

or

$$°C = \frac{°F - 32}{1.8}$$

*This traditional value for "normal body temperature" was established in 1868. A recent assessment places the value at 98.2°F with a range of 4.8°F.
**The boiling point referred to in the Celsius and Fahrenheit scales pertains to pure water at standard sea-level pressure. It is necessary to remember this fact, for the boiling point of water gradually decreases with altitude.

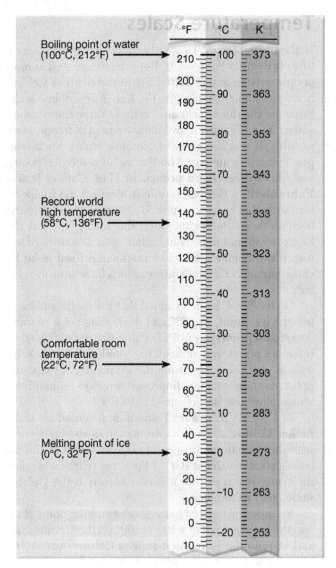

FIGURE 3-26 The three temperature scales compared.

You can see that the formulas adjust for degree size with the 1.8 factor, and adjust for the different 0° points with the ±32 factor.

The Fahrenheit scale is best known in the United States, where its official use is declining along with the British system of weights and measures. In other parts of the world as well as in the scientific community, where the metric system is used, the Celsius temperature scale is also used.

For some scientific purposes a third temperature scale is used, the **Kelvin** or **absolute scale.** On this scale, degrees Kelvin are called *Kelvins* (abbreviated K). It is similar to the Celsius scale because its divisions are exactly the same; there are 100° separating the melting point of ice and the boiling point of water. However, on the Kelvin scale, the ice point is set at 273 and the steam point at 373 (see Figure 3–26). The reason is that the zero point represents the temperature at which all molecular motion is presumed to cease (called

absolute zero). Thus, unlike the Celsius and Fahrenheit scales, it is not possible to have a negative value when using the Kelvin scale, for there is no temperature lower than absolute zero. The relationship between Kelvin and Celsius scales is easily written as follows:

$$°C = K\ 273 \ \text{ or } \ K = °C + 273$$

Applications of Temperature Data

To make weather data more useful to people, many different applications have been developed over the years. In this section, we examine some commonly used practical applications. First, we will look at three indices that all have the term *degree-days* as part of their name: heating degree-days, cooling degree-days, and growing degree-days. The first two are relative measures that allow us to evaluate the weather-produced needs and costs of heating and cooling. The third is a simple index used by farmers to estimate the maturity of crops.

Heating Degree-Days

Developed by heating engineers early in the twentieth century, **heating degree-days** represent a practical method for evaluating energy demand and consumption. It starts from the assumption that heating is not required in a building when the daily mean temperature is 65°F (18.3°C) or higher.* Simply, each degree of temperature below 65°F is counted as 1 heating degree-day. Therefore, heating degree-days are determined each day by subtracting the daily mean below 65°F from 65°F. Thus, a day with a mean temperature of 50°F has 15 heating degree-days (65 − 50 = 15), and one with an average temperature of 65°F or higher has none.

The amount of heat required to maintain a certain temperature in a building is proportional to the total heating degree-days. This linear relationship means that doubling the heating degree-days usually doubles the fuel consumption. Consequently, a fuel bill will generally be twice as high for a month with 1000 heating degree-days as for a month with just 500. When seasonal totals are compared for different places, we can estimate differences in seasonal fuel consumption (Table 3–2). For example, more than five times as much fuel is required to heat a building in Chicago (nearly 6500 total heating degree-days) than to heat a similar building in Los Angeles (almost 1300 heating degree-days). This statement is true, however, only if we assume that building construction and living habits in these areas are the same.

*Because the National Weather Service and the news media in the United States still compute and report degree-day information in Fahrenheit degrees, we will use the Fahrenheit scale throughout this discussion.

TABLE 3-2 Average annual heating and cooling degree-days for selected cities (1971–2000)*		
City	Heating degree-days	Cooling degree-days
Anchorage, AK	10470	3
Baltimore, MD	3807	1774
Boston, MA	5630	777
Chicago, IL.	6498	830
Denver, CO	6128	695
Detroit, MI.	6422	736
Great Falls, MT	7828	288
International Falls, MN	10269	233
Las Vegas, NV	2239	3214
Los Angeles, CA	1274	679
Miami, FL	149	4361
New York City, NY	4754	1151
Phoenix, AZ	1125	4189
San Antonio, TX	1573	3038
Seattle, WA	4797	173

*Source: NOAA, National Climatic Data Center

Each day, the previous day's accumulation is reported as well as the total thus far in the season. For reporting purposes the heating season is defined as the period from July 1 through June 30. These reports often include a comparison with the total up to this date last year or with the long-term average for this date or both, and so it is a relatively simple matter to judge whether the season thus far is above, below, or near normal.

Cooling Degree-Days

Just as fuel needs for heating can be estimated and compared by using heating degree-days, the amount of power required to cool a building can be estimated by using a similar index called the **cooling degree-day.** Because the 65°F base temperature is also used in calculating this index, cooling degree-days are determined each day by subtracting 65°F from the daily mean. Thus, if the mean temperature for a given day is 80°F, 15 cooling degree-days would be accumulated. Mean annual totals of cooling degree-days for selected cities are shown in Table 3–2. By comparing the totals for Baltimore and Miami, we can see that the fuel requirements for cooling a building in Miami are almost two and a half times as great as for a similar building in Baltimore. The "cooling season" is conventionally measured from January 1 through December 31. Therefore, when cooling degree-day totals are reported, the number represents the accumulation since January 1 of that year.

Although indices that are more sophisticated than heating and cooling degree-days have been proposed to take into account the effects of wind speed, solar radiation, and humidity, degree-days continue to be widely used.

Growing Degree-Days

Another practical application of temperature data is used in agriculture to determine the approximate date when crops will be ready for harvest. This simple index is called the **growing degree-day.**

The number of growing degree-days for a particular crop on any day is the difference between the daily mean temperature and the base temperature of the crop, which is the minimum temperature required for it to grow. For example, the base temperature for sweet corn is 50°F and for peas it is 40°F. Thus, on a day when the mean temperature is 75°F, the number of growing degree-days for sweet corn is 25 and the number for peas is 35.

Starting with the onset of the growth season, the daily growing degree-day values are added. Thus, if 2000 growing degree-days are needed for that crop to mature, it should be ready to harvest when the accumulation reaches 2000 (Figure 3–27). Although many factors important to plant growth are not included in the index, such as moisture conditions and sunlight, this system nevertheless serves as a simple and widely used tool in determining approximate dates of crop maturity.

Temperature and Comfort

A more familiar use of temperature data relates to human perception of temperature. Television weather reports use indices that attempt to portray levels of human comfort and discomfort. Such indices are based on the fact that our sensation of temperature is often quite different from the actual air temperature recorded by a thermometer.

FIGURE 3-27 Growing degree-days are used to determine the approximate date when crops will be ready for harvest. *(Photo by Alice Garik/Peter Arnold, Inc.)*

The human body is a heat generator that continually releases energy. Anything that influences the rate of heat loss from the body also influences our sensation of temperature, thereby affecting our feeling of comfort. Several factors control the thermal comfort of the human body, and certainly air temperature is a major one. Other environmental conditions are also significant, such as relative humidity, wind, and solar radiation.

Because evaporation is a cooling process, the evaporation of perspiration from skin is a natural means of regulat-

FIGURE 3-28 Strong winds make winter days seem much colder. New Yorkers had to cope with frigid temperatures, strong winds, and lots of snow during this January blizzard in 1996. *(Photo by Kaz Chiba Photography/Getty Images, Inc.-Liaison)*

ing body temperature. When the air is very humid, however, heat loss by evaporation is reduced. As a result, a hot and humid day feels warmer and more uncomfortable than a hot and dry day. This is the basis for a commonly used expression of summertime discomfort known as the *heat stress index* or simply the *heat index*. Because of its link to humidity, this index is the focus of a special-interest box in Chapter 4.

Wind is another significant factor affecting the sensation of temperature. A cold and windy winter day may feel much colder than the air temperature indicates (Figure 3–28). Box 3–5 focuses on this frequently used wintertime application known as *windchill*.

Students Sometimes Ask...

What impact does windchill have on exposed water pipes or my car's radiator?

The only effect windchill has on inanimate objects, such as the ones you mentioned, is to shorten the amount of time it takes for the object to cool. The inanimate object will not cool below the actual air temperature. For example, if the temperature outside is –5°F and the windchill temperature is –31°F, then your car's radiator will not drop lower than –5°F.

Chapter Summary

- Temperature is one of the basic elements of weather and climate. The *daily mean temperature* is determined by averaging the 24 hourly readings or by adding the maximum and minimum temperatures for a 24-hour period and dividing by two. The *daily temperature range* is computed by finding the difference between the maximum and minimum temperatures. Other temperature data involving longer periods include the *monthly mean temperature* (the sum of the daily means for each day of the month divided by the number of days in the month), the *annual mean temperature* (the average of the twelve monthly mean temperatures), and the *annual temperature range* (the difference between the warmest and coldest monthly mean temperatures).

- The *controls of temperature*—those factors that cause temperature to vary from place to place—are (1) differential heating of land and water; (2) ocean currents; (3) altitude; (4) geographic position; and (5) cloud cover and albedo.

- On maps illustrating the world distribution of temperature, *isotherms*, lines that connect points of equal temperature, generally trend east and west and show a decrease in temperature poleward. Moreover, the isotherms illustrate a latitudinal shifting of temperatures caused by the seasonal migration of the Sun's vertical rays and also reveal the presence of ocean currents. The north-south migration of isotherms is more pronounced over the continents because the temperatures do not fluctuate as much over water.

- Annual temperature range is small near the equator and increases with an increase in latitude. Outside the tropics, annual temperature range also increases with an increase in continentality.

- The primary control of the daily cycle of air temperature is Earth's rotation. However, the magnitude of these changes is variable and influenced by locational factors, local weather conditions, or both.

- As a consequence of the mechanism by which Earth's atmosphere is heated, the months of the highest and lowest temperatures do not coincide with the periods of maximum and minimum incoming solar radiation. In the Northern Hemisphere the greatest intensity of solar radiation occurs at the time of the summer solstice, yet the months of July and August are generally the warmest of the year. Conversely, in the Northern Hemisphere a minimum of solar energy is received in December at the time of the winter solstice, but January and February are usually colder.

- *Thermometers* measure temperature either mechanically or electrically. Most *mechanical thermometers* are based on the ability of a substance to expand when heated and contract when cooled. One type of mechanical thermometer, the liquid-in-glass thermometer, includes maximum thermometers, which use mercury, and minimum thermometers, which contain a liquid of low density, such as alcohol. A bimetal strip mechanical thermometer is frequently used in a thermograph, an instrument that continuously records temperature. *Electrical thermometers* use a thermistor (a thermal resistor) to measure temperature.

- Temperature scales use reference points, called *fixed points*. Three common temperature scales are (1) the *Fahrenheit scale*, which is defined by using the ice point (32°) and steam point (212°), (2) the *Celsius scale*, a decimal scale on which the melting point of ice is set at 0° and the boiling point of water at 100°, and (3) the *Kelvin* or *absolute scale*, where the zero point represents the temperature at which all molecular motion is presumed to cease (called *absolute zero*), the ice point is set at 273, and the steam point at 373.

- Three common applications of temperature data are (1) *heating degree-days*, where each degree of temperature below 65°F is counted as one heating degree day, (2) *cooling degree-days*, which are determined by subtracting 65°F from the daily mean, and (3) *growing degree-days*,

BOX 3-5   Windchill: The Cooling Power of Moving Air

Most everyone is familiar with the wintertime cooling power of moving air. When the wind blows on a cold day, we realize that comfort would improve if the wind were to stop. A stiff breeze penetrates ordinary clothing and reduces its capacity to retain body heat while causing exposed parts of the body to chill rapidly. Not only is cooling by evaporation heightened in this situation but the wind is also acting to carry heat away from the body by constantly replacing warmer air next to the body with colder air.

On November 1, 2001, the U.S. National Weather Service (NWS) and the Meteorological Services of Canada (MSC) implemented a new Wind Chill Temperature (WCT) index that is designed to more accurately calculate how the wind and cold feel on human skin (Figure 3–H). The index formerly used by the United States and Canada was developed in the 1940s and based on research conducted in Antarctica. The experiments measured the cooling rate of water in a container hanging from a tall pole outside.

FIGURE 3-H This windchill chart came into use in November 2001. Fahrenheit temperatures are used here because this is how the National Weather Service and the news media in the United States commonly report windchill information. The shaded areas on the chart indicate frostbite danger. Each shaded zone shows how long a person can be exposed before frostbite develops. *(After NOAA, National Weather Service)*

Wind (mph)	Calm	40	35	30	25	20	15	10	5	0	-5	-10	-15	-20	-25	-30	-35	-40	-45
5		36	31	25	19	13	7	1	-5	-11	-16	-22	-28	-34	-40	-46	-52	-57	-63
10		34	27	21	15	9	3	-4	-10	-16	-22	-28	-35	-41	-47	-53	-59	-66	-72
15		32	25	19	13	6	0	-7	-13	-19	-26	-32	-39	-45	-51	-58	-64	-71	-77
20		30	24	17	11	4	-2	-9	-15	-22	-29	-35	-42	-48	-55	-61	-68	-74	-81
25		29	23	16	9	3	-4	-11	-17	-24	-31	-37	-44	-51	-58	-64	-71	-78	-84
30		28	22	15	8	1	-5	-12	-19	-26	-33	-39	-46	-53	-60	-67	-73	-80	-87
35		28	21	14	7	0	-7	-14	-21	-27	-34	-41	-48	-55	-62	-69	-76	-82	-89
40		27	20	13	6	-1	-8	-15	-22	-29	-36	-43	-50	-57	-64	-71	-78	-84	-91
45		26	19	12	5	-2	-9	-16	-23	-30	-37	-44	-51	-58	-65	-72	-79	-86	-93
50		26	19	12	4	-3	-10	-17	-24	-31	-38	-45	-52	-60	-67	-74	-81	-88	-95
55		25	18	11	4	-3	-11	-18	-25	-32	-39	-46	-54	-61	-68	-75	-82	-89	-97
60		25	17	10	3	-4	-11	-19	-26	-33	-40	-48	-55	-62	-69	-76	-84	-91	-98

Temperature (°F)

Frostbite Times   ☐ 30 minutes   ☐ 10 minutes   ☐ 5 minutes

which are determined from the difference between the daily mean temperature and the base temperature of the crop, the minimum temperature required for it to grow.

- One familiar use of temperature data relates to human perception of temperature. The *heat stress index* (or *heat index*), a commonly used expression of summertime discomfort, links humidity and temperature to determine the thermal comfort of the human body. *Windchill,* a typical wintertime index, uses both wind and air temperature to calculate the human sensation of temperature.

Vocabulary Review

absolute zero (p. 88)
annual mean temperature (p. 66)
annual temperature range (p. 66)
bimetal strip (p. 86)
Celsius scale (p. 87)
controls of temperature (p. 68)
cooling degree-day (p. 89)
daily mean temperature (p. 66)
daily temperature range (p. 66)

Fahrenheit scale (p. 87)
fixed points (p. 87)
growing degree-days (p. 89)
heating degree-days (p. 88)
ice point (p. 87)
isotherm (p. 67)
Kelvin or absolute scale (p. 88)
liquid-in-glass thermometer (p. 83)
maximum thermometer (p. 83)

minimum thermometer (p. 83)
monthly mean temperature (p. 66)
specific heat (p. 68)
steam point (p. 87)
temperature gradient (p. 67)
thermistor (p. 86)
thermograph (p. 86)
thermometers (p. 82)

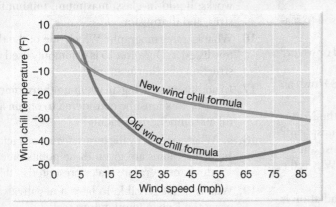

FIGURE 3-I This graph compares windchill temperatures using the old and new calculations, assuming the air temperature is 5°F. Overall, the new index is significantly warmer than the previous index, especially when wind speeds exceed 15 miles per hour. *(After NOAA, National Weather Service)*

Because a container of water freezes faster than flesh, the previous windchill index *underestimated* the time to freezing and *overestimated* the chilling effect of the wind (Figure 3-I).

The new index accounts for wind effects at face level and more accurately portrays body heat–loss estimates. Moreover, it was tested on human subjects in a chilled wind tunnel. The results of those trials were used to validate and improve the accuracy of the new formula.

Unlike the previous index, the new Wind Chill Chart includes a frostbite indicator, showing the points where temperature, wind speed, and exposure time will produce frostbite on humans (Figure 3–I). For example, a temperature of 0°F and a wind speed of 15 miles per hour will produce a windchill temperature of −19°F. Under these conditions, exposed skin can freeze in 30 minutes.

It is worth pointing out that in contrast to a cold and windy day, a calm and sunny day in winter feels *warmer* than the thermometer reading. In this situation the warm feeling is caused by the absorption of direct solar radiation by the body. Currently the new index does not take into account any offsetting effect for windchill due to solar radiation. Such a factor may be added at a later date.

It is important to remember that the windchill temperature is only an *estimate* of human discomfort. The degree of discomfort felt by different people will vary because it is influenced by many factors. Even if clothing is assumed to be the same, individuals vary widely in their responses because of such factors as age, physical condition, state of health, and level of activity. Nevertheless, as a relative measure, WCT is useful because it allows people to make more informed judgments regarding the potential harmful effects of wind and cold.

*Based in part on material prepared by the U.S. National Weather Service.

Review Questions

1. How are the following temperature data calculated: daily mean, daily range, monthly mean, annual mean, and annual range?

2. What are isotherms and what is their purpose?

3. Why are summertime maximum temperatures so high in Death Valley, California? (See Box 3–1.)

4. a. State the relationship between the heating and cooling of land versus water.

   b. List and explain the factors that cause the difference between the heating and cooling of land and water.

   c. We are studying the atmosphere, so why are we concerned with the heating characteristics at Earth's surface?

5. How does the annual temperature range near the equator compare with the annual temperature ranges in the middle to high latitudes? Explain.

6. Three cities are at the same latitude (about 45° N). One city is located along a windward coast, another in the center of the continent, and the third along a leeward coast. Compare the annual temperature ranges of these cities.

7. Quito, Ecuador, is on the equator and is not a coastal city. It has an annual mean temperature of only 13°C. What is the likely cause for this low annual mean temperature?

8. How does the daily march of temperature on a completely overcast day compare with that on a cloudless, sunny day? Explain your answer.

9. Examine Figure 3–14 and explain why Yangon's monthly mean temperature for April is higher than the July monthly mean.

10. Answer the following questions about world temperature distribution (you may wish to refer to the January and July isotherm maps).

a. Isotherms generally trend east–west. Why?

b. Isotherms bend (poleward, equatorward) over continents in summer. Underline the correct answer and explain.

c. Isotherms shift north and south from season to season. Why?

d. Where do isotherms shift most, over land or water? Explain.

e. How do isotherms show ocean currents? How can you tell if the current is warm or cold?

f. Why are the isotherms more irregular in the Northern Hemisphere than in the Southern Hemisphere?

11. Which area on Earth experiences the highest annual temperature range? (Refer to Figure 3–17). Why is the annual range so high in this region?

12. Although the intensity of incoming solar radiation is greatest at local noon, the warmest part of the day is most often midafternoon. Why? Use Figure 3–20 to explain your answer.

13. List at least three factors that contribute to the urban heat island. (See Box 3–4.)

14. The magnitude of the daily temperature range can vary significantly from place to place and from time to time. List and describe at least three factors that might cause such variations.

15. Describe how each of the following thermometers works: liquid-in-glass, maximum, minimum, bimetal strip, and thermistor.

16. What is a thermograph? Which one of the thermometers listed in Question 15 is commonly used in the construction of a thermograph?

17. In addition to having an accurate thermometer, which other factors must be considered to obtain a meaningful air temperature reading?

18. a. What is meant by the terms *steam point* and *ice point*?

b. What values are given these points on each of the three temperature scales presented in this chapter?

19. Why is it not possible to have a negative value when using the Kelvin temperature scale?

20. When heating and cooling degree-day totals for different places are examined to compare fuel consumption, what important assumption is made?

21. How are growing degree-days calculated? For what purpose is this index used?

Problems

1. If you were asked to identify the coldest city in the United States (or any other designated region), what statistics could be used? Can you list at least three different ways of selecting the coldest city?

2. Refer to the thermograph record in Figure 3–18. Determine the maximum and minimum temperature for each day of the week. Use these data to calculate the daily mean and daily range for each day.

3. By referring to the world maps of temperature distribution for January and July (Figures 3–15 and 3–16), determine the approximate January mean, July mean, and annual temperature range for a place located at 60° north latitude, 80° east longitude, and a place located at 60° south latitude, 80° east longitude.

4. Calculate the annual temperature range for three cities in Appendix F. Try to choose cities with different ranges and explain these differences in terms of the controls of temperature.

5. Referring to Figure 3–H in Box 3–5, determine wind-chill temperatures under the following circumstances:
a. Temperature = 5°F, wind speed = 15 mph.
b. Temperature = 5°F, wind speed = 30 mph.

6. The mean temperature is 55°F on a particular day. The following day the mean drops to 45°F. Calculate the number of heating degree-days for each day. How much more fuel would be needed to heat a building on the second day compared with the first day?

7. Use the appropriate formula to convert the following temperatures:

$$20°C = \underline{\hspace{1cm}} °F$$
$$-25°C = \underline{\hspace{1cm}} K$$
$$59°F = \underline{\hspace{1cm}} °C$$

Atmospheric Science Online

The Atmosphere 10e web site uses the resources and flexibility of the Internet to aid in your study of the topics in this chapter. Written and developed by meteorology instructors, this site will help improve your understanding of meteorology. Visit **http://www .prenhall.com/lutgens** and click on the cover of *The Atmosphere 10e* to find:

- **Online review quizzes**
- **Critical thinking exercises**
- **Links to chapter-specific web resources**
- **Internet-wide key term searches**

http://www.prenhall.com/lutgens

MOISTURE and ATMOSPHERIC STABILITY

Clouds and morning fog over Toulumne
Meadows in California's Yosemite
National Park. *(Photo by Marc Muench)*

ater vapor is an odorless, colorless gas that mixes freely with the other gases of the atmosphere. Unlike oxygen and nitrogen—the two most abundant components of the atmosphere—water can change from one state of matter to another (solid, liquid, or gas) at the temperatures and pressures experienced on Earth. (By contrast, nitrogen will not condense to a liquid unless its temperature is lowered to −196°C [−371°F]). Because of this unique property, water freely leaves the oceans as a gas and returns again as a liquid.

As you observe day-to-day weather changes, you might ask: Why is it generally more humid in the summer than in the winter? Why do clouds form on some occasions but not on others? Why do some clouds look thin and harmless, whereas others form gray and ominous towers? Answers to these questions involve the role of water vapor in the atmosphere, the central theme of this chapter.

Movement of Water Through the Atmosphere

GEODe

Moisture and Cloud Formation

▶ Movement of Water Through the Atmosphere

Water is everywhere on Earth—in the oceans, glaciers, rivers, lakes, the air, soil, and in living tissue (Figure 4–1). All of these "reservoirs" constitute Earth's hydrosphere. In all, the water content of Earth's hydrosphere is about 1.36 billion cubic kilometers (326 million cubic miles).

The increasing demands on this finite resource have led scientists to focus on the continuous exchange of water among the oceans, the atmosphere, and the continents (Figure 4–2). This unending circulation of Earth's water supply has come to be called the **hydrologic cycle** (or water cycle).

The hydrologic cycle is a gigantic system powered by energy from the Sun in which the atmosphere provides the vital link between the oceans and continents. Water from the oceans and, to a much lesser extent, from the continents, evaporates into the atmosphere. Winds transport this moisture-laden air, often over great distances.

Complex processes of cloud formation eventually result in precipitation. The precipitation that falls into the ocean has ended its cycle and is ready to begin another by evaporating again. The water that falls on the continents, however, must still flow back to the oceans.

Once precipitation has fallen on land, a portion of the water soaks into the ground, some of it moving downward, then laterally, and finally seeping into lakes and streams or directly into the ocean. Much of the water that soaks in or runs off eventually finds its way back to the atmosphere. In addition to evaporation from the soil, lakes, and streams, some water that infiltrates the ground is absorbed by plants through their roots. They then release it into the atmosphere, a process called **transpiration.**

FIGURE 4-1 Steam fog over a lake in Maine. *(Photo by Sara Gray/Getty Image Inc.-Stone Allstock)*

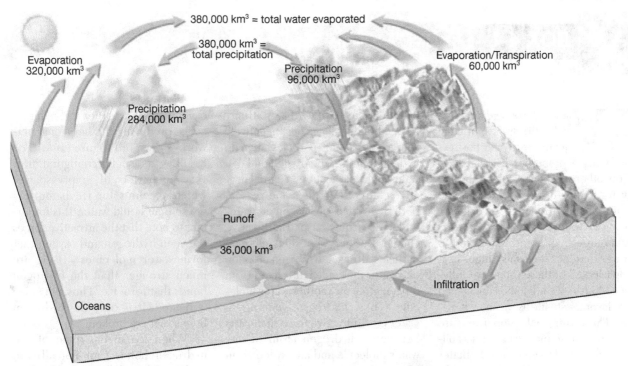

380,000 km³ = total water evaporated

380,000 km³ = total precipitation

Evaporation 320,000 km³

Precipitation 284,000 km³

Precipitation 96,000 km³

Evaporation/Transpiration 60,000 km³

Runoff

36,000 km³

Infiltration

Oceans

FIGURE 4-2 Earth's water balance. About 320,000 cubic kilometers of water are evaporated annually from the oceans, whereas evaporation from the land (including lakes and streams) contributes 60,000 cubic kilometers of water. Of this total of 380,000 cubic kilometers of water, about 284,000 cubic kilometers fall back to the ocean, and the remaining 96,000 cubic kilometers fall on Earth's land surface. Because 60,000 cubic kilometers of water leave the land through evaporation and transpiration, 36,000 cubic kilometers of water remain to erode the land during the journey back to the oceans.

Figure 4–2 not only shows Earth's hydrologic cycle but also its *water balance*. The water balance is a quantitative view of the hydrologic cycle. Although the amount of water vapor in the air is just a tiny fraction of Earth's total water supply, the absolute quantities that are cycled through the atmosphere in a year are immense, some 380,000 cubic kilometers (91,000 cubic miles). This is enough to cover Earth's surface uniformly to a depth of about 1 meter (3.3 feet). Estimates show that over North America almost six times more water is carried within the moving currents of air than is transported by all the continent's rivers.

Because the total amount of water vapor in the entire global atmosphere remains about the same, the average annual precipitation over Earth must be equal to the quantity of water evaporated. However, for the continents, precipitation exceeds evaporation. Conversely, over the oceans, evaporation exceeds precipitation. Because the level of the world ocean is consistent, runoff from land areas must balance the deficit of precipitation over the oceans.

In summary, the hydrologic cycle depicts the continuous movement of water from the oceans to the atmosphere, from the atmosphere to the land, and from the land back to the sea. The movement of water through the cycle holds the key to the distribution of moisture over the surface of our planet and is intricately related to all atmospheric phenomena.

Water's Changes of State

GEODe Moisture and Cloud Formation
▶ Water's Changes of State

Water is the only substance that exists in the atmosphere as a solid (ice), liquid, and gas (water vapor). It is made of hydrogen and oxygen atoms that are bonded together to form water molecules (H_2O). In all three states of matter (even ice) these molecules are in constant motion—the higher the temperature, the more vigorous the movement. The chief difference among liquid water, ice, and water vapor is the arrangement of the water molecules.

Ice, Liquid Water, and Water Vapor

Ice is composed of water molecules that have low kinetic energies (motion) and are held together by mutual molecular attractions (see Box 4–1). Here the molecules form a tight, orderly network as shown in Figure 4–3. As a consequence, the water molecules in ice are not free to move relative to each other but rather vibrate about fixed sites. When ice is heated, the molecules oscillate more rapidly. When the rate of molecular movement increases sufficiently, the bonds between some of the water molecules are broken, resulting in melting.

BOX 4-1 Water: A Unique Substance

ater is the only *liquid* found at Earth's surface in large quantities. Water has several unusual properties that set it apart from other substances, for instance: 1) water is readily converted from one state of matter to another (solid, liquid, gas); 2) water's solid phase, ice, is less dense than liquid water; and 3) water has an unusually high heat capacity. All of these properties influence Earth's weather and climate and are favorable to life as we know it.

These unusual properties are largely a consequence of water's ability to form hydrogen bonds. To better grasp the nature of hydrogen bonds, let's examine a water molecule. A water molecule (H_2O) consists of two hydrogen atoms that are strongly bonded to an oxygen atom. Because oxygen atoms have a greater affinity for the bonding electrons (negatively charged subatomic particles) than do hydrogen atoms, the oxygen end of a water molecule acquires a partial negative charge. For the same reason, both hydrogen atoms on a water molecule acquire a partial positive charge. Because oppositely charged particles attract, a hydrogen atom on one water molecule is attracted to an oxygen atom on another water molecule. Thus, *hydrogen bonding* in water is an attractive force that exists between a hydrogen atom in one water molecule and an oxygen atom of any other water molecule.

Hydrogen bonds are what hold water molecules together to form the solid we call *ice*. In ice, hydrogen atoms form hydrogen bonds with oxygen atoms in other water molecules, producing the hexagonal network shown in Figure 4–A. The resulting molecular configuration is very open (lots of empty space), which accounts for ice being less dense than liquid water. It is important to note that the attractive forces between hydrogen and oxygen that form water molecules (H_2O) are much stronger than the hydrogen bonds that form ice. Thus, when ice is heated, it is only the hydrogen bonds that are broken.

When ice melts, some of the hydrogen bonds (but not all) are broken. This allows for the more compact arrangement shown in Figure 4–B. Consequently, the liquid phase of water is denser than the solid phase. Should water's temperature

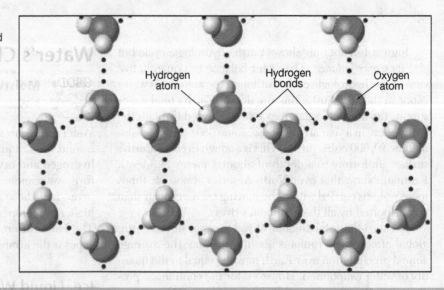

FIGURE 4-A Illustration of the crystalline structure of ice. Water molecules are joined together by hydrogen bonds (shown with dotted lines) that connect a hydrogen atom on one water molecule with an oxygen atom on another. Oxygen atoms are represented by red spheres and hydrogen atoms by small blue spheres. For simplicity the three-dimensional nature of ice has not been illustrated.

Hydrogen atom

Hydrogen bonds

Oxygen atom

In the liquid state, water molecules are still tightly packed but are moving fast enough that they are able to easily slide past one another. As a result, liquid water is fluid and will take the shape of its container.

As liquid water gains heat from its environment, some of the molecules will acquire enough energy to break the remaining molecular attractions and escape from the surface, becoming water vapor. Water-vapor molecules are widely spaced compared to liquid water and exhibit very energetic random motion. What distinguishes a gas from a liquid is its compressibility (and expandability). For exam-ple, you can easily put more and more air into a tire and increase its volume only slightly. However, don't try to put 10 gallons of gasoline into a five-gallon can.

To summarize, when water changes state, it does not turn into a different substance; only the distances and inter-actions among the water molecules changes.

Latent Heat

Whenever water changes state, heat is exchanged between water and its surroundings. When water evaporates, heat is absorbed (Figure 4–3). Meteorologists often measure heat

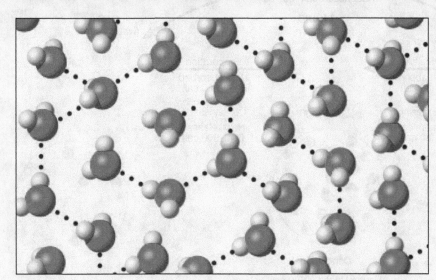

FIGURE 4-B Water in the liquid state consists of clusters of water molecules joined together by hydrogen bonds. As these clusters move about, they continually break up and are replaced by new ones.

rise, more hydrogen bonds will break, and the liquid will become even denser, until it reaches 4°C (39°F) when maximum density is achieved. At higher temperatures water gradually becomes less dense because of increased molecular motion—just like most other substances. However, even at higher temperatures, liquid water has significant hydrogen bonding that tends to form clusters of water molecules that are free to move relative to each other. These clusters continually break up and are replaced by new ones.

As a body of water freezes, ice forms on top because ice is less dense than the water beneath it. This has far-reaching effects, both for our daily weather and for aquatic life. When ice forms on a water body, it insulates the underlying liquid and limits further freezing. If a water body froze from the bottom, imagine the consequences. Many lakes would freeze solid during the winter, killing the aquatic life. In addition, deep bodies of water, such as the Arctic Ocean, would never be ice-covered. This would alter Earth's heat budget, which in turn would modify global atmospheric and oceanic circulations.

Water's heat capacity is also related to hydrogen bonding. When water is heated, some of the energy is used to break hydrogen bonds rather than to increase molecular motion. (Recall that an increase in average molecular motion corresponds to an increase in temperature.) Thus, under similar conditions, water heats up and cools down more slowly than most common substances. This contributes to the differential heating of land and water discussed in Chapter 3. Large water bodies tend to moderate temperatures by remaining warmer than adjacent landmasses in winter and remaining cooler in summer.

Hydrogen bonds are also broken as water evaporates. Thus, water molecules need "extra energy" to give them the motion needed to break the molecular attractions and escape the surface of the liquid to become a gas. (When liquids evaporate, the energy absorbed by the gas molecules is called *latent heat of vaporization.*) Water vapor molecules contain an unusually large amount of "stored energy," which is an important factor influencing weather and climate. When water vapor condenses in the atmosphere, this energy is released, warming the surrounding air and giving it buoyancy. If the moisture content of air is high, this process can spur the development of thunderstorms and contribute to hurricane formation in the tropics.

energy in calories. One **calorie** is the amount of heat required to raise the temperature of 1 gram of water 1°C (1.8°F). Thus, when 10 calories of heat are absorbed by 1 gram of water, the molecules vibrate faster and a 10°C (18°F) temperature rise occurs.

Under certain conditions, heat may be added to a substance without an accompanying rise in temperature. For example, when a glass of ice water is warmed, the temperature of the ice-water mixture remains a constant 0°C (32°F) until all the ice has melted. If adding heat does not raise the temperature, where does this energy go? In this case, the added energy went to break the molecular attractions that bind water molecules into a crystalline structure.

Because the heat used to melt ice does not produce a temperature change, it is referred to as **latent heat.** (Latent means *hidden,* like the latent fingerprints hidden at a crime scene.) This energy can be thought of as being stored in liquid water, and it is not released to its surroundings as heat until the liquid returns to the solid state.

It requires 80 calories to melt one gram of ice, an amount referred to as *latent heat of melting.* Freezing, the reverse process, releases these 80 calories per gram to the

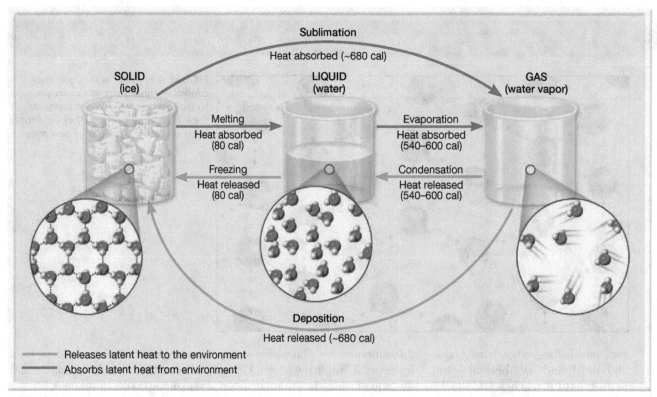

FIGURE 4-3 Change of state always involves an exchange of heat. The amounts of heat are expressed in calories and are shown here for the change of 1 gram of water from one state of matter to another.

environment as *latent heat of fusion*. We will consider the importance of latent heat of fusion in Chapter 5 in the section on frost prevention.

Evaporation and Condensation.   We saw that heat is absorbed when ice is converted to liquid water. Heat is also absorbed during **evaporation,** the process of converting a liquid to a gas (vapor). The energy absorbed by water molecules during evaporation is used to give them the motion needed to escape the surface of the liquid and become a gas. This energy is referred to as the **latent heat of vaporization** and varies from about 600 calories per gram for water at 0°C to 540 calories per gram at 100°C. (Notice from Figure 4–3 that it takes much more energy to evaporate 1 gram of water than it does to melt the same amount of ice.) During the process of evaporation, it is the higher-temperature (faster-moving) molecules that escape the surface. As a result, the average molecular motion (temperature) of the remaining water is reduced—hence, the common expression "Evaporation is a cooling process." You have undoubtedly experienced this cooling effect on stepping dripping wet from a swimming pool or bathtub. In this situation the energy used to evaporate water comes from your skin—hence, you feel cool.

Condensation, the reverse process, occurs when water vapor changes to the liquid state. During condensation, water-vapor molecules release energy (**latent heat of condensation**) in an amount equivalent to what was absorbed during evaporation. When condensation occurs in the

atmosphere, it results in the formation of such phenomena as fog and clouds (Figure 4–4).

As you will see, latent heat plays an important role in many atmospheric processes. In particular, when water vapor condenses to form cloud droplets, latent heat of condensation is released, warming the surrounding air and giving it buoyancy. When the moisture content of air is high, this process can spur the growth of towering storm clouds. Furthermore, the evaporation of water over the tropical oceans and the subsequent condensation at higher latitudes results in significant energy transfer from equatorial to more poleward locations.

Sublimation and Deposition.   You are probably least familiar with the last two processes illustrated in Figure 4–3—sublimation and deposition. **Sublimation** is the conversion of a solid directly to a gas without passing through the liquid state. Examples you may have observed include the gradual shrinking of unused ice cubes in the freezer and the rapid conversion of dry ice (frozen carbon dioxide) to wispy clouds that quickly disappear.

Deposition refers to the reverse process, the conversion of a vapor directly to a solid. This change occurs, for example, when water vapor is deposited as ice on solid objects such as grass or windows (Figure 4–5). These deposits are called *white frost* or *hoar frost* and are frequently referred to simply as *frost*. A household example of the process of deposition is the "frost" that accumulates in a freezer. As shown in Figure 4–3, deposition releases an amount of energy equal to the total amount released by condensation and freezing.

FIGURE 4-4 Condensation of water vapor generates phenomena such as clouds and fog. *(Photo by Jeremy Walker/Getty Image Inc.-Stone Allstock)*

FIGURE 4-5 White frost on a window pane. *(Photo by Craig F. Bohren)*

Humidity: Water Vapor in the Air

GEODe **Moisture and Cloud Formation**
▶ Humidity: Water Vapor in the Air

Water vapor constitutes only a small fraction of the atmosphere, varying from as little as one-tenth of 1 percent up to about 4 percent by volume. But the importance of water in the air is far greater than these small percentages would indicate. Indeed, scientists agree that *water vapor* is the most important gas in the atmosphere when it comes to understanding atmospheric processes.

Humidity is the general term used to describe the amount of water vapor in the air Figure 4–6. Meteorologists employ several methods to express the water-vapor content of the air, including (1) absolute humidity, (2) mixing ratio, (3) vapor pressure, (4) relative humidity, and (5) dew point. Two of these methods, *absolute humidity* and *mixing ratio*, are similar in that both are expressed as the quantity of water vapor contained in a specific amount of air.

Absolute humidity is *the mass of water vapor in a given volume of air* (usually as grams per cubic meter).

$$\text{Absolute humidity} = \frac{\text{mass of water vapor (grams)}}{\text{volume of air (cubic meters)}}$$

As air moves from one place to another, changes in pressure and temperature cause changes in its volume. When such volume changes occur, the absolute humidity also changes, even if no water vapor is added or removed. Consequently, it is difficult to monitor the water-vapor content of a moving mass of air if absolute humidity is the index

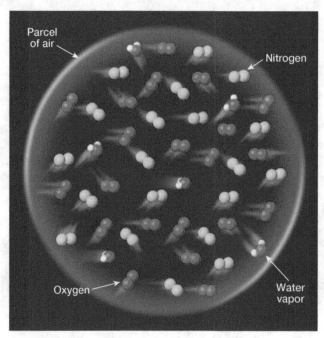

FIGURE 4-6 Meteorologists use several methods to express the water-vapor content of air.

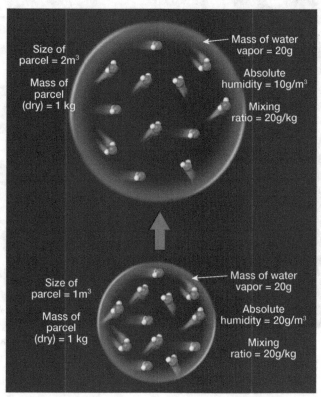

FIGURE 4-7 Comparison of absolute humidity and mixing ratio for a rising parcel of air. Note that the mixing ratio is not affected by changes in pressure as the parcel of air rises and expands.

being used. Therefore, meteorologists generally prefer to employ mixing ratio to express the water-vapor content of air.

The **mixing ratio** is *the mass of water vapor in a unit of air compared to the remaining mass of dry air.*

$$\text{mixing ratio} = \frac{\text{mass of water vapor (grams)}}{\text{mass of dry air (kilograms)}}$$

Because it is measured in units of mass (usually grams per kilogram), the mixing ratio is not affected by changes in pressure or temperature. (Figure 4–7).[*]

Neither the absolute humidity nor the mixing ratio, however, can be easily determined by direct sampling. Therefore, other methods are also used to express the moisture content of the air. These include vapor pressure, relative humidity, and dew point.

Vapor Pressure and Saturation

Another measure of the moisture content of the air is obtained from the pressure exerted by water vapor. To understand how water vapor exerts pressure imagine a closed container half full of pure water and overlain by dry air, as shown in Figure 4–8a. Almost immediately some of the water molecules begin to leave the water surface and evaporate into the dry air above. The addition of water vapor into the air can be detected by a small increase in pressure

(Figure 4–8b). This increase in pressure is the result of the motion of the water-vapor molecules that were added to the air through evaporation. In the atmosphere, this pressure is called **vapor pressure** and is defined as *that part of the total atmospheric pressure attributable to its water-vapor content.*

Initially, many more molecules will leave the water surface (evaporate) than will return (condense). However, as more and more molecules evaporate from the water surface, the steadily increasing vapor pressure in the air above forces more and more water molecules to return to the liquid. Eventually a balance is reached in which the number of water molecules returning to the surface balances the number leaving. At that point the air is said to have reached an equilibrium called **saturation** (Figure 4–8c). When air is saturated, the pressure exerted by the motion of the water-vapor molecules is called the **saturation vapor pressure.**

Now suppose we were to disrupt the equilibrium by heating the water in our closed container, as illustrated in Figure 4–8d. The added energy would increase the rate at which the water molecules would evaporate from the surface. This in turn would cause the vapor pressure in the air above to increase until a new equilibrium was reached between evaporation and condensation. Thus, we conclude that the saturation vapor pressure is temperature-dependent, such that at higher temperatures it takes more water vapor to saturate air (Figure 4–9). The amount of

---

[*]Another commonly used expression is "specific humidity," which is the mass of water vapor in a unit mass of air, including the water vapor. Because the amount of water vapor in the air rarely exceeds a few percent of the total mass of the air, the specific humidity of air is equivalent to its mixing ratio for all practical purposes.

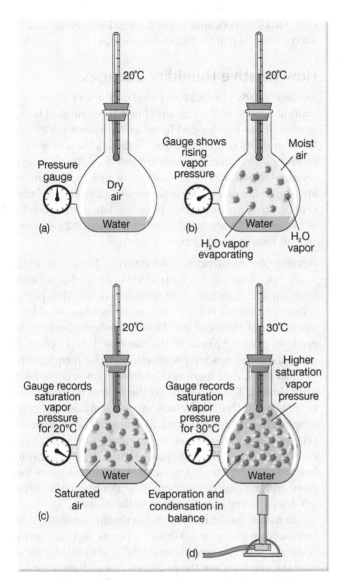

FIGURE 4-8 The relationship between vapor pressure and saturation. (a) Initial conditions—dry air at 20°C with no observable vapor pressure. (b) Evaporation generates measurable vapor pressure. (c) As more and more molecules escape from the water surface, the steadily increasing vapor pressure forces more and more of these molecules to return to the liquid. Eventually, the number of water-vapor molecules returning to the surface will balance the number leaving. At that point the air is said to be saturated. (d) When the container is heated from 20° to 30°C, the rate of evaporation increases, causing the vapor pressure to increase until a new balance is reached.

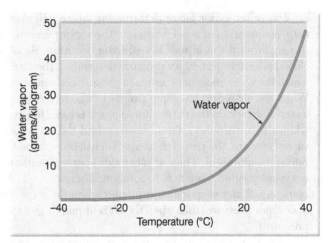

FIGURE 4-9 The amount of water vapor required to saturate 1 kilogram of dry air at various temperatures.

stantly evaporating from liquid surfaces (such as lakes or cloud droplets) and other vapor molecules are arriving. However, in nature a balance is not always achieved. More often than not, more water molecules are leaving the surface of a water puddle than are arriving, causing what meteorologists call *net evaporation*. By contrast, during the formation of fog, more water molecules are condensing than are evaporating from the tiny fog droplets, resulting in *net condensation*.

What determines whether the rate of evaporation exceeds the rate of condensation (net evaporation) or vice versa? One of the major factors is the temperature of the surface water, which in turn determines how much motion (kinetic energy) the water molecules possess. At higher temperatures the molecules have more energy and can more readily escape. Thus, under otherwise similar conditions, because hot water has more energy, it will evaporate faster than cold water.

water vapor required for the saturation of 1 kilogram (2.2 pounds) of dry air at various temperatures is shown in Table 4–1. Note that for every 10°C (18°F) increase in temperature, the amount of water vapor needed for saturation almost doubles. Thus, roughly four times more water vapor is needed to saturate 30°C (86°F) air than 10°C (50°F) air.

The atmosphere behaves in much the same manner as our closed container. In nature, gravity, rather than a lid, prevents water vapor (and other gases) from escaping into space. Also like our container, water molecules are con-

TABLE 4-1	Saturation mixing ratio (at sea-level pressure)
Temperature °C (°F)	**Saturation mixing ratio g/kg**
−40 (−40)	0.1
−30 (−22)	0.3
−20 (−4)	0.75
−10 (14)	2
0 (32)	3.5
5 (41)	5
10 (50)	7
15 (59)	10
20 (68)	14
25 (77)	20
30 (86)	26.5
35 (95)	35
40 (104)	47

The other major factor determining which will dominate, evaporation or condensation, is the vapor pressure in the air around the liquid. Recall from our example of a closed container that vapor pressure determines the rate at which the water molecules return to the surface (condense). When the air is dry (low vapor pressure), the rate at which water molecules return to the liquid phase is low. However, when the air around a liquid has reached the saturation vapor pressure, the rate of condensation will be equal to the rate of evaporation. Thus, at saturation there is neither a net condensation nor a net evaporation. Therefore, all else being equal, net evaporation is greater when the air is dry (low vapor pressure) than when the air is humid (high vapor pressure).

In addition to vapor pressure and temperature, other factors exist in nature that affect rates of evaporation and condensation. Although these factors are of minimal importance to most of the processes operating at Earth's surface, they are significant in the atmosphere where clouds and precipitation form. Thus, we will revisit this idea when we consider the formation of clouds and precipitation in Chapter 5.

Students Sometimes Ask

Why do the sizes of snow piles seem to shrink a few days after a snowfall, even when the temperatures remain below freezing?

On clear, cold days following a snowfall, the air can be very dry. This fact, plus solar heating, causes the ice crystals to sublimate—turn from a solid to a gas. Thus, even without any appreciable melting, these accumulations of snow gradually get smaller.

Relative Humidity

 GEODe **Moisture and Cloud Formation**
ATMOSPHERE
▶ Humidity: Water Vapor in the Air

The most familiar and, unfortunately, the most misunderstood term used to describe the moisture content of air is relative humidity. **Relative humidity** *is a ratio of the air's actual water-vapor content compared with the amount of water vapor required for saturation at that temperature (and pressure).* Thus, relative humidity indicates how near the air is to saturation rather than the actual quantity of water vapor in the air (see Box 4–2).

To illustrate, we see from Table 4–1 that at 25°C, air is saturated when it contains 20 grams of water vapor per kilogram of air. Thus, if the air contains 10 grams per kilogram on a 25°C day, the relative humidity is expressed as 10/20, or 50 percent. Further, if air with a temperature of 25°C had a water-vapor content of 20 grams per kilogram, the relative humidity would be expressed as 20/20 or 100 per-

cent. On those occasions when the relative humidity reaches 100 percent, the air is said to be saturated.

How Relative Humidity Changes

Because relative humidity is based on the air's water-vapor content, as well as the amount of moisture required for saturation, it can be changed in either of two ways. First, relative humidity can be changed by the addition or removal of water vapor. Second, because the amount of moisture required for saturation is a function of air temperature, relative humidity varies with temperature. (Recall that the saturation vapor pressure is temperature dependent, such that at higher temperatures, it takes more water vapor to saturate air than at lower temperatures.)

Adding or Subtracting Moisture. Notice in Figure 4–10. that when water vapor is added to a parcel of air, its relative humidity increases until saturation occurs (100 percent relative humidity). What if even more moisture is added to this parcel of saturated air? Does the relative humidity exceed 100 percent? Normally, this situation does not occur. Instead, the excess water vapor condenses to form liquid water.

You may have experienced such a situation while taking a hot shower. The water leaving the shower is composed of very energetic (hot) molecules, which means that the rate of evaporation is high. As long as you run the shower, the process of evaporation continually adds water vapor to the unsaturated air in the bathroom. Therefore, if you stay in a hot shower long enough, the air eventually becomes saturated and the excess water vapor condenses on the mirror, window, tile, and other surfaces in the room.

In nature, moisture is added to the air mainly via evaporation from the oceans. However, plants, soil, and smaller bodies of water do make substantial contributions. Unlike your shower, however, the processes that add water vapor to the air generally do not operate at rates fast enough to cause saturation to occur directly. One exception is when you exhale on a cold winter day and "see your breath." What is happening is the warm moist air from your lungs mixes with the cold outside air, which has a very low saturation vapor pressure. Your breath has enough moisture to saturate a small quantity of cold outside air and the result is a miniature "cloud." Almost as fast as the "cloud" forms, it mixes with more of the dry outside air and quickly evaporates.

Changes with Temperature. The second condition that affects relative humidity is air temperature (see Box 4–3). Examine Figure 4–11 carefully. Note that in Figure 4–11a, when air at 20°C contains 7 grams of water vapor per kilogram, it has a relative humidity of 50 percent. This can be verified by referring to Table 4–1. Here we can see that at 20°C, air is saturated when it contains 14 grams of water vapor per kilogram of air. Because the air in Figure 4–11a contains 7 grams of water vapor, its relative humidity is 7/14 or 50 percent.

How does cooling affect relative humidity? When the flask in Figure 4–11a is cooled from 20° to 10°C, as shown in Figure 4–11b, the relative humidity increases from 50 to

BOX 4-2   Dry Air at 100 Percent Relative Humidity?

A common misconception relating to meteorology is the notion that air with a high relative humidity must have a greater water-vapor content than air with a lower relative humidity. Frequently, this is not the case (Figure 4–C). To illustrate, let us compare a typical January day at International Falls, Minnesota, to one in the desert near Phoenix, Arizona. On this hypothetical day the temperature in International Falls is a cold −10°C (14°F) and the relative humidity is 100 percent. By referring to Table 4–1, we can see that saturated −10°C (14°F)

air has a water-vapor content (mixing ratio) of 2 grams per kilogram (g/kg). By contrast, the desert air at Phoenix on this January day is a warm 25°C (77°F), and the relative humidity is just 20 percent. A look at Table 4–1 reveals that 25°C (77°F) air has a saturation mixing ratio of 20 g/kg. Therefore, with a relative humidity of 20 percent, the air at Phoenix has a water-vapor content of 4 g/kg (20 grams × 20 percent). Consequently, the "dry" air at Phoenix actually contains twice the water vapor as the "wet" air at International Falls.

This should make clear why places that are very cold are also very dry. The low water-vapor content of frigid air (even when saturated) helps to explain why many arctic areas receive only meager amounts of precipitation and are sometimes referred to as "polar deserts." This also helps us understand why people frequently experience dry skin and chapped lips during the winter months. The water vapor content of cold air is low, even when compared to some hot, arid regions.

FIGURE 4-C Moisture content of hot air versus frigid air. Hot desert air with a low relative humidity generally has a higher water-vapor content than frigid air with a high relative humidity. *(Top photo by E. J. Tarbuck, bottom photo by Matt Duvall)*

FIGURE 4-10 Relative humidity. At a constant temperature the relative humidity will increase as water vapor is added to the air. Here, the saturation mixing ratio remains constant at 20 grams per kilogram and the relative humidity rises from 25 to 100 percent as the water-vapor content increases.

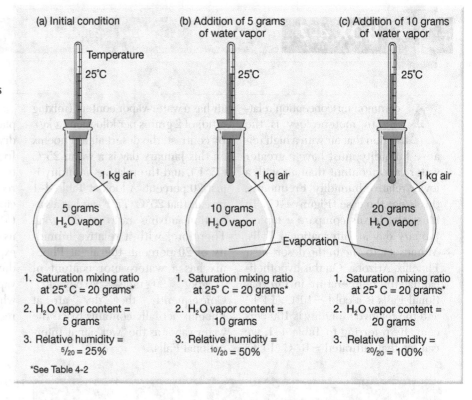

(a) Initial condition

Temperature
25°C

1 kg air

5 grams
H_2O vapor

1. Saturation mixing ratio at 25° C = 20 grams*

2. H_2O vapor content = 5 grams

3. Relative humidity = $^{5}/_{20}$ = 25%

*See Table 4-2

(b) Addition of 5 grams of water vapor

25°C

1 kg air

10 grams
H_2O vapor

1. Saturation mixing ratio at 25° C = 20 grams*

2. H_2O vapor content = 10 grams

3. Relative humidity = $^{10}/_{20}$ = 50%

(c) Addition of 10 grams of water vapor

25°C

1 kg air

20 grams
H_2O vapor

Evaporation

1. Saturation mixing ratio at 25° C = 20 grams*

2. H_2O vapor content = 20 grams

3. Relative humidity = $^{20}/_{20}$ = 100%

100 percent. We can conclude from this that when the water-vapor content remains constant, a decrease in temperature results in an increase in relative humidity.

But there is no reason to assume that cooling would cease the moment the air reached saturation. What happens when the air is cooled below the temperature at which saturation occurs? Figure 4–11c illustrates this situation.

Notice from Table 4–1 that when the flask is cooled to 0°C, the air is saturated at 3.5 grams of water vapor per kilogram of air. Because this flask originally contained 7 grams of water vapor, 3.5 grams of water vapor will condense to form liquid droplets that collect on the walls of the container. In the meantime, the relative humidity of the air inside remains at 100 percent. This raises an important concept. When air

BOX 4-3   Humidifiers and Dehumidifiers

In summer, stores sell *dehumidifiers*. As winter rolls around, these same merchants feature *humidifiers*. Why do you suppose so many homes are equipped with both a humidifier and a dehumidifier? The answer lies in the relationship between temperature and relative humidity. Recall that if the water-vapor content of air remains at a constant level, an increase in temperature lowers the relative humidity and a lowering of temperature increases the relative humidity.

During the summer months, warm, moist air frequently dominates

the weather of the central and eastern United States. When hot and humid air enters a home, some of it circulates into the cool basement. As a result, the temperature of this air drops and its relative humidity increases. The result is a damp, musty-smelling basement. In response, the homeowner installs a dehumidifier to alleviate the problem. As air is drawn over the cold coils of the dehumidifier, water vapor condenses and collects in a bucket or flows down a drain. This process reduces the relative humidity and makes for a drier, more comfortable basement.

By contrast, during the winter months, outside air is cool and dry. When this air is drawn into the home, it is heated to room temperature. This process in turn causes the relative humidity to plunge, often to uncomfortably low levels of 40 percent or lower. Living with dry air can mean static electrical shocks, dry skin, sinus headaches, or even nose bleeds. Consequently, the homeowner may install a humidifier, which adds water to the air and increases the relative humidity to a more comfortable level.

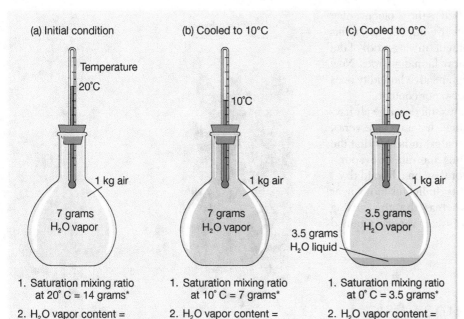

(a) Initial condition

Temperature
20°C

1 kg air

7 grams
H₂O vapor

1. Saturation mixing ratio
   at 20° C = 14 grams*

2. H₂O vapor content =
   7 grams

3. Relative humidity =
   ⁷/₁₄ = 50%

*See Table 4-2

(b) Cooled to 10°C

10°C

1 kg air

7 grams
H₂O vapor

1. Saturation mixing ratio
   at 10° C = 7 grams*

2. H₂O vapor content =
   7 grams

3. Relative humidity =
   ⁷/₇ = 100%

(c) Cooled to 0°C

0°C

1 kg air

3.5 grams
H₂O vapor

3.5 grams
H₂O liquid

1. Saturation mixing ratio
   at 0° C = 3.5 grams*

2. H₂O vapor content =
   3.5 grams

3. Relative humidity =
   ³·⁵/₃.₅ = 100%

FIGURE 4-11 Relative humidity varies with temperature. When the water-vapor content (mixing ratio) remains constant, the relative humidity can be changed by increasing or decreasing the air temperature. In this example, when the temperature of the air in the flask was lowered from 20° to 10°C, the relative humidity increased from 50 to 100 percent. Further cooling (from 10° to 0°C) causes one-half of the water vapor to condense. In nature, cooling of air below its saturated mixing ratio generally causes condensation in the form of clouds, dew, or fog.

aloft is cooled below its saturation level, some of the water vapor condenses to form clouds. As clouds are made of liquid droplets, this moisture is no longer part of the water-vapor content of the air.

Let us return to Figure 4–11 and see what would happen should the flask in Figure 4–11a be heated to 35°C. From Table 4–1 we see that at 35°C, saturation occurs at 35 grams of water vapor per kilogram of air. Consequently, by heating the air from 20° to 35°C, the relative humidity would drop from 7/14 (50 percent) to 7/35 (20 percent).

We can summarize the effects of temperature on relative humidity as follows. When the water-vapor content of air remains at a constant level, a decrease in air temperature results in an increase in relative humidity, and an increase in temperature causes a decrease in relative humidity.

Natural Changes in Relative Humidity

In nature there are three major ways that air temperatures change (over relatively short time spans) to cause corresponding changes in relative humidity. These are:

1. Daily changes in temperatures (daylight versus nighttime temperatures).
2. Temperature changes that result as air moves horizontally from one location to another.
3. Temperature changes caused as air moves vertically in the atmosphere.

The importance of the last two processes in creating weather will be discussed later. The effect of the typical daily temperature cycle on relative humidity is shown in Figure 4–12. Notice that during the warmer midday period, relative

FIGURE 4-12 Typical daily variation in temperature and relative humidity during a spring day at Washington, DC.

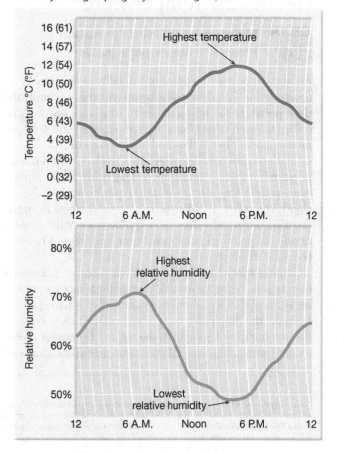

humidity reaches its lowest level, whereas the cooler evening hours are associated with higher relative humidities. In this example, the actual water-vapor content (mixing ratio) of the air remains unchanged; only the relative humidity varies. Now we can better understand why a high relative humidity does not necessarily indicate a high water-vapor content.

Despite the previous example, we still describe air having a low relative humidity as being "dry" and vice versa. The use of the word "dry" in this context indicates that the air is far from being saturated. Thus, the rate of evaporation on a dry day is generally higher than on a humid day.

In summary, relative humidity indicates how near the air is to being saturated, whereas the air's mixing ratio denotes the actual quantity of water vapor contained in that air.

Students Sometimes Ask

Why do my lips get chapped in the winter?

During the winter months, outside air is comparatively cool and dry. When this air is drawn into the home, it is heated, which causes the relative humidity to plunge. Unless your home is equipped with a humidifier, you are likely to experience chapped lips and dry skin at that time of year.

Dew-Point Temperature

 Moisture and Cloud Formation
▶ Humidity: Water Vapor in the Air

Another important measure of humidity is the dew-point temperature. The **dew point temperature,** or simply the **dew point,** is the temperature to which air needs to be cooled to reach saturation. For example, in Figure 4–11 the unsaturated air in the flask had to be cooled to 10°C before saturation occurred. Therefore, 10°C is the dew-point temperature for this air. In nature, cooling below the dew point causes water vapor to condense, typically as dew, fog, or clouds (Figure 4–13). The term *dew point* stems from the fact that during nighttime hours, objects near the ground often cool below the dew-point temperature and become coated with dew.*

Unlike relative humidity, which is a measure of how near the air is to being saturated, dew-point temperature is a measure of the *actual moisture content* of a parcel of air. Because the dew-point temperature is directly related to the amount of water vapor in the air, and because it is easy to determine, it is one of the most useful measures of humidity.

*Normally we associate dew with grass. Because of transpiration by the blades of grass, the relative humidity on a calm night is much higher near the grass than a few inches above the surface. Consequently, dew forms on grass before it does on most other objects.

FIGURE 4-13 Condensation, or "dew," occurs when a cold drinking glass chills the surrounding layer of air to the dew-point temperature. *(Photo by © Dorling Kindersley)*

Recall that the saturation vapor pressure is temperature-dependent and that for every 10°C (18°F) increase in temperature, the amount of water vapor needed for saturation doubles. Therefore, relatively cold *saturated air* (0°C or 32°F) contains about half the water vapor of *saturated air* having a temperature of 10°C (50°F) and roughly one-fourth that of hot *saturated air* with a temperature of 20°C (68°F). Because the dew point is the temperature at which saturation occurs, we can conclude that high dew-point temperatures equate to moist air and low dew-point temperatures indicate dry air (Table 4–2). More precisely, based on what we have learned about vapor pressure and saturation, we can state that for every 10°C (18°F) increase in the dew-point temperature, air contains about twice as much water vapor. Therefore, we know that when the dew-point temperature is 25°C (77°F), air contains about twice the water vapor as when the dew point is 15°C (59°F) and four times that of air with a dew point of 5°C (41°F).

Because the dew-point temperature is a good measure of the amount of water vapor in the air, it is the measure of atmospheric moisture that appears on a variety of weather

TABLE 4-2 Dew-point thresholds

Dew-point temperature	
≤ 10°F	Significant snowfall is inhibited.
≥ 55°F	Minimum for severe thunderstorms to form.
≥ 65°F	Considered humid by most people.
≥ 70°F	Typical of the rainy tropics.
≥ 75°F	Considered oppressive by most.

maps. Notice on the map in Figure 4–14 that many of the places located near the warm Gulf of Mexico have dew-point temperatures that exceed 70°F (21°C). When the dew point exceeds 65°F (18°C), it is considered humid by most people, and air with a dew point 75°F (24°C) or higher is oppressive. Also notice in Figure 4–14 that although the Southeast is dominated by humid conditions (dew points above 65°F), most of the remainder of the country is experiencing comparatively drier air.

Students Sometimes Ask

Is frost just frozen dew?

Contrary to popular belief, frost is not frozen dew. Rather, white frost (*hoar frost*) forms on occasions when saturation occurs at temperature of 0°C (32°F) or below (a temperature called the *frost point*). Thus, frost forms when water vapor changes directly from a gas into a solid (ice) without entering the liquid state. This process, called *deposition,* produces delicate patterns of ice crystals that often decorate windows during winter.

Humidity Measurement

Aside from the fact that humidity is important meteorologically, many of us are interested in humidity because it influences comfort (see Box 4–4). Here we will look at the various ways that humidity is measured.

Absolute humidity and mixing ratio are difficult to measure directly, but if the relative humidity is known, they can be readily computed from a table or graph. How is relative humidity measured?

A variety of instruments, called **hygrometers,** can be used to measure relative humidity. One of the simplest hygrometers, a **psychrometer,** consists of two identical thermometers mounted side by side (Figure 4–15). One thermometer, called the *wet bulb,* has a thin muslin wick tied around the end.

To use the psychrometer, the cloth wick is saturated with water and a continuous current of air is passed over the wick, either by swinging the instrument freely in the air or by fanning air past it. As a result, water evaporates from the wick, absorbing heat energy from the thermometer to do so, and the temperature of the wet bulb drops. The amount of cooling that takes place is directly proportional to the dryness of the air. The drier the air, the greater the cooling. Therefore, the larger the difference between the wet- and dry-bulb temperatures, the lower the relative humidity; the smaller the difference, the higher the relative humidity. If the air is saturated, no evaporation will occur, and the two thermometers will have identical readings.

Tables have been devised to obtain both the relative humidity and the dew-point temperature. (Please refer to Appendix C, Table C–1 and Table C–2.) All that is required is to record the air (dry-bulb) temperature and calculate the difference between the dry- and wet-bulb readings. The difference is known as the *depression of the wet bulb.* Assume, for instance, that the dry-bulb temperature is 20°C and that the wet-bulb reading after swinging or fanning is 14°C. To determine the relative humidity, find the dry-bulb temperature on the left-hand column of Table C–1 of Appendix C and the depression of the wet bulb across the top. The relative humidity is found where the two meet. In this example, the relative humidity is 51 percent. The dew point can be determined in the same way, using Table C–2. In this case, it would be 10°C.

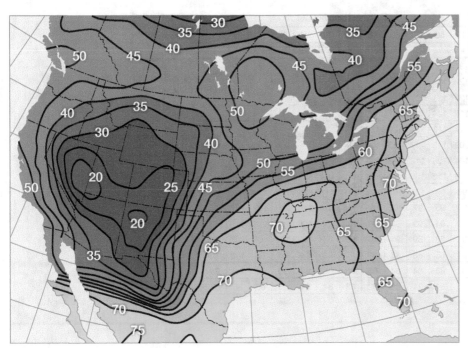

FIGURE 4-14 Surface map showing dew-point temperatures for September 15, 2005. Dew-point temperatures above 60°F dominate the southeastern United States, indicating that this region is blanketed with humid air.

BOX 4-4 Atmospheric Hazard: Humidity and Heat Stress

During a heat wave in 1995 more than 500 heat-related fatalities occurred in the greater Chicago area. Although this was an exceptional event, the stress of high summer temperatures and exposure to the Sun claim about 175 American lives in an average year.

High humidity contributes significantly to the discomfort people feel during a heat wave. Why are hot, muggy days so uncomfortable? Humans, like other mammals, are warm-blooded creatures who maintain a constant body temperature regardless of the temperature of the environment. One of the ways the body prevents overheating is by perspiring or sweating. However, this process does little to cool the body unless the perspiration can evaporate. It is the cooling created by the evaporation of perspiration that reduces body temperature. Because high humidity retards evaporation, people are more uncomfortable on a hot and humid day than on a hot and dry day.

Generally, temperature and humidity are the most important elements influencing summertime human comfort. Several indices combine these factors to establish the level or degree of comfort or discomfort. One index widely used by the National Weather Service was developed by R. G. Steadman and is called the *heat stress index*, or simply the *heat index*. It is a measure of *apparent temperature*, the air temperature that an individual perceives. It indicates how "hot" an average person feels given various combinations of temperature and relative humidity (Table 4–A).

For example, we can see from Table 4–A that if the air temperature is 90°F and the relative humidity is 60 percent, it should feel like 100°F. Note that as the relative humidity increases, the apparent temperature, and thus heat stress, increases as well. Further, when the relative humidity is low, the apparent temperature can have a value that is less than the actual air temperature.

To advise the public on the potential danger from heat stress, the National Weather Service uses the apparent temperature to determine the level of human discomfort, as shown in Table 4–A. This method categorizes the impact that various apparent temperatures will have on the well-being of individuals. It is important to note that factors such as the length of exposure to direct sunlight, the wind speed, and the general health of the individual greatly affect the amount of stress a person will experience. Further, while a period of hot, humid weather in New Orleans might be tolerable, a similar event in Minneapolis, Minnesota, would tax that population. This is because hot and humid weather is more taxing on people who live where it is less common than it is on people who live where prolonged periods of heat and humidity are the rule.

TABLE 4-A Heat index

Air Temperature (°F)	Relative Humidity (%)													With prolonged exposure and/or physical activity
	40	45	50	55	60	65	70	75	80	85	90	95	100	
110	136													**Extreme danger** Heat stroke or sunstroke highly likely
108	130	137												
106	124	130	137											
104	119	124	131	137										
102	114	119	124	130	137									**Danger** Sunstroke, muscle cramps, and/or heat exhaustion likely
100	109	114	118	124	129	136								
98	105	109	113	117	123	128	134							
96	101	104	108	112	116	121	126	132						
94	97	100	102	106	110	114	119	124	129	135				**Extreme caution** Sunstroke, muscle cramps, and/or heat exhaustion possible
92	94	96	99	101	105	108	112	116	121	126	131			
90	91	93	95	97	100	103	106	109	113	117	122	127	132	
88	88	89	91	93	95	98	100	103	106	110	113	117	121	
86	85	87	88	89	91	93	95	97	100	102	105	108	112	**Caution** Fatigue possible
84	83	84	85	86	88	89	90	92	94	96	98	100	103	
82	81	82	83	84	84	85	86	88	89	90	91	93	95	
80	80	80	81	81	82	82	83	84	84	85	86	86	87	

FIGURE 4-15 Sling psychrometer. This instrument is used to determine relative humidity and dew point. The dry-bulb thermometer gives the current air temperature. The thermometers are spun until the temperature of the wet-bulb thermometer (covered with a cloth wick) stops declining. Then both thermometers are read, and the data are used in conjunction with Tables C–1 and C–2 in Appendix C. (*Photo by E. J. Tarbuck*)

Another instrument used for measuring relative humidity, the *hair hygrometer*, can be read directly without using tables. The hair hygrometer operates on the principle that hair changes length in proportion to changes in relative humidity. Hair lengthens as relative humidity increases and shrinks as relative humidity drops. People with naturally curly hair experience this phenomenon, for in humid weather their hair lengthens and hence becomes curlier. The hair hygrometer uses a bundle of hairs linked mechanically to an indicator that is calibrated between 0 and 100 percent. Thus, we need only glance at the dial to read directly the relative humidity. Unfortunately, the hair hygrometer is less accurate than the psychrometer. Furthermore, it requires frequent calibration and is slow in responding to changes in humidity, especially at low temperatures.

A different type of hygrometer is used in remote-sensing instrument packages, such as radiosondes, that transmit upper-air observations back to ground stations. The electric hygrometer contains an electrical conductor coated with a moisture-absorbing chemical. It works on the principle that electric current flow varies as the relative humidity varies. Most surface weather stations have converted from tradi-

tional hygrometers to electric hygrometers of the type used for upper-air observations.

Adiabatic Temperature Changes

 Moisture and Cloud Formation
▶ The Basis of Cloud Formation: Adiabatic Cooling

So far we have considered some basic properties of water vapor and how its variability in the atmosphere is measured. We are now ready to examine the critical role that water vapor plays in our daily weather.

Recall that condensation occurs when water vapor is cooled enough to change to a liquid. Condensation may produce dew, fog, or clouds. Although each type of condensation is different, all require saturated air to form. As indicated earlier, saturation occurs either when sufficient water vapor is added to the air or, more commonly, when the air is cooled to its dew-point temperature.

Heat near Earth's surface is readily exchanged between the ground and the air above. As the ground loses heat in the evening (radiation cooling), dew may condense on the grass and fog may form in the air near the surface. Thus, surface cooling that occurs after sunset accounts for some condensation. However, cloud formation often takes place during the warmest part of the day. Clearly some other mechanism must operate aloft that cools air sufficiently to generate clouds.

The process that generates most clouds is easily visualized. Have you ever pumped up a bicycle tire with a hand pump and noticed that the pump barrel became very warm? When you applied energy to compress the air, the motion of the gas molecules increased and the temperature of the air rose. Conversely, if you allow air to escape from a bicycle tire, it expands; the gas molecules move less rapidly and the air cools. You have probably felt the cooling effect of the propellant gas expanding as you applied hair spray or spray deodorant.

The temperature changes just described, in which heat was neither added nor subtracted, are called **adiabatic temperature changes.** They result when air is compressed or allowed to expand. In summary, *when air is allowed to expand, it cools; when air is compressed, it warms.*

Adiabatic Cooling and Condensation

To simplify the following discussion, it helps if we imagine a volume of air enclosed in a thin elastic cover. Meteorologists call this imaginary volume of air a **parcel.** Typically, we consider a parcel to be a few hundred cubic meters in volume, and we assume that it acts independently of the surrounding air. It is also assumed that no heat is transferred into, or out of, the parcel. Although highly idealized, over short time spans, a parcel of air behaves in a manner much like an actual volume of air moving vertically in the atmosphere. In nature, sometimes the surrounding air infiltrates a vertically moving column of air, a process called **entrainment.** For the following discussion we will assume no mixing of this type is occurring.

Any time a parcel of air moves upward, it passes through regions of successively lower pressure. As a result, ascending air expands and it cools adiabatically. Unsaturated air cools at a constant rate of 10°C for every 1000 meters of ascent (5.5°F per 1000 feet). Conversely, descending air comes under increasing pressure and is compressed and heated 10°C for every 1000 meters of descent (Figure 4–16). This rate of cooling or heating applies only to vertically moving unsaturated air and is known as the **dry adiabatic rate** ("dry" because the air is unsaturated).

If a parcel of air rises high enough, it will eventually cool to its dew point. Here the process of condensation begins. The altitude at which a parcel reaches saturation and cloud formation begins is called the **lifting condensation level.** At the lifting condensation level an important thing happens: The latent heat that was absorbed by the water vapor when it evaporated is liberated. Although the parcel will continue to cool adiabatically, the release of this latent heat slows the rate of cooling. In other words, when a parcel of air ascends above the lifting condensation level, the rate of cooling is reduced because the release of latent heat partially offsets the cooling due to expansion. This slower rate of cooling caused by the release of latent heat is called the **wet adiabatic rate** of cooling ("wet" because the air is saturated).

Because the amount of latent heat released depends on the quantity of moisture present in the air (generally between 0 and 4 percent), the wet adiabatic rate varies from 5°C per 1000 meters for air with a high moisture content to 9°C per 1000 meters for air with a low moisture content. (Figure 4–17) illustrates the role of adiabatic cooling in the formation of clouds. Note that from the surface up to the lifting condensation level, the air cools at the faster, dry adiabatic rate. The slower, wet adiabatic rate commences at the point where condensation begins.

Processes That Lift Air

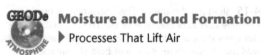 **Moisture and Cloud Formation**
▶ Processes That Lift Air

To review, when air rises, it expands and cools adiabatically. If air is lifted sufficiently, it will eventually cool to its dewpoint temperature, saturation will occur, and clouds will develop. But why does air rise on some occasions and not on others?

FIGURE 4-16 Whenever an unsaturated parcel of air is lifted it expands and cools at the *dry adiabatic rate* of 10°C per 1000 meters. Conversely, when air sinks, it is compressed and heats at the same rate.

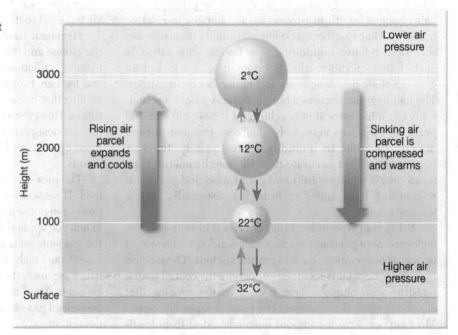

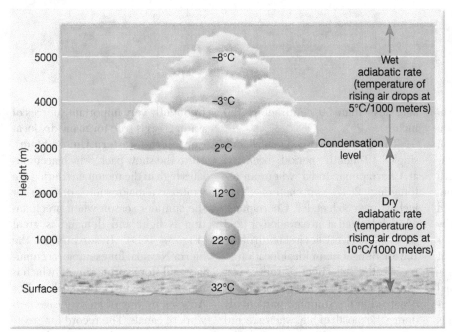

FIGURE 4-17 Rising air expands and cools at the dry adiabatic rate of 10°C per 1000 meters until the air reaches the dew point and condensation (cloud formation) begins. As air continues to rise, the latent heat released by condensation reduces the rate of cooling. The wet adiabatic rate is therefore always less than the dry adiabatic rate.

It turns out that in general the tendency is for air to resist vertical movement. Therefore, air located near the surface tends to stay near the surface, and air aloft tends to remain aloft. Exceptions to this rule, as we shall see, include conditions in the atmosphere that give air sufficient buoyancy to rise without the aid of outside forces. In many situations, however, when you see clouds forming, there is some mechanical phenomenon at work that forces the air to rise (at least initially).

We will look at four mechanisms that cause air to rise. These are:

1. *Orographic lifting*—air is forced to rise over a mountainous barrier.
2. *Frontal wedging*—warmer, less dense air, is forced over cooler, denser air.
3. *Convergence*—a pile-up of horizontal air flow results in upward movement.

4. *Localized convective lifting*—unequal surface heating causes localized pockets of air to rise because of their buoyancy.

In later chapters, we will consider other mechanisms that contribute to vertical airflow. In particular, horizontal airflow at upper levels significantly contributes to vertical lifting across the middle latitudes.

Orographic Lifting

Orographic lifting occurs when elevated terrains, such as mountains, act as barriers to the flow of air (Figure 4–18). As air ascends a mountain slope, adiabatic cooling often generates clouds and copious precipitation. In fact, many of the rainiest places in the world are located on windward mountain slopes (see Box 4–5).

In addition to providing lift, mountains remove additional moisture in other ways. By slowing the horizontal flow of air, they cause convergence and retard the passage of storm systems. Moreover, the irregular topography of mountains enhances the differential heating that causes some localized convective lifting. These combined effects account for the generally higher precipitation associated with mountainous regions compared with surrounding lowlands.

By the time air reaches the leeward side of a mountain, much of its moisture has been lost. If the air descends, it warms adiabatically, making condensation and precipitation even less likely. As shown in Figure 4–18, the result can be a **rain shadow desert** (see Box 4–6). The Great Basin Desert of the western United States lies only a few hundred kilometers from the Pacific Ocean, but it is effectively cut off from the ocean's moisture by the imposing Sierra Nevada (Figure 4–19). The Gobi Desert of Mongolia, the Takla

FIGURE 4-18 Orographic lifting occurs where air is forced over a topographic barrier.

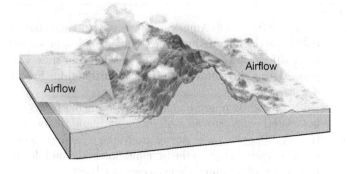

BOX 4-5   Precipitation Records and Mountainous Terrain

Many of the rainiest places in the world are located on windward mountain slopes. Typically, these rainy areas occur because the mountains act as a barrier to the general circulation. Thus, the prevailing winds are forced to ascend the sloping terrain, thereby generating clouds and often abundant precipitation. A station at Mount Waialeale, Hawaii, for example, records the highest average annual rainfall in the world, some 1234 centimeters (486 inches). The station is located on the windward (northeast) coast of the island of Kauai at an elevation of 1569 meters (5148 feet). Incredibly, only 31 kilometers (19 miles) away lies sunny Barking Sands, with annual precipitation that averages less than 50 centimeters (20 inches).

The greatest recorded rainfall for a single 12-month period occurred at Cherrapunji, India, where an astounding 2647 centimeters (1042 inches), over 86 feet, fell. Cherrapunji, which is located at an elevation of 1293 meters (4309 feet), lies just north of the Bay of Bengal in an ideal location to receive the full effect of India's wet summer monsoon. Most of this rainfall occurred in the summer, particularly during the month of July, when a record 930 centimeters (366 inches) fell. For comparison, 10 times more rain fell in a single month at Cherrapunji, India, than falls in an average year at Chicago.

Because mountains can be sites of abundant precipitation, they are frequently very important sources of water. This is true for many dry locations in the western United States. Here the snow pack, which accumulates high in the mountains during the winter, is a major source of water for the summer season when precipitation is light and demand is great (Figure 4–D). Reservoirs in the Sierra Nevada, for example, accumulate and store spring runoff, which is then delivered to cities such as Los Angeles by way of an extensive network of canals. The record for greatest annual snowfall in the United States goes to the Mount Baker ski area north of Seattle, Washington, where 2896 centimeters (1140 inches) of snow were measured during the winter of 1998–1999.

FIGURE 4-D Heavy snow pack along Trail Ridge Road, in Colorado's Rocky Mountain National Park. *(Photo by Henry Lansford)*

Makan of China, and the Patagonia Desert of Argentina are other examples of deserts that exist because they are on the leeward sides of mountains.

Frontal Wedging

If orographic lifting were the only mechanism that forced air aloft, the relatively flat central portion of North America would be an expansive desert instead of the nation's breadbasket. Fortunately, this is not the case.

In central North America, masses of warm and cold air collide producing a **front.** Here the cooler, denser air acts as a barrier over which the warmer, less dense air rises. This process, called **frontal wedging,** is illustrated in (Figure 4–20).

It should be noted that weather-producing fronts are associated with storm systems called *middle-latitude cyclones.* Because these storms are responsible for producing a high percentage of the precipitation in the middle latitudes, we will examine them closely in Chapter 9.

FIGURE 4-19 Rain-shadow desert. The arid conditions in California's Death Valley can be partially attributed to the adjacent mountains, which orographically remove the moisture from air originating over the Pacific. *(Photo by James E. Patterson/James Patterson Collection)*

Convergence

We saw that the collision of contrasting air masses forces air to rise. In a more general sense, whenever air in the lower troposphere flows together, lifting results. This phenomenon is called **convergence.** When air flows in from more than one direction, it must go somewhere. As it cannot go down, it goes up (Figure 4–21). This, of course, leads to adiabatic cooling and possibly cloud formation.

Convergence can also occur whenever an obstacle slows or restricts horizontal air flow (wind). We saw earlier that mountains slow winds and cause convergence. Further, when air moves from a relatively smooth surface, such as the ocean, onto an irregular landscape its speed is reduced. The result is a pileup of air (convergence). This is similar to what happens when people leave a well-attended sporting event and pileup results at the exits. When air converges, the air molecules do not simply squeeze closer together (like people); rather, there is a net upward flow.

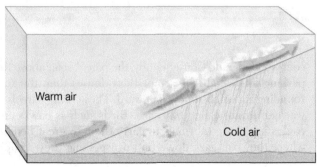

FIGURE 4-20 Frontal wedging. Colder, denser air acts as a barrier over which warmer, less dense air rises.

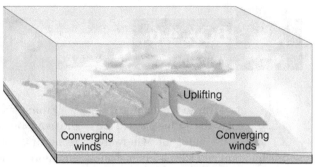

FIGURE 4-21 Convergence. When surface air converges, it increases in height to allow for the decreased area it occupies.

The Florida peninsula provides an excellent example of the role that convergence can play in initiating cloud development and precipitation. On warm days, the airflow is from the ocean to the land along both coasts of Florida. This leads to a pileup of air along the coasts and general convergence over the peninsula. This pattern of air movement and the uplift that results is aided by intense solar heating of the land. The result is that the peninsula of Florida experiences the greatest frequency of mid-afternoon thunderstorms in the United States (Figure 4–22).

More important, convergence as a mechanism of forceful lifting is a major contributor to the weather associated with middle-latitude cyclones and hurricanes. The low-level horizontal airflow associated with these systems is inward and upward around their centers. These important weather producers will be covered in more detail later, but for now remember that convergence near the surface results in a general upward flow.

FIGURE 4-22 Southern Florida viewed from the space shuttle. On warm days, airflow from the Atlantic Ocean and Gulf of Mexico onto the Florida peninsula generates many mid-afternoon thunderstorms. *(Photo by NASA/Media Services)*

BOX 4-6   Orographic Effects: Windward Precipitation and Leeward Rain Shadows

good way to see the role that orographic lifting plays in the development of windward precipitation and leeward rain shadows is to examine a simplified hypothetical situation. In Figure 4–E, prevailing winds force warm, moist air over a 3000-meter-high mountain range. As the unsaturated air ascends the windward side of the range, it cools at the rate of 10°C per 1000 meters (dry adiabatic rate) until it reaches the dew-point temperature of 20°C. Because the dew-point temperature is reached at 1000 meters, we can say that this height represents the lifting condensation level and the height of the cloud base. Notice in Figure 4–E that above the lifting condensation level, latent heat is released, which results in a slower rate of cooling, called the *wet adiabatic rate*.

From the cloud base to the top of the mountain, water vapor within the rising air is condensing to form more and more cloud droplets. As a result, the windward side of the mountain range experiences abundant precipitation.

For simplicity, we will assume that the air that was forced to the top of the mountain is cooler than the surrounding air and hence begins to flow down the leeward slope of the mountain. As the air descends, it is compressed and *heated* at the dry adiabatic rate (Figure 4–E). Upon reaching the base of the mountain range, the temperature of the descending air has risen to 40°C, or 10°C warmer than the temperature at the base of the mountain on the windward side. The higher temperature on the leeward side is the result of the latent heat that was released

during condensation as the air ascended the windward slope of the mountain range.

Two reasons account for the rain shadow commonly observed on leeward mountain slopes. First, water is extracted from air in the form of precipitation on the windward side. Second, the air on the leeward side is warmer than the air on the windward side. (Recall that whenever the temperature of air rises, the relative humidity drops.)

It should be emphasized that the hypothetical example provided here is only a rough approximation of conditions in the natural world. Most often, only a small percentage (sometimes none) of the moisture that condenses to form clouds actually falls as precipitation. Nevertheless, warmer and dryer conditions are the rule on the leeward side of a mountainous

FIGURE 4-E Orographic lifting and the formation of rain shadow deserts.

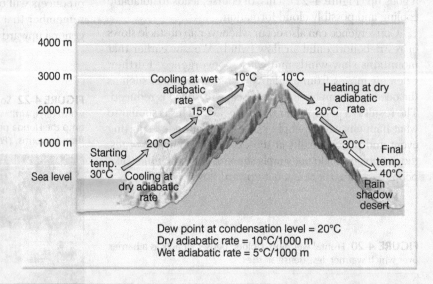

Dew point at condensation level = 20°C
Dry adiabatic rate = 10°C/1000 m
Wet adiabatic rate = 5°C/1000 m

Localized Convective Lifting

On warm summer days, unequal heating of Earth's surface may cause pockets of air to be warmed more than the surrounding air (Figure 4–23). For instance, air above a paved parking lot will be warmed more than the air above an adja-

cent wooded park. Consequently, the parcel of air above the parking lot, which is warmer (less dense) than the surrounding air, will be buoyed upward. These rising parcels of warmer air are called *thermals*. Birds such as hawks and eagles use these thermals to carry them to great heights where they can gaze down on unsuspecting prey. People

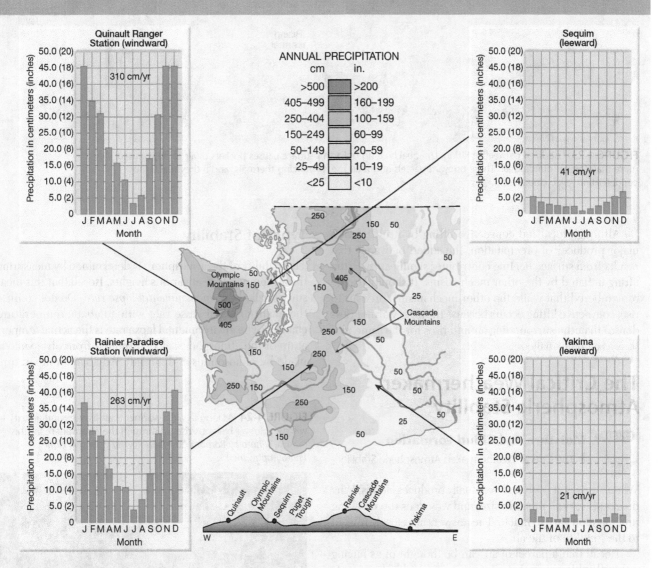

FIGURE 4-F Distribution of precipitation in western Washington State. Data from four stations provide examples of wetter windward locations and drier leeward rain shadows. (After Robert W. Christopherson).

barrier as compared to the rainier, windward side.

A classic example of windward precipitation and leeward rain shadows is found in western Washington State. As moist Pacific air flows inland over the Olympic and Cascade mountains, orographic precipitation is abundant (Figure 4–F). On the other hand, precipitation data for Sequim and Yakima indicate the presence of rain shadows on the leeward side of these highlands.

have learned to employ these rising parcels using hang gliders as a way to "fly."

The phenomenon that produces rising thermals is called **localized convective lifting.** When these warm parcels of air rise above the lifting condensation level, clouds form, which on occasion produce mid-afternoon rain showers. The height of clouds produced in this fashion is somewhat limited, for instability caused solely by unequal surface heating is confined to, at most, the first few kilometers of the atmosphere. Also, the accompanying rains, although occasionally heavy, are of short duration and widely scattered.

FIGURE 4-23 Localized convective lifting. Unequal heating of Earth's surface causes pockets of air to be warmed more than the surrounding air. These buoyant parcels of hot air rise, producing thermals, and if they reach the condensation level, clouds form.

Although localized convective lifting by itself is not a major producer of precipitation, the added buoyancy that results from surface heating contributes significantly to the lifting initiated by the other mechanisms. It should also be remembered that while the other mechanisms force air to rise, convective lifting occurs because the air is warmer (less dense) than the surrounding air and rises for the same reasons as a hot air balloon.

The Critical Weathermaker: Atmospheric Stability

 Moisture and Cloud Formation
▶ The Critical Weathermaker: Atmospheric Stability

When air rises, it cools and eventually produces clouds. Why do clouds vary so much in size, and why does the resulting precipitation vary so much? The answers are closely related to the *stability* of the air.

Recall that a parcel of air can be thought of as having a thin flexible cover that allows it to expand but prevents it from mixing with the surrounding air (picture a hot-air balloon). If this parcel were forced to rise, its temperature would decrease because of expansion. By comparing the parcel's temperature to that of the surrounding air, we can determine its stability. If the parcel were *cooler* than the surrounding environment, it would be more dense; and if allowed to do so, it would sink to its original position. Air of this type, called **stable air,** resists vertical movement.

If, however, our imaginary rising parcel were *warmer* and hence less dense than the surrounding air, it would continue to rise until it reached an altitude where its temperature equaled that of its surroundings. This is exactly how a hot-air balloon works, rising as long as it is warmer and less dense than the surrounding air (Figure 4–24). This type of air is classified as **unstable air.** In summary, stability is a property of air that describes its tendency to remain in its original position (stable), or to rise (unstable).

Types of Stability

The stability of the atmosphere is determined by measuring the air temperature at various heights. Recall that this measure is called the *environmental lapse rate*. Do not confuse the environmental lapse rate with adiabatic temperature changes. The environmental lapse rate is the actual temperature of the atmosphere, as determined from observations made by radiosondes and aircraft. Adiabatic temperature

FIGURE 4-24 As long as air is warmer than its surroundings, it will rise. Hot-air balloons rise up through the atmosphere for this reason. *(Photo by Barbara Cushman Rowell/Mountain Light Photography, Inc.)*

changes are changes in temperature that a parcel of air would experience if it moved vertically through the atmosphere.

To illustrate how the stability of the atmosphere is determined, consider a situation in which the prevailing environmental lapse rate is 5°C per 1000 meters (Figure 4-25). Under this condition, when the air at the surface has a temperature of 25°C, the air at 1000 meters will be 5°C cooler, or 20°C, whereas the air at 2000 meters will have a temperature of 15°C, and so forth.

Examine Figure 4-25 and note that the air at the surface appears to be less dense than the air at 1000 meters, for it is 5°C warmer. However, if the air near the surface were to rise to 1000 meters, it would expand and cool at the dry adiabatic rate of 1°C per 100 meters. Therefore, on reaching 1000 meters, the temperature of the rising parcel would have dropped from 25°C to 15°C, a total of 10°C. Being 5°C cooler than its environment, it would be more dense and would tend to sink to its original position. Thus, we say that the air near the surface is *potentially cooler* than the air aloft and therefore it will not rise on its own.

By similar reasoning, if the air at 1000 meters subsided, adiabatic heating would increase its temperature 10°C by the time it reached the surface, making it warmer than the surrounding air; thus, its buoyancy would cause it to return to its original position. The air just described is stable and resists vertical movement.

With that background, we will now look at three fundamental conditions of the atmosphere: absolute stability, absolute instability, and conditional instability.

Absolute Stability. Stated quantitatively, **absolute stability** prevails when *the environmental lapse rate is less than the wet adiabatic rate.* Figure 4–26 depicts this situation by using an environmental lapse rate of 5°C per 1000 meters and a wet adiabatic rate of 6°C per 1000 meters. Note that at 1000 meters the temperature of the surrounding air is 15°C and that the rising parcel of air has cooled by expansion to 10°C and so is the denser air. Even if this stable air were forced above the condensation level, it would remain cooler and denser than its environment and would have a tendency to return to the surface.

The most stable conditions occur when the temperature in a layer of air actually increases with altitude. When such a reversal occurs, a *temperature inversion* exists. Many circumstances can create temperature inversions. Temperature inversions frequently occur on clear nights as a result of radiation cooling at Earth's surface. Under these conditions an inversion is created because the ground and the air next to it will cool more rapidly than the air aloft.

Temperature inversions also occur in winter when warm air from the Gulf of Mexico invades the cold, snow-covered surface of the midcontinent. Anytime warmer air overlies cooler air, the resulting layer is extremely stable and resists appreciable vertical mixing. Because of this, temperature inversions are responsible for trapping pollutants in a narrow zone near Earth's surface. This idea will be explored more fully in Chapter 13.

Absolute Instability. At the other extreme, a layer of air is said to exhibit **absolute instability** when *the environmental lapse rate is greater than the dry adiabatic rate.* As shown in Figure 4–27, the ascending parcel of air is always warmer than its environment and will continue to rise because of its own buoyancy. Absolute instability occurs most often during the warmest months and on clear days when solar heating is intense. Under these conditions the lowermost layer of the atmosphere is heated to a much higher temperature than the air aloft. This results in a steep environmental lapse rate and a very unstable atmosphere.

Instability produced mainly by strong surface heating is generally confined to the first few kilometers of the atmosphere. Above this height the environmental lapse rate assumes a more "normal" value. Stated another way, the temperature drops more slowly with altitude, creating a more stable temperature regime. Consequently, clouds produced by surface heating lack great vertical height and thus rarely produce violent weather.

Conditional Instability. A more common type of atmospheric instability is called **conditional instability.** This situation prevails when *moist air has an environmental lapse rate between the dry and wet adiabatic rates* (between about 5° and 10°C per 1000 meters). Simply stated, the atmosphere is said to be conditionally unstable when it is *stable* with respect to an *unsaturated* parcel of air, but *unstable* with respect to a *saturated* parcel of air. Notice in

FIGURE 4-25 In a stable atmosphere, as an unsaturated parcel of air is lifted, it expands and cools at the dry adiabatic rate of 10°C per 1000 meters. Because the temperature of the rising parcel of air is lower than that of the surrounding environment, it will be heavier and, if allowed to do so, will sink to its original position.

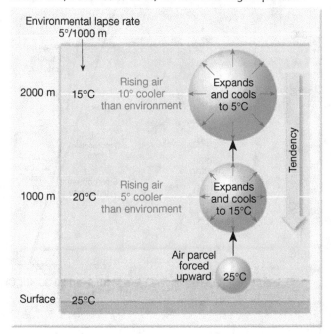

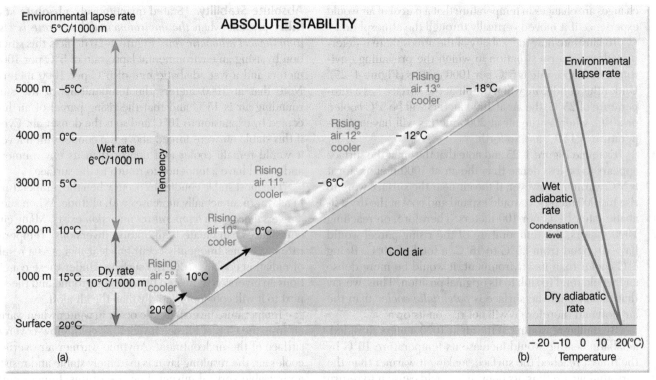

FIGURE 4-26 *Absolute stability* prevails when the environmental lapse rate is less than the wet adiabatic rate. (a) The rising parcel of air is always cooler and heavier than the surrounding air, producing stability. (b) Graphic representation of the conditions shown in part (a).

FIGURE 4-27 Illustration of *absolute instability* that develops when solar heating causes the lowermost layer of the atmosphere to be warmed to a higher temperature than the air aloft. The result is a steep environmental lapse rate that renders the atmosphere unstable. (b) Graphic representation of the conditions shown in part (a).

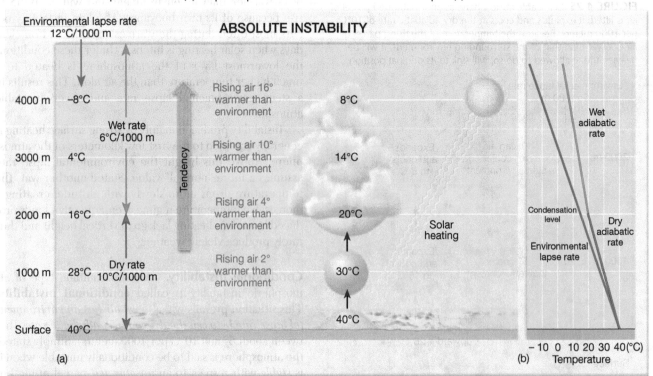

Figure 4–28 that the rising parcel of air is cooler than the surrounding air for the first 4000 meters. With the release of latent heat above the lifting condensation level, the parcel becomes warmer than the surrounding air. From this point along its ascent, the parcel will continue to rise without an outside force.

Thus, conditional instability depends on whether or not the rising air is saturated. The word "conditional" is used because the air must be forced upward before it reaches the level where it becomes unstable and rises on its own.

In summary, the stability of air is determined by measuring the temperature of the atmosphere at various heights (environmental lapse rate). In simple terms, a column of air is deemed unstable when the air near the bottom of this layer is significantly warmer (less dense) than the air aloft, indicating a steep environmental lapse rate. Under these conditions, the air actually turns over because the warm air below rises and displaces the colder air aloft. Conversely, the air is considered to be stable when the temperature

decreases gradually with increasing altitude. The most stable conditions occur during a temperature inversion when the temperature actually increases with height. Under these conditions, there is very little vertical air movement.

Stability and Daily Weather

From the previous discussion, we can conclude that stable air resists vertical movement and that unstable air ascends freely because of its own buoyancy. How do these facts manifest themselves in our daily weather?

When stable air is forced aloft, the clouds that form are widespread and have little vertical thickness compared with their horizontal dimension. Precipitation, if any, is light to moderate. In contrast, clouds associated with unstable air are towering and are usually accompanied by heavy precipitation. Thus, we can conclude that on a dreary and overcast day with light drizzle, stable air was forced aloft. Conversely, on a day when cauliflower-shaped clouds appear to be growing

FIGURE 4-28 Illustration of *conditional instability,* where warm air is forced to rise along a frontal boundary. Note that the environmental lapse rate of 9°C per 1000 meters lies between the dry and wet adiabatic rates. (a) The parcel of air is cooler than the surrounding air up to nearly 3000 meters, where its tendency is to sink toward the surface (stable). Above this level, however, the parcel is warmer than its environment and will rise because of its own buoyancy (unstable). Thus, when conditionally unstable air is forced to rise, the result can be towering cumulus clouds. (b) Graphic representation of the conditions shown in part (a).

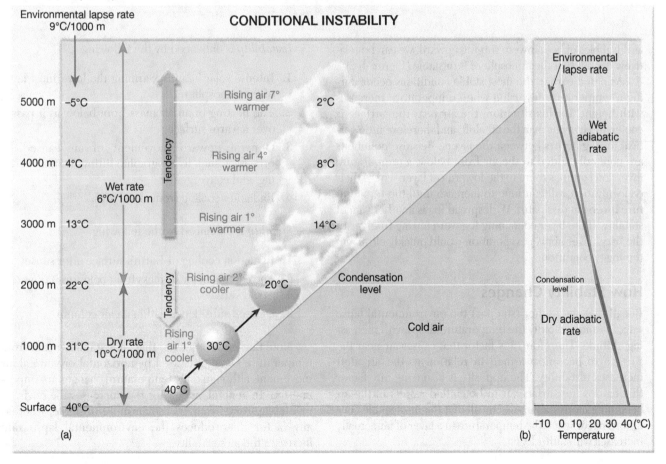

FIGURE 4-29 Cauliflower-shaped clouds provide evidence of unstable conditions in the atmosphere. *(Photo by Tom Bean/DRK Photo)*

as if bubbles of hot air were surging upward, we can be relatively certain that the atmosphere is unstable (Figure 4–29).

As noted earlier, the most stable conditions occur during a temperature inversion when temperature increases with height. In this situation, the air near the surface is cooler and heavier than the air aloft, and therefore little vertical mixing occurs between the layers. Because pollutants are generally added to the air from below, a temperature inversion confines them to the lowermost layer, where their concentration will continue to increase until the temperature inversion dissipates. Widespread fog is another sign of stability. If the layer containing fog were mixing freely with the "dry" layer above, evaporation would quickly eliminate the foggy condition.

How Stability Changes

Recall that the higher (steeper) the environmental lapse rate, the more rapidly the temperature drops with increasing altitude. Therefore, any factor that causes air near the surface to become warmed in relation to the air aloft increases instability. The opposite is also true; any factor that causes the surface air to be chilled results in the air becoming more stable. Also recall that the most stable conditions occur when the temperature in a layer of air actually increases with altitude.

Instability is enhanced by the following:

1. Intense solar heating warming the lowermost layer of the atmosphere.
2. The heating of an air mass from below as it passes over a warm surface.
3. General upward movement of air caused by processes such as orographic lifting, frontal wedging, and convergence.
4. Radiation cooling from cloud tops.

Stability is enhanced by the following:

1. Radiation cooling of Earth's surface after sunset.
2. The cooling of an air mass from below as it traverses a cold surface.
3. General subsidence within an air column.

Note that most processes that alter stability result from temperature changes caused by horizontal or vertical air movement, although daily temperature changes are important too. In general, any factor that increases the environmental lapse rate renders the air more unstable, whereas any factor that reduces the environmental lapse rate increases the air's stability.

Temperature Changes and Stability

As stated earlier, on a clear day when there is abundant surface heating, the lower atmosphere often becomes warmed sufficiently to cause parcels of air to rise. After the Sun sets, surface cooling generally renders the air stable again.

Similar changes in stability occur as air moves horizontally over a surface having markedly different temperatures. In the winter, warm air from the Gulf of Mexico moves northward over the cold, snow-covered Midwest. Because the air is cooled from below, it becomes more stable, often producing widespread fog.

The opposite occurs when wintertime polar air moves southward over the open waters of the Great Lakes. Although we would die of hypothermia in a few minutes if we fell into these cold waters (perhaps 5°C or 41°F), compared to the frigid air temperatures, these waters are warm. Recall from our discussion of vapor pressure that the temperature of the water surface and the vapor pressure of the surrounding air determine the rate at which water will evaporate. Because the water of the Great Lakes is comparatively warm and because the polar air is dry (low vapor pressure) the rate of evaporation will be high. The moisture and heat added to the frigid polar air from the water below are enough to make it unstable and generate the clouds that produce heavy snowfalls on the downwind shores of these lakes (called "lake-effect snows"—see Chapter 8).

Radiation Cooling from Clouds. On a smaller scale the loss of heat by radiation from cloud tops during evening hours adds to their instability and growth. Unlike air, which is a poor radiator of heat, cloud droplets emit energy to space nearly as well as does Earth's surface. Towering clouds that owe their growth to surface heating lose that source of energy at sunset. After sunset, however, radiation cooling at their tops steepens the lapse rate near the top of the cloud and can lead to additional upward flow of warmer parcels from below. This process is believed responsible for producing nocturnal thunderstorms from clouds whose growth prematurely ceased at sunset.

Vertical Air Movement and Stability

Vertical movements of air also influence stability. When there is a general downward airflow, called **subsidence,** the upper portion of the subsiding layer is heated by compression, more so than the lower portion. Usually the air near the surface is not involved in the subsidence and so its temperature remains unchanged. The net effect is to stabilize the air, for the air aloft is warmed in relation to the surface air. The warming effect of a few hundred meters of subsidence is enough to evaporate the clouds found in any layer of the atmosphere. Thus, one sign of subsiding air is a deep blue, cloudless sky. Subsidence can also produce a temperature inversion aloft. The most intense and prolonged temperature inversions and associated air pollution episodes are caused by subsidence, a topic discussed more fully in Chapter 13.

Upward movement of air generally enhances instability, particularly when the lower portion of the rising layer has a higher moisture content than the upper portion, which is usually the situation. As the air moves upward, the lower portion becomes saturated first and cools at the lesser wet adiabatic rate. The net effect is to increase the lapse rate within the rising layer. This process is especially important in producing the instability associated with thunderstorms. In addition, recall that conditionally unstable air can become unstable if lifted sufficiently.

In summary, the role of stability in determining our daily weather cannot be overemphasized. The air's stability, or lack of it, determines to a large degree whether clouds develop and produce precipitation and whether that precipitation will come as a gentle shower or a violent downpour. In general, when stable air is forced aloft, the associated clouds have little vertical thickness, and precipitation, if any, is light. In contrast, clouds associated with unstable air are towering and are frequently accompanied by heavy precipitation.

Chapter Summary

- The unending circulation of Earth's water supply is called the *hydrologic cycle* (or water cycle). The cycle illustrates the continuous movement of water from the oceans to the atmosphere, from the atmosphere to the land, and from the land back to the sea.
- *Water vapor,* an odorless, colorless gas, can change from one state of matter (solid, liquid or gas) to another at the temperatures and pressures experienced on Earth. The heat energy involved in the change of state of water is often measured in *calories*. The processes involved in

changes of state include *evaporation* (liquid to gas), *condensation* (gas to liquid), *melting* (solid to liquid), *freezing* (liquid to solid), *sublimation* (solid to gas), and *deposition* (gas to solid). During each change, *latent* (hidden, or stored) *heat* energy is either absorbed or released.
- *Humidity* is the general term used to describe the amount of water vapor in the air. The methods used to express humidity quantitatively include (1) *absolute humidity,* the mass of water vapor in a given volume of air, (2) *mixing ratio,* the mass of water vapor in a unit of

air compared to the remaining mass of dry air, (3) *vapor pressure,* that part of the total atmospheric pressure attributable to its water-vapor content, (4) *relative humidity,* the ratio of the air's actual water-vapor content compared with the amount of water vapor required for saturation at that temperature, and (5) *dew point,* the temperature to which a parcel of air would need to be cooled to reach saturation. When air is *saturated,* the pressure exerted by the water vapor, called the *saturation vapor pressure,* produces a balance between the number of water molecules leaving the surface of the water and the number returning. Because the saturation vapor pressure is temperature-dependent, at higher temperatures more water vapor is required for saturation to occur.

- Relative humidity can be changed in two ways: (1) by changing the amount of moisture in the air or (2) by changing the air's temperature. Adding moisture to the air while keeping the temperature constant increases the relative humidity. Removing moisture lowers the relative humidity. When the water vapor content of air remains at a constant level, a decrease in air temperature results in an increase in relative humidity, and an increase in temperature causes a decrease in relative humidity. In nature there are three major ways that air temperatures change to cause corresponding changes in relative humidity: (1) daily (daylight versus nighttime) changes in temperature, (2) temperature changes that result as air moves horizontally from one location to another, and (3) changes caused as air moves vertically in the atmosphere.

- An important concept related to relative humidity is the *dew-point temperature* (or simply *dew point*), which is the temperature to which a parcel of air would need to be cooled to reach saturation. Unlike relative humidity, which is a measure of how near the air is to being saturated, dew-point temperature is a measure of the air's actual moisture content. High dew-point temperatures equate to moist air, and low dew-point temperatures indicate dry air. Because the dew-point temperature is a good measure of the amount of water vapor in the air, it is the measure of atmospheric moisture that appears on daily weather maps.

- A variety of instruments, called *hygrometers,* can be used to measure relative humidity. One of the simplest hygrometers, a *psychrometer,* consists of two identical thermometers mounted side by side. One thermometer, called the wet-bulb thermometer, has a thin muslin wick tied around the bulb. After spinning or fanning air past the instrument and noting the difference between the dry- and wet-bulb readings (known as the depression of the wet bulb), tables are consulted to determine the relative humidity. A second instrument, the *hair hygrometer,* can be read directly without using tables.

- When air is allowed to expand, it cools. When air is compressed, it warms. Temperature changes produced in this manner, in which heat is neither added nor subtracted, are called *adiabatic temperature changes.* The rate of cooling or warming of vertically moving unsaturated ("dry") air is 10°C for every 1000 meters (5.5°F per 1000 feet), the *dry adiabatic rate.* At the *lifting condensation level* (the altitude where a rising parcel of air has reached saturation and cloud formation begins), latent heat is released, and the rate of cooling is reduced. The slower rate of cooling, called the *wet adiabatic rate* of cooling ("wet" because the air is saturated) varies from 5°C per 1000 meters for air, with a high-moisture content to 9°C per 1000 meters for air with a low-moisture content.

- When air rises, it expands and cools adiabatically. If air is lifted sufficiently high, it will eventually cool to its dew-point temperature, and clouds will develop. Four mechanisms that cause air to rise are (1) *orographic lifting,* where air is forced to rise over a mountainous barrier, (2) *Frontal wedging,* where warmer, less dense air is forced over cooler, denser air along a *front,* (3) *convergence,* a pile-up of horizontal airflow resulting in an upward flow, and (4) *localized convective lifting,* where unequal surface heating causes localized pockets of air to rise because of their buoyancy.

- When air rises, it cools and can eventually produce clouds. *Stable air* resists vertical movement, whereas *unstable air* rises because of its buoyancy. The stability of air is determined by knowing the *environmental lapse rate,* the temperature of the atmosphere at various heights. The three fundamental conditions of the atmosphere are (1) *absolute stability,* when the environmental lapse rate is less than the wet adiabatic rate, (2) *absolute instability,* when the environmental lapse rate is greater than the dry adiabatic rate, and (3) *conditional instability,* when moist air has an environmental lapse rate between the dry and wet adiabatic rates. In general, when stable air is forced aloft, the associated clouds have little vertical thickness, and precipitation, if any, is light. In contrast, clouds associated with unstable air are towering and frequently accompanied by heavy rain.

- Any factor that causes air near the surface to become warmed in relation to the air aloft increases the air's instability. The opposite is also true; any factor that causes the surface air to be chilled results in the air becoming more stable. Most processes that alter atmospheric stability result from temperature changes caused by horizontal or vertical air movements, although daily temperature changes are important too. Changes in stability occur as air moves horizontally over a surface having a markedly different temperature than the air. Furthermore, *subsidence* (a general downward airflow) generally stabilizes the air, while upward air movement enhances instability.

Vocabulary Review

absolute humidity (p. 103)
absolute instability (p. 121)
absolute stability (p. 121)
adiabatic temperature changes (p. 114)
calorie (p. 101)
condensation (p. 102)
conditional instability (p. 121)
convergence (p. 117)
deposition (p. 102)
dew point (p. 110)
dew point temperature (p. 110)
dry adiabatic rate (p. 114)
entrainment (p. 114)

evaporation (p. 102)
front (p. 116)
frontal wedging (p. 116)
humidity (p. 103)
hydrologic cycle (p. 98)
hygrometer (p. 111)
latent heat (p. 101)
latent heat of condensation (p. 102)
latent heat of vaporization (p. 102)
lifting condensation level (p. 114)
localized convective lifting (p. 119)
mixing ratio (p. 104)
orographic lifting (p. 115)

parcel (p. 114)
psychrometer (p. 111)
rain shadow desert (p. 115)
relative humidity (p. 106)
saturation (p. 104)
saturation vapor pressure (p. 104)
stable air (p. 120)
sublimation (p. 102)
subsidence (p. 125)
transpiration (p. 98)
unstable air (p. 120)
vapor pressure (p. 104)
wet adiabatic rate (p. 114)

Review Questions

1. Describe the movement of water through the hydrologic cycle.

2. The quantity of water lost to evaporation over the oceans is not equaled by precipitation. Why, then, does the sea level not drop?

3. Summarize the processes by which water changes from one state to another. Indicate whether heat is absorbed or liberated.

4. After reviewing Table 4–1, write a generalization relating temperature and the amount of water vapor needed to saturate the air.

5. How do absolute humidity and mixing ratio differ? What do they have in common? How is relative humidity different from absolute humidity and the mixing ratio?

6. Refer to Figure 4–12 and then answer the following questions.
   a. When is relative humidity highest during a typical day? When is it lowest?
   b. At what time of day would dew most likely form?
   c. Write a generalization relating changes in air temperature to changes in relative humidity.

7. If temperature remains unchanged, and if the mixing ratio decreases, how will relative humidity change?

8. How much more water vapor does a mass of air having a dew-point temperature of 24°C (75°F) contain than air having a dew-point temperature of 4°C (39°F)?

9. Explain the principle of both the psychrometer and the hair hygrometer.

10. What are the disadvantages of the hair hygrometer? Does this instrument have any advantages over the psychrometer?

11. What name is given to the processes whereby the temperature of the air changes without the addition or subtraction of heat?

12. At what rate does unsaturated air cool when it rises through the atmosphere?

13. Why does air expand as it moves upward through the atmosphere?

14. Explain why air warms whenever it sinks.

15. Why does the adiabatic rate of cooling change when condensation begins? Why is the wet adiabatic rate not a constant figure?

16. The contents of an aerosol can are under very high pressure. When you push the nozzle on such a can, the spray feels cold. Explain.

17. How do orographic lifting and frontal wedging act to force air to rise?

18. Explain why the Great Basin area of the western United States is dry. What term is applied to such a situation?

19. How is localized convective lifting different from the other three processes that cause air to rise?

20. How does stable air differ from unstable air?

21. Explain the difference between the environmental lapse rate and adiabatic cooling.

22. How is the stability of air determined?

23. Write a statement relating the environmental lapse rate to stability.

24. What weather conditions would lead you to believe that air is unstable?

25. List four ways instability can be enhanced.

26. List three ways stability can be enhanced.

Problems

1. Using Table 4–1, answer the following:
   a. If a parcel of air at 25°C contains 10 grams of water vapor per kilogram of air, what is its relative humidity?
   b. If a parcel of air at 35°C contains 5 grams of water vapor per kilogram of air, what is its relative humidity?
   c. If a parcel of air at 15°C contains 5 grams of water vapor per kilogram of air, what is its relative humidity?
   d. If the temperature of this same parcel of air dropped to 5°C, how would its relative humidity change?
   e. If 20°C air contains 7 grams of water vapor per kilogram of air, what is its dew point?

2. Using the standard tables (Appendix C Tables C–1 and C–2), determine the relative humidity and dew-point temperature if the dry-bulb thermometer reads 22°C and the wet-bulb thermometer reads 16°C. How would the relative humidity and dew point change if the wet-bulb reading were 19°C?

3. If unsaturated air at 20°C were to rise, what would its temperature be at a height of 500 meters? If the dew-point temperature at the lifting condensation level were 11°C, at what elevation would clouds begin to form?

4. Using Figure 4–30, answer the following. (*Hint:* Read Box 4–6.)
   a. What is the elevation of the cloud base?

   b. What is the temperature of the ascending air when it reaches the top of the mountain?
   c. What is the dew-point temperature of the rising air at the top of the mountain? (Assume 100 percent relative humidity.)
   d. Estimate the amount of water vapor that must have condensed (in grams per kilogram) as the air moved from the cloud base to the top of the mountain.
   e. What will the temperature of the air be if it descends to point B? (Assume that the moisture that condensed fell as precipitation on the windward side of the mountain.)
   f. What is the approximate capacity of the air to hold water vapor at point B?
   g. Assuming that no moisture was added or subtracted from the air as it traveled downslope, estimate the relative humidity at point B.
   h. What is the *approximate* relative humidity at point A? (Use the dew-point temperature at the condensation level for the surface dew point.)
   i. Give *two* reasons for the difference in relative humidity between points A and B.
   j. Needles, California, is situated on the dry leeward side of a mountain range similar to the position of point B. What term describes this situation?

5. If a lake is ice covered, what is the temperature of the water at the bottom of the lake? (*Hint:* See Box 4–1.)

FIGURE 4-30 Orographic lifting problem.

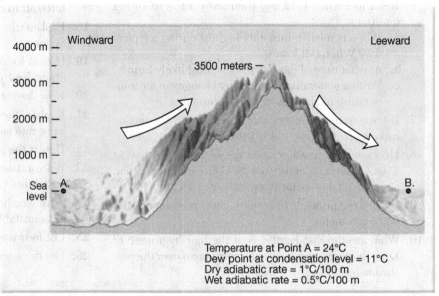

Temperature at Point A = 24°C
Dew point at condensation level = 11°C
Dry adiabatic rate = 1°C/100 m
Wet adiabatic rate = 0.5°C/100 m

Atmospheric Science Online

The Atmosphere 10e web site uses the resources and flexibility of the Internet to aid in your study of the topics in this chapter. Written and developed by meteorology instructors, this site will help improve your understanding of meteorology. Visit **http://www .prenhall.com/lutgens** and click on the cover of *The Atmosphere 10e* to find:

• **Online review quizzes**
• **Critical thinking exercises**
• **Links to chapter-specific web resources**
• **Internet-wide key term searches**

http://www.prenhall.com/lutgens

FORMS OF
CONDENSATION
and
PRECIPITATION

Cirrus clouds over Lake Superior near Eagle Harbor on Michigan's Keweenaw Peninsula. *(Photo by Jim Wark/AirPhoto)*

Clouds, fog, rain, snow, and sleet are among the most observable weather phenomena (Figure 5–1). This chapter will provide a basic understanding of each. In addition to learning the basic scheme for classifying and naming clouds, you will learn that the formation of an average raindrop involves complex processes requiring water from roughly a million cloud droplets. Can scientists make rain by triggering these processes? Can modern weather-modification technology increase the precipitation that falls from a cloud? Can we control weather events such as fog and frost?

Cloud Formation

Clouds can be defined as *visible aggregate of minute droplets of water, or tiny crystals of ice, or a mixture of both.* In addition to being prominent and sometimes spectacular features in the sky, clouds are of continual interest to meteorologists because they provide a visible indication of what is going on in the atmosphere.

Condensation Aloft

Clouds are a form of condensation produced when water vapor condenses in the atmosphere. Clearly the most important cloud-forming process is *adiabatic cooling*. To review, any time a parcel of air ascends, it passes through regions of successively lower pressure. As a result, rising air expands and cools adiabatically. At a height called the *lifting condensation level,* the ascending parcel has cooled to its dew-point temperature, and further ascent (cooling) causes condensation.

As you learned earlier, condensation occurs when water vapor changes to a liquid. The result of this process may be dew, fog, or clouds. Although each type of condensation is somewhat different, they all form when two conditions are met. First, for any form of condensation to occur, the air must be *saturated* (or nearly so). Saturation occurs most often when air is cooled to its dew point. (Condensation may also occur when sufficient water vapor is added to a layer of the atmosphere.) Second, there generally must be a *surface* on which the water vapor can condense. When dew forms, objects at or near the ground, like blades of grass, serve this purpose.

When condensation occurs aloft, tiny particles known as **cloud condensation nuclei** serve as surfaces on which water vapor condenses. Nuclei are important because, if they are absent, a relative humidity well in excess of 100 percent is necessary to produce cloud droplets. (At very low temperatures—low kinetic energies—water molecules will "stick together" in tiny clusters without the presence of condensation nuclei.) Cloud condensation nuclei include microscopic dust, smoke, and salt particles, all of which are profuse in the lower atmosphere. Consequently, in the troposphere the relative humidity seldom exceeds 100 percent.

Growth of Cloud Droplets

Particles that are the most effective sites for condensation are called **hygroscopic** (*water-seeking*) **nuclei.** Some familiar food items, such as crackers and cereals, are hygroscopic, which is why they quickly absorb moisture when exposed to humid air and become stale.

FIGURE 5-1 A pedestrian dashes across the street in downtown Minneapolis. At the time the rainfall rate was about 5 centimeters (2 inches) per hour. *(Photo by Jerry Holt/Star Tribune/NewsCom.)*

Over the ocean, salt particles are released into the atmosphere when sea spray evaporates. Because salt is hygroscopic, water droplets begin to form around sea salt particles at relative humidities less than 100 percent. As a result, the cloud droplets that form on salt are generally much larger than those that grow on **hydrophobic** (*water-repelling*) **nuclei.** Although hydrophobic particles are not efficient condensation nuclei, cloud droplets will form on them whenever the relative humidity reaches 100 percent.

Dust storms, volcanic eruptions, and pollen are major sources of cloud condensation nuclei on land. In addition, hygroscopic nuclei are introduced into the atmosphere as a by-product of combustion (burning) from such sources as forest fires, automobiles, and coal-burning furnaces. Because cloud condensation nuclei have a wide range of affinities for water, cloud droplets of various sizes often coexist in the same cloud. This fact has important consequences for the formation of precipitation.

Initially, the growth of cloud droplets is rapid. However, the rate of growth quickly diminishes because the available water vapor is consumed by the large number of competing droplets. The result is the formation of a cloud consisting of billions of tiny water droplets, all so small that they remain suspended in air. Even in very moist air, the growth of cloud droplets by additional condensation is quite slow. Furthermore, the immense size difference between cloud droplets and raindrops (it takes about a million cloud droplets to form a single raindrop) suggests that condensation alone is not responsible for the formation of drops (or ice crystals) large enough to fall to the ground without evaporating. We will investigate this idea later when we examine the processes that generate precipitation.

Cloud Classification

 GEODe **Forms of Condensation and Precipitation**
▶ Classifying Clouds

Anyone who observes clouds finds a bewildering variety of these white and gray masses streaming across the sky. Once the basic classification scheme for clouds is known, however, most of the confusion vanishes.

Prior to the beginning of the nineteenth century, there were no generally accepted names for clouds. In 1803 Luke Howard, an English naturalist, published a cloud classification that met with great success and subsequently served as the basis of our present-day system.

Clouds are classified on the basis of two criteria: *form* and *height* (Figure 5–2). Three basic cloud forms are recognized:

- **Cirrus** clouds are high, white, and thin. They are separated or detached and form delicate veil-like patches or extended wispy fibers and often have a feathery appearance. (*Cirrus* is a Latin word meaning "curl" or "filament.")
- **Cumulus** clouds consist of globular individual cloud masses. Normally they exhibit a flat base and appear as rising domes or towers. Such clouds are frequently described as having a cauliflower-like structure.
- **Stratus** clouds are best described as sheets or layers (strata) that cover much or all of the sky. Although there may be minor breaks, there are no distinct individual cloud units.

All clouds have one of these three basic forms or combinations or modifications of them.

Looking at the second aspect of cloud classification—height—three levels are recognized: high, middle, and low. **High clouds** normally have bases above 6000 meters (20,000 feet); **middle clouds** generally occupy heights from 2000 to 6000 meters; **low clouds** form below 2000 meters (6500 feet). These altitudes are not hard and fast. They vary somewhat by season of the year and by latitude. At high (poleward) latitudes or during cold winter months, high clouds generally occur at lower altitudes. Further, some clouds extend vertically to span more than one height range. These are called **clouds of vertical development.**

Definite weather patterns can be associated with specific clouds or combinations of clouds, so it is important to become familiar with cloud characteristics.

Ten basic cloud types are recognized internationally. We describe them below and summarize them in Table 5–1.

High Clouds

Three cloud types make up the family of high clouds (above 6000 meters/20,000 feet). They are *cirrus, cirrostratus,* and *cirrocumulus.* Because of the low temperatures and small quantities of water vapor present at high altitudes, all high clouds are thin and white and made up primarily of ice crystals.

Cirrus are detached clouds composed of white, delicate icy filaments. Winds aloft often cause these fibrous ice trails to bend or curl. As shown in Figure 5–3a, cirrus clouds with hooked filaments are called "mares' tails" (see Box 5–1).

Cirrostratus is a transparent, whitish cloud veil of fibrous or sometimes smooth appearance that may cover much or all of the sky. This cloud is easily recognized when it pro-

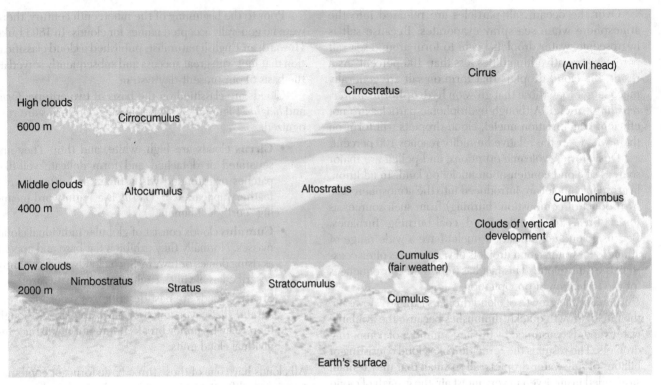

FIGURE 5-2 Classification of clouds according to height and form. *(After Ward's Natural Science Establishment, Inc., Rochester, N.Y.)*

TABLE 5-1 Basic cloud types		
Cloud family and height	**Cloud type**	**Characteristics**
High clouds—above 6000 m (20,000 ft)	Cirrus (Ci)	Thin, delicate, fibrous ice-crystal clouds. Sometimes appear as hooked filaments called "mares' tails" (cirrus uncinus; Figure 5–3a).
	Cirrostratus (Cs)	Thin sheet of white ice-crystal clouds that may give the sky a milky look. Sometimes produces halos around the Sun and Moon (Figure 5–3b).
	Cirrocumulus (Cc)	Thin, white ice-crystal clouds. In the form of ripples or waves, or globular masses all in a row. May produce a "mackerel sky." Least common of high clouds (Figure 5–3c).
Middle clouds—2000–6000 m (6500 to 20,000 ft)	Altocumulus (Ac)	White to gray clouds often made up of separate globules; "sheepback" clouds (Figure 5–4a).
	Altostratus (As)	Stratified veil of clouds that is generally thin and may produce very light precipitation. When thin, the Sun or Moon may be visible as a "bright spot," but no halos are produced (Figure 5–4b).
Low clouds—below 2000 m (6500 ft)	Stratus (St)	Low uniform layer resembling fog but not resting on the ground. May produce drizzle.
	Stratocumulus (Sc)	Soft, gray clouds in globular patches or rolls. Rolls may join together to make a continuous cloud.
	Nimbostratus (Ns)	Amorphous layer of dark gray clouds. One of the chief precipitation-producing clouds (Figure 5–5).
Clouds of vertical development	Cumulus (Cu)	Dense, billowy clouds often characterized by flat bases. May occur as isolated clouds or closely packed (Figure 5–6).
	Cumulonimbus (Cb)	Towering cloud, sometimes spreading out on top to form an "anvil head." Associated with heavy rainfall, thunder, lightning, hail, and tornadoes (Figure 5–7).

(a)

(b)

(c)

FIGURE 5-3 Three basic cloud types make up the family of high clouds: (a) cirrus, (b) cirrostratus, and (c) cirrocumulus. *(Photos (a) and (c) by E. J. Tarbuck, (b) by A. and J. Verkaik/CORBIS/Stock Market)*

duces a halo around the Sun or Moon (Figure 5–3b). On occasions, cirrostratus may be so thin and transparent that the clouds are barely discernible. With the approach of a warm front, cirrostratus clouds generally thicken and grade into middle-level altostratus clouds.

Cirrocumulus clouds appear as white patches composed of very small cells or ripples (Figure 5–3c). Most often the masses that make up these clouds have an apparent width similar to that of the Sun. Furthermore, these small globules, which may be merged or separate, are often arranged in a regular pattern. This pattern is commonly called "mackerel sky" because of the similarity to the pattern formed by fish scales.

High clouds generally are not precipitation makers. However, when cirrus clouds give way to cirrocumulus clouds that cover even more of the sky, they may warn of impending stormy weather. The following mariner's saying is based on this observation: *Mackerel scales and mares' tails make lofty ships carry low sails.*

Middle Clouds

Clouds that appear in the middle altitude range (2000 to 6000 meters/6500 to 20,000 feet) have the prefix *alto* as part of their name. There are two types: *altocumulus* and *altostratus*.

Altocumulus tend to form in large patches composed of rounded masses or rolls that may or may not merge (Figure 5–4a). Because they are generally composed of water droplets rather than ice crystals, the individual cells usually have a more distinct outline. Altocumulus are most easily confused with two other cloud types: cirrocumulus (which are smaller and less dense) and stratocumulus (which are larger).

135

FIGURE 5-4 Two forms of clouds are generated in the middle-altitude range. (a) Altocumulus tend to form in patches composed of rolls or rounded masses. (b) Altostratus occur as grayish sheets covering a large portion of the sky. When visible, the Sun appears as a bright spot through these clouds. *(Photos by E. J. Tarbuck)*

Altostratus is the name given to a formless layer of grayish clouds covering all or a large portion of the sky. Generally, the Sun is visible through these clouds as a bright spot, but with the edge of its disc not discernible (Figure 5–4b). However, unlike cirrostratus clouds, altostratus do not produce halos. Infrequent precipitation in the form of light snow or drizzle may accompany these clouds. Altostratus clouds are commonly associated with warm fronts. As the front approaches, the clouds thicken into a dark gray layer of nimbostratus that is capable of producing copious rainfall.

Low Clouds

There are three members of the family of low clouds (below 2000 meters/6500 feet): *stratus, stratocumulus,* and *nimbostratus*.

Stratus is a uniform layer that frequently covers much of the sky and, on occasion, may produce light precipitation. When stratus clouds develop a scalloped bottom that appears as long parallel rolls or broken globular patches, they are called *stratocumulus* clouds.

Nimbostratus clouds derive their name from the Latin *nimbus,* "rain cloud," and *stratus,* "to cover with a layer" (Figure 5–5). As the name implies, nimbostratus clouds are one of the chief precipitation producers. Nimbostratus clouds form in association with stable conditions. We might not expect clouds to grow or persist in stable air, yet cloud growth of this type is common when air is forced to rise, as along a front or near the center of a cyclone where converging winds cause air to ascend. Such forced ascent of stable air leads to the formation of a stratified cloud layer that is large horizontally compared to its thickness. Precipitation associated with nimbostratus clouds is generally light to moderate but of long duration and widespread.

Clouds of Vertical Development

Some clouds do not fit into any one of the three height categories. Such clouds have their bases in the low height range and extend upward into the middle or high altitudes; they are referred to as *clouds of vertical development*. Vertically developed clouds are all closely related and are associated with unstable air. There are two types, *cumulus* and *cumulonimbus*.

Cumulus clouds are individual masses that develop into vertical domes or towers, the tops of which often resemble cauliflower. Cumulus clouds most often form on clear days when unequal surface heating causes parcels of air to rise convectively above the lifting condensation level (Figure 5–6). This level is often apparent to an observer because the flat cloud bottoms define it.

On days when cumulus clouds are present, we usually notice an increase in cloudiness into the afternoon as solar heating intensifies. Furthermore, because small cumulus clouds (*cumulus humilis*) rarely produce appreciable precipitation, and because they form on "sunny" days, they are often called "fair-weather clouds."

Although cumulus clouds are associated with fair weather, they may, under the proper circumstances, grow dramatically in height. Once upward movement is triggered, acceleration is powerful, and clouds with great vertical extent are formed. As the cumulus enlarges, its top leaves the low height range, and it is called a *cumulus congestus*. Finally, when the cloud becomes even more towering and rain begins to fall, it becomes a cumulonimbus.

Cumulonimbus are dark, dense, billowy clouds of considerable vertical extent in the form of huge towers (Figure 5–7). In its later stages of development, the upper part of a cumulonimbus turns to ice and appears fibrous. Furthermore, the tops of these clouds frequently spread out in the shape of an anvil. Cumulonimbus towers extend from a few hundred meters above the surface upward to 12 kilometers (7 miles) or, on rare occasions, 20 kilometers (12 miles). These huge towers produce heavy precipitation with accompanying lightning and thunder and occasionally hail. We will consider the development of these important weather producers in Chapter 10, which considers thunderstorms and tornadoes.

Cloud Varieties

In addition to the names given to the 10 basic cloud types, adjectives may also be used to describe variations of a particular cloud type. For example, the term *uncinus*, meaning "hook-shaped," is applied to streaks of cirrus clouds that are shaped like a comma resting on its side. Cirrus uncinus are often precursors of bad weather.

When stratus or cumulus clouds appear to be broken into smaller pieces, the adjective *fractus* may be used in their description. In addition, some clouds have rounded protuberances on their bottom surface, not unlike the udders of cows. When these structures are present, the term *mammatus* can be applied. This configuration is sometimes associated with stormy weather and cumulonimbus clouds.

Lens-shaped clouds are referred to as *lenticular*. They are common in areas that have rugged or mountainous topography, where they are called *lenticular altocumulus* (Figure 5–8a). Although lenticular clouds can form whenever the airflow undulates sharply in the vertical, they most

FIGURE 5-5 Nimbostratus clouds are one of the chief precipitation producers. These dark gray layers often exhibit a ragged-appearing base. *(Photo by E. J. Tarbuck)*

frequently form on the lee side of mountains. As air passes over mountainous terrain, a wave pattern develops, as shown in Figure 5–8b. Clouds form where the wavy flow causes air to ascend, whereas areas with descending air are cloud-free.

FIGURE 5-6 Cumulus clouds. These small, white, billowy clouds generally form on sunny days and, therefore, are often called "fair weather clouds." *(Photo by E. J. Tarbuck)*

BOX 5-1 Aircraft Contrails and Cloudiness

You have undoubtedly seen a *contrail* (from *con*densation *trail*), in the wake of an aircraft flying on a clear day (Figure 5–A). Contrails are produced by jet aircraft engines that expel large quantities of hot, moist air. As this air mixes with the frigid air aloft, a streamlined cloud

FIGURE 5-A Aircraft contrails. Condensation trails produced by jet aircraft often spread out to form broad bands of cirrus clouds. *(Photo by J. F. Towers/CORBIS/ Stock Market)*

is produced. Because it often takes a few seconds for sufficient cooling to occur, the contrail usually forms a short distance behind the aircraft.

Why do contrails occur on some occasions and not on others? Contrails form under the same conditions as any other cloud—that is, when the air reaches saturation and condensation nuclei exist in sufficient numbers. Most contrails form when the exhaust gases add sufficient water vapor to the air to cause saturation. Further, it has been demonstrated that the exhaust gases of aircraft engines supply abundant sulfate molecules that serve as nuclei to promote the development of contrails.

Contrails typically form above 9 kilometers (6 miles) where air temperatures are a frigid −50°C (−58°F) or colder. Thus, it is not surprising that contrails are composed of minute ice crystals. Most contrails have a very short life span. Once formed, these streamlined clouds mix with surrounding cold, dry air and ultimately evaporate. However, if the air aloft is near saturation, contrails may survive for long periods. Under these conditions, the upper airflow usually spreads the streamlike clouds into broad bands of clouds called *contrail cirrus*.

With the increase in air traffic during the last few decades, an overall increase in cloudiness has been recorded, particularly near major transportation hubs (Figure 5–B). This is most evident in the American Southwest, where aircraft contrails persist in otherwise cloudless or mostly clear skies.

In addition to the added cloud cover associated with increasing levels of jet aircraft traffic, other less noticeable effects are of concern. Research is currently under way to assess the impact of contrail-produced cirrus clouds on the planet's heat budget. Recall from Chapter 3 that high, thin clouds are effective transmitters of solar radiation (most radiation reaches the surface) but are good absorbers of outgoing infrared radiation emitted from Earth's surface. As a consequence, high cirrus clouds tend to have an overall warming effect. However, research indicates that most contrails differ markedly from typical cirrus clouds, which are generated under quite different conditions. Although the results of these studies are inconclusive, it appears that human-induced cirrus clouds may actually lead to surface cooling rather than warming.

Students Sometimes Ask...

How much water is found in a cloud?

That depends a lot on the size of the cloud. Let's consider a modest size cumulonimbus cloud that is roughly 3000 meters (about 2 miles) in width and depth and 10,000 meters high. If our hypothetical cloud contains an average of 0.5 cubic centimeter of liquid per cubic meter, it would contain 45 billion cubic centimeters of water (3000 × 3000 × 10,000 × 0.5). That equates to 13 million gallons—enough to fill a small pond.

Types of Fog

GEODe
Forms of Condensation and Precipitation
▶ Types of Fog

Fog is generally considered an atmospheric hazard. When it is light, visibility is reduced to 2 or 3 kilometers (1 or 2 miles). When it is dense, visibility may be cut to a few dozen meters or less, making travel by any mode not only difficult but dangerous. Official weather stations report fog only when the visibility is reduced to 1 kilometer or

FIGURE 5-B This photograph, taken through the window of the International Space Station, shows contrails over the Rhone Valley in eastern France. It is estimated that these "artificial clouds" cover 0.1 percent of the planet's surface, and the percentages are far higher in some places, such as southern California and part of Europe, as illustrated here. *(Photo courtesy of NASA).*

Additional research is still needed to accurately determine the impact of contrails on climate change.

One effect of contrails that is known with some certainty is how these "artificial" clouds impact daily temperature ranges (that is, the difference between daily maximum and minimum temperatures). During the three-day commercial flight hiatus following the September 11 terrorist attacks, contrails all but disappeared. As a result, during these days of "clearer skies," the differences between the high and low temperatures increased by 2°F (1.1°C). This data supports the view that contrails reduce the transfer of both incoming solar radiation and outgoing terrestrial radiation. Consequently, cities located near major air-traffic centers experience lower daily highs and higher daily lows than would be the case if jet aircraft did not produce contrails.

---

less. Although arbitrary, this figure does permit a more objective criterion for comparing fog frequencies at different locations.

Fog is defined as *a cloud with its base at or very near the ground.* Physically, there is basically no difference between a fog and a cloud; their appearance and structure are the same. The essential difference is the method and place of formation. Clouds result when air rises and cools adiabatically. Fog results from cooling or by the addition of enough water vapor to cause saturation. Let us look at fogs, first those formed by cooling and then those formed by the addition of water vapor.

Fogs Formed by Cooling

When the temperature of a layer of air in contact with the ground falls below its dew point, condensation produces fog. Depending upon the prevailing conditions, the ground may become shrouded in radiation fog, advection fog, or upslope fog.

Radiation Fog. As the name implies, **radiation fog** results from radiation cooling of the ground and adjacent air. It is a nighttime phenomenon requiring clear skies and a fairly high relative humidity. Under these circumstances, the ground and the air immediately above it will cool

FIGURE 5-7 Cumulonimbus clouds. These dense, billowy clouds have great vertical extent and can produce heavy precipitation. *(Photo by Doug Millar/Science Source/Photo Researchers, Inc.)*

(a)

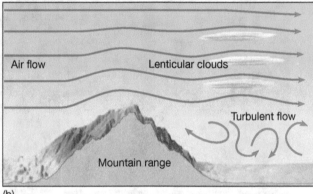

(b)

FIGURE 5-8 Lenticular clouds. (a) These lens-shaped clouds are relatively common in mountainous areas. *(Photo by Dennis Tasa)* (b) This diagram depicts the formation of lenticular clouds in the turbulent flow that develops in the lee of a mountain range.

rapidly. Because the relative humidity is high, just a small amount of cooling will lower the temperature to the dew point. If the air is calm, the fog may be patchy and less than a meter deep. For radiation fog to be more extensive vertically, a light breeze of 3 to 5 kilometers (2 to 3 miles) per hour is necessary. Then the light wind creates enough turbulence to carry the fog upward 10 to 30 meters (30 to 100 feet) without dispersing it.

Because the air containing the fog is relatively cold and dense, it drains downslope in hilly terrain. As a result, radiation fog is thickest in valleys, whereas the surrounding hills are clear (Figure 5–9). Normally these fogs dissipate within one to three hours after sunrise. Often the fog is said to "lift." However, it does not rise. Instead, the Sun warms the ground, which in turn heats the lowest layer of air first. Consequently, the fog evaporates from the bottom up, giving the impression of lifting. The last vestiges of radiation fog may appear to be a low stratus cloud layer.

In the eastern United States, radiation fog may also form when the skies clear after a rainfall. In these situations the air near the surface is close to saturation and only a small amount of radiation cooling is needed to promote condensation. Radiation fog of this type often occurs around sunset and can make driving hazardous.

Advection Fog.   When warm and moist air is blown over a cold surface, it becomes chilled by contact and, to a certain extent, by mixing with the cold air created by the cold surface below. If cooling is sufficient, the result will be a blanket of fog called **advection fog.** The term *advection* refers to air moving horizontally. Therefore, advection fogs are a consequence of air giving up heat to the surface below during horizontal movement. A classic example is the frequent advection fog around San Francisco's Golden Gate Bridge (Figure 5–10).

A certain amount of turbulence is needed for proper development of advection fog. Thus, winds between 10 and

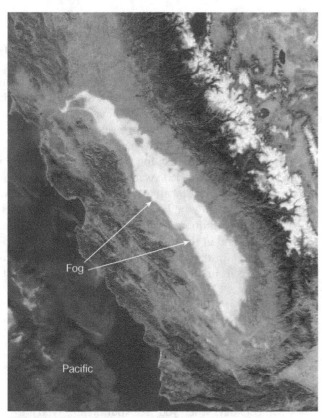

FIGURE 5-9 Satellite image of dense fog in California's San Joaquin Valley on November 20, 2002. This early morning radiation fog was responsible for several car accidents in the region, including a 14-car pileup. The white areas to the east of the fog are the snow-capped Sierra Nevadas. *(NASA image)*

30 kilometers (6 and 18 miles) per hour are usually associated with it. Not only does the turbulence facilitate cooling through a thicker layer of air but it also carries the fog to greater heights. Unlike radiation fogs, advection fogs are often thick (300 to 600 meters deep) and persistent.

Examples of such fogs are common. The foggiest location in the United States is Cape Disappointment, Washington. The name is indeed appropriate because the station averages 2552 hours (106 days) of fog each year. The fog experienced at Cape Disappointment, as well as that at other West Coast locations during the summer and early autumn, is produced when warm, moist air from the Pacific Ocean moves over the cold California Current (Figure 5–10). It is then carried onshore by westerly winds or a local sea breeze.

Advection fog is also a common wintertime phenomenon along the Gulf and Atlantic coasts. Here, comparatively warm, moist air from the Gulf of Mexico and Atlantic moves over cold and occasionally snow-covered surfaces to produce widespread foggy conditions. These fogs are frequently thick and produce hazardous driving conditions.

Upslope Fog. As its name implies, **upslope fog** is created when relatively humid air moves up a gradual sloping plain or, in some cases, up the steep slopes of a mountain. Because of the upward movement, air expands and cools adiabatically (this is the only type of fog that forms adiabatically). If the dew point is reached, an extensive layer of fog may form.

FIGURE 5-10 Advection fog rolling into San Francisco Bay. *(Photo by Ed Pritchard/Getty Images Inc.-Stone Allstock)*

It is easy to visualize how upslope fog might form in mountainous terrain. However, in the United States upslope fog also occurs in the Great Plains. Here, when humid Gulf air moves westward from the Mississippi River toward the Rocky Mountains, it gradually glides upslope. (Recall that Denver, Colorado, is called the "mile-high city," and the Gulf of Mexico is at sea level.) Air flowing "up" the Great Plains expands and cools adiabatically by as much as 12°C (22°F). The result can be an extensive upslope fog in the western plains.

Fogs Formed by Evaporation

When saturation occurs primarily because of the addition of water vapor, the resulting fogs are called *evaporation fogs.* Two types of evaporation fogs are recognized: steam fog and frontal (precipitation) fog.

Steam Fog. When cool air moves over warm water, enough moisture may evaporate from the water surface to saturate the air immediately above. As the rising water vapor meets the cold air, it condenses and rises with the air that is being warmed from below. Because the rising air looks like the "steam" that forms above a hot cup of coffee, the phenomenon is called **steam fog** (Figure 5–11). It is a fairly common occurrence over lakes and rivers on clear, crisp mornings in the fall when the waters are still relatively warm while the air is rather cold. Steam fog is often shallow, for as it rises, the water droplets evaporate as they mix with the unsaturated air above.

Steam fogs can be dense, however. During the winter, cold arctic air pours off the continents and ice shelves onto the comparatively warm open ocean. The temperature contrast between the warm ocean and cold air has been known to exceed 30°C (54°F). The result is an intense steam fog produced as the rising water vapor saturates a large volume of air. Because of its source and appearance, this type of steam fog is given the name *arctic sea smoke.*

Frontal Fog. When frontal wedging occurs, warm air is lifted over colder air. If the resulting clouds yield rain, and the cold air below is near the dew point, enough rain can evaporate to produce fog. A fog formed in this manner is called **frontal** or **precipitation fog.** The result is a more or less continuous zone of condensed water droplets reaching from the ground up through the clouds.

In summary, both steam fog and frontal fog result from the addition of moisture to a layer of air. As you saw, the air is usually cool or cold and already near saturation. Thus, only a relatively modest amount of evaporation is necessary to produce saturated conditions and fog.

The frequency of dense fog varies considerably from place to place (Figure 5–12). As might be expected, fog incidence is highest in coastal areas, especially where cold currents prevail, as along the Pacific and New England coasts. Relatively high frequencies are also found in the Great Lakes region and in the humid Appalachian Mountains of the East. In contrast, fogs are rare in the interior of the continent, especially in the arid and semiarid areas of the West.

> ## Students Sometimes Ask...
> *Why do I see my
> breath on cold mornings?*
>
> On cold days when you "see your breath," you are actually creating steam fog. The moist air that you exhale saturates a small volume of cold air, causing tiny droplets to form. Like most steam fogs, the droplets quickly evaporate as the "fog" mixes with the unsaturated air around it.

Dew and Frost

Clouds and fog are the most conspicuous and meteorologically important forms of condensation. Dew and white frost must be considered minor by comparison. These common forms of condensation generally result from radiation cooling on clear, cool nights.

FIGURE 5-11 Steam fog rising from upper St. Regis Lake, Adirondack Mountains, New York. *(Photo by Jim Brown/CORBIS/Stock Market)*

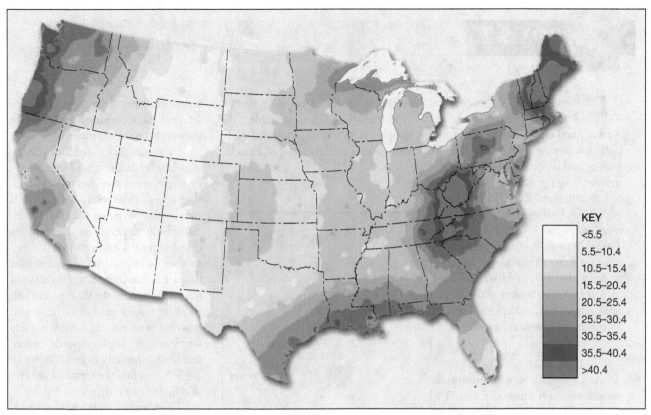

FIGURE 5-12 Map showing average number of days per year with heavy fog. Notice that the frequency of dense fog varies considerably from place to place. Coastal areas, particularly the Pacific Northwest and New England where cold currents prevail, have high occurrences of dense fog.

KEY
<5.5
5.5–10.4
10.5–15.4
15.5–20.4
20.5–25.4
25.5–30.4
30.5–35.4
35.5–40.4
>40.4

Dew is the condensation of water vapor on objects that have radiated sufficient heat to lower their temperature below the dew point of the surrounding air. Because different objects radiate heat at different rates, dew may form on some surfaces but not on others. An automobile, for example, may be covered with dew shortly after sunset, whereas the concrete driveway surrounding the car remains free of condensation throughout the night.

Dew is a common sight on lawns in the early morning. In fact, the grass will frequently have a coating of dew when nothing else does. Dew is more frequent on grass because the transpiration of water vapor by the blades raises the relative humidity to higher levels directly above the grass. Therefore, only modest radiation cooling may be necessary to bring about saturation and condensation.

Although dew is an unimportant source of moisture in humid areas, plant life in some arid regions depends on it for survival. In parts of Israel, for example, dew may supply as much as 55 millimeters (2.17 inches) of water annually. Further, this moisture is available mainly during the dry summer months when plants are experiencing the greatest stress.

Contrary to popular belief, white frost is not frozen dew. Rather, **white frost** (*hoar frost*) forms when the dew point of the air is below freezing. Thus, frost forms when water vapor changes directly from a gas into a solid (ice), without entering the liquid state. This process, called *deposition*, produces delicate patterns of ice crystals that frequently decorate windows in northern winters (see Figure 4–5, p. 103).

How Precipitation Forms

 Forms of Condensation and Precipitation
▶ How Precipitation Forms

Although all clouds contain water, why do some produce precipitation and others drift placidly overhead? This seemingly simple question perplexed meteorologists for many years. Before examining the processes that generate precipitation, we need to examine a couple of facts.

First, cloud droplets are very tiny, 20 micrometers (0.02 millimeter) in diameter (Figure 5–13). (One micrometer equals 0.001 millimeter.) For comparison, a human hair is about 75 micrometers in diameter. The small size of cloud droplets results mainly because condensation nuclei are usually very abundant and the available water is distributed among numerous droplets rather than concentrated into fewer large droplets.

Second, because of their small size, the rate at which cloud droplets fall is incredibly slow (see Box 5–2). An

BOX 5-2   Forces Acting on Cloud Droplets and Raindrops

Gregory J. Carbone*

Two opposing forces act on cloud droplets—*gravity* and *friction*. Gravitational force pulls a water droplet toward Earth's surface and is equal to the mass of the droplet times gravitational acceleration (gravitational force = droplet mass × 9.8 m/s²). Because 1 cubic centimeter (1 cm³) of volume equals 1 gram of mass, we can substitute volume for mass in the above equation and say that the gravitational force of a droplet increases with its volume. Assuming the droplet is a sphere, its volume is calculated as follows:

$$\text{Volume} = \tfrac{4}{3}\pi r^3$$

As a droplet falls, it encounters air resistance, or frictional force. The magnitude of this force depends on the size of the drop's "bottom"—that is, the surface area resisting the fall (Figure 5–C). Again, assuming the droplet is spherical, frictional force will change with the area of a circle:

$$\text{Area} = \pi r^2$$

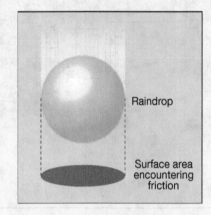

FIGURE 5-C Raindrops and friction.

Frictional drag increases as a droplet accelerates, because a faster droplet encounters more air molecules.

Eventually, frictional and gravitational forces balance, and the droplet no longer accelerates but falls at a constant speed. This speed is referred to as the droplet's *terminal velocity*. Terminal velocity depends on size. Smaller droplets have a lower terminal velocity than do larger droplets, because as droplet radius increases, gravitational force increases to the third power and frictional force increases to the second power. Consequently, larger droplets accelerate to higher speeds before reaching terminal velocity. (Refer to Table 5–3 to find the terminal velocity of different-sized droplets.)

The terminal velocity of individual droplets is important because it

---

average cloud droplet falling from a cloud base at 1000 meters would require several hours to reach the ground. However, it would never complete its journey. This cloud droplet would evaporate before it fell a few meters from the cloud base into the unsaturated air below.

How large must a droplet grow in order to fall as precipitation? A typical raindrop has a diameter of about 2000

FIGURE 5-13 Comparative diameters of particles involved in condensation and precipitation processes.

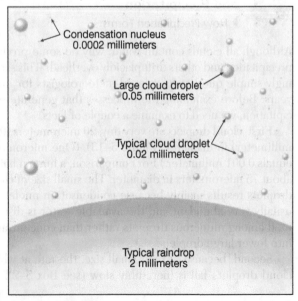

Condensation nucleus
0.0002 millimeters

Large cloud droplet
0.05 millimeters

Typical cloud droplet
0.02 millimeters

Typical raindrop
2 millimeters

micrometers (2 millimeters), or 100 times that of the average cloud droplet having a diameter of 20 micrometers (0.02 millimeter). However, as shown in Box 5–2, the *volume* of a typical raindrop is a million times that of a cloud droplet. Thus, for precipitation to form, cloud droplets must grow in volume by roughly 1 million times. You might suspect that additional condensation creates drops large enough to survive the descent to the surface. However, clouds consist of many billions of tiny cloud droplets that all compete for the available water. Thus, condensation provides an inefficient means of raindrop formation.

Two processes are responsible for the formation of precipitation: the Bergeron process and the collision–coalescence process.

Students Sometimes Ask...

Why does it often seem like the roads are slippery when it rains after a long dry period?

It appears that a buildup of debris on roads during dry weather causes more slippery conditions after a rainfall. One recent traffic study indicates that if it rains today, there will be no increase in risk of fatal crashes if it also rained yesterday. However, if it has been two days since the last rain, then the risk for a deadly accident increases by 3.7 percent. Furthermore, if it has been 21 days since the last rain, the risk increases to 9.2 percent.

determines the probability that a droplet will reach Earth without evaporating or being carried in updrafts. In fact, it is possible to estimate the maximum fall distance before evaporation for droplets of various size. Table 5–A shows such values assuming a barometric pressure of 900 mb, temperature of 5°C, and relative humidity equal to 90 percent. Note that droplets with a radius less than 100 μm (micrometers) are unlikely to reach Earth's surface because cloud bases are typically higher than their maximum fall distance.

Because most cloud droplets are too small to reach the surface, precipitation requires processes that cause droplet growth. But condensation is a very slow growth process. Consider a typical cloud droplet of

TABLE 5-A Maximum fall distance before evaporation

Drop diameter (μm)	Maximum fall distance (m)
2500	280,000
1000	42,000
100	150
10	0.033
0	0.0000033

10-μm radius. To grow to the size of a typical raindrop (1000 μm, or 100 times its original size), the cloud droplet must increase its volume by 1 million times:

$$\text{Volume}_{10\,\mu m} = \tfrac{4}{3} \times \pi \times (10\ \mu m)^3$$
$$= 4,189\ \mu m^3$$
$$\text{Volume}_{100\,\mu m} = \tfrac{4}{3} \times \pi \times (1000\ \mu m)^3$$
$$4,189,000,000\ \mu m^3/4,189\ \mu m^3$$
$$= 1,000,000$$

Clearly, condensation provides an inefficient means of cloud droplet growth, thus emphasizing the importance of other mechanisms, such as the collision–coalescence and Bergeron process.

*Professor Carbone is a faculty member in the Department of Geography at the University of South Carolina.

Precipitation from Cold Clouds: The Bergeron Process

You have probably watched a TV documentary in which mountain climbers brave intense cold and ferocious snowstorms as they scale an ice-covered peak. Although it is hard to imagine, very similar conditions exist in the upper portions of towering cumulonimbus clouds, even on sweltering summer days. (In fact, in the upper troposphere where commercial aircraft cruise, the temperature typically approaches −50°C (−58°F) or lower.) It turns out that the frigid conditions high in the troposphere provide an ideal environment to initiate precipitation. In fact, in the middle latitudes much of the rain that falls begins with the birth of snowflakes high in the cloud tops, where temperatures are considerably below freezing. Obviously, in the winter, even low clouds are cold enough to trigger precipitation.

The process that generates much of the precipitation in the middle latitudes is named the **Bergeron process** for its discoverer, the highly respected Swedish meteorologist, Tor Bergeron (see Box 5–3). The Bergeron process, which involves ice-crystal growth, depends on the coexistence of water vapor, liquid cloud droplets, and ice crystals. To understand just how this mechanism operates, we must first examine two important properties of water. First, *cloud droplets do not freeze at 0°C as expected.* In fact, pure water suspended in air does not freeze until it reaches a temperature of nearly −40°C (−40°F). Water in the liquid state below

0°C (32°F) is referred to as **supercooled.** Supercooled water will readily freeze if it impacts an object, which explains why airplanes collect ice when they pass through a liquid cloud made up of supercooled droplets. This also explains why the stuff we call *freezing rain* or *glaze* falls as a liquid but then turns to a sheet of ice when it strikes the pavement or a tree branch.

In addition, supercooled droplets will freeze on contact with solid particles that have a crystal form closely resembling that of ice (silver iodide is an example). These materials are called **freezing nuclei.** The need for freezing nuclei to initiate the freezing process is similar to the requirement for condensation nuclei in the process of condensation.

In contrast to condensation nuclei, however, freezing nuclei are sparse in the atmosphere and do not generally become active until the temperature reaches −10°C (14°F) or below. Thus, at temperatures between 0 and −10°C, clouds consist mainly of supercooled water droplets. Between −10 and −20°C, liquid droplets coexist with ice crystals, and below −20°C (−4°F), clouds are generally composed entirely of ice crystals—for example, high-altitude cirrus clouds.

This brings us to a second important property of water. *The saturation vapor pressure above ice crystals is somewhat lower than above supercooled liquid droplets.* This occurs because ice crystals are solid, which means that the individual water molecules are held together more tightly

BOX 5-3 Science and Serendipity*

Serendipity is defined by Nobel Laureate Irving Langmuir as "the art of profiting from unexpected occurrences." In other words, if you are observing something and the entirely unexpected happens, and if you see in this accident a new and meaningful discovery, then you have experienced serendipity. Most nonscientists, some scientists, and, alas, many teachers are not aware that many of the great discoveries in science were serendipitous.

An excellent example of serendipity in science occurred when Tor Bergeron, the great Swedish meteorologist, discovered the importance of ice crystals in the initiation of precipitation in supercooled clouds. Bergeron's discovery occurred when he spent several weeks at a health resort at an altitude of 430 meters (1400 feet) on a hill near Oslo. During his stay, Bergeron noted that this hill was often "fogged in" by a layer of supercooled clouds. As he walked along a narrow road in the fir forest along the hillside, he noticed that the "fog" did not enter the "road tunnel" at temperatures below −5°C, but did enter it when the temperature was warmer than 0°C. (Profiles of the hill, trees, and fog for the two temperature regimes is shown in Figure 5–D.)

Bergeron immediately concluded that at temperatures below about −5°C the branches of the firs acted as freezing nuclei upon which some of the supercooled droplets crystallized. Once the ice crystals developed, they grew rapidly at the expense of the remaining water droplets (Figure 5–D). The result was the growth of ice crystals (rime) on the branches of the firs accompanied

FIGURE 5-D Distribution of fog when the temperature is above freezing and when the temperature falls to −10°C.

by a "clearing-off" between the trees and along the "road-tunnel."

From this experience, Bergeron realized that if ice crystals somehow were to appear in the midst of a cloud of supercooled droplets, they would grow rapidly as water molecules diffused toward them from the evaporating cloud droplets. This rapid growth forms snow crystals that, depending on the air temperature beneath the cloud, fall to the ground as snow or rain. Bergeron had thus discovered one way that minuscule cloud droplets can grow large enough to fall as precipitation (see the section entitled "Precipitation from Cold Clouds: The Bergeron Process" on page 145).

Serendipity influences the entire realm of science. Can we conclude that anyone who makes observations will necessarily make a major discovery? Not at all. A perceptive and inquiring mind is required, a mind that has been searching for order in a labyrinth of facts. As Langmuir said, the unexpected occurrence is not enough; you must know how to profit from it. Louis Pasteur observed that "in the field of observation, chance favors only the prepared mind." The discoverer of vitamin C, Nobel Laureate Albert Szent-Gyorgyi, remarked that discoveries are made by those who "see what everybody else has seen, and think what nobody else has thought." Serendipity is at the heart of science itself.

*Based on material prepared by Duncan C. Blanchard.

---

than those forming a liquid droplet. As a result, it is easier for water molecules to escape from the supercooled liquid droplets. Consequently, when air is saturated (100 percent relative humidity) with respect to liquid droplets, it is supersaturated with respect to ice crystals. Table 5–2, for example, shows that at −10°C (14°F), when the relative humidity is 100 percent with respect to water, the relative humidity with respect to ice is about 110 percent.

With these facts in mind, we can now explain how the Bergeron process produces precipitation. Visualize a cloud

at a temperature of −10°C (14°F), where each ice crystal is surrounded by many thousands of liquid droplets (Figure 5–14). Because the air was initially saturated (100 percent) with respect to liquid water, it will be supersaturated (over 100 percent) with respect to the newly formed ice crystals. As a result of this supersaturated condition, the ice crystals collect more water molecules than they lose by sublimation. Thus, continued evaporation from the liquid drops provides a source of water vapor to feed the growth of ice crystals (Figure 5–14).

TABLE 5-2 Relative humidity with respect to ice when relative humidity with respect to water is 100 percent

Temperature (°C)	Relative humidity with respect to:	
	Water	Ice
0	100%	100%
−5	100%	105%
−10	100%	110%
−15	100%	115%
−20	100%	121%

Because the level of supersaturation with respect to ice can be great, the growth of snow crystals is generally sufficiently rapid to generate crystals large enough to fall. During their descent, these crystals enlarge as they intercept cloud drops that freeze on them. Air movement will sometimes break up these delicate crystals, and the fragments will serve as freezing nuclei for other liquid droplets. A chain reaction develops and produces many snow crystals, which, by accretion, will form into larger masses called snowflakes. Large snowflakes may consist of 10 to 30 individual crystals.

In summary, the Bergeron process can produce precipitation throughout the year in the middle latitudes, provided at least the upper portions of clouds are cold enough to generate ice crystals. The type of precipitation (snow, sleet, rain, or freezing rain) that reaches the ground depends on the temperature profile in the lower few kilometers of the atmosphere. When the surface temperature is above 4°C (39°F), snowflakes usually melt before they reach the ground and continue their descent as rain. Even on a hot summer day a heavy downpour may have begun as a snowstorm high in the clouds overhead.

Precipitation from Warm Clouds: The Collision–Coalescence Process

A few decades ago meteorologists believed that the Bergeron process was responsible for the formation of most precipitation except for light drizzle. Later it was discovered that copious rainfall is often associated with clouds located well below the freezing level (called *warm clouds*), especially in the tropics. Clearly, a second mechanism also must trigger precipitation. Researchers discovered the **collision–coalescence process.**

Research has shown that clouds made entirely of liquid droplets must contain some droplets larger than 20 micrometers (0.02 millimeters) if precipitation is to form. These large droplets form when "giant" condensation nuclei are present, or when hygroscopic particles exist (such as sea salt). Recall that hygroscopic particles begin to remove water vapor from the air at relative humidities under 100 percent.

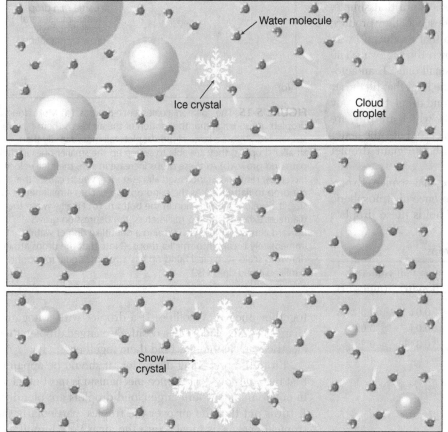

FIGURE 5-14 The Bergeron process. Ice crystals grow at the expense of cloud droplets until they are large enough to fall. The size of these particles has been greatly exaggerated.

Because the rate at which drops fall is size-dependent, these "giant" droplets fall most rapidly. (Table 5–3 summarizes drop size and falling velocities.)

As the larger droplets fall through a cloud, they collide with the smaller, slower droplets and coalesce (see Box 5–2). Becoming larger in the process, they fall even more rapidly (or, in an updraft, they rise more slowly) and increase their chances of collision and rate of growth (Figure 5–15a). After collecting the equivalent of a million or so cloud droplets, they are large enough to fall to the surface without evaporating.

Because of the huge number of collisions required for growth to raindrop size, clouds that have great vertical thickness and contain large cloud droplets have the best chance of producing precipitation. Updrafts also aid this process because they allow the droplets to traverse the cloud repeatedly, colliding with more droplets.

As raindrops grow in size, their fall velocity increases. This in turn increases the frictional resistance of the air, which causes the drop's "bottom" to flatten out (Figure 5–15b). As the drop approaches 4 millimeters in diameter, it develops a depression as shown in Figure 5–15c. Raindrops can grow to a maximum of 5 millimeters when they fall at the rate of 33 kilometers (20 miles) per hour. At this size and speed, the water's surface tension, which holds the drop together, is surpassed by the frictional drag of the air. At this point the depression grows almost explosively, forming a donutlike ring that immediately breaks apart. The resulting breakup of a large raindrop produces numerous smaller drops that begin anew the task of sweeping up cloud droplets (Figure 5–15d).

The collision–coalescence process is not that simple, however. First, as the larger droplets descend, they produce an airstream around them similar to that produced by an automobile when driven rapidly down the highway. The airstream repels objects, especially small ones. If an automobile is driven at night and we use the bugs that fill the air on a summer evening as being like cloud droplets, it is easy to visualize how most cloud droplets, which are tiny, are swept aside. The larger the cloud droplet (or bug), the better chance it will have of colliding with the giant droplet (or car).

Next, collision does not guarantee coalescence. Experimentation has indicated that the presence of atmospheric electricity may be the key to what holds these droplets

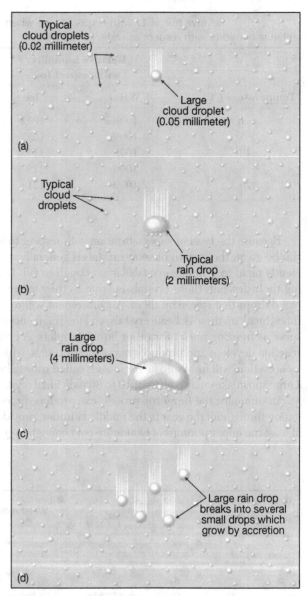

(a)

(b)

(c)

(d)

FIGURE 5-15 The collision–coalescence process. (a) Most cloud droplets are so small that the motion of the air keeps them suspended. Because large cloud droplets fall more rapidly than smaller droplets, they are able to sweep up the smaller ones in their path and grow. (b) As these drops increase in size, their fall velocity increases, resulting in increased air resistance, which causes the raindrop to flatten. (c) As the raindrop approaches 4 millimeters in size, it develops a depression in the bottom. (d) Finally, when the diameter exceeds about 5 millimeters, the depression grows upward almost explosively, forming a donutlike ring of water that immediately breaks into smaller drops. (Note that the drops are not drawn to scale—a typical raindrop has a volume equal to roughly 1 million cloud droplets.)

together once they collide. If a droplet with a negative charge should collide with a positively charged droplet, their electrical attraction may bind them together.

From the preceding discussion, it should be apparent that the collision–coalescence mechanism is most efficient in environments where large cloud droplets are plentiful. It turns out that the air over the tropics, particularly the tropical oceans, is ideal. Here the air is very humid and

TABLE 5-3 Fall velocity of water drops

Types	Diameter (millimeters)	Fall velocity (km/hr)	(miles/hr)
Small cloud droplets	0.01	0.01	0.006
Typical cloud droplets	0.02	0.04	0.03
Large cloud droplets	0.05	0.3	0.2
Drizzle drops	0.5	7	4
Typical rain drops	2.0	23	14
Large rain drops	5.0	33	20

Data from Smithsonian Meteorological Tables

relatively clean, so fewer condensation nuclei exit compared to the air over more populated regions. With fewer condensation nuclei to compete for available water vapor (which is plentiful), condensation is fast-paced and produces comparatively few large cloud droplets. Within developing cumulus clouds, the largest drops quickly gather smaller droplets to generate the warm afternoon showers associated with tropical climates.

In the middle latitudes the collision–coalescence process may contribute to the precipitation from a large cumulonimbus cloud by working in tandem with the Bergeron process—particularly during the hot, humid summer months. High in these towers the Bergeron process generates snow that melts as it passes below the freezing level. Melting generates relatively large drops with fast fall velocities. As these large drops descend, they overtake and coalesce with the slower and smaller cloud droplets that comprise much of the lower regions of the cloud. The result can be a heavy downpour.

In summary, two mechanisms are known to generate precipitation: the *Bergeron process* and the *collision–coalescence process*. The Bergeron process is dominant in the middle latitudes where cold clouds (or cold cloud tops) are the rule. In the tropics, abundant water vapor and comparatively few condensation nuclei are the norm. This leads to the formation of fewer, larger drops with fast fall velocities that grow by collision and coalescence. No matter which process initiates precipitation, further growth in drop size is through collision–coalescence.

> ## Students Sometimes Ask...
> ### *What is the largest annual rainfall ever recorded?*
>
> The greatest recorded rainfall for a single 12-month period occurred at Cherrapunji, India, where an astounding 2647 centimeters (1042 inches), over 86 feet, fell. Cherrapunji is located at an elevation of 1293 meters (4309 feet), where orographic lifting of the onshore, monsoon winds greatly contributed to the total.

FIGURE 5-16 Four precipitation types and their temperature profiles.

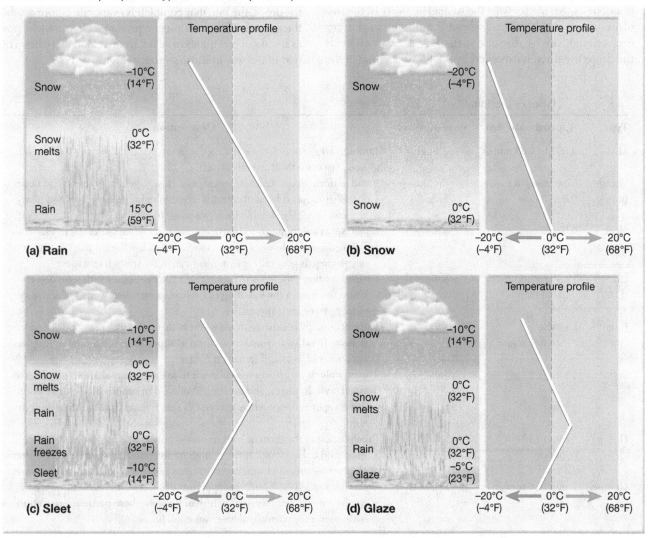

Forms of Precipitation

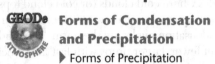

**Forms of Condensation
and Precipitation**

▶ Forms of Precipitation

Because atmospheric conditions vary greatly both geographically and seasonally, several different forms of precipitation are possible (Figure 5–16). Rain and snow are the most common and familiar forms, but others listed in Table 5–4 are important as well. The occurrence of sleet, glaze, and hail is often associated with important weather events. Although limited in occurrence and sporadic in both time and space, these forms, especially glaze and hail, may on occasion cause considerable damage.

Rain

In meteorology the term **rain** is restricted to drops of water that fall from a cloud and have a diameter of at least 0.5 millimeter. (This excludes drizzle and mist, which have smaller droplets.) Most rain originates in either nimbostratus clouds or in towering cumulonimbus clouds that are capable of producing unusually heavy rainfalls known as *cloudbursts*. No matter what the rainfall intensity is, the size of raindrops rarely exceeds about 5 millimeters. Larger drops cannot survive, because surface tension, which holds the drops together, is exceeded by the frictional drag of the air. Consequently, large raindrops regularly break apart into smaller ones.

Much of the world's rainfall begins as snow crystals or other solid forms such as hail or graupel, as shown in Figure 5–16a. Entering the warmer air below the cloud, these ice particles often melt and reach the ground as raindrops. In some parts of the world, particularly the subtropics, precipitation often forms in clouds that are warmer than 0°C (32°F). These rains frequently occur over the ocean where cloud condensation nuclei are not plentiful and those that do exist vary in size. Under such conditions, cloud droplets can grow rapidly by the collision–coalescence process to produce copious amounts of rain.

Fine, uniform drops of water having a diameter less than 0.5 millimeter are called *drizzle*. Drizzle and small raindrops generally are produced in stratus or nimbostratus clouds where precipitation may be continuous for several hours, or on rare occasions for days.

Precipitation containing the very smallest droplets able to reach the ground is called *mist*. Mist can be so fine that the tiny droplets appear to float and their impact is almost imperceptible.

As rain enters the unsaturated air below the cloud, it begins to evaporate. Depending on the humidity of the air and size of the drops, the rain may completely evaporate before reaching the ground. This phenomenon produces *virga*, which appear as streaks of precipitation falling from a cloud that extend only part of the way to Earth's surface (Figure 5–17).

TABLE 5-4 Types of precipitation			
Type	**Approximate size**	**State of water**	**Description**
Mist	0.005 to 0.05 mm	Liquid	Droplets large enough to be felt on the face when air is moving 1 meter/second. Associated with stratus clouds.
Drizzle	Less than 0.5 mm	Liquid	Small uniform drops that fall from stratus clouds, generally for several hours.
Rain	0.5 to 5 mm	Liquid	Generally produced by nimbostratus or cumulonimbus clouds. When heavy, size can be highly variable from one place to another.
Sleet	0.5 to 5 mm	Solid	Small, spherical to lumpy ice particles that form when raindrops freeze while falling through a layer of subfreezing air. Because the ice particles are small, any damage is generally minor. Sleet can make travel hazardous.
Glaze	Layers 1 mm to 2 cm thick	Solid	Produced when supercooled raindrops freeze on contact with solid objects. Glaze can form a thick coating of ice having sufficient weight to seriously damage trees and power lines.
Rime	Variable accumulations	Solid	Deposits usually consisting of ice feathers that point into the wind. These delicate frostlike accumulations form as supercooled cloud or fog droplets encounter objects and freeze on contact.
Snow	1 mm to 2 cm	Solid	The crystalline nature of snow allows it to assume many shapes, including six-sided crystals, plates, and needles. Produced in supercooled clouds where water vapor is deposited as ice crystals that remain frozen during their descent.
Hail	5 mm to 10 cm or larger	Solid	Precipitation in the form of hard, rounded pellets or irregular lumps of ice. Produced in large convective, cumulonimbus clouds, where frozen ice particles and supercooled water coexist.
Graupel	2 mm to 5 mm	Solid	Sometimes called "soft hail," graupel forms as rime collects on snow crystals to produce irregular masses of "soft" ice. Because these particles are softer than hailstones, they normally flatten out upon impact.

FIGURE 5-17 Virga, latin for "streak."In the arid west, rain frequently evaporates before reaching the ground. *(Photo by Pekka Parviainen/Science Photo Library/Photo Researchers, Inc.)*

Snow

Snow is precipitation in the form of ice crystals (snowflakes) or, more often, aggregates of ice crystals (Figure 5–16b). The size, shape, and concentration of snowflakes depend to a great extent on the temperature at which they form.

Recall that at very low temperatures, the moisture content of air is small. The result is the generation of very light and fluffy snow made up of individual six-sided ice crystals (Figure 5–18). This is the "powder" that downhill skiers talk so much about. By contrast, at temperatures warmer than about −5°C (23°F), the ice crystals join together into larger clumps consisting of tangled aggregates of crystals. Snowfalls consisting of these composite snowflakes are generally heavy and have a high moisture content, which makes them ideal for making snowballs. (For more on winter weather, see Box 5–4.)

Sleet and Glaze

Sleet is a wintertime phenomenon and refers to the fall of small particles of ice that are clear to translucent. Figures 5–16c and 5–19 show how sleet is produced: An above-freezing air layer must overlie a subfreezing layer near the ground. When the raindrops, which are often melted snow, leave the warmer air and encounter the colder air below, they freeze and reach the ground as small pellets of ice roughly the size of the raindrops from which they formed.

On some occasions, when the vertical distribution of temperatures is similar to that associated with the formation of sleet, **freezing rain** or **glaze** results instead. In such situations the subfreezing air near the ground is not thick enough to allow the raindrops to freeze (Figure 5–16d). The raindrops, however, do become supercooled as they fall through the cold air and turn to ice. The result can be a thick coating of ice having sufficient weight to break tree limbs, to down power lines, and to make walking and driving extremely hazardous.

In January 1998 an ice storm of historic proportions caused enormous damage in southeastern Canada. Here five days of freezing rain deposited a heavy layer of ice on all exposed surfaces from eastern Ontario to the Atlantic coast. The 8 centimeters (3 inches) of precipitation caused trees, power lines, and high-voltage towers to collapse, leaving over a million households without power—many for nearly a month following the storm (Figure 5–20).

At least 25 deaths were blamed on the storm, which caused damages in excess of $1 billion. Much of the damage was to the electrical grid, which one Canadian climatologist summed up this way: "What it took human beings a half-century to construct, took nature a matter of hours to knock down."

Hail

Hail is precipitation in the form of hard, rounded pellets or irregular lumps of ice. Large hailstones, when cut in half, often reveal nearly concentric shells of differing densities and degrees of opaqueness (Figure 5–21). The layers of ice accumulate as the hailstone travels up and down in a strong convective cloud.

FIGURE 5-18 All snow crystals are six-sided, but they come in an infinite variety of forms. *(Courtesy of NOAA, Seattle)*

BOX 5-4   Atmospheric Hazard: Worst Winter Weather

Extremes, whether they be the tallest building or the record low temperature for a location, fascinate us. When it comes to weather, some places take pride in claiming to have the worst winters on record. In fact, Fraser, Colorado, and International Falls, Minnesota, have both proclaimed themselves the "ice box of the nation." Although Fraser recorded the low temperature for the 48 contiguous states 23 times in 1989, its neighbor, Gunnison, Colorado, recorded the low temperature 62 times, far more than any other location.

Such facts do not impress the residents of Hibbing, Minnesota, where the temperature dropped to −38°C (−37°F) during the first week of March 1989. But this is mild stuff, say the old-timers in Parshall, North Dakota, where the temperature fell to −51°C (−60°F) on February 15, 1936. Not to be left out, Browning, Montana, holds the record for the most dramatic 24-hour temperature drop. Here the temperature plummeted 56°C (100°F), from a cool 7°C (44°F) to a frosty −49°C (−56°F) during a January evening in 1916.

Although impressive, the temperature extremes cited here represent only one aspect of winter weather. What about snowfall (Figure 5–E)? Cooke City holds the seasonal snowfall record for Montana, with 1062 centimeters (418.1 inches) during the winter of 1977–1978. But what about cities like Sault Ste. Marie, Michigan, or Buffalo, New York? The winter snowfalls associated with the Great Lakes are legendary. Even larger snowfalls occur in many sparsely inhabited mountainous areas.

Try telling residents of the eastern United States that heavy snowfall by itself makes for the worst weather. A blizzard in March 1993 produced heavy snowfall along with hurricane-force winds and record low temperatures that immobilized much of the region from Alabama to the Maritime Provinces of eastern Canada. This event quickly earned the well-deserved title of Storm of the Century.

As we can see, determining which location has the worst winter weather depends on how you measure it. Most snowfall in a season? Longest cold spell? Coldest temperature? Most disruptive storm?

Here are the meanings of some common terms used by the National Weather Service for winter weather events.

Snow flurries Snow falling for short durations at intermittent periods and resulting in generally little or no accumulation.

Blowing snow Snow lifted from the surface by the wind and blown about to a degree that horizontal visibility is reduced.

Drifting snow Significant accumulations of falling or loose snow caused by strong wind.

Blizzard A winter storm characterized by winds of at least 56 kilometers (35 miles) per hour for at least three hours. The storm must also be accompanied by low temperatures and considerable falling and/or blowing snow that reduces visibility to a quarter of a mile or less.

Severe blizzard A storm with winds of at least 72 kilometers (45 miles) per hour, a great amount of falling or drifting snow, and temperatures −12°C (10°F) or lower.

Heavy snow warning A snowfall in which at least 4 inches in 12 hours or 6 inches in 24 hours is expected.

FIGURE 5-19 Sleet forms when rain passes through a cold layer of air and freezes into ice pellets. This occurs most often in the winter when warm air is forced over a layer of cold air.

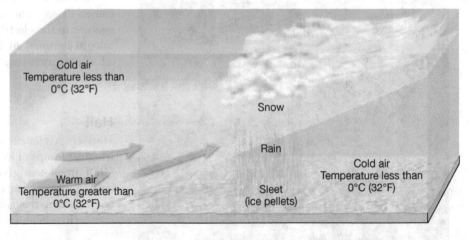

Cold air
Temperature less than
0°C (32°F)

Snow

Rain

Cold air
Temperature less than
0°C (32°F)

Warm air
Temperature greater than
0°C (32°F)

Sleet
(ice pellets)

FIGURE 5-E Rochester, NY, was hit by blizzard conditions that left 24 inches of snow in 24 hours on March 4, 1999. *(Photo by AP/Wide World Photos)*

Freezing rain Rain falling in a liquid form through a shallow sub-freezing layer of air near the ground. The rain (or drizzle) freezes on impact with the ground or other objects, resulting in a clear coating of ice known as *glaze*.

Sleet Also called *ice pellets*. Sleet is formed when raindrops or melted snowflakes freeze as they pass through a subfreezing layer of air near Earth's surface. Sleet does not stick to trees and wires, and it usually bounces when it hits the ground. An accumulation of sleet sometimes has the consistency of dry sand.

Travelers' advisory Issued to inform the public of hazardous driving conditions caused by snow, sleet, freezing precipitation, fog, wind, or dust.

Cold wave A rapid fall of temperature in a 24-hour period, usually signifying the beginning of a spell of very cold weather.

Windchill A measure of apparent temperature that uses the effects of wind and temperature on the human body by translating the cooling power of wind to a temperature under calm conditions. It is an approximation only for the human body and has no meaning for cars, buildings, or other objects. (See Box 3–5 for more details.)

FIGURE 5-20 Glaze forms when supercooled raindrops freeze on contact with objects. In January 1998 an ice storm of historic proportions caused enormous damage in New England and southeastern Canada. Nearly five days of freezing rain (glaze) left millions without electricity—some for as long as a month. *(Photo by Syracuse Newspapers/The Image Works)*

FIGURE 5-21 Hail. A cross section of the Coffeyville hailstone. This record-breaking hailstone fell over Coffeyville, Kansas, in 1970 and weighed 0.75 kilogram (1.67 pounds). *(Photo courtesy of University Corporation for Atmospheric Research/National Science Foundation/Visual Communications NCAR)*

Most hailstones have diameters between 1 centimeter (pea size) and 5 centimeters (golf ball size), although some can be as big as an orange or even bigger. Occasionally, hailstones weighing a pound or more have been reported. Many of these were probably composites of several stones frozen together.

The largest hailstone ever recorded in the United States fell during violent thunderstorms that pounded southeastern Nebraska on June 22, 2003. In the town of Aurora, a seven-inch (17.8-centimeter)-wide chunk of ice, almost as large as a volleyball, was recovered. However, this hailstone was not the heaviest hailstone ever measured. Apparently, a chunk of this stone was broken off when it hit the gutter of a house.

The heaviest hailstone in North America fell on Coffeyville, Kansas, in 1970. Having a 5.5 inch (14 centimeter) diameter, this hailstone weighed 1.67 pounds (766 grams).

Even heavier hailstones have reportedly been recorded in Bangladesh, where a hailstorm in 1987 killed more than 90 people. It is estimated that large hailstones hit the ground at speeds exceeding 100 miles (160 kilometers) per hour.

The destructive effects of large hailstones are well known, especially to farmers whose crops have been devastated in a few minutes and to people whose windows, roofs, and cars have been damaged (Figure 5–22). In the United States, hail damage each year can run into the hundreds of millions of dollars. One of the costliest hailstorms to occur in North America took place on June 11, 1990, in Denver, Colorado. Total damage was estimated to exceed $625 million.

Hail is produced only in large cumulonimbus clouds where updrafts can sometimes reach speeds approaching 160 kilometers (100 miles) per hour, and where there is an abundant supply of supercooled water. Figure 5–23 shows the process. Hailstones begin as small embryonic ice pellets that grow by collecting supercooled droplets as they fall through the cloud. If they encounter a strong updraft, they may be carried upward again and begin the downward journey anew. Each trip through the supercooled portion of the cloud might be represented by an additional layer of ice. Hailstones can also form from a single descent through an updraft. Either way, the process continues until the hailstone encounters a downdraft or grows too heavy to remain suspended by the thunderstorm's updraft.

Hailstones may contain several layers that alternate between clear and milky ice. High in the clouds, rapid freezing of small, supercooled water droplets traps air bubbles, which cause the milky appearance. By contrast, the clear ice is produced in the lower and warmer regions of the clouds where colliding droplets wet the surface of the hailstones. As these droplets slowly freeze, they produce relatively bubble-free clear ice.

FIGURE 5-22 Hail damage to a used car lot in Fort Worth, Texas, May 6, 1995. This storm, which packed high winds and hail the size of baseballs, killed at least nine people and injured more than 100 as it swept through the northern part of the state. *(Photo by Ron Heflin/AP/Wide World Photos)*

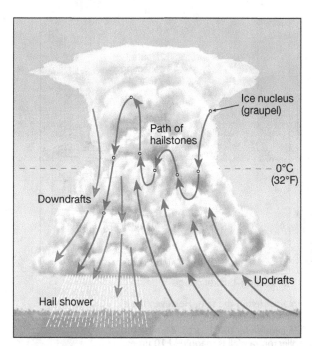

FIGURE 5-23 Growth of hailstones. Hailstones begin as small ice pellets that grow by adding supercooled water droplets as they move through a cloud. Strong updrafts may carry stones upward in several cycles, increasing the size of the hail by adding a new layer with each cycle. Eventually, the hailstones encounter a downdraft or grow too large to be supported by the updraft.

Students Sometimes Ask...

What is the difference between a winter storm warning and a blizzard warning?

A winter storm warning is usually issued when heavy snow exceeding six inches in 12 hours or possible icing conditions are likely. It is interesting to note that in Upper Michigan and mountainous areas where snowfall is abundant, winter storm warnings are issued only if eight or more inches of snow is expected in 12 hours. By contrast, blizzard warnings are issued for periods when considerable falling or blowing snow is accompanied by winds of 35 or more miles per hour. Thus, a blizzard is a type of winter storm in which winds are the determining factor, not the amount of snowfall.

Rime

Rime is a deposit of ice crystals formed by the freezing of supercooled fog or cloud droplets on objects whose surface temperature is below freezing. When rime forms on trees, it adorns them with its characteristic ice feathers, which can be spectacular to behold (Figure 5–24). In these situations, objects such as pine needles act as freezing nuclei, causing the supercooled droplets to freeze on contact. On occasions when the wind is blowing, only the windward surfaces of objects will accumulate the layer of rime.

FIGURE 5-24 Rime consists of delicate ice crystals that form when supercooled fog or cloud droplets freeze on contact with objects. *(Photo by John Cancalosi/Stock Boston)*

Precipitation Measurement

The most common form of precipitation, rain, is probably the easiest to measure. Any open container that has a consistent cross section throughout can be a rain gauge (Figure 5–25a). In general practice, however, more sophisticated devices are used to measure small amounts of rainfall more accurately and to reduce loss from evaporation.

Standard Instruments

The **standard rain gauge** (Figure 5–25b) has a diameter of about 20 centimeters (8 inches) at the top. Once the water is caught, a funnel conducts the rain through a narrow opening into a cylindrical measuring tube that has a cross-sectional area only one-tenth as large as the receiver. Consequently, rainfall depth is magnified 10 times, which allows for accurate measurements to the nearest 0.025 centimeter (0.01 inch), and the narrow opening minimizes evaporation. When the amount of rain is less than 0.025

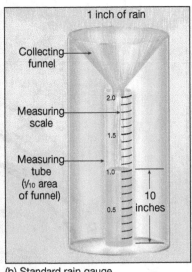

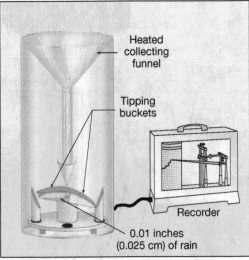

(a) Simple rain gauge   (b) Standard rain gauge   (c) Tipping–bucket gauge

FIGURE 5-25 Precipitation measurement. (a) The simplest gauge is any container left in the rain. However, these homemade devices are hard to read precisely. (b) The standard rain gauge increases the height of water collected by a factor of 10, allowing for accurate rainfall measurement to the nearest 0.025 centimeter (0.01 inch). Because the cross-sectional area of the measuring tube is only one-tenth as large as the collector, rainfall is magnified 10 times. (c) The tipping-bucket rain gauge contains two "buckets" that hold the equivalent of 0.025 centimeter (0.01 inch) of precipitation. When one bucket fills, it tips and the other bucket takes its place. Each event is recorded as 0.01 inch of rainfall.

centimeter (0.01 inch), it is generally reported as being a **trace of precipitation.**

In addition to the standard rain gauge, several types of recording gauges are routinely used. These instruments not only record the amount of rain, but also its time of occurrence and intensity (amount per unit of time). Two of the most common gauges are the tipping-bucket gauge and the weighing gauge.

As can be seen in Figure 5–25c, the **tipping-bucket gauge** consists of two compartments, each one capable of holding 0.025 centimeter (0.01 inch) of rain, situated at the base of a funnel. When one "bucket" fills, it tips and empties its water. Meanwhile, the other "bucket" takes its place at the mouth of the funnel. Each time a compartment tips, an electrical circuit is closed and 0.025 centimeter (0.01 inch) of precipitation is automatically recorded on a graph.

The **weighing gauge,** as the name would indicate, works on a different principle. Precipitation is caught in a cylinder that rests on a spring balance. As the cylinder fills, the movement is transmitted to a pen that records the data.

Measuring Snowfall

When snow records are kept, two measurements are normally taken—depth and water equivalent. Usually, the depth of snow is measured with a calibrated stick. The actual measurement is not difficult, but choosing a representative spot can be. Even when winds are light or moderate, snow drifts freely. As a rule, it is best to take several measurements in an open place away from trees and obstructions and then average them. To obtain the water

equivalent, samples may be melted and then weighed or measured as rain.

Sometimes large cylinders are used to collect snow. A major problem that hinders accurate measurement by snow gauges is the wind. Snow will blow around the top of the cylinder instead of falling into it. Therefore, the amount caught by the gauge is generally less than the actual fall. As is often the practice with rain gauges, shields designed to break up wind eddies are placed around the snow gauge to ensure a more accurate catch.

The quantity of water in a given volume of snow is not constant. A general ratio of 10 units of snow to 1 unit of water is often used when exact information is not available. You may have heard TV weathercasters use this ratio, saying, "Every 10 inches of snow equals 1 inch of rain." But the actual water content of snow may deviate widely from this figure. It may take as much as 30 centimeters of light and fluffy dry snow (30:1) or as little as 4 centimeters of wet snow (4:1) to produce 1 centimeter of water.

Measurement Errors

We tend to be unquestioning when we hear weather reports concerning the past day's events. However, unlike temperature and pressure, which tend to vary only slightly over a few dozen miles, precipitation on one side of the street can be significantly greater than on the other. Further, by its very nature precipitation is difficult to collect, and the techniques used have numerous potential sources for error.

When measuring rain, a certain amount goes unrecorded—some because it splashes out upon impact, and some "wets" the collection funnel and never makes it into the cylinder. Snow in particular is often underestimated by rain gauges. In addition, in certain climates evaporation removes some of the precipitation before it is measured.

No matter which rain gauge is used, proper exposure is critical. Errors arise when gauges are located too close to buildings, trees, or other high objects that block obliquely falling rain. For best results the instrument should be twice as far away from such obstructions as the objects are high. Another cause for error is wind. It has been shown that as wind speed strengthens, turbulence increases, and it becomes more difficult to collect a representative quantity of rain. To offset this effect, a windscreen is often placed around the instrument so that rain falls into the gauge and is not carried across it (Figure 5–26).

Studies have shown that in the United States, annual precipitation errors range between about 7 and 20 percent. Most often the precipitation is underestimated. In some high latitudes, percentage errors are thought to exceed 80 percent.

Precipitation Measurement by Weather Radar

Today's TV weathercasts show helpful maps, like the one in Figure 5–27, to depict precipitation patterns. The instrument that produces these images is the *weather radar*.

The development of radar has given meteorologists an important tool to probe storm systems that may be up to a few hundred kilometers away. All radar units have a transmitter that sends out short pulses of radio waves. The specific wavelengths that are used depend on the objects the user wants to detect. When radar is used to monitor precipitation, wavelengths between 3 and 10 centimeters are employed.

These wavelengths can penetrate small cloud droplets but are reflected by larger raindrops, ice crystals, or hailstones. The reflected signal, called an *echo,* is received and displayed on a TV monitor. Because the echo is "brighter" when the precipitation is more intense, modern radar is able to depict not only the regional extent of the precipitation but also the rate of rainfall. Figure 5–27 is a typical radar display in which colors show precipitation intensity. As you will see in Chapters 10 and 12, weather radar can also measure the rate and direction of storm movement.

Intentional Weather Modification

Intentional weather modification is deliberate human intervention to influence atmospheric processes that constitute the weather—that is, to alter the weather for human purposes. This desire to change the weather is nothing new. From earliest recorded times people have used prayer, wizardry, dances, and even black magic in attempts to alter the weather.

During the American Civil War, rainfall seemed to increase following some battles, leading to experiments in which cannons were fired into clouds to trigger more rain. These experiments and many others proved unsuccessful. However, by the nineteenth century, smudge pots, sprinklers, and wind machines were used successfully to fight frost.

Weather-modification strategies fall into three broad categories. The first employs energy to forcefully alter the weather. Examples are the use of intense heat sources or the mechanical mixing of air (such as by helicopters) to disperse fog at some airports.

The second category involves modifying land and water surfaces to change their natural interaction with the lower atmosphere. One often discussed but untried example is the blanketing of a land area with a dark substance. The additional solar energy absorbed by this dark surface would warm the layer of air near the surface and encourage the development of updrafts that might aid cloud formation.

FIGURE 5-26 This standard rain gauge is fitted with metal slats that serve as a windscreen to minimize the undercatch that results because of windy conditions. *(Photo by Bobbé Christopherson)*

FIGURE 5-27 Doppler radar display commonly seen on The Weather Channel and local TV weathercasts. Colors indicate different intensities of precipitation. Note the band of heavy precipitation extending from northerneastern Iowa to Milwaukee, Wisconsin.

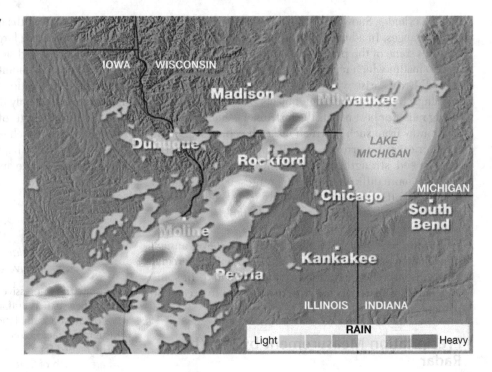

The third category involves triggering, intensifying, or redirecting atmospheric processes. The seeding of clouds with agents such as dry ice (frozen carbon dioxide) and silver iodide to stimulate precipitation is the primary example. Because **cloud seeding** sometimes seems to show promising results and is a relatively inexpensive technique, it has been a primary focus of modern weather-modification technology.

Cloud Seeding

The first breakthrough in weather modification came in 1946 when Vincent J. Schaefer discovered that dry ice, dropped into a supercooled cloud, spurred the growth of ice crystals. Recall that once ice crystals form in a supercooled cloud, they grow larger at the expense of the remaining liquid cloud droplets and, on reaching a sufficient size, fall as precipitation.

Later it was learned that silver iodide could also be used for cloud seeding. The similarity in the structure of silver iodide crystals and ice crystals accounts for silver iodide's ability to initiate ice crystal growth. Thus, unlike dry ice, which simply chills the air, silver iodide crystals act as freezing nuclei. Because silver iodide can be more easily delivered to clouds from burners on the ground or from aircraft, it is a better alternative than dry ice (Figure 5–28).

If cloud seeding is to trigger precipitation, certain atmospheric conditions must exist. Clouds must be present, for seeding cannot create clouds. Also, a portion of the cloud must be supercooled—it must be made of liquid droplets below 0°C (32°F) in temperature.

One type of cloud seeding assumes that cold cumulus clouds are deficient in freezing nuclei and that adding them will stimulate precipitation. The object is to produce just

enough ice crystals so they will grow large enough (via the Bergeron process) to fall as precipitation. Overseeding will simply produce billions of ice crystals that are too tiny to fall.

Seeding of winter clouds that form along mountain barriers (orographic clouds) has been tried repeatedly. These clouds are thought to be good candidates for seeding because only a small percentage of the water that condenses in cold orographic clouds actually falls as precipitation. The idea is to increase the winter snowpack, which melts and runs off during warmer months and is collected in reservoirs for irrigation and hydroelectric power generation. Since 1977 Colorado's Vail and Beaver Creek ski areas have used this method to increase winter snows.

In recent years the seeding of warm convective clouds with hygroscopic (water-seeking) particles has received renewed attention. The interest in this technique arose

FIGURE 5-28 Cloud seeding using silver iodide flares is one way that freezing nuclei are supplied to clouds. *(Courtesy of University Corporation for Atmospheric Research/National Science Foundation/National Center for Atmospheric Research)*

when it was discovered that a pollution-belching paper mill near Nelspruit, South Africa, seemed to be triggering precipitation. Flying through clouds near the paper mill, research aircraft collected samples of the particulate matter emitted from the mill. It turned out that the mill was emitting tiny salt crystals (potassium chloride and sodium chloride), which rose with updrafts into the clouds. Because these salts attract moisture, they quickly form large cloud droplets, which grow into raindrops by the collision–coalescence process. Ongoing experiments being conducted over the arid landscape of northern Mexico are attempting to duplicate this process by seeding clouds using flares mounted on airplanes that spread hygroscopic salts. Although the results of these studies are promising, conclusive evidence that such seeding can increase rainfall over economically significant areas is not yet available.

More than two dozen countries around the globe have weather modification programs, mainly rainfall enhancement. China appears to have the greatest number of projects, including efforts in cloud dispersal, which they hope to employ for the 2008 Beijing Olympics. Other projects are aimed at bringing drought relief and hail suppression to a large part of central China.

In the United States, over 50 weather modification projects are currently underway in 10 states. Some of the most promising results come from western Texas, where researchers estimate a 10 percent increase in rainfall from silver iodide–seeded clouds compared to unseeded ones.

In summary, researchers are gaining confidence that precipitation can be enhanced by seeding supercooled clouds. Further, the use of large hygroscopic particles to seed warm convective clouds appears to hold promise, although the processes involved are poorly understood. However, because these studies have been limited in scope, the economic viability of cloud seeding remains uncertain. The major outcome of the last five decades of cloud-seeding experimentation has been the sobering realization that even the simplest weather events are exceedingly complex and not yet fully understood.

Fog and Cloud Dispersal

One of the most successful applications of cloud seeding involves spreading dry ice, particles of solid carbon dioxide at temperatures of $-78°C$ ($-108°F$), into layers of supercooled fog or stratus clouds to disperse them and thereby improve visibility. Airports, harbors, and foggy stretches of interstate highway are obvious candidates. Such applications trigger a transformation in cloud composition from supercooled water droplets to ice crystals. The ice crystals then settle out, leaving an opening in the cloud or fog (Figure 5–29). Initially the ice crystals are too small to fall to the ground, but as the Bergeron process proceeds and they grow at the expense of the remaining water droplets, and as turbulent air disperses them, they can grow large enough to produce a snow shower. The snowfall is light, and visibility almost always improves. Often a large hole is opened in the stratus clouds or supercooled fog.

FIGURE 5-29 Effects produced by seeding a cloud deck with dry ice. Within one hour a hole developed over the seeded area. *(Photo courtesy of E. J. Tarbuck)*

The U.S. Air Force has practiced this technology for many years at airbases, and commercial airlines have used this method at selected foggy airports in the western United States. The possibility of opening large holes in winter clouds to increase the solar radiation reaching the ground in northerly locations has been discussed, but little experimentation has followed.

FIGURE 5-30 Hail damage to a soybean field north of Sioux Falls, South Dakota. *(AP/Wide World Photos)*

BOX 5-5   The Hail Cannons of Europe

Some of history's more interesting efforts at weather modification have focused on suppressing hail. During the 1500s, village priests often rang church bells and called for prayers to shield nearby farms from hail. Near the turn of the twentieth century, serious attempts at hail suppression in Europe involved the firing of cannons into developing thunderstorms. It was thought that the formation of hailstones could be prevented by injecting smoke particles as condensation nuclei into the developing clouds.

These "hail cannons" were vertical muzzle-loading mortars that resembled huge megaphones. The one shown in Figure 5–F weighed 9000 kilograms (10 tons), was 9 meters (30 feet) tall, and pivoted in all directions. When fired, these cannons produced a loud whistling noise and a large smoke ring that rose to a height of about 300 meters.

During a two-year test of hail cannons in Austria, no hail was observed. At the same time, nearby provinces suffered severe hail damage. Believing from this that hail cannons were effective, these devices spread to other areas in Europe where crops of great value, such as vineyards, frequently experienced hail losses. Soon much of Europe acquired "cannon fever," and by 1899 over 2000 cannons were in use in Italy alone. How-

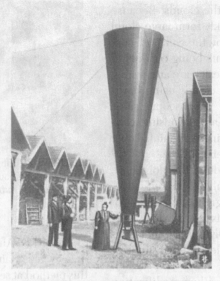

FIGURE 5-F Around 1900, cannons like this fired smoke particles into thunderstorms to prevent the formation of hail. However, hail shooting proved to be ineffective, and the practice was abandoned after a decade. *(Photo courtesy of J. Loreena Ivens, Illinois State Water Survey)*

ever, the hail cannons proved to be ineffective, and the practice was abandoned during the next decade.

It is interesting to note, however, that by the 1960s, Russian scientists were experimenting with a similar approach to hail suppression. Their experiments employed rockets and artillery shells to carry freezing nuclei into the clouds. However, like earlier efforts at hail suppression, the Russian attempts were not much more effective than ringing church bells.

Modern attempts at hail suppression have introduced silver iodide crystals into storm clouds to interrupt the formation and growth of hailstones. It is assumed that each of these crystals, acting as a freezing nucleus, attracts a portion of the cloud's water supply and thereby increases the competition for the available supercooled water droplets. With a diminished supply of supercooled water droplets, hailstones cannot grow large enough to be destructive.

Because of dramatic crop and property losses, hail-suppression technology has been the focus of many field and laboratory studies. The results, however, have been mixed at best. In Russia during the 1960s, scientists used rocket and artillery shells to carry freezing nuclei to the clouds, and they claimed to have extraordinary success.

In the United States during the 1970s, the federal government established the National Hail Research Experiment in northeastern Colorado. This experiment included a randomized seeding test to verify the Russian experience. An analysis of the data collected after three years revealed no statistically significant difference in the occurrence of hail between the seeded and nonseeded clouds, cutting short the planned five-year experiment.

Unfortunately, most fog does not consist of supercooled water droplets. The more common "warm fogs" are more expensive to combat because seeding will not diminish them. Successful attempts at dispersing warm fogs have involved mixing drier, warmer air from above into the fog, or heating the air. When the layer of fog is very shallow, helicopters have been used. By flying just above the fog, the helicopter creates a strong downdraft that forces drier air toward the surface, where it mixes with the saturated foggy air.

At some airports where warm fogs are common, it has become more usual to heat the air and thus evaporate the

fog. A sophisticated thermal fog-dissipation system, called Turboclair, was installed in 1970 at Orly Airport in Paris. It uses eight jet engines in underground chambers along the upwind edge of the runway. Although expensive to install, the system is capable of improving visibility for about 900 meters along the approach and landing zones.

Hail Suppression

Hail causes serious crop loss and property damage in many parts of the world (Figure 5–30). Consequently, hail-suppression efforts date from classical Greece to the present. A

(a)

(b)

FIGURE 5-31 Two common frost-prevention methods. (a) Sprinklers distribute water, which releases latent heat as it freezes on citrus. (b) Wind machines mix warmer air aloft with cooler surface air. *(Photos by (a) Bruce Borich/Silver Image Photo Agency, Inc. and (b) Christi Carter/Grant Heilman Photography, Inc.)*

major attempt in Europe near the turn of the twentieth century actually involved firing cannons at thunderstorms (see Box 5–5).

One of the newest attempts to suppress hail-storm damage comes from a Canadian company called HailStop. This company has developed machines that produce 120-decibel sound waves that are fired into storm clouds at 6-second intervals. The intent is to disrupt the hail cycle and decrease the size of the stones or even eliminate them. Although all methods of hail suppression remain unproved, the car manufacturer Nissan is using the HailStop system at one of its plants in Jackson, Mississippi.

Frost Prevention

Frost, the fruit grower's plight, occurs when the air temperature falls to 0°C (32°F) or below. Thus, frost conditions are dependent on temperature and need not be accompanied by deposits of ice crystals (called *white frost*), which only form if the air becomes saturated.

A frost hazard is produced by two conditions: when a cold air mass moves into a region or when sufficient radiation cooling occurs on a clear night. Frost associated with an invasion of cold air is characterized by low daytime temperatures and long periods of freezing conditions that inflict widespread crop damage. By contrast, frost induced by radiation cooling is strictly a nighttime phenomenon that tends to be confined to low-lying areas. Obviously, the latter phenomenon is much easier to combat.

Several methods of frost prevention are being used with varying success. They either conserve heat (reduce the heat lost at night) or add heat to warm the lowermost layer of air.

Heat-conservation methods include covering plants with insulating material, such as paper or cloth, or generating particles that, when suspended in air, reduce the rate of radiation cooling. *Smudge fires,* which produce dense black smoke, have been used to fill the air with carbon particles. Generally, this method has proved unsatisfactory. In addition to polluting the air, the carbon particles impede daytime warming by reducing the solar radiation that can reach the surface.

Warming methods employ water sprinklers, air-mixing techniques, and/or orchard heaters. Sprinklers (Figure 5–31a) add heat in two ways: first, from the warmth of the water and, more important, from the latent heat of fusion released when the water freezes. As long as an ice-water mixture remains on the plants, the latent heat released will keep the temperature from dropping below 0°C (32°F).

Air mixing works best when the air temperature 15 meters (50 feet) above the ground is at least 5°C (9°F) warmer than the surface temperature. By using a wind machine, the warmer air aloft is mixed with the colder surface air (Figure 5–31b).

FIGURE 5-32 Orchard heaters used to prevent frost damage to pear trees, Hood River, Oregon. *(Photo by Bruce Hands/The Image Works)*

Orchard heaters probably produce the most successful results (Figure 5–32). However, because as many as 30 to 40 heaters per acre are required, fuel cost can be significant.

Understanding the Role of Clouds in the Climate System

Views of Earth from space show that clouds are abundant (see Figure 1-11, p. 13). Covering up to 75 percent of our planet at any given time, clouds play a prominent role in determining how much sunlight reaches Earth's surface and how much is reflected back to space. Furthermore, the amount and type of cloud cover strongly influences the amount of heat that escapes the surface in the form of long-wave radiation. In short, clouds play a central role in Earth's climate system.

Recently a new tool has become available that will help researchers better understand and predict climate change. The false-color image shown in Figure 5-33 shows a one-month composite of cloud optical thickness measured by Moderate-resolution Imaging Spectroradiometer (MODIS). Optical thickness is a measure of how much solar radiation is able to penetrate the atmosphere. Areas shown in red and yellow indicate very cloudy skies, whereas areas that are green and light blue show moderately cloudy skies. Regions with little or no cloud cover appear dark blue.

MODIS is one of five sensors aboard NASA's *Terra* satellite. In addition to determining cloud thickness, it can determine whether a cloud is composed of ice or liquid water (or both), and it can estimate the size of cloud particles. This instrument is one more tool that will help scientists better understand the complex workings of Earth's climate system.

FIGURE 5-33 This false-color image shows a one-month composite of cloud optical thickness measured for April 2001. Optical thickness is a measure of how much solar radiation penetrates the atmosphere. *(Data from NASA)*

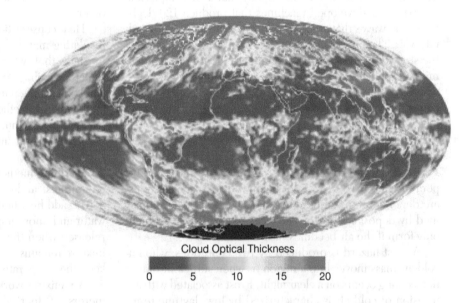

Cloud Optical Thickness

0   5   10   15   20

Chapter Summary

- *Condensation* occurs when water vapor changes to a liquid. For condensation to take place, the air must be saturated and there must be a surface on which the vapor can condense. In the air above the ground, tiny particles known as *cloud condensation nuclei* serve as the surfaces on which water vapor condenses.

- *Clouds,* visible aggregates of minute droplets of water or tiny crystals of ice, are one form of condensation. Clouds are classified on the basis of two criteria: form and height. The three basic cloud forms are *cirrus* (high, white, and thin), *cumulus* (globular, individual cloud masses), and *stratus* (sheets or layers). Cloud heights can be either *high*, with bases above 6000 meters (20,000 feet); *middle*, from 2000 to 6000 meters; or *low*, below 2000 meters (6500 feet). Based on the two criteria, 10 basic cloud types, including *cirrostratus, altocumulus,* and *stratocumulus,* are recognized.

- *Fog,* generally considered an atmospheric hazard, is a cloud with its base at or very near the ground. Fogs formed by cooling include *radiation fog* (from radiation cooling of the ground and adjacent air), *advection fog* (when warm and moist air flows over a cold surface), and *upslope fog* (created when air moves up a slope and cools adiabatically). Those formed by the addition of water vapor are *steam fog* (when water vapor evaporates from a warm water body and condenses in cool air above) and *frontal fog* (when warm air that is lifted over colder air generates precipitation that evaporates as it descends and saturates the air near the surface).

- *Dew* is the condensation of water vapor on objects that have radiated sufficient heat to lower their temperature below the dew point of the surrounding air. *White frost (hoar frost)* forms when the dew point of the air is below freezing.

- For precipitation to form, millions of cloud droplets must somehow coalesce into drops large enough to sustain themselves during their descent. The two mechanisms that have been proposed to explain this phenomenon are: the *Bergeron process,* which produces precipitation from cold clouds primarily in the middle latitudes, and the warm-cloud process most associated with the tropics called the *collision–coalescence process.*

- The two most common and familiar forms of precipitation are *rain* (drops of water that fall from a cloud and have a diameter of at least 0.5 millimeter) and *snow* (precipitation in the form of ice crystals or, more often, aggregates of ice crystals). Other forms include *sleet* (falling small particles of ice that are clear to translucent), *glaze* (formed when supercooled raindrops turn to ice on colliding with solid objects), *hail* (hard, rounded pellets or irregular lumps of ice produced in large cumulonimbus clouds), and *rime* (a deposit of ice crystals formed by the freezing of supercooled fog or cloud droplets on objects whose surface temperature is below freezing).

- Rain, the most common form of precipitation, is probably the easiest to measure. The most common instruments used to measure rain are the *standard rain gauge,* which is read directly, and the *tipping bucket gauge* and *weighing gauge,* both of which record the amount and intensity of rain. The two most common measurements of snow are depth and water equivalent. Although the quantity of water in a given volume of snow is not constant, a general ratio of 10 units of snow to 1 unit of water is often used when exact information is not available.

- *Intentional weather modification* is deliberate human intervention to influence atmospheric processes that constitute the weather. Weather modification falls into three categories: (1) the use of energy to forcefully alter the weather, (2) modifying land and water surfaces to change their natural interaction with the lower atmosphere, and (3) triggering, intensifying, or redirecting atmospheric processes. The focus of intentional weather modification using modern weather technology is on *cloud seeding, fog and cloud dispersal, hail suppression,* and *frost prevention.*

Vocabulary Review

advection fog (p. 140)
Bergeron process (p. 145)
cirrus (p. 133)
cloud condensation nuclei (p. 132)
clouds (p. 132)
cloud seeding (p. 158)
clouds of vertical development
  (p. 133)
collision–coalescence process
  (p. 147)

cumulus (p. 133)
dew (p. 143)
fog (p. 139)
freezing nuclei (p. 145)
freezing rain (p. 151)
frontal or precipitation fog (p. 142)
frost (p. 161)
glaze (p. 151)
hail (p. 151)
high clouds (p. 133)

hydrophobic nuclei (p. 133)
hygroscopic nuclei (p. 132)
intentional weather modification
  (p. 157)
low clouds (p. 133)
middle clouds (p. 133)
radiation fog (p. 139)
rain (p. 150)
rime (p. 155)
sleet (p. 151)

Review Questions

1. Clouds are classified on the basis of two criteria. Name them.
2. Why are high clouds always thin in comparison to low and middle clouds?
3. Which cloud types are associated with the following characteristics: thunder, halos, precipitation, hail, mackerel sky, lightning, and mares' tails?
4. What do layered clouds indicate about the stability of the air? What do clouds of vertical development indicate about the stability of air?
5. What is the importance of condensation nuclei?
6. Distinguish between clouds and fog.
7. List five types of fog and discuss how they form.
8. What actually happens when a radiation fog "lifts"?
9. Identify the fogs described in the following situations.
   a. You have stayed the night in a motel and decide to take an early morning swim. As you approach the heated swimming pool, you notice a fog over the water.
   b. You are located in the western Great Plains, and the winds are from the east and fog is extensive.
   c. You are driving through hilly terrain during the early morning hours and experience fog in the valleys but clearing on the hills.
10. Why is there a relatively high frequency of dense fog along the Pacific Coast?
11. Describe the steps in the formation of precipitation according to the Bergeron process. Be sure to include (a) the importance of supercooled cloud droplets, (b) the role of freezing nuclei, and (c) the difference in saturation vapor pressure between liquid water and ice.
12. How does the collision–coalescence process differ from the Bergeron process?
13. If snow is falling from a cloud, which process produced it? Explain.
14. Describe sleet and glaze and the circumstances under which they form. Why does glaze result on some occasions and sleet on others?
15. How does hail form? What factors govern the ultimate size of hailstones?
16. Although an open container can serve as a rain gauge, what advantages does a standard rain gauge provide?
17. How do recording rain gauges work? Do they have advantages over a standard rain gauge?
18. Describe some of the factors that could lead to an inaccurate measurement of rain or snow.
19. Why are silver iodide crystals used to seed supercooled clouds?
20. If cloud seeding is to have a chance of success, certain atmospheric conditions must exist. Name them.
21. How do frost and white frost differ?
22. Describe how smudge fires, sprinkling, and air mixing are used in frost prevention.
23. List three factors that contribute to greater precipitation in and downwind of cities.

Problems

1. Suppose that the air temperature is 20°C (68°F) and the relative humidity is 50 percent at 6:00 P.M., and that during the evening the air temperature drops but its water vapor content does not change. If the air temperature drops 1°C (1.8°F) every two hours, will fog occur by sunrise (6:00 A.M.) the next morning? Explain your answer. (*Hint:* The data you need are found in Table 4–1, p. 105.)

2. By using the same conditions as in Problem 1, will fog occur if the air temperature drops 1 degree every hour? If so, when will it first appear? What name is given to fog of this type that forms because of surface cooling during the night?

3. Assuming the air is still, how long would it take a large raindrop (5 mm) to reach the ground if it fell from a cloud base at 3000 meters? (See Table 5–3, p. 148.) How long would a typical raindrop (2 mm) take if it fell from the same cloud? How about a drizzle drop (0.5 mm)?

4. Assuming the air is still, how long would it take for a typical cloud droplet (0.02 mm) to reach the ground if it fell from a cloud base at 1000 meters? (See Table 5–3) It is very unlikely that a cloud droplet would ever reach the ground, even if the air were perfectly still. Can you explain why?

5. What is the volume of a small raindrop that is 1000 μm diameter (1 mm diameter)? (*Hint:* See Box 5–2.)

6. A large raindrop 5000 μm (5 mm) in diameter is 100 times the diameter of a large cloud droplet (50 μm in diameter). How many times greater is the volume of a large raindrop than a cloud droplet? (*Hint:* See Box 5–2.)

7. What is the area of the "bottom" of a falling drop of 1 mm diameter?

8. How many times greater is the "bottom" area of a falling 5-mm drop?

Atmospheric Science Online

The Atmosphere 10e web site uses the resources and flexibility of the Internet to aid in your study of the topics in this chapter. Written and developed by meteorology instructors, this site will help improve your understanding of meteorology. Visit **http://www.prenhall.com/lutgens** and click on the cover of *The Atmosphere 10e* to find:

- **Online review quizzes**
- **Critical thinking exercises**
- **Links to chapter-specific web resources**
- **Internet-wide key term searches**

http://www.prenhall.com/lutgens

AIR PRESSURE
and WINDS

An April blizzard in Minnesota. *(Photo by Jim Brandenburg/Minden Pictures)*

Of the various elements of weather and climate, changes in air pressure are the least noticeable. In listening to a weather report, generally we are interested in moisture conditions (humidity and precipitation), temperature, and perhaps wind. It is the rare person, however, who wonders about air pressure. Although the hour-to-hour and day-to-day variations in air pressure are not perceptible to human beings, they are very important in producing changes in our weather. For example, it is variations in air pressure from place to place that generate winds that in turn can bring changes in temperature and humidity (Figure 6–1). Air pressure is one of the basic weather elements and a significant factor in weather forecasting. As we shall see, air pressure is closely tied to the other elements of weather (temperature, moisture, and wind) in a cause-and-effect relationship.

Understanding Air Pressure

In Chapter 1 we noted that **air pressure** is simply the pressure exerted by the weight of air above. Average air pressure at sea level is about 1 kilogram per square centimeter, or 14.7 pounds per square inch. This is roughly the same pressure that is produced by a column of water 10 meters (33 feet) in height. With some simple arithmetic you can cal-

culate that the air pressure exerted on the top of a small (50 centimeter by 100 centimeter) school desk exceeds 5000 kilograms (11,000 pounds), or about the weight of a 50 passenger school bus. Why doesn't the desk collapse under the weight of the ocean of air above? Simply, air pressure is exerted in all directions—down, up, and sideways. Thus, the air pressure pushing down on the desk exactly balances the air pressure pushing up on the desk.

You might be able to visualize this phenomenon better if you imagine a tall aquarium that has the same dimensions as the desktop. When this aquarium is filled to a height of 10 meters (33 feet), the water pressure at the bottom equals 1 atmosphere (14.7 pounds per square inch). Now imagine what will happen if this aquarium is placed on top of our student desk so that all the force is directed downward. Compare this to what results when the desk is placed inside the aquarium and allowed to sink to the bottom. In the latter situation the desk survives because the water pressure is exerted in all directions, not just downward, as in our earlier example. The desk, like your body, is "built" to withstand the pressure of 1 atmosphere. It is important to note that although we do not generally notice the pressure exerted by the ocean of air around us, except when ascending or descending in an elevator or airplane, it is nonetheless substantial. The pressurized suits used by astronauts on space walks are designed to duplicate the atmospheric pressure experienced at Earth's surface. Without these protec-

FIGURE 6-1 Gale force winds created waves that battered the coast at Blackpool, UK in February 2002. *(Photo by John Giles/NewsCom)*

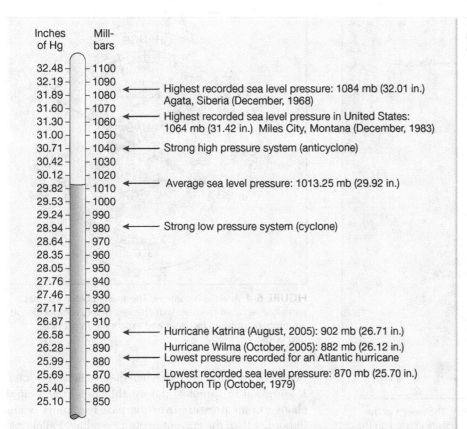

FIGURE 6-2 A comparison of atmospheric pressure in inches of mercury and millibars.

tive suits to keep body fluids from boiling away, astronauts would perish in minutes.

The concept of air pressure can be better understood if we examine the behavior of gases. Gas molecules, unlike those of the liquid and solid phases, are not "bound" to one another but are freely moving about, filling all space available to them. When two gas molecules collide, which happens frequently under normal atmospheric conditions, they bounce off each other like very elastic balls. If a gas is confined to a container, this motion is restricted by its sides, much like the walls of a handball court redirect the motion of the handball. The continuous bombardment of gas molecules against the sides of the container exerts an outward push that we call air pressure. Although the atmosphere is without walls, it is confined from below by Earth's surface and effectively from above because the force of gravity prevents its escape. Here we define *air pressure* as the force exerted against a surface by the continuous collision of gas molecules.

Measuring Air Pressure

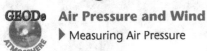 **Air Pressure and Wind**

▶ Measuring Air Pressure

To measure atmospheric pressure, meteorologists use a unit of force from the science of physics called the **newton**.° At sea level the standard atmosphere exerts a force of 101,325

newtons per square meter. To simplify this large number, the U.S. National Weather Service adopted the **millibar** (mb), which equals 100 newtons per square meter. Thus, standard sea-level pressure is stated as 1013.25 millibars (Figure 6–2)°. The millibar has been the unit of measure on all U.S. weather maps since January 1940.

Although millibars are used almost exclusively by meteorologists, you might be better acquainted with the expression "inches of mercury," which is used by the media to describe atmospheric pressure. This expression dates from 1643 when Torricelli, a student of the famous Italian scientist Galileo, invented the **mercury barometer.** Torricelli correctly described the atmosphere as a vast ocean of air that exerts pressure on us and all things about us. To measure this force, he closed one end of a glass tube and filled it with mercury. He then inverted the tube into a dish of mercury (Figure 6–3). Torricelli found that the mercury flowed out of the tube until the weight of the mercury column was balanced by the pressure exerted on the surface of the mercury by the air above. In other words, the weight of the mercury in the column equaled the weight of a similar diameter column of air that extended from the ground to the top of the atmosphere.

Torricelli noted that when air pressure increased, the mercury in the tube rose; conversely, when air pressure

°A newton is the force needed to accelerate a 1 kilogram mass 1 meter per second squared.

°The standard unit of pressure in the SI system is the pascal, which is the name given to a newton per square meter (N/m^2). In this notation a standard atmosphere has a value of 101,325 pascals, or 101.325 kilopascals. If the National Weather Service officially converts to the metric system, it will probably adopt this unit.

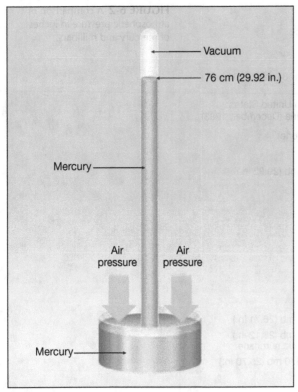

FIGURE 6-3 Simple mercury barometer. The weight of the column of mercury is balanced by the pressure exerted on the dish of mercury by the air above. If the pressure decreases, the column of mercury falls; if the pressure increases, the column rises.

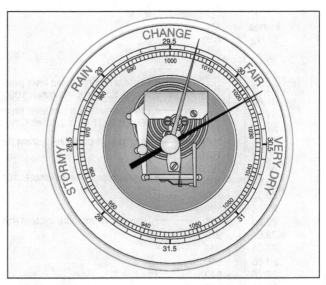

FIGURE 6-4 Aneroid barometer. The aneroid barometer has a partially evacuated chamber that changes shape, compressing as atmospheric pressure increases and expanding as pressure decreases.

decreased, so did the height of the column of mercury. The length of the column of mercury, therefore, became the measure of the air pressure, or "inches of mercury." With some refinements the mercury barometer invented by Torricelli is still the standard pressure-measuring instrument used today. Standard atmospheric pressure at sea level equals 29.92 inches (760 millimeters) of mercury. In the United States the National Weather Service converts millibar values to inches of mercury for public and aviation use (Figure 6–3).

The need for a smaller and more portable instrument for measuring air pressure led to the development of the **aneroid barometer** (*aneroid* means without liquid). Instead of having a mercury column held up by air pressure, the aneroid barometer uses a partially evacuated metal chamber (Figure 6–4). The chamber, being very sensitive to variations in air pressure, changes shape, compressing as the pressure increases and expanding as the pressure decreases. A series of levers transmits the movements of the chamber to a pointer on a dial that is calibrated to read in inches of mercury and/or millibars.

As shown in Figure 6–4, the face of an aneroid barometer intended for home use is inscribed with words like *fair, change, rain,* and *stormy.* Notice that "fair weather" corresponds with high-pressure readings, whereas "rain" is associated with low pressures. Although barometric readings may indicate the present weather, this is not always the case. The dial may point to "fair" on a rainy day, or you may be

experiencing "fair" weather when the dial indicates "rainy." If you want to "predict" the weather in a local area, the change in air pressure over the past few hours is more important than the current pressure reading. Falling pressure is often associated with increasing cloudiness and the possibility of precipitation, whereas rising air pressure generally indicates clearing conditions. It is useful to remember, however, that particular barometer readings or trends do not always correspond to specific types of weather.

One advantage of the aneroid barometer is that it can easily be connected to a recording mechanism. The resulting instrument is a **barograph,** which provides a continuous record of pressure changes with the passage of time (Figure 6–5). Another important adaptation of the aneroid barometer is its use to indicate altitude for aircraft, mountain climbers, and mapmakers (see Box 6–1).

As we shall see later, meteorologists are most concerned with pressure differences that occur horizontally across the globe. Thus, they obtain pressure readings from a number

FIGURE 6-5 An aneroid barograph makes a continuous record of pressure changes. *(Photo courtesy of Qualimetrics, Inc., Sacramento, California.)*

BOX 6–1 Air Pressure and Aviation

The cockpit of nearly every aircraft contains a *pressure altimeter*, an instrument that allows a pilot to determine the altitude of a plane. A pressure altimeter is essentially an aneroid barometer and, as such, responds to changes in air pressure. Recall that air pressure decreases with an increase in altitude and that the pressure distribution with height is well established. To make an altimeter, an aneroid is simply marked in meters instead of millibars. For example, we see in Table 6–1 that a pressure of 795 millibars "normally" occurs at a height of 2000 meters. Therefore, if such a pressure were experienced, the altimeter would indicate an altitude of 2000 meters.

Because of temperature variations and moving pressure systems, actual conditions are usually different from those represented as standard. Con-

sequently, the altitude of an aircraft is seldom exactly that shown by its altimeter. When the barometric pressure aloft is lower than specified by the standard atmosphere, the plane will be flying lower than the height indicated by the altimeter. This could be especially dangerous if the pilot is flying a small plane through mountainous terrain with poor visibility. To correct for these situations, pilots make altimeter corrections before takeoffs and landings, and in some cases corrections are made en route.

Above 5.5 kilometers (18,000 feet), where commercial jets fly and pressure changes are more gradual, corrections cannot be made as precisely as at lower levels. Consequently, such aircraft have their altimeters set at the standard atmosphere and fly paths of constant pressure instead of constant altitude

(Figure 6–A). Stated another way, when an aircraft flies at a constant altimeter setting, a pressure variation will result in a change in the plane's elevation. When pressure increases along a flight path, the plane will climb, and when pressure decreases, the plane will descend. There is little risk of midair collisions because all high-flying aircraft adjust their altitude in a similar manner.

Large commercial aircraft also use radio altimeters to measure heights above the terrain. The time required for a radio signal to reach the surface and return is used to accurately determine the height of the plane above the ground. This system is not without its drawbacks. Because a radio altimeter provides the elevation above the ground rather than above sea level, a knowledge of the underlying terrain is required.

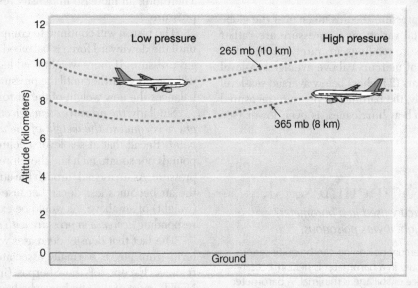

FIGURE 6-A Aircraft above 5.5 kilometers (18,000 feet) generally fly paths of constant pressure instead of constant altitude.

FIGURE 6-6 To compare atmospheric pressures, meteorologists first convert all pressure measurements to sea-level values. This is done by adding the pressure that would be exerted by an imaginary column of air (shown in red) to the station's pressure reading.

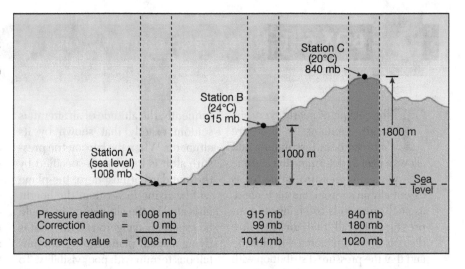

Pressure reading	=	1008 mb	915 mb	840 mb
Correction	=	0 mb	99 mb	180 mb
Corrected value	=	1008 mb	1014 mb	1020 mb

of stations. To compare pressure readings from various weather stations, compensation must be made for the *elevation* of each station. This is done by converting all pressure measurements to sea-level equivalents (Figure 6–6). Doing so requires meteorologists to determine the pressure that would be exerted by an imaginary column of air equal in height to the elevation of the recording station and adding it to the station's pressure reading. Because temperature greatly affects the density, and hence the weight of this imaginary column, temperature also must be considered in the calculations. Thus, the corrected reading would give the pressure, at that time, as if it were taken at sea level under the same conditions.°

A comparison of pressure records taken over the globe reveals that horizontal variations in pressure are rather small. Extreme pressure readings are rarely greater than 30 millibars (1 inch of mercury) above average sea-level pressure or 60 millibars (2 inches) below average sea-level pressure. Occasionally, the barometric pressure measured in severe storms, such as hurricanes, is even lower (see Figure 6–2).

Students Sometimes Ask...

Why is mercury used in a barometer?
I thought it was poisonous.

You are correct—mercury poisoning can be quite serious. However, the mercury in a barometer is held in a reservoir where the chance of spillage is minimal. A barometer could be constructed using any number of different liquids, including water. The problem with a water-filled barometer is size. Because water is 13.6 times less dense than mercury, the height of a water column at standard sea-level pressure would be 13.6 times taller than that of a mercurial barometer. Consequently, a water-filled barometer would need to be nearly 34 feet tall.

°Appendix D explains how barometer corrections can be computed.

Pressure Changes with Altitude

Let us consider the decrease in pressure with altitude mentioned in Chapter 1. The relationship between air pressure and density largely explains this observed decrease. To illustrate, imagine a cylinder fitted with a movable piston, as shown in Figure 6–7. If the temperature is kept constant and weights are added to the piston, the downward force exerted by gravity will squeeze (compress) the gas molecules together. The result is to increase the density of the gas and hence the number of gas molecules (per unit area) bombarding the cylinder wall as well as the bottom of the piston. Therefore, an increase in density results in an increase in pressure.

The piston will continue to compress the air molecules until the downward force is balanced by the ever increasing gas pressure. If more weight is added to the piston, the air will compress further until the pressure of the gas once again balances the new weight of the piston.

Similarly, *the pressure at any given altitude in the atmosphere is equal to the weight of the air directly above that point.* Recall that at sea level a column of air weighs 14.7 pounds per square inch and therefore exerts that amount of pressure. As we ascend through the atmosphere, we find that the air becomes less dense because of the lesser amount (weight) of air above. As would be expected, there is a corresponding *decrease in pressure with an increase in altitude.*

The fact that density decreases with altitude is why the term "thin air" is normally associated with mountainous regions. Except for the Sherpas (indigenous peoples of Nepal), most of the climbers who have reached the summit of Mount Everest (elevation 8852 meters or 29,029 feet) and survived used supplementary oxygen for the final leg of the journey. Even with the aid of supplementary oxygen, most of these climbers experienced periods of disorientation because of an inadequate supply of oxygen to their brains. The decrease in pressure with altitude also affects the boiling temperature of water, which at sea level is 100°C (212°F). For example, in Denver, Colorado—the Mile High City—water boils at 95°C (203°F). Although water comes to a boil faster

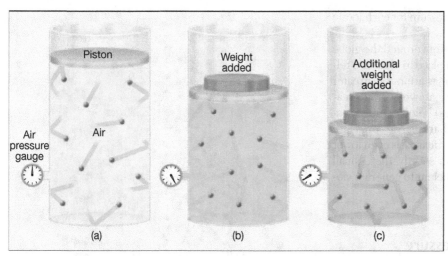

FIGURE 6-7 Schematic drawing showing the relationship between air pressure and density. Cylinder (a) of air fitted with movable piston. As more weight is added (b and c) to the piston, the increased number of molecules per unit volume (density) causes an increase in the pressure exerted on the walls of the cylinder and the gauge.

in Denver than in San Diego because of its lower boiling temperature, it takes longer to cook spaghetti in Denver.

Recall in Chapter 1 that the rate at which pressure decreases with altitude is not a constant. The rate of decrease is much greater near Earth's surface, where pressure is high, than aloft, where air pressure is low. The "normal" decrease in pressure experienced with increased altitude is provided by the standard atmosphere in Table 6–1. The **standard atmosphere** depicts the idealized vertical distribution of atmospheric pressure (as well as temperature and density), which is taken to represent average conditions in the real atmosphere. We see from Table 6–1

that atmospheric pressure is reduced by approximately one-half for each 5-kilometer increase in altitude. Therefore, at 5 kilometers the pressure is one-half its sea-level value; at 10 kilometers it is one-fourth; at 15 kilometers it is one-eighth; and so forth. Thus, at the altitude at which commercial jets fly (10 kilometers), the air exerts a pressure equal to only one-fourth that at sea level.

TABLE 6-1 U.S. standard atmosphere

Height (km)	Pressure (mb)	Temperature (°C)
50.0	0.798	−2
40.0	2.87	−22
35.0	5.75	−36
30.0	11.97	−46
25.0	25.49	−51
20.0	55.29	−56
18.0	75.65	−56
16.0	103.5	−56
14.0	141.7	−56
12.0	194.0	−56
10.0	265.0	−50
9.0	308.0	−43
8.0	356.5	−37
7.0	411.0	−30
6.0	472.2	−24
5.0	540.4	−17
4.0	616.6	−11
3.5	657.8	−8
3.0	701.2	−4
2.5	746.9	−1
2.0	795.0	2
1.5	845.6	5
1.0	898.8	9
0.5	954.6	12
0	1013.2	15

Students Sometimes Ask...

Why do my ears sometimes feel pain when I fly?

When airplanes take off and land, some people experience pain in their ears because of a change in cabin pressure. (Although most commercial airplanes are designed to keep the cabin pressure relatively constant, small changes in pressure do occur.) Normally the air pressure in one's middle ear is the same as the pressure of the surrounding atmosphere because the Eustachian tube connects the ear to the throat. However, when an individual has a cold, his or her Eustachian tubes may become blocked, preventing the flow of air either into or out of the middle ear. The resulting pressure difference can cause mild discomfort or, less often, excruciating pain, which subsides when the ears "pop," equalizing the pressure.

Horizontal Variations in Air Pressure

Although pressure changes with altitude are important, meteorologists are most interested in pressure differences that occur horizontally across the globe. To compare pressure readings from various weather stations, compensation must be made for the *elevation* of each station (see Figure

6–6). The adjusted reading gives the pressure for each locale as if it were taken at sea level.°

A comparison of pressure records from around the globe reveals that pressure differences from place to place are relatively small. Extreme pressure readings are rarely greater than 30 millibars (1 inch of mercury) above average sea-level pressure or 60 millibars (2 inches) below average sea-level pressure. Occasionally, the barometric pressure measured in severe storms, such as hurricanes, is even lower (see Figure 6–2). As we shall discover shortly, these small differences in air pressure can be sufficient to generate violent winds.

Influence of Temperature and Water Vapor on Air Pressure

How do pressure differences arise? One of the easiest ways to envision this is to picture northern Canada in midwinter. Here the snow-covered surface is continually radiating heat to space, while receiving little incoming solar radiation. The frigid ground cools the air above so that daily lows of −34°C (−30°F) are common and extremes of −46°C (−50°F) can occur.

Recall that temperature is a measure of the average molecular motion (kinetic energy) of a substance. Therefore, cold Canadian air is composed of comparatively slow-moving gas molecules that are packed closely together. As the density of a column of air increases, so does the pressure it exerts on the surface (Figure 6–8). Thus, a mass of cold air moving into the Midwest from Canada is quite dense and will be labeled a **High,** for *high barometric pressure,* on a weather map.

In contrast, the air over the Gulf of Mexico in January is relatively warm. Because the gas molecules in warm air have abundant kinetic energy, they are more widely spaced (less dense). Warm air masses that produce *low barometric pressure* are labeled **Low** on a weather map.

It is important to remember, however, that factors other than temperature affect the amount of pressure a column of air will exert. For example, the amount of water vapor contained in a volume of air influences its density. Contrary to popular perception, water vapor *reduces* the density of air. The air may feel "heavy" on hot, humid days, but it is not. You can easily verify this fact for yourself by examining a periodic table of the elements and noting that the molecular weights of nitrogen (N_2) and oxygen (O_2) are greater than that of water vapor (H_2O). In a mass of air the molecules of these gases are intermixed, and each takes up roughly the same amount of space. As the water content of an air mass increases, lighter water vapor molecules displace heavier nitrogen and oxygen molecules. Therefore, humid air is lighter (less dense) than dry air. Nevertheless, even very humid air is only about 2 percent less dense than dry air at the same temperature.

°The relationship among pressure, temperature, and density described in this section is stated in the *ideal gas law.* A mathematical treatment of the ideal gas law is provided in Appendix D.

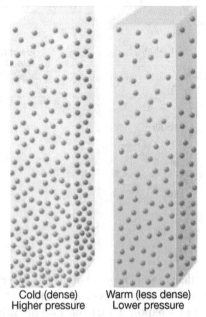

FIGURE 6-8 A comparison of the density of a column of cold air with a column of warm air. All else being equal, cold, dense air exerts more pressure than warm, less dense air.

Cold (dense) Higher pressure — Warm (less dense) Lower pressure

From the preceding discussion we can conclude that a cold, dry air mass will produce higher surface pressures than a warm, humid air mass. Further, a warm, dry air mass will exhibit higher pressure than an equally warm, but humid, air mass. Consequently, large air masses are responsible for some of the pressure variations observed at Earth's surface.

Airflow and Pressure

The movement of air can also cause variations in air pressure. For example, in situations where there is a net flow of air into a region, a phenomenon called **convergence,** the air piles up. Stated another way, as air converges horizontally, it must increase in height to allow for the decreased area it now occupies. This results in a "taller" and therefore heavier air column that exerts more pressure at the surface. By contrast, in regions where there is a net outflow of air, a situation referred to as **divergence,** the surface pressure drops.

As you might expect, atmospheric processes involve significantly more complex variables than have just been described. Sometimes divergence at the surface is accompanied by convergence higher in the atmosphere. In this situation, surface pressure will rise when convergence outpaces divergence, or fall when divergence exceeds convergence. We will return to this important mechanism for producing areas of high and low pressure later in this chapter.

In summary, cold, dry air masses are dense and associated with high pressure. In contrast, warm, humid air masses are less dense and tend to exhibit low pressure. Further, the pressure at the surface will increase when there is a net convergence in a region and decrease when there is a net divergence.

The importance of atmospheric pressure to Earth's weather cannot be overemphasized. As you shall see shortly, differences in air pressure create global winds that become organized into the systems that "bring us our weather." Thus, much of the remainder of this book will consider the relationship between air temperature and air pressure and the effect of air pressure on airflow, and vice versa.

Factors Affecting Wind

GEODe **Air Pressure and Wind**
▶ Factors Affecting Wind
ATMOSPHERE

We discussed the upward movement of air and its importance in cloud formation. As important as vertical motion is, far more air is involved in horizontal movement, the phenomenon we call **wind.** Although we know that air will move vertically if it is warmer and thus more buoyant than surrounding air, what causes air to move horizontally?

Simply stated, *wind is the result of horizontal differences in air pressure.* Air flows from areas of higher pressure to areas of lower pressure. You may have experienced this condition when opening a vacuum-packed can of coffee. The noise you hear is caused by air rushing from the area of higher pressure outside the can to the lower pressure inside. Wind is nature's attempt to balance inequalities in air pressure. Because unequal heating of Earth's surface continually generates these pressure differences, solar radiation is the ultimate energy source for most wind.

If Earth did not rotate and if there were no friction, air would flow directly from areas of higher pressure to areas of lower pressure. Because both factors exist, however, wind is controlled by a combination of forces, including:

1. the pressure-gradient force
2. the Coriolis force
3. friction

Pressure-Gradient Force

To get anything to accelerate (change its velocity) requires an unbalanced force in one direction. The force that generates winds results from horizontal pressure differences. When air is subjected to greater pressure on one side than on another, the imbalance produces a force that is directed from the region of higher pressure toward the area of lower pressure. Thus, pressure differences cause the wind to blow, and the greater these differences, the greater the wind speed.

Variations in air pressure over Earth's surface are determined from barometric readings taken at hundreds of weather stations. These pressure data are shown on surface weather maps by means of isobars. **Isobars** are lines connecting places of equal air pressure (*iso* = equal, *bar* = pressure), as shown in Figure 6–9. The *spacing* of

FIGURE 6-9 Isobars are lines connecting places of equal sea-level pressure. They are used to show the distribution of pressure on daily weather maps. Isobars are seldom straight, but usually form broad curves. Concentric rings of isobars indicate cells of high and low pressure. The "wind flags" indicate the expected airflow surrounding pressure cells and are plotted as "flying" with the wind (that is, the wind blows toward the station circle). Notice on this map that the isobars are more closely spaced and the wind speed is faster around the low-pressure center than around the high.

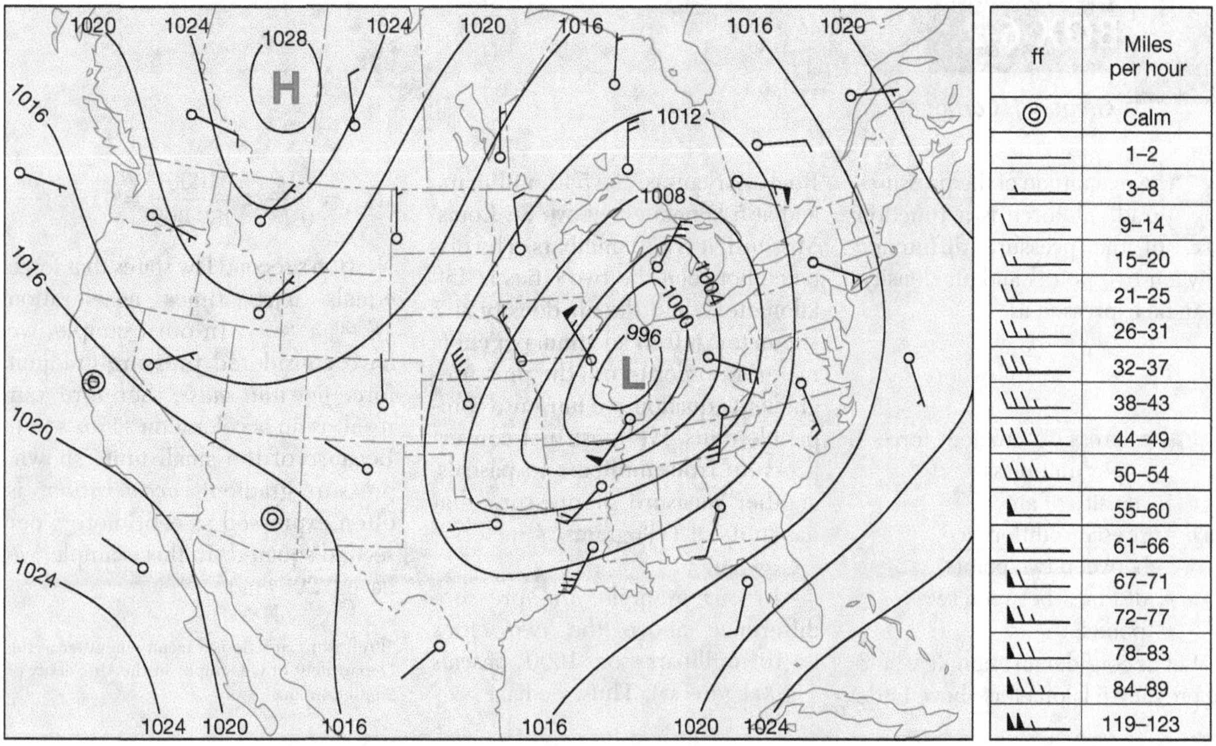

1020
1024
1028
H
1024
1020
1016
1016
1020
1016
1012
1008
1004
1000
996
L
1016
1020
1024
1024
1020
1016
1016
1020
1024
ff
Miles per hour
Calm
1–2
3–8
9–14
15–20
21–25
26–31
32–37
38–43
44–49
50–54
55–60
61–66
67–71
72–77
78–83
84–89
119–123

the isobars indicates the amount of pressure change occurring over a given distance and is expressed as the **pressure gradient.** The mathematical expression of the pressure gradient force is provided in Box 6–2.

You might find it easier to visualize the concept of a pressure gradient if you think of it as being analogous to the slope of a hill. A steep pressure gradient, like a steep hill, causes greater acceleration of a parcel of air than does a weak pressure gradient (a gentle hill). Thus, the relationship between wind speed and the pressure gradient is straightforward. Closely spaced isobars indicate a steep pressure gradient and strong winds; widely spaced isobars indicate a weak pressure gradient and light winds. Figure 6–10 illustrates the relationship between the spacing of isobars and wind speed. Note also that the pressure-gradient force is always directed at *right angles* to the isobars.

Pressure differences observed on the daily weather map result from complex factors. However, the underlying cause of these differences is simply *unequal heating of Earth's land–sea surface*.

Horizontal Pressure Gradients and Wind. To illustrate how temperature differences can generate a horizontal pressure gradient and thereby create winds, let us look at a common example, the *sea breeze*. Figure 6–11a shows a vertical cross-section of a coastal location just before sunrise. At this time we are assuming that temperatures and pressures do not vary horizontally at any level. This assumption is shown in Figure 6–11a by the horizontal pressure surfaces that indicate the equal pressure at equal heights. Because there is no horizontal variation in pressure (zero horizontal pressure gradient), there is no wind.

After sunrise, however, the unequal rates at which land and water heat will initiate pressure differences and, therefore, airflow (Figure 6–11b). Recall from Chapter 3 that surface temperatures over the ocean change only slightly on a daily basis. On the other hand, land surfaces and the air above can be substantially warmed during a single daylight period. As air over the land warms, it expands, causing a reduction in density. This in turn results in pressure surfaces that are bent upward, as shown in Figure 6–11b. Although this warming does not by itself produce a surface pressure change, a given pressure surface aloft does become elevated over the land compared to over the ocean. The resultant pressure gradient aloft causes the air aloft to move from the land toward the ocean.

The mass transfer of air seaward creates a surface high-pressure area over the ocean, where the air is collecting, and a surface low over the land. The surface circulation that develops from this redistribution of air aloft is from the sea toward the land (sea breeze), as shown in Figure 6–11c. Thus, a simple thermal circulation develops, with a seaward flow aloft and a landward flow at the surface. Note that *vertical* movement also is required to make the circulation complete. (We will consider the vertical pressure gradient next.)

An important relationship exists between pressure and temperature, as you saw in the preceding discussion. Temperature variations create pressure differences and hence wind. The greater these temperature differences, the stronger the horizontal pressure gradient and resultant wind.

BOX 6-2 Pressure-Gradient Force

Gregory J. Carbone*

The magnitude of the pressure-gradient force is a function of the pressure difference between two points and air density. It can be expressed as

$$F_{PG} = \frac{1}{d} \times \frac{\Delta_p}{\Delta_n}; \text{ where}$$

F_{PG} = pressure-gradient force per unit mass
d = density of air
p = pressure difference between two points
n = distance between two points

Let us consider an example where the pressure 5 kilometers above Little Rock, Arkansas, is 540 millibars, and at 5 kilometers above St. Louis, Missouri, it is 530 millibars. The distance between the two cities is 450 kilometers, and the air density at 5 kilometers is 0.75 kilogram per cubic meter. In order to use the pressure-gradient equation, we must use compatible units. We must first convert pressure from millibars to pascals, another measure of pressure that has units of (kilograms × meters^{-1} × second^2).

In our example, the pressure difference above the two cities is 10 millibars, or 1000 pascals (1000 kg/m · s^2). Thus, we have

$$F_{PG} = \frac{1}{0.75} \times \frac{1000}{450,000} = 0.0029 \frac{m}{s^2}$$

Newton's second law states that force equals mass times acceleration ($F = m \times a$). In our example, we have considered pressure-gradient force *per unit mass;* therefore, our result is an acceleration ($F/m = a$). Because of the small units shown, pressure-gradient *acceleration* is often expressed as centimeters per second squared. In this example, we have 0.296 cm/s^2.

*Professor Carbone is a faculty member in the Department of Geography at the University of South Carolina.

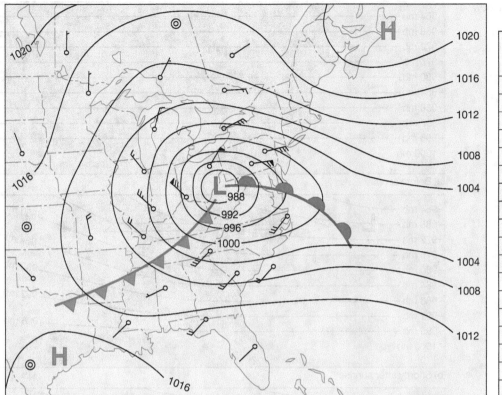

ff	Miles per hour
◎	Calm
———	1–2
〴	3–8
＼	9–14
＼	15–20
＼	21–25
＼	26–31
＼＼	32–37
＼＼	38–43
＼＼	44–49
＼＼	50–54
＿	55–60
＿	61–66
＿	67–71
＿	72–77
＿	78–83
＿	84–89
＿	119–123

FIGURE 6-10 Pressure-gradient force. Closely spaced isobars indicate a strong pressure gradient and high wind speeds, whereas widely spaced isobars indicate a weak pressure gradient and low wind speeds.

Daily temperature differences and the pressure gradients so generated are generally confined to a zone that is only a few kilometers thick. On a global scale, however, variations in the amount of solar radiation received due to variations in Sun angle with latitude generate the much larger pressure systems that in turn produce the planetary atmospheric circulation. This is the topic of the next chapter.

If the pressure-gradient force was the only force acting on the wind, air would flow directly from areas of higher pressures to areas of lower pressure and the lows would be quickly filled. Thus, the well-developed high and low pressure systems that dominate our daily weather maps could never sustain themselves. Instead, Earth's atmosphere would, at best, develop only very weak and short-lived pressure systems. Therefore, most locations would experience long periods of very still air that would occasionally be disrupted by gentle breezes.

Fortunately, for those of us who like more varied weather, this is not the case. Once the pressure-gradient force starts the air in motion, the Coriolis force, friction, and other forces come into play. Although these forces cannot generate wind (with the exception of gravity), they do *greatly modify airflow*. By doing so, these forces help sustain and even enhance the development of the Earth's pressure systems. We will consider some of these important *modifying* forces shortly.

Vertical Pressure Gradient. As you learned earlier, airflow is from areas of higher pressure to areas of lower

pressure. Further, you are aware that air pressure is highest near Earth's surface and gets progressively lower as you move upward through the atmosphere. Combining these two ideas, you might wonder why air does not rapidly accelerate upward and escape into space. In fact, it would do just that if it were not for the force of gravity, which acts in the opposite direction to the upward directed, *vertical pressure gradient*. The important balance that is usually maintained between these two opposing forces is called **hydrostatic equilibrium.**

In general, the atmosphere is in or near hydrostatic balance. On those occasions when the gravitational force slightly exceeds the vertical pressure-gradient force, slow downward airflow results. This occurs, for example, within a dense Arctic air mass, where cold air is subsiding and spreading out at the surface. Most large-scale downward (and upward) motions are slow, averaging a few centimeters per second (less than 1 mile per day). However, some smaller-scale vertical motions are much more rapid. For example, strong updrafts and downdrafts associated with severe thunderstorms can reach 100 kilometers (62 miles) per hour or more. Fortunately, these phenomena are sporadic and localized. Overall, the state of the atmosphere is in hydrostatic equilibrium, where the upward pressure-gradient force is balanced by the downward force of gravity.

In summary, the horizontal pressure gradient is the driving force of wind. It has both magnitude and direction. Its magnitude is determined from the spacing of isobars, and

FIGURE 6-11 Cross-sectional view illustrating the formation of a sea breeze. (a) Just before sunrise; (b) after sunrise; (c) sea breeze established.

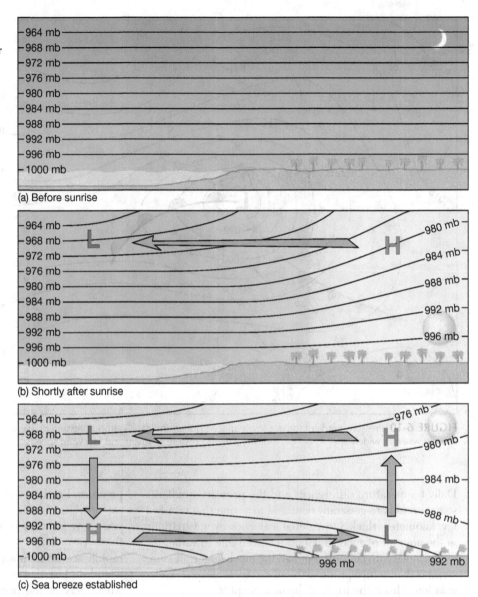

(a) Before sunrise

(b) Shortly after sunrise

(c) Sea breeze established

Coriolis Force

the direction of force is always from areas of higher pressure to areas of lower pressure and at right angles to the isobars. By contrast, the vertical pressure gradient is usually in, or near, balance with gravity. Thus, upward and downward flow in the atmosphere is comparatively slow (with the exception of localized updrafts and downdrafts).

Coriolis Force

The weather map in Figure 6–9 shows the typical air movements associated with surface high- and low-pressure systems. As expected, the air moves out of the regions of higher pressure and into the regions of lower pressure. However, the wind does not cross the isobars at right angles, as the pressure-gradient force directs. This deviation is the result of Earth's rotation and has been named the **Coriolis force** after the French scientist Gaspard Gustave Coriolis, who first expressed its magnitude quantitatively.

All free-moving objects, including wind, are deflected to the *right* of their path of motion in the Northern Hemi-

sphere and the *left* in the Southern Hemisphere. The reason for this deflection can be illustrated by imagining the path of a rocket launched from the North Pole toward a target on the equator (Figure 6–12). If the rocket took an hour to reach its target, Earth would have rotated 15° to the east during its flight. To someone standing on Earth, it would look as if the rocket veered off its path and hit Earth 15° west of its target. The true path of the rocket was straight and would appear so to someone out in space looking down at Earth. It was Earth turning under the rocket that gave it its apparent deflection. Note that the rocket was deflected to the right of its path of motion because of the counter-clockwise rotation of the Northern Hemisphere. Clockwise rotation produces a similar deflection in the Southern Hemisphere, but to the left of the path of motion.

Although it is usually easy for people to visualize the Coriolis deflection when the motion is from north to south, as in our rocket example, it is not so easy to see how a west-to-east flow would be deflected. Figure 6–13 illustrates this situation using winds blowing eastward at four different

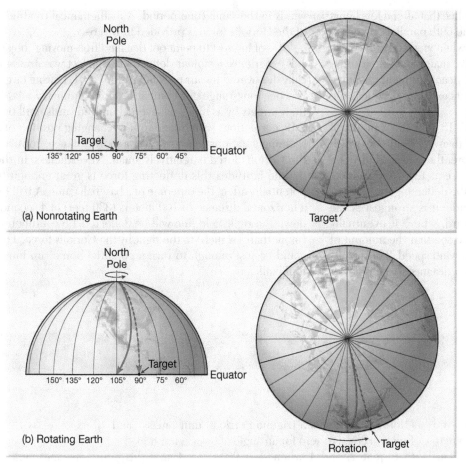

FIGURE 6-12 The Coriolis force illustrated using the one-hour flight of a rocket traveling from the North Pole to a location on the equator. (a) On a nonrotating Earth the rocket would travel straight to its target. (b) However, Earth rotates 15° each hour. Thus, although the rocket travels in a straight line, when we plot the path of the rocket on Earth's surface, it follows a curved path that veers to the right of the target.

FIGURE 6-13 Coriolis deflection of winds blowing eastward at different latitudes. After a few hours the winds along the 20th, 40th, and 60th parallels appear to veer off course. This deflection (which does not occur at the equator) is caused by Earth's rotation, which changes the orientation of the surface over which the winds are moving.

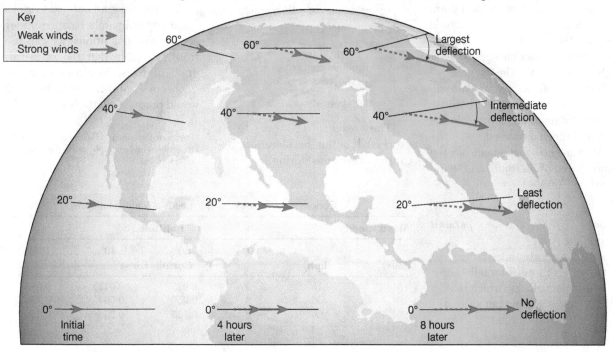

latitudes (0°, 20°, 40°, and 60°). Notice that after a few hours the winds along the 20th, 40th, and 60th parallels appear to be veering off course. However, when viewed from space, it is apparent that these winds have maintained their original direction. It is the North American continent changing its orientation as Earth turns on its axis that produces the deflection we observe.

We can also see in Figure 6–13 that the amount of deflection is greater at 60° latitude than at 40° latitude, which is greater than at 20°. Furthermore, there is no deflection observed for the airflow along the equator. We conclude, therefore, that the magnitude of the deflecting force (Coriolis force) is dependent on latitude; it is strongest at the poles, and it weakens equatorward, where it eventually becomes nonexistent. We can also see that the amount of Coriolis deflection increases with wind speed. This results because faster winds cover a greater distance than do slower winds in the same time period. A mathematical treatment of the Coriolis force is provided in Box 6–3.

It is of interest to point out that any "free-moving" object will experience a similar deflection. This fact was dramatically discovered by our navy in World War II. During target practice long-range guns on battleships continually missed their targets by as much as several hundred yards until ballistic corrections were made for the changing position of a seemingly stationary target. Over a short distance, however, the Coriolis force is relatively small. Nevertheless, in the middle latitudes this deflecting force is great enough to potentially affect the outcome of a baseball game. A ball hit a horizontal distance of 100 meters (330 feet) in 4 seconds down the right field line will be deflected 1.5 centimeters (more than 1/2 inch) to the right by the Coriolis force. This could be just enough to turn a potential home run into a foul ball!

BOX 6–3 Coriolis Force As a Function of Wind Speed and Latitude

Gregory J. Carbone*

Figure 6–13 shows how wind speed and latitude conspire to affect the Coriolis force. Consider a west wind at four different latitudes (0°, 20°, 40°, and 60°). After several hours Earth's rotation has changed the orientation of latitude and longitude of all locations except the equator such that the wind appears to be deflected to the right. The degree of deflection for a given wind speed increases with latitude because the orientation of latitude and longitude lines changes more at higher latitudes. The degree of deflection of a given latitude increases with wind speed because greater distances are covered in the period of time considered.

We can show mathematically the importance of latitude and wind speed on Coriolis force:

$$F_{CO} = 2v\,\Omega\,\sin\phi$$

where F_{CO} = Coriolis force *per unit mass of air*

v = wind speed

Ω = Earth's rate of rotation or angular velocity (which is 7.29×10^{-5} radians per second)

ϕ = latitude

[Note that sin ϕ is a trigonometric function equal to zero for an angle of 0° (equator) and 1 when $\phi = 90°$ (poles).]

As an example, the Coriolis force per unit mass that must be considered for a 10-meter-per-second (m/s) wind at 40° is calculated as:

$$F_{CO} = 2\Omega\,\sin\phi v$$

$$F_{CO} = 2\Omega\,\sin 40 \times 10 \text{ m/s}$$

$$F_{CO} = 2(7.29 \times 10^{-5}\text{ s}^{-1})\,0.64(10/\text{ms})$$

$$F_{CO} = 0.00094 \text{ meter per second squared}$$

$$= 0.094 \text{ cm s}^{-2}$$

The result $(0.094 \text{ cm s}^{-2})$ is expressed as an acceleration because we are considering force per unit mass and force = mass $\times$ acceleration.

Using this equation, one could calculate the Coriolis force for any latitude or wind speed. Consider Table 6–A, which shows the Coriolis force per unit mass for three specific wind speeds at various latitudes. All values are expressed in centimeters per second squared (cm s^{-2}). Because pressure gradient and Coriolis force approximately balance under geostrophic conditions, we can see from our table that the pressure-gradient force (per unit mass) of 0.296 cm s^{-2} illustrated in Box 6–2 would produce relatively high winds.

*Professor Carbone is a faculty member in the Department of Geography at the University of South Carolina.

TABLE 6-A Coriolis force for three wind speeds at various latitudes

Wind speed		Latitude (ϕ)			
		0°	20°	40°	60°
(m/s)	(kph)	Coriolis force (cm/s²)			
5	18	0	0.025	0.047	0.063
10	36	0	0.050	0.094	0.126
25	90	0	0.125	0.235	0.316

In summary, on a rotating Earth the Coriolis force acts to change the direction of a moving body to the right in the Northern Hemisphere and to the left in the Southern Hemisphere. This deflecting force (1) is always directed at right angles to the direction of airflow; (2) affects only wind direction, not wind speed; (3) is affected by wind speed (the stronger the wind, the greater the deflecting force); and (4) is strongest at the poles and weakens equatorward, becoming nonexistent at the equator.

Students Sometimes Ask…

*I've been told that water goes down a sink
in one direction in the Northern Hemisphere
and in the opposite direction
in the Southern Hemisphere. Is that true?*

No! The origin of this myth comes from applying a scientific principle to a situation where it does not fit. Recall that the Coriolis deflection causes cyclonic systems to rotate counterclockwise in the Northern Hemisphere and clockwise in the Southern Hemisphere. It was inevitable that someone would suggest (without checking) that a sink should drain in a similar manner. However, a cyclone is more than 1000 kilometers in diameter and may exist for several days. By contrast, a typical sink is less than a meter in diameter and drains in a matter of seconds. On this scale, the Coriolis force is minuscule. Therefore, the shape of the sink and how level it is has more to do with the direction of water flow than the Coriolis force.

Friction

Earlier we stated that the pressure-gradient force is the primary driving force of the wind. As an unbalanced force, it causes air to accelerate from regions of higher pressure to regions of lower pressure. Thus, wind speeds should continually increase (accelerate) for as long as this imbalance exists. But we know from personal experience that winds do not become faster indefinitely. Some other force, or forces, must oppose the pressure-gradient force to moderate airflow. From our everyday experience we know that friction acts to slow a moving object. Although friction significantly influences airflow near Earth's surface, its effect is negligible above a height of a few kilometers (Figure 6–14). For this reason, we will divide our discussion. First, we will examine the flow aloft, where the effect of friction is small. Then we will analyze surface winds, where friction significantly influences airflow.

Winds Aloft and Geostrophic Flow

This section will deal only with airflow above a few kilometers, where the effects of friction are small enough to disregard.

Aloft, the Coriolis force is responsible for balancing the pressure-gradient force and thereby directing airflow. Figure 6–15 shows how a balance is reached between these opposing forces. For illustration only, we assume a nonmoving parcel of air at the starting point in Figure 6–15. (Remember

FIGURE 6-14 (a) Wind increases in strength with an increase in altitude because it is less affected by friction from objects near Earth's surface. (b) This snow-covered tree shows the effects of strong winds in a high mountain setting. *(Photo by E. J. Tarbuck)*

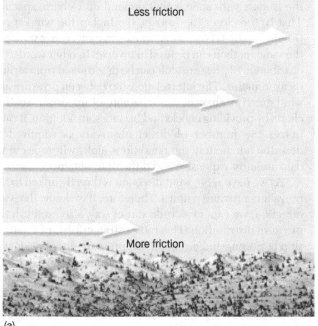

Less friction

More friction

(a)

(b)

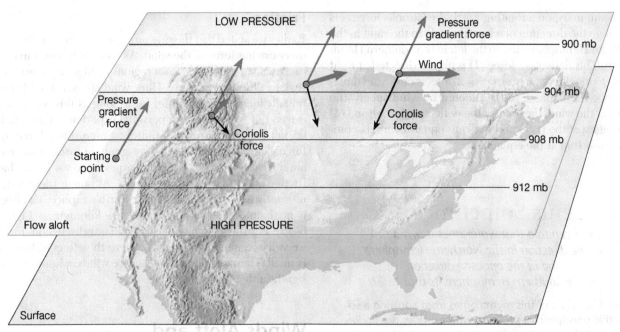

FIGURE 6-15 The geostrophic wind. The only force acting on a stationary parcel of air is the pressure-gradient force. Once the air begins to accelerate, the Coriolis force deflects it to the right in the Northern Hemisphere. Greater wind speeds result in a stronger Coriolis force (deflection) until the flow is parallel to the isobars. At this point the pressure-gradient force and Coriolis force are in balance and the flow is called a *geostrophic wind*. It is important to note that in the "real" atmosphere, airflow is continually adjusting for variations in the pressure field. As a result, the adjustment to geostrophic equilibrium is much more irregular than shown.

that air is rarely stationary in the atmosphere.) Because our parcel of air has no motion, the Coriolis force exerts no influence; only the pressure-gradient force can act at the starting point. Under the influence of the pressure-gradient force, which is always directed perpendicularly to the isobars, the parcel begins to accelerate directly toward the area of low pressure. As soon as the flow begins, the Coriolis force comes into play and causes a deflection to the right for winds in the Northern Hemisphere. As the parcel continues to accelerate, the Coriolis force intensifies (recall that the magnitude of the Coriolis force is proportional to wind speed). Thus, the increased speed results in further deflection.

Eventually the wind turns so that it is flowing parallel to the isobars. When this occurs, the pressure-gradient force is balanced by the opposing Coriolis force, as shown in Figure 6–15. As long as these forces remain balanced, the resulting wind will continue to flow parallel to the isobars at a constant speed. Stated another way, the wind can be considered to be coasting (not accelerating or decelerating) along a pathway defined by the isobars.

Under these idealized conditions, when the Coriolis force is exactly equal and opposite to the pressure-gradient force, the airflow is said to be in *geostrophic balance*. The winds generated by this balance are called **geostrophic winds** (geostrophic means "turned by Earth"). Geostrophic winds flow in a straight path, parallel to the isobars, with velocities proportional to the pressure-gradient force. A steep pressure gradient creates strong winds, and a weak pressure gradient produces light winds.

It is important to note that the geostrophic wind is an idealized model that only approximates the actual behavior of airflow aloft. In the real atmosphere, winds are never purely geostrophic. Nonetheless, the geostrophic model offers a useful approximation of the actual winds aloft. By measuring the pressure field (orientation and spacing of isobars) that exists aloft, meteorologists can determine both wind direction and speed (Figure 6–16).

The idealized geostrophic flow predicts winds parallel to the isobars with speeds that depend on isobaric spacing. That is, the closer the isobars, the higher the wind speed (Figure 6–16). Of equal importance to meteorologists is that the same method can be used in reverse. In other words, the distribution of pressure aloft can be determined from airflow measurements. The interrelationship between pressure and wind greatly enhances the reliability of upper-air weather charts by providing checks and balances. In addition, it minimizes the number of direct observations required to describe adequately the conditions aloft, where accurate data are most expensive and difficult to obtain.

As we have seen, wind direction is directly linked to the prevailing pressure pattern. Therefore, if we know the wind direction, we can, in a crude sort of way, also establish the pressure distribution. This rather straightforward relationship between wind direction and pressure distribution was first formulated by the Dutch meteorologist Buys Ballot in 1857. Essentially, **Buys Ballot's law** states: In the Northern Hemisphere *if you stand with your back to the wind, low pressure will be found to your left and high pressure to*

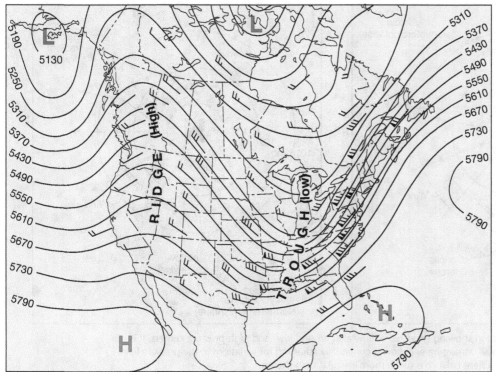

(a) Upper-level weather chart

ff	Miles per hour
◎	Calm
——	1–2
⌐—	3–8
⌐—	9–14
⌐—	15–20
⌐—	21–25
⌐—	26–31
⌐—	32–37
⌐—	38–43
⌐—	44–49
⌐—	50–54
▬—	55–60
▬—	61–66
▬—	67–71
▬—	72–77
▬—	78–83
▬—	84–89
▬—	119–123

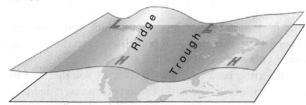

(b) Representation of upper-level chart

FIGURE 6-16 Upper-air weather chart. (a) This simplified weather chart shows the direction and speed of the upper-air winds. Note from the flags that the airflow is almost parallel to the contours. Like most upper-air charts, this one shows variations in the height (in meters) at which a selected pressure (500 millibars) is found, instead of showing variations in pressure at a fixed height like surface maps. Do not let this confuse you, because there is a simple relationship between height contours and pressure. Places experiencing 500-millibar pressure at higher altitudes (toward the south) are experiencing higher pressures than places where the height contours indicate lower altitudes. Thus, *higher-elevation* contours indicate *higher* pressures, and *lower-elevation* contours indicate *lower* pressures. (b) Representation of the 500-millibar surface shown in the upper-air weather chart above.

your right. In the Southern Hemisphere, the situation is reversed.

Although Buys Ballot's law holds for airflow aloft, it must be used with caution when applied to surface winds. At the surface, friction and topography interfere with the idealized circulation. At the surface, if you stand with your back to the wind, then turn clockwise about 30°, low pressure will be to your left and high pressure to your right.

In summary, winds above a few kilometers can be considered geostrophic—that is, they flow in a straight path parallel to the isobars at speeds that can be calculated from the pressure gradient. The major discrepancy from true geostrophic winds involves the flow along highly curved paths, a topic considered next.

Curved Flow and the Gradient Wind

Even a casual glance at a weather map shows that the isobars are not generally straight; instead, they make broad, sweeping curves (see Figure 6–9). Occasionally the isobars connect to form roughly circular cells of either high or low pressure. Thus, unlike geostrophic winds that flow in a straight path parallel to the isobars, winds around cells of high or low pressure follow curved paths in order to parallel the isobars. Winds of this nature, which blow at a constant speed parallel to curved isobars, are called **gradient winds.**

Let us examine how the pressure-gradient force and Coriolis force combine to produce gradient winds. Figure 6–17a

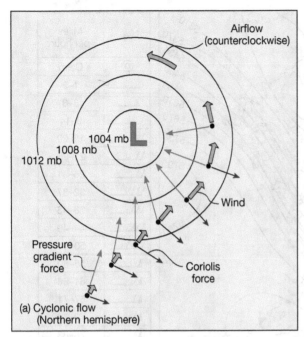

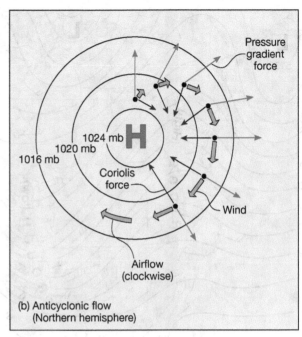

FIGURE 6-17 Idealized illustration showing expected airflow aloft around low- and high-pressure centers. It is important to note that in the "real" atmosphere, airflow is continually adjusting for variations in the pressure field. As a result, the adjustment to gradient balance is much more irregular than shown.

shows the gradient flow around a center of low pressure. As soon as the flow begins, the Coriolis force causes the air to be deflected. In the Northern Hemisphere, where the Coriolis force deflects the flow to the right, the resulting wind blows counterclockwise about a low (Figure 6–17a). Conversely, around a high-pressure cell, the outward-directed pressure-gradient force is opposed by the inward-directed Coriolis force, and a clockwise flow results (Figure 6–17b).

Because the Coriolis force deflects the winds to the left in the Southern Hemisphere, the flow is reversed there—clockwise around low-pressure centers and counterclockwise around high-pressure centers.

It is common practice to call all centers of low pressure **cyclones** and the flow around them cyclonic. **Cyclonic flow** has the same direction of rotation as Earth: counterclockwise in the Northern Hemisphere and clockwise in the Southern Hemisphere. Centers of high prsssure are frequently called **anticyclones** and exhibit **anticyclonic flow** (opposite that of Earth's rotation). Whenever isobars curve to form elongated regions of low and high pressure, these areas are called **troughs** and **ridges,** respectively (Figure 6–16). The flow about a trough is cyclonic; the flow around a ridge is anticyclonic.

Now let us consider the forces that produce the gradient flow associated with cyclonic and anticyclonic circulations. Wherever the flow is curved, a force has deflected the air (changed its direction), even when no change in speed results. This is a consequence of Newton's first law of motion, which states that a moving object will continue to move in a straight line unless acted upon by an unbalanced force. You have undoubtedly experienced the effect of New-

ton's law when the automobile in which you were riding made a sharp turn and your body tried to continue moving straight ahead (see Appendix E).

Referring back to Figure 6–17a, we see that in a low-pressure center, the inward-directed pressure-gradient force is opposed by the outward-directed Coriolis force. But to keep the path curved (parallel to the isobars), the inward pull of the pressure-gradient force must be strong enough to balance the Coriolis force as well as to turn (accelerate) the air inward. The inward turning of the air is called *centripetal acceleration.* Stated another way, the pressure-gradient force must exceed the Coriolis force to overcome the air's tendency to continue moving in a straight line.*

The opposite situation exists in anticyclonic flows, where the inward-directed Coriolis force must balance the pressure-gradient force as well as provide the inward acceleration needed to turn the air. Notice in Figure 6–17 that the pressure-gradient and Coriolis force are not balanced (the arrow lengths are different), as they are in geostrophic flow. This imbalance provides the change in direction (centripetal acceleration) that generates curved flow.

Despite the importance of centripetal acceleration in establishing curved flow aloft, near the surface, friction comes into play and greatly overshadows this much weaker force. Consequently, except for rapidly rotating storms such as tornadoes and hurricanes, the effect of centripetal acceleration is negligible and therefore is not considered in the discussion of surface circulation.

---

*The tendency of a particle to move in a straight line when rotated creates an imaginary outward force called *centrifugal force.*

BOX 6-4 — Do Baseballs Really Fly Farther at Denver's Coors Field?

Since Denver's Coors Field was built, in 1995, it has become known as the "homerun hitter's ballpark" (Figure 6–B). This notoriety is warranted since Coors Field led all major-league ballparks in both the total home runs and home runs per at-bat during seven of its first eight seasons.

In theory, a well-struck baseball should travel roughly 10 percent farther in Denver (elevation 5280 feet) than it would in a ballpark at sea level. This so-called elevation enhancement results from low air density at mile-high Coors Field. According to Robert Adair, Sterling Professor Emeritus of Physics at Yale University, a 400-foot blast in Atlanta could carry perhaps 425 feet in Denver, although Adair admits that calculating the actual difference is tricky for

reasons having to do with subtleties of fluid dynamics.

Recently a group of researchers at the University of Colorado at Denver tested the assumption that batted balls travel farther in the "thin air" at Coors Field than in ballparks near sea level. They concluded that the assumed elevation enhancement of flyball distance has been greatly overestimated. Instead, they suggest that the hitter-friendly conditions should be attributed to the prevailing weather conditions of the nearby Front Range of the Rocky Mountains and the effects of low air density on the act of pitching a baseball.

For example, wind can make or break a home run. According to Professor Adair, if there's a 10-mile-an-hour breeze behind a batter, it will add an extra 30 feet to a 400-foot home run.

Conversely, if the wind is blowing in toward home plate at 10 miles per hour, the flight of the ball will be reduced by about 30 feet. During the summer months winds most frequently blow from the south and southwest in the Denver area. Because of the orientation of Coors Field, these winds are blowing toward the outfield, thus aiding the hitters rather than the pitchers. Speaking of pitchers, the act of pitching a baseball is also greatly affected by air density. In particular, part of what determines how much a curveball will curve is air density. At higher elevations, thinner air causes a ball to break less, which makes it easier for a batter to hit a pitch.

In summary, it appears that several factors have contributed to Coors Field being known as a hitter's paradise.

FIGURE 6–B Denver's Coors Field, home of the Colorado Rockies, is nearly one mile above sea-level. It is known as a "hitter's ballpark." *(Photo by Ronald Martinez/Getty Images)*

Surface Winds

Friction as a factor affecting wind is important only within the first few kilometers of Earth's surface. We know that friction acts to slow the movement of air (Figure 6–18). By slowing air movement, friction also reduces the Coriolis force, which is proportional to wind speed. Because the pressure-gradient force is not affected by wind speed, it wins the tug of war against the Coriolis force and wind direction changes (Figure 6–19). The result is the movement of air at an angle across the isobars, toward the area of lower pressure.

The roughness of the terrain determines the angle at which the air will flow across the isobars as well as influence the speed at which it will move. Over the relatively smooth ocean surface, where friction is low, air moves at an angle of 10° to 20° to the isobars and at speeds roughly two-thirds of geostrophic flow. Over rugged terrain, where friction is high, the angle can be as great as 45° from the isobars, with wind speeds reduced by as much as 50 percent.

Near the surface, friction plays a major role in redistributing air within the atmosphere by changing the direction of airflow. This is especially noticeable when considering the motion around surface cyclones and anticyclones, two of the most common features on surface weather maps.

We have learned that above the friction layer in the Northern Hemisphere, winds blow counterclockwise around a cyclone and clockwise around an anticyclone, with winds nearly parallel to the isobars. When we add the effect of friction, we notice that the airflow crosses the isobars at varying angles, depending on the roughness of the terrain, but always from higher to lower pressure. In a cyclone, in which pressure decreases inward, friction causes a net flow *toward* its center (Figure 6–20). In an anticyclone just the opposite is true: The pressure decreases outward, and friction causes a net flow *away*

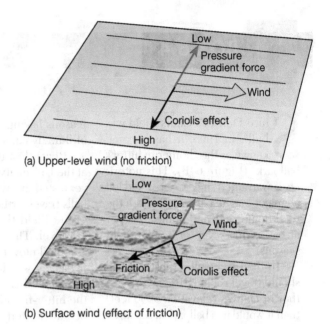

(a) Upper-level wind (no friction)

(b) Surface wind (effect of friction)

FIGURE 6-19 Comparison between upper-level winds and surface winds showing the effects of friction on airflow. Friction slows surface wind speed, which weakens the Coriolis force, causing the winds to cross the isobars.

from the center. Therefore, the resultant winds blow into and counterclockwise about a surface cyclone (Figure 6–21), and outward and clockwise about a surface anticyclone. Of course, in the Southern Hemisphere the Coriolis force deflects the winds to the left and reverses the direction of flow.

In whatever hemisphere, however, friction causes a net inflow (*convergence*) around a cyclone and a net outflow (*divergence*) around an anticyclone. This very important relationship between cyclonic flow and convergence and anticyclonic flow and divergence will be considered again.

FIGURE 6-18 A snow fence slows the wind, thereby decreasing the wind's ability to transport snow. As a result, snow accumulates on the downwind side of the fence. *(Photo by Stephen Trimble)*

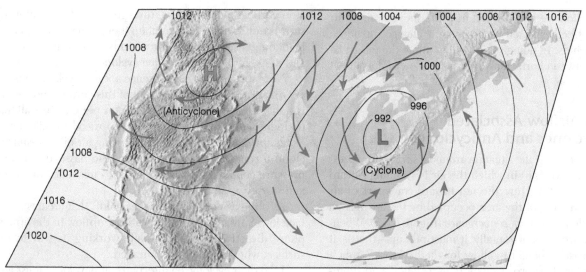

FIGURE 6-20 Cyclonic and anticyclonic winds in the Northern Hemisphere. Arrows show the winds blowing inward and counterclockwise around a low, and outward and clockwise around a high.

How Winds Generate Vertical Air Motion

 Air Pressure and Wind
▶ Highs and Lows

So far we have discussed wind without regard to how airflow in one region might affect airflow elsewhere. As one researcher put it, a butterfly flapping its wings in South America can generate a tornado in the United States. Although this is an exaggeration, it does illustrate how airflow in one region might cause a change in weather at some later time and at a different location.

Of particular importance is the question of how horizontal airflow (winds) relates to vertical flow. Although vertical transport is small compared to horizontal motion, it is very important as a weather maker. Rising air is associated with cloudy conditions and precipitation, whereas subsidence produces adiabatic heating and clearing conditions.

FIGURE 6-21 Cyclonic circulation in the Northern and Southern hemispheres. The cloud patterns in these images allow us to "see" the circulation pattern in the lower atmosphere. (a) This satellite image shows a large low-pressure center in the Gulf of Alaska on August 17, 2004. The cloud pattern clearly shows an inward and *counterclockwise* spiral. (b) This image from March 26, 2004, shows a strong cyclonic storm in the South Atlantic near the coast of Brazil. The cloud pattern reveals an inward and *clockwise* circulation. *(NASA Images)*

(a)

(b)

In this section we will discern how the movement of air (dynamic effect) can itself create pressure change and hence generate winds. In doing so, we will examine the interrelationship between horizontal and vertical flow and its effect on the weather.

Vertical Airflow Associated with Cyclones and Anticyclones

Let us first consider the situation around a surface low-pressure system (cyclone) in which the air is spiraling inward (see Figure 6–20). Here the net inward transport of air causes a shrinking of the area occupied by the air mass, a process called *horizontal convergence* (Figure 6–22). Whenever air converges horizontally, it must pile up—that is, it must increase in height to allow for the decreased area it now occupies. This process generates a "taller" and therefore heavier air column, yet a surface low can exist only as long as the column of air above remains light. We seem to have encountered a paradox—low-pressure centers cause a net accumulation of air, which increases their pressure. Consequently, a surface cyclone should quickly eradicate itself in a manner not unlike what happens to the vacuum in a coffee can when it is opened.

You can see that for a surface low to exist for very long, compensation must occur aloft. For example, surface convergence could be maintained if *divergence* (spreading out) aloft occurred at a rate equal to the inflow below. Figure 6–22 diagrammatically shows the relationship between surface convergence (inflow) and the divergence aloft (outflow) that is needed to maintain a low-pressure center.

Divergence aloft may even exceed surface convergence, thereby resulting in intensified surface inflow and acceler-

ated vertical motion. Thus, divergence aloft can intensify storm centers as well as maintain them. On the other hand, inadequate divergence aloft permits surface flow to "fill" and weaken the accompanying cyclone.

Note that surface convergence about a cyclone causes a *net upward movement.* The rate of this vertical movement is slow, generally less than 1 kilometer per day. (Recall that updrafts in thunderstorms sometimes exceed 100 kilometers per hour.) Nevertheless, because rising air often results in cloud formation and precipitation, the passage of a low-pressure center generally is related to unstable conditions and stormy weather.

As often as not, it is divergence aloft that creates a surface low. Spreading out aloft initiates upflow in the atmosphere directly below, eventually working its way to the surface, where inflow is encouraged.

Like their cyclonic counterparts, anticyclones must also be maintained from above. Outflow near the surface is accompanied by convergence aloft and general subsidence of the air column (Figure 6–22). Because descending air is compressed and warmed, cloud formation and precipitation are unlikely in an anticyclone. Thus, fair weather can usually be expected with the approach of a high-pressure system.

For reasons that should now be obvious, it has been common practice to write the word "stormy" at the low end of household barometers and "fair" at the high end (Figure 6–23). By noting the pressure trend—rising, falling, or steady—we have a good indication of forthcoming weather. Such a determination, called the **pressure tendency** or **barometric tendency,** is useful in short-range weather prediction. The generalizations relating cyclones and anticyclones to weather conditions are stated nicely in this verse ("glass" refers to the barometer):

FIGURE 6-22 Airflow associated with surface cyclones and anticyclones. A low, or cyclone, has converging surface winds and rising air causing cloudy conditions. A high, or anticyclone, has diverging surface winds and descending air, which leads to clear skies and fair weather.

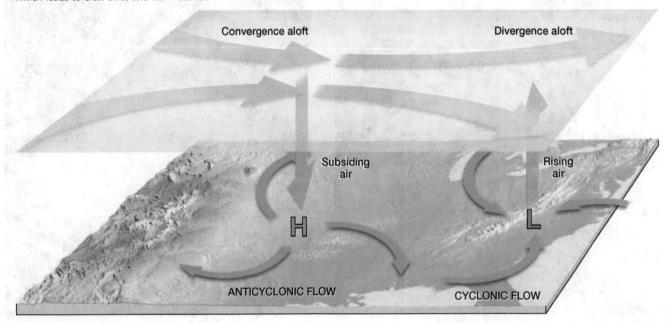

(a)

(b)

FIGURE 6-23 These two photographs illustrate the basic weather generalizations associated with pressure centers. (a) A sea of umbrellas on a rainy day in Shanghai, China. Centers of low pressure are frequently associated with cloudy conditions and precipitation. *(Photo by Stone/Getty Images, Inc.-Stone Allstock)* (b) By contrast, clear skies and "fair" weather may be expected when an area is under the influence of high pressure. Sunbathers on a beach at Cape Henlopen, Delaware. *(Photo by Mark Gibson/DRK Photo)*

When the glass falls low,

Prepare for a blow;

When it rises high,

Let all your kites fly.

In conclusion, you should now be better able to understand why local television weather broadcasters emphasize the positions and projected paths of cyclones and anticyclones. The "villain" on these weather programs is always the cyclone, which produces "bad" weather in any season. Lows move in roughly a west-to-east direction across the United States and require from a few days to more than a week for the journey. Because their paths can be erratic, accurate prediction of their migration is difficult and yet essential for short-range forecasting. Meteorologists must also determine if the flow aloft will intensify an embryo storm or act to suppress its development.

Factors That Promote Vertical Airflow

Because of the close tie between vertical motion in the atmosphere and our daily weather, we will consider some other factors that contribute to surface convergence (uplifting) and surface divergence (subsidence).

Friction can cause convergence and divergence in several ways. When air moves from the relatively smooth ocean surface onto land, for instance, the increased friction causes an abrupt drop in wind speed. This reduction of wind speed downstream results in a pile-up of air upstream. Thus, converging winds and ascending air accompany flow off the ocean. This effect contributes to the cloudy conditions over land often associated with a sea breeze in a humid region like Florida. Conversely, when air moves from land onto the ocean, general divergence and subsidence accompany the seaward flow of air because of lower friction and increasing wind speed over the water. (It should be noted that if cool air moves over a comparatively warm water body, heating from below tends to destabilize the air.)

Mountains also hinder the flow of air and cause divergence and convergence. As air passes over a mountain range, it is compressed vertically, which produces horizontal spreading (divergence) aloft. On reaching the lee side of the mountain, the air experiences vertical expansion, which causes horizontal convergence. This effect greatly influences the weather in the United States east of the Rocky Mountains, as we shall examine later. When air flows equatorward, where the Coriolis force is weakened, divergence and subsidence prevail; during poleward migration, convergence and slow uplift are favored.

As a result of the close tie between surface conditions and those aloft, great emphasis has been placed on understanding total atmospheric circulation, especially in the midlatitudes. Once we have examined the workings of global atmospheric circulation in the next chapter, we will again consider the close tie between horizontal airflow and vertical motion in light of this information.

FIGURE 6-24 Wind vane (right) and cup anemometer (left). The wind vane shows wind direction, and the anemometer measures wind speed. *(Photo by Belfort Instrument Company)*

Wind Measurement

Two basic wind measurements—direction and speed—are important to the weather observer. Winds are always labeled by the direction *from* which they blow. A north wind blows from the north toward the south; an east wind blows from the east toward the west. One instrument that is commonly used to determine wind direction is the **wind vane** (Figure 6–24). This instrument, which is a common sight on many buildings, always points into the wind. Sometimes the wind direction is shown on a dial that is connected to the wind vane. The dial indicates the direction of the wind either by points of the compass—that is, N, NE, E, SE, and so on—or by a scale of 0 to 360°. On the latter scale 0° (or 360°) is north, 90° is east, 180° is south, and 270° is west.

When the wind consistently blows more often from one direction than from any other, it is called a **prevailing wind.** You may be familiar with the prevailing westerlies that dominate the circulation in the mid-latitudes. In the United States, for example, these winds consistently move the "weather" from west to east across the continent. Embedded within this general eastward flow are cells of high and low pressure with their characteristic clockwise and counterclockwise flow. As a result, the winds associated with the westerlies, as measured at the surface, often vary considerably from day to day and from place to place. By contrast, the direction of airflow associated with the belt of trade winds is much more consistent, as can be seen in Figure 6–25.

A *wind rose* provides a method of representing prevailing winds by indicating the percentage of time the wind blows from various directions (Figure 6–25). The length of the lines on the wind rose indicates the percentage of time the wind blew from that direction. Knowledge of the wind patterns for a particular area can be useful. For example, during the construction of an airport, the runways are aligned with the prevailing wind to

Students Sometimes Ask...

What causes "mountain sickness"?

When visitors drive up to a mountain pass above 3000 meters (10,000 feet) and take a walk, they typically notice a shortness of breath and possibly fatigue. These symptoms are caused by breathing air that has roughly 30 percent less oxygen than at sea level. At these altitudes our bodies try to compensate for air that is deficient in oxygen by breathing more deeply and increasing the heart rate, thereby pumping more blood to the body's tissues. The additional blood is thought to cause brain tissues to swell, resulting in headaches, insomnia, and nausea—the main symptoms of *acute mountain sickness*. Mountain sickness is generally not life threatening and usually can be alleviated with a night's rest at a lower altitude. Occasionally people become a victim of *high-altitude pulmonary edema*. This life-threatening condition involves a buildup of fluid in the lungs and requires prompt medical attention.

FIGURE 6-25 Wind roses showing the percentage of time airflow is from various directions. (a) Wind frequency for the winter in the eastern United States. (b) Wind frequency for the winter in northern Australia. Note the reliability of the southeast trades in Australia as compared to the westerlies in the eastern United States. *(Data from G. T. Trewartha)*

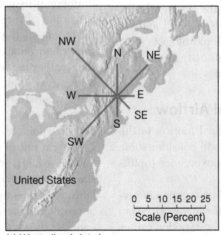

(a) Westerlies (winter)

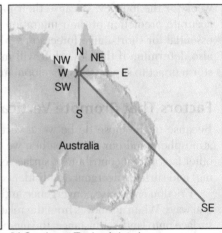

(b) Southeast Trades (winter)

FIGURE 6-26 An aerovane. *(Photo by Warren Faidley/ Weatherstock)*

Wind speed is often measured with a **cup anemometer** (Figure 6–24). The wind speed is read from a dial much like the speedometer of an automobile. Sometimes an **aerovane** is used instead of a wind vane and cup anemometer. As can be seen in Figure 6–26, this instrument resembles a wind vane with a propeller at one end. The fin keeps the propeller facing into the wind, allowing the blades to rotate at a rate that is proportional to the wind speed. This instrument is commonly attached to a recorder to keep a continuous record of wind speed and direction. Places where winds are steady and speeds are relatively high are potential sites for tapping wind energy (see Box 6–5).

At small airstrips *wind socks* are frequently used. They consist of a cone-shaped bag that is open at both ends and free to change position with shifts in wind direction. The degree to which the sock is inflated is an indication of the strength of the wind.

Recall that 70 percent of Earth's surface is covered by water where conventional methods of measuring wind speed are not possible. Although weather buoys and ships at sea do provide some coverage, weather forecasts have improved dramatically since the 1990s due to the availability of satellite-derived wind data. One way wind speed and direction can be established is by using satellite images to track cloud movements. This is currently being accomplished by comparing a sequence of GOES images separated by intervals of 5 to 30 minutes (Figure 6–27). This innovation has been especially useful in predicting the timing and location of where a hurricane will make landfall.

assist in takeoffs and landings. Furthermore, prevailing winds greatly affect the weather and climate of a region. North–south trending mountain ranges, such as the Cascade Range of the Pacific Northwest, for example, causes the ascent of the prevailing westerlies. Thus, the windward (west) slopes of these ranges are rainy, whereas the leeward (east) sides are dry.

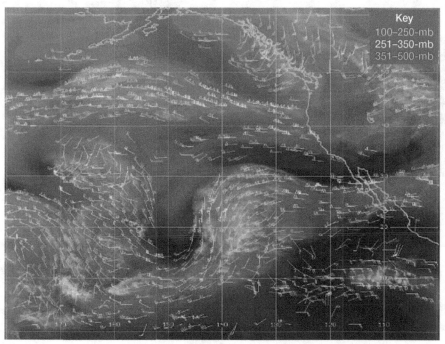

Key
100–250-mb
251–350-mb
351–500-mb

FIGURE 6–27 Upper-level winds obtained from the GOES meteorological satellite.

BOX 6-5   Wind Energy: An Alternative with Potential

ir has mass, and when it moves (that is, when the wind blows), it contains the energy of that motion—kinetic energy. A portion of that energy can be converted into other forms—mechanical force or electricity—that we can use to perform work (Figure 6–C).

Mechanical energy from wind is commonly used for pumping water in rural or remote places. The "farm windmill," still a familiar site in many rural areas, is an example. Mechanical energy converted from wind can also be used for other purposes, such as sawing logs, grinding grain, and propelling sailboats. By contrast, wind-powered electric turbines generate electricity for homes, businesses, and for sale to utilities.

Approximately 0.25 percent (one-quarter of 1 percent) of the solar energy that reaches the lower atmosphere is transformed into wind. Although it is just a minuscule percentage, the absolute amount of energy is enormous. According to one estimate, North Dakota alone is theoretically capable of producing enough wind-generated power to meet more than one-third of U.S. electricity demand. Wind speed is a crucial element in determining whether a place is a suit-

FIGURE 6-C These wind turbines are operating near Palm Springs, California. California is the state in which the most wind-power development has occurred. As of January 2004, California had a total of 2043 megawatts of installed capacity (nearly one-third of total U.S. capacity). That's enough electricity to supply between 500,000 and 600,000 average American households. *(Photo by John Mead/Science Photo Library/Photo Researchers, Inc.)*

able site for installing a wind-energy facility. Generally a minimum, annual average wind speed of 21 kilometers (13 miles) per hour is necessary for a utility-scale wind-power plant.

The power available in the wind is proportional to the cube of its speed. Thus, a turbine operating at a site with an average wind speed of 12 mph could in theory generate about 33 percent more electricity than one at an 11-mph site, because the cube of 12 (1768) is 33 percent larger than the cube of 11 (1331). (In the real world, the turbine will not produce quite that much more electricity, but it will still generate much more than the 9 percent difference in wind speed.) The important thing to understand is that what seems like a small difference in wind speed can mean a large difference in available energy and in electricity produced, and

therefore a large difference in the cost of the electricity generated. Also, there is little energy to be harvested at very low wind speeds (6-mph winds contain less than one-eighth the energy of 12-mph winds).[*]

As technology has improved, efficiency has increased and the costs of wind-generated electricity have become more competitive. Between 1983 and 2004 technological advances cut the cost of wind power by more than 85 percent. As a result, the growth of installed capacity has grown dramatically. Worldwide the total amount of installed wind power grew more than 600 percent from 7636 megawatts in 1997 to 47,000 megawatts in 2004 (Table 6–B). 47,000 megawatts is enough to supply 10.5 million average American households, or as much as could be generated by 14 large nuclear power plants.

By the end of 2005, U.S. capacity reached nearly 9200 megawatts (Figure 6–D). By 2008 or 2009 the United States is expected to add at least 3000 megawatts of new utility wind-power projects.

The U.S. Department of Energy has announced a goal of obtaining 5 percent of U.S. electricity from wind by the year 2020—a goal that seems consistent with the current growth rate of wind energy nationwide. Thus, wind-generated electricity seems to be shifting from being an "alternative" to being a "mainstream" energy source.

[*]American Wind Energy Association. "Wind Energy Basics" http://www.awea.org/faq/tutorial/wwt_basics.html

TABLE 6-B	World leaders in wind capacity (2004)
Country	**Capacity (megawatts[*])**
Germany	16,629
Spain	8,263
United States	6,740
Denmark	3,117
India	3,000
Italy	1125
Netherlands	1078
United Kingdom	888
Japan	874
China	764

[*]1 megawatt is enough electricity to supply 250–300 average American households. The "top 10" nations listed in this table account for over 95 percent of the total wind energy produced.

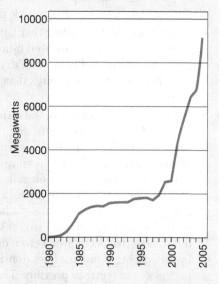

FIGURE 6-D U.S.-installed wind-power capacity (in megawatts at the end of 2005). Growth in recent years has been dramatic. (*Data from U.S. Department of Energy and American Wind Energy Association*)

Chapter Summary

- *Air pressure* is the pressure exerted by the weight of air above. Average air pressure at sea level is about 1 kilogram per square centimeter, or 14.7 pounds per square inch. Another way to define air pressure is that it is the force exerted against a surface by the continuous collision of gas molecules.

- The *newton* is the unit of force used by meteorologists to measure atmospheric pressure. A *millibar* (mb) equals 100 newtons per square meter. Standard sea-level pressure is 1013.25 millibars. Two instruments used to measure atmospheric pressure are the *mercury barometer*, where the height of a mercury column provides a measure of air pressure (standard atmospheric pressure at sea level equals 29.92 inches or 760 millimeters), and the *aneroid barometer*, which uses a partially evacuated metal chamber that changes shape as air pressure changes.

- The pressure at any given altitude is equal to the weight of the air above that point. Furthermore, the rate at which pressure decreases with an increase in altitude is much greater near Earth's surface. The "normal" decrease in pressure experienced with increased altitude is provided by the *standard atmosphere*, which depicts the idealized vertical distribution of atmospheric pressure.

- In calm air, the two factors that largely determine the amount of air pressure exerted by an air mass are temperature and humidity. A cold, dry air mass will produce higher surface pressures than a warm, humid air mass.

- *Wind* is the result of horizontal differences in air pressure. If Earth did not rotate and there were no friction, air would flow directly from areas of higher pressure to areas of lower pressure. However, because both factors exist, wind is controlled by a combination of (1) the *pressure-gradient force*, (2) the *Coriolis force*, and (3) *friction*. The pressure-gradient force is the primary driving force of wind that results from pressure differences that occur over a given distance, as depicted by the spacing of *isobars*, lines drawn on maps that connect places of equal air pressure. The spacing of isobars indicates the amount of pressure change occurring over a given distance, expressed as the *pressure gradient*. Closely spaced isobars indicate a steep pressure gradient and strong winds; widely spaced isobars indicate a weak pressure gradient and light winds. There is also an upward-directed vertical pressure gradient, which is usually balanced by gravity in what is referred to as *hydrostatic equilibrium*. On those occasions when the gravitational force slightly exceeds the vertical pressure gradient force, slow downward airflow results. The Coriolis force produces a deviation in the path of wind due to Earth's rotation (to the right in the Northern Hemisphere and to the left in the Southern Hemisphere). The amount of deflection is greatest at the poles and decreases to zero at the equator. The amount

of Coriolis deflection also increases with wind speed. Friction, which significantly influences airflow near Earth's surface, is negligible above a height of a few kilometers.

- Above a height of a few kilometers, the effect of friction on airflow is small enough to disregard. Here, as the wind speed increases, the deflection caused by the Coriolis force also increases. Winds in which the Coriolis force is equal to and opposite the pressure gradient force are called *geostrophic winds*. Geostrophic winds flow in a straight path, parallel to the isobars, with velocities proportional to the pressure-gradient force.

- Winds that blow at a constant speed parallel to curved isobars are termed *gradient winds*. In centers of low pressure, called *cyclones*, the circulation of air, referred to as *cyclonic flow*, is counterclockwise in the Northern Hemisphere and clockwise in the Southern Hemisphere. Centers of high pressure, called *anticyclones*, exhibit *anticyclonic flow*, which is clockwise in the Northern Hemisphere and counterclockwise in the Southern Hemisphere. Whenever isobars curve to form elongated regions of low and high pressure, these areas are called *troughs* and *ridges*, respectively.

- Near the surface, friction plays a major role in redistributing air within the atmosphere by changing the direction of airflow. The result is a movement of air at an angle across the isobars, toward the area of lower pressure. Therefore, the resultant winds blow into and counterclockwise about a Northern Hemisphere surface cyclone. In a Northern Hemisphere surface anticyclone, winds blow outward and clockwise. Regardless of the hemisphere, friction causes a net inflow (*convergence*) around a cyclone and a net outflow (*divergence*) around an anticyclone.

- A surface low-pressure system with its associated horizontal convergence is maintained or intensified by divergence (spreading out) aloft. Inadequate divergence aloft will weaken the accompanying cyclone. Because surface convergence about a cyclone accompanied by divergence aloft causes a net upward movement of air, the passage of a low pressure center is often associated with stormy weather. By contrast, fair weather can usually be expected with the approach of a high-pressure system. As a result of the general weather patterns usually associated with cyclones and anticyclones, the *pressure tendency* or *barometric tendency* (the nature of the change of the barometer over the past several hours) is useful in short-range weather prediction.

- Two basic wind measurements—direction and speed—are important to the weather observer. Wind direction is commonly determined using a *wind vane*. When the wind consistently blows more often from one direction than from any other, it is called a *prevailing wind*. Wind speed is often measured with a *cup anemometer*.

Vocabulary Review

aerovane (p. 191)
air pressure (p. 168)
aneroid barometer (p. 170)
anticyclone (p. 184)
anticyclonic flow (p. 184)
barograph (p. 170)
barometric tendency (p. 188)
Buys Ballot's law (p. 182)
convergence (p. 174)
Coriolis force (p. 178)
cup anemometer (p. 191)

cyclone (p. 184)
cyclonic flow (p. 184)
divergence (p. 174)
geostrophic wind (p. 182)
gradient wind (p. 183)
high (p. 174)
hydrostatic equilibrium (p. 177)
isobar (p. 175)
low (p. 174)
mercury barometer (p. 169)

millibar (p. 169)
newton (p. 169)
pressure gradient (p. 176)
pressure tendency (p. 188)
prevailing wind (p. 190)
ridge (p. 184)
standard atmosphere (p. 173)
trough (p. 184)
wind (p. 175)
wind vane (p. 190)

Review Questions

1. What is standard sea-level pressure in millibars? In inches of mercury? In pounds per square inch?

2. Describe the operating principles of the mercury barometer and the aneroid barometer. List two advantages of the aneroid barometer.

3. Explain why air pressure decreases with an increase in altitude.

4. Explain why a cold, dry air mass produces a higher surface pressure than a warm, humid air mass.

5. Compare convergence with divergence.

6. What force is responsible for *generating* wind?

7. Write a generalization relating the spacing of isobars to the speed of wind.

8. Temperature variations create pressure differences, which in turn produce winds. On a small scale, the sea breeze illustrates this principle nicely. Describe how a sea breeze forms.

9. Although vertical pressure differences may be great, such variations do not generate strong vertical currents. Explain.

10. Briefly describe how the Coriolis force modifies the movement of air.

11. Which two factors influence the magnitude of the Coriolis force?

12. Explain the formation of a geostrophic wind.

13. Unlike winds aloft, which blow nearly parallel to the isobars, surface winds generally cross the isobars. Explain what causes this difference.

14. Prepare a diagram (isobars and wind arrows) showing the winds associated with surface cyclones and anticyclones in both the Northern and Southern Hemispheres.

15. For surface low pressure to exist for an extended period, what condition must exist aloft?

16. What are the general weather conditions to be expected when the pressure tendency is rising? When the pressure tendency is falling?

17. Converging winds and ascending air are often associated with the flow of air from the oceans onto land. Conversely, divergence and subsidence often accompany the flow of air from land to sea. What causes this convergence over land and divergence over the ocean?

18. A southwest wind blows from the _____ (direction) toward the _____ (direction).

19. The wind direction is 315°. From what compass direction is the wind blowing?

Problems

1. Calculate the magnitude of the pressure-gradient force (per unit mass) between two cities 500 kilometers apart if pressure at the respective cities is 1010 mb and 1017 mb?

2. Calculate the magnitude of Coriolis force acting on air moving at:

a. 36 kilometers per hour (10 meters per second) at 35° latitude.

b. 36 kilometers per hour (10 meters per second) at 65° latitude.

c. 54 kilometers per hour (15 meters per second) at 35° latitude.

Atmospheric Science Online

The Atmosphere 10e web site uses the resources and flexibility of the Internet to aid in your study of the topics in this chapter. Written and developed by meteorology instructors, this site will help improve your understanding of meteorology. Visit **http://www .prenhall.com/lutgens** and click on the cover of *The Atmosphere 10e* to find:

- **Online review quizzes**
- **Critical thinking exercises**
- **Links to chapter-specific web resources**
- **Internet-wide key term searches**

http://www.prenhall.com/lutgens

CIRCULATION
of the ATMOSPHERE

Sailboats in a Norwegian fiord. *(Photo by The Image Bank/Getty Images, Inc.)*

The main goal of this chapter is to gain an understanding of Earth's highly integrated wind system. Global atmospheric circulation can be thought of as a series of deep rivers of air that encircle the planet. Embedded in the main currents are vortices of various sizes including hurricanes, tornadoes, and midlatitude cyclones (Figure 7–1). Like eddies in a stream, these rotating wind systems develop and die out with somewhat predictable regularity. In general, the smallest eddies, such as dust devils, last only a few minutes, whereas larger and more complex systems, such as hurricanes, may survive for several days.

Recall from Chapter 6 that winds are generated by pressure differences that arise because of unequal heating of Earth's surface. Global winds are generated because the tropics receive more solar radiation than Earth's polar regions. Thus, Earth's winds blow in an unending attempt to balance inequalities in surface temperatures. Because the zone of maximum solar heating migrates with the seasons— moving northward during the Northern Hemisphere summer and southward as winter approaches—the wind patterns that make up the general circulation also migrate latitudinally.

Although we will focus on the global circulation, local wind systems will also be considered. The chapter concludes with a discussion of global precipitation patterns. As you will see, the global distribution of precipitation is closely linked to the patterns of atmospheric pressure and thus the global wind system.

Scales of Atmospheric Motion

Those who live in the United States are familiar with the term "westerlies" to describe the winds that predominately blow from west to east. But all of us have experienced winds from the south and north and even directly from the east. You may even recall being in a storm when shifts in wind direction and speed came in such rapid succession that it was impossible to determine the wind's direction. With such variations, how can we describe our winds as westerly? The answer lies in our attempt to simplify descriptions of the atmospheric circulation by sorting out events according to *size*. On the scale of a weather map, for instance, where observing stations are spaced about 150 kilometers apart, small whirlwinds that carry dust skyward are far too small to show up. Instead, weather maps reveal larger-scale wind patterns, such as those associated with traveling cyclones and anticyclones.

Not only do we separate winds according to the size of the system, but equal consideration is also given to the time frame in which they occur. In general, large weather patterns have longer life spans than do their smaller counterparts. For

FIGURE 7-1 In this satellite image, low clouds reveal a swirling wind pattern on the lee of Guadalupe Island. The airflow develops substantial rotation when it is too stable to flow over the top of a barrier such as this isolated island. *(Photo courtesy of NASA/Visuals Unlimited, Inc.)*

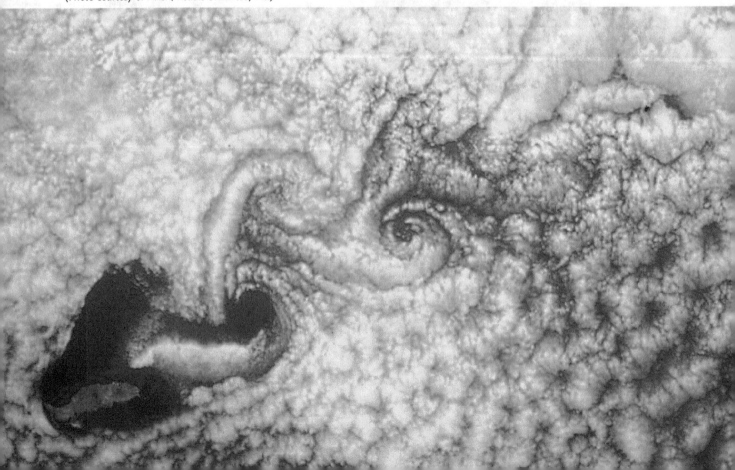

TABLE 7-1	Time and space scales for atmospheric motions		
Scale	**Time scale**	**Distance scale**	**Examples**
Macroscale			
Planetary	Weeks or longer	1000–40,000 km	Westerlies and trade winds
Synoptic	Days to weeks	100–5000 km	Mid-latitude cyclones, anticyclones, and hurricanes
Mesoscale	Minutes to hours	1–100 km	Thunderstorms, tornadoes, and land–sea breeze
Microscale	Seconds to minutes	<1 km	Turbulence, dust devils, and gusts

example, dust devils usually last a few minutes and rarely occur for more than an hour. By contrast, midlatitude cyclones typically take a few days to cross the United States and occasionally dominate the weather for a week or longer. The time and size scales we will use for atmospheric motions are provided in Table 7–1.

Large- and Small-Scale Circulation

The wind systems shown in Figure 7–2 illustrate the three major categories of atmospheric circulation: macroscale, mesoscale and microscale. *Macroscale* circulation includes large planetary-scale flow, such as the trade winds that blow consistently for weeks or longer as well as smaller features like hurricanes (Figure 7–2a). *Mesoscale* circulation is associated with tornadoes, thunderstorms, and numerous *local winds* that generally last from minutes to hours. Finally, *microscale* events have life spans of from a few seconds to minutes and include dust devils, gusts, and general atmospheric turbulence.

Macroscale Winds. The largest wind patterns, called **macroscale winds,** are exemplified by the westerlies and trade winds that carried sailing vessels back and forth across the Atlantic during the opening of the New World. These *planetary-scale* flow patterns extend around the entire globe and can remain essentially unchanged for weeks at a time.

A somewhat smaller macroscale circulation is called *synoptic scale*, or *weather-map scale*. Two well-known synoptic scale systems are the individual traveling cyclones and anticyclones that appear on weather maps as areas of low and high pressure, respectively. These weather producers are found in the middle latitudes where they move from west to east as part of the larger westerly flow. Furthermore, these rotating systems usually persist for days or occasionally weeks and have a horizontal dimension of hundreds to thousands of kilometers. Recall that the direction of surface flow around a cyclone is toward the center with a general upward component. Anticyclones, in contrast, are areas of subsidence associated with outward flow near the surface. The average rate of vertical motion within these systems is slow, typically less than 1 kilometer per day.

Somewhat smaller macroscale systems are the tropical cyclones and hurricanes that develop in late summer and early fall over the warm tropical oceans. Airflow in these systems is inward and upward as in the larger midlatitude

cyclones. However, the rate of horizontal flow associated with hurricanes is usually more rapid than that of their more poleward cousins.

Mesoscale Winds. **Mesoscale winds** generally last for several minutes and may exist for hours. These middle-size phenomena are usually less than 100 kilometers (62 miles) across. Further, some mesoscale winds—for example, thunderstorms and tornadoes—also have a strong vertical component (Figure 7–2b). It is important to remember that thunderstorms and tornadoes are always imbedded within and thus move as part of the larger macroscale circulation. Further, much of the vertical air movement within a midlatitude cyclone, or hurricane, is provided by thunderstorms, where updrafts in excess of 100 kilometers (62 miles) per hour have been measured. Land and sea breezes, as well as mountain and valley winds, also fall into this category and will be discussed in the next section along with other mesoscale winds.

Microscale Winds. The smallest scale of air motion is referred to as **microscale circulation.** These small, often chaotic winds normally last for seconds or at most minutes. Examples include simple gusts, which hurl debris into the air (Figure 7–2c) and small, well-developed vortices such as dust devils (see Box 7–1).

Structure of Wind Patterns

Although it is common practice to divide atmospheric motions according to scale, remember that global winds are a composite of all scales of motion—much like a meandering river that contains large eddies composed of smaller eddies containing still smaller eddies. For example, let us examine the flow associated with hurricanes that form over the North Atlantic. When we view one of these tropical cyclones on a satellite image, the storm appears as a large whirling cloud migrating slowly across the ocean (see Figure 7–2a). From this perspective, which is at the weather-map (synoptic) scale, the general counterclockwise rotation of the storm can be easily seen.

When we average the winds of hurricanes, we find that they often have a net motion from east to west, thereby indicating that these larger eddies are embedded in a still larger flow (planetary scale) that is moving westward across the tropical portion of the North Atlantic.

FIGURE 7-2 Three scales of atmospheric motion. (a) Satellite image of Hurricane Nora, an example of macroscale circulation. (b) Tornadoes exemplfy mesoscale wind systems. (c) Gusts illustrate microscale winds. *(Photos by (a) NASA/Science Photo Library/Photo Researchers, Inc., (b) A. and J. Verkaik/CORBIS/The Stock Market, (c) E.J. Tarbuck)*

If we examine a hurricane more closely by flying an airplane through it, some of the small-scale aspects of the storm become noticeable. As the plane approaches the outer edge of the system, it becomes evident that the large rotating cloud that we saw in the satellite images is made of many individual cumulonimbus towers (thunderstorms). Each of these mesoscale phenomena lasts for only a few hours and must be continually replaced by new ones if the hurricane is to persist. As we fly into these storms, we quickly realize that the individual clouds are made up of even smaller-scale turbulences. The small thermals of rising air that occur in these clouds make for a rather rough trip.

Thus, a typical hurricane exhibits several scales of motion, including many mesoscale thunderstorms, which, in turn, consist of numerous microscale turbulences. Furthermore, the counterclockwise circulation of the hurricane (weather-map scale) is imbedded in the global winds (planetary scale) that flow from east to west in the tropical North Atlantic.

Local Winds

Before examining the large macroscale circulation for Earth, let us turn to some mesoscale winds (time frame of minutes to hours and size of 1 to 100 kilometers—Table 7–1). Remem-

200

BOX 7-1 Dust Devils

A common phenomenon in arid regions of the world is the whirling vortex called the *dust devil* (Figure 7–A). Although they resemble tornadoes, dust devils are generally much smaller and less intense than their destructive cousins. Most dust devils are only a few meters in diameter and reach heights no greater than about 100 meters (300 feet). Further, these whirlwinds are usually short-lived microscale phenomena. Most form and die out within minutes. In rare instances dust devils have lasted for hours.

Unlike tornadoes, which are associated with convective clouds, dust devils form on days when clear skies dominate. Further, these whirlwinds form from the ground upward, exactly opposite of tornadoes. Because surface heating is critical to their formation, dust devils occur most frequently in the afternoon when surface temperatures are highest.

Recall that when the air near the surface is considerably warmer than the air a few dozen meters overhead, the layer of air near Earth's surface becomes unstable. In this situation warm surface air begins to rise, causing air near the ground to be drawn into the developing whirlwind. The rotating winds that are associated with dust devils are produced by the same phenomenon that causes ice skaters to spin faster as they pull their arms closer to their body. (For an expanded discussion of this process, see Box 11–1, Chapter 11.) As the inwardly spiraling air rises, it carries sand, dust, and other loose debris dozens of meters into the air. It is this material that makes a dust devil visible. Occasionally, dust devils form above vegetated surfaces. Under these conditions, the vortices may go undetected unless they interact with objects at the surface.

Most dust devils are small and short-lived; consequently, they are not generally destructive. Occasionally, however, these whirlwinds grow to be 100 meters or more in diameter and over a kilometer high. With wind speeds that may reach 100 kilometers (60 miles) per hour, large dust devils can do considerable damage. Fortunately, such occurrences are few and far between.

FIGURE 7-A Dust devil. Although these whirling vortices resemble tornadoes, they have different origins and are much smaller and less intense. *(Courtesy of St. Meyers/ Okapia/Photo Researchers, Inc.)*

ber that all winds have the same cause: pressure differences that arise because of temperature differences caused by unequal heating of Earth's surface. Local winds are medium-scale winds produced by a locally generated pressure gradient.

Although many winds are given local names, some are actually part of the global wind system. The "norther" of Texas, for instance, is a cold southward flow produced by the circulation around anticyclones that invade the United States from Canada in the winter. Because these winds are not locally generated, they cannot be considered true local winds. Others, like those about to be described, are truly mesoscale and are caused either by topographic effects or variations in local surface composition.

Recall that winds are named for the direction *from which they blow*. This holds true for local winds. Thus, a sea breeze originates over water and blows toward the land, whereas a valley breeze blows upslope away from its source.

Land and Sea Breezes

The daily temperature contrast between the land and the sea, and the pressure pattern that generates a sea breeze, was discussed in the preceding chapter (see Figure 6–11). Recall that land is heated more intensely during daylight hours than is an adjacent body of water. As a result, the air above the land surface heats and expands, creating an area of low pressure. A **sea breeze** then develops, as cooler air over the water moves onto the land (Figure 7–3a). At night, the reverse may take place; the land cools more rapidly than the sea and a **land breeze** develops (Figure 7–3b).

The sea breeze has a significant moderating influence on coastal temperatures. Shortly after the breeze begins, air temperatures over the land may drop by as much as 5° to 10°C. However, the cooling effect of these breezes generally reaches a maximum of only about 100 kilometers (60 miles) inland in the tropics and often less than half that distance in the middle latitudes. These cool sea breezes generally begin shortly before noon and reach their greatest intensity, about 10 to 20 kilometers per hour, in the midafternoon.

Smaller-scale sea breezes can also develop along the shores of large lakes. People who live in a city near the Great Lakes, such as Chicago, recognize the "lake effect," especially in the summer. Residents are reminded daily by reports of the cooler temperatures near the lake compared to warmer outlying areas. In many places sea breezes also affect the amount of cloud cover and rainfall. The peninsula of Florida, for example, experiences a summer precipitation maximum caused partly by the convergence of sea breezes from both the Atlantic and Gulf coasts.

The intensity and extent of land and sea breezes depend on the location and the time of year. Tropical areas where intense solar heating is continuous throughout the year experience more frequent and stronger sea breezes than do mid-latitude locations. The most intense sea breezes develop along tropical coastlines adjacent to cool ocean currents. In the middle latitudes, sea breezes are most common during the warmest months, but the counterpart, the land breeze, is often missing, for the land does not always cool below the ocean temperature. In the higher middle latitudes the frequent migration of high- and low-pressure systems dominates the circulation, so land and sea breezes are less noticeable.

Mountain and Valley Breezes

A daily wind similar to land and sea breezes occurs in many mountainous regions. During the day, air along mountain slopes is heated more intensely than air at the same elevation over the valley floor (Figure 7–4a). This warmer air glides up along the mountain slope and generates a **valley breeze.** The occurrence of these daytime upslope breezes can often be identified by the isolated cumulus clouds that develop over adjacent mountain peaks (Figure 7–5). This also causes the late afternoon thundershowers so common on warm summer days in the mountains. After sunset the pattern is reversed. Rapid radiation heat loss along the mountain slopes cools the air, which drains into the valley below and causes a **mountain breeze** (Figure 7–4b). Similar cool air drainage can occur in regions that have little slope. The result is that the coldest pockets of air are usually found in the lowest spots, a phenomenon you likely have experienced while walking in hilly terrain. Consequently, low areas are the first to experience radiation fog and are the most likely spots for frost damage to crops.

Like many other winds, mountain and valley breezes have seasonal preferences. Although valley breezes are most common during the warm season when solar heating is most intense, mountain breezes tend to be more frequent during the cold season.

FIGURE 7-3 Illustration of a sea breeze and a land breeze. (a) During the daylight hours the air above the land heats and expands, creating an area of lower pressure. Cooler and denser air over the water moves onto the land, generating a sea breeze. (b) At night the land cools more rapidly than the sea, generating an offshore flow called a *land breeze.*

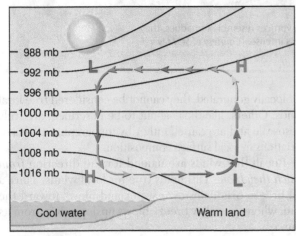

(a) Sea breeze

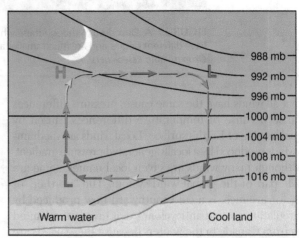

(b) Land breeze

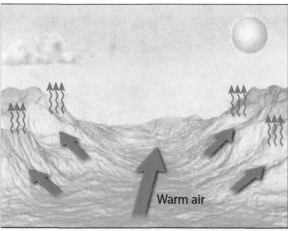

(a) Valley breeze

(b) Mountain breeze

FIGURE 7-4 Valley and mountain breezes. (a) Heating during the daylight hours warms the air along the mountain slopes. This warm air rises, generating a valley breeze. (b) After sunset, cooling of the air near the mountain can result in cool air drainage into the valley, producing the mountain breeze.

Chinook (Foehn) Winds

Warm, dry winds sometimes move down the east slopes of the Rockies, where they are called **chinooks,** and the Alps, where they are called **foehns.** Such winds are often created when a strong pressure gradient develops in a mountainous region. As the air descends the leeward slopes of the mountains, it is heated adiabatically (by compression). Because condensation may have occurred as the air ascended the windward side, releasing latent heat, the air descending the leeward side will be warmer and drier than at a similar elevation on the windward side. Although the temperature of these winds is generally less than 10°C (50°F), which is not particularly warm, they usually occur in the winter and spring when the affected area may be experiencing subfreezing temperatures. Thus, by comparison, these dry, warm winds often bring drastic change. Within minutes of the arrival of a chinook, the temperature may climb 20°C (36°F). When the ground has a snow cover, these winds melt it in short order. The Native American word *chinook* means "snoweater."

The chinook is viewed by some as beneficial to ranchers east of the Rockies, for it keeps their grasslands clear of snow during much of the winter, but this benefit is offset by the loss of moisture that the snow would bequeath to the land if it remained until the spring melt.

Another chinooklike wind that occurs in the United States is the **Santa Ana.** Found in southern California, these hot, desiccating winds greatly increase the threat of fire in this already dry area (see Box 7–2).

Katabatic (Fall) Winds

In the winter, areas adjacent to highlands may experience a local wind called a **katabatic wind** or **fall wind.** These winds originate when cold air, situated over a highland area such as the ice sheets of Greenland or Antarctica, is set in motion. Under the influence of gravity, the cold air cascades over the rim of a highland like a waterfall. Although the air is heated adiabatically, as are chinooks, the initial temperatures are so low that the wind arrives in the lowlands still colder and more dense than the air it displaces. In fact, this air *must* be colder than the air it invades, for it is the air's greater density that causes it to descend. As this frigid air descends, it occasionally is channeled into narrow valleys, where it acquires velocities capable of great destruction.

FIGURE 7-5 The occurrence of a daytime upslope (valley) breeze is identified by cloud development on mountain peaks, sometimes progressing to a midafternoon thunderstorm. *(Photo by James E. Patterson/James Patterson Collection)*

BOX 7-2   Atmospheric Hazard: Santa Ana Winds and Wildfires

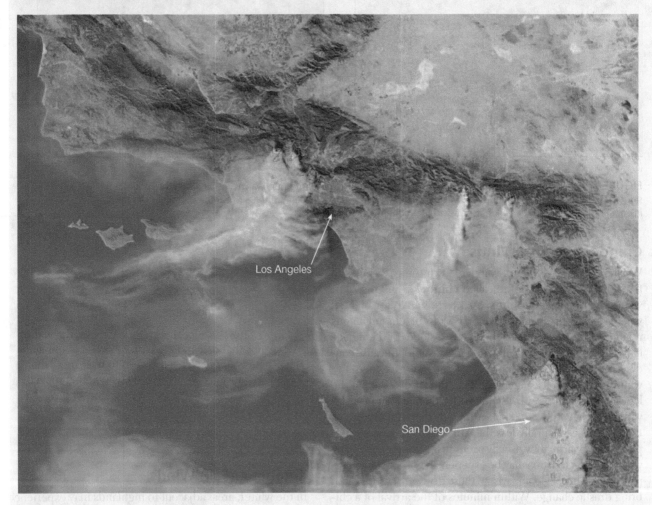

Los Angeles

San Diego

FIGURE 7-B Ten large wildfires rage across southern California in this image taken on October 27, 2003, by NASA's *Aqua* satellite. *(Photo courtesy of NASA)*

A few of the better-known katabatic winds have local names. Most famous is the **mistral,** which blows from the French Alps toward the Mediterranean Sea. Another is the **bora,** which originates in the mountains of Yugoslavia and blows to the Adriatic Sea.

Country Breezes

One mesoscale wind, called a **country breeze,** is associated with large urban areas. As the name implies, this circulation pattern is characterized by a light wind blowing into the city from the surrounding countryside. The country breeze is best developed on relatively clear, calm nights. Under these conditions cities, because they contain massive buildings composed of rocklike materials, tend to retain the heat accumulated during the day more than the less built up outlying areas (see Box 3–4 on the urban heat island). The result is that the warm, less dense air over the city rises, which in turn initiates the country-to-city flow.

One investigation in Toronto showed that heat accumulated within this city created a rural/city pressure difference that was sufficient to cause an inward and counterclockwise circulation centered on the downtown area. One of the unfortunate consequences of the country breeze is that pollutants emitted near the urban perimeter tend to drift in and concentrate near the city's center.

Global Circulation

Our knowledge of global winds comes from two sources: the patterns of pressure and winds observed worldwide, and theoretical studies of fluid motion. We first consider the classical model of global circulation that was developed largely from average worldwide pressure distribution. We then add to this idealized circulation more recently discovered aspects of the atmosphere's complex motions.

People living in southern California are well aware of chinook-type winds called the *Santa Anas*. These hot, dry, dust-bearing winds invade California most often in autumn when they bring temperatures that often approach 32°C (90°F) and may occasionally exceed 38°C (100°F). When a strong anticyclone is centered over the Great Basin, the clockwise flow directs desert air from Arizona and Nevada westward toward the Pacific. The wind gains speed as it is funneled through the canyons of the Coast Ranges, in particular the Santa Ana Canyon, from which the winds derive their name. Compressional heating of this already warm, dry air as it descends mountain slopes further accentuates the already parched conditions. Vegetation, seared by the summer heat, is dried even further by these desiccating winds.

In late October 2003, Santa Anas began blowing toward the coast of southern California, with speeds that sometimes exceeded 100 kilometers (60 miles) per hour. Much of this area is covered by brush known as chaparral and related shrubs. It didn't take much—a careless camper or motorist, a lightning strike, or an arsonist—to ignite a fire. Soon a number of outbreaks occurred in portions of Los Angeles, San Bernardino, Riverside, and San Diego counties (Figure 7–B). Several developed quickly into wildfires that moved almost as fast as the ferocious Santa Ana winds sweeping through the canyons.

FIGURE 7-C Flames from a wildfire fanned by Santa Ana winds move toward a home south of Valley Center, California, on October 27, 2003. *(Photo by Denis Poroy/Associated Press)*

Within a few days more than 13,000 firefighters were on firelines that extended from north of Los Angeles to the Mexican border. Nearly two months later, when all the fires were officially extinguished, more than 742,000 acres had been scorched, over 3000 homes destroyed, and 26 people killed (Figure 7–C). The Federal Emergency Management Agency put the dollar losses at over $2.5 billion. The 2003 southern California wildfires became the worst fire disaster in the state's history.

Strong Santa Ana winds, coupled with dry summers, have produced wildfires in southern California for a millennia. These fires are nature's way of burning out chaparral thicket and sage scrub to prepare the land for new growth. The problem began when people started to crowd into the fire-prone area between Santa Barbara and San Diego. Residents have compounded the danger by landscaping their yards with highly flammable eucalyptus and pine trees. Furthermore, successful fire prevention has allowed the buildup of even more flammable material. Clearly, wildfires will remain a major threat in these areas into the foreseeable future.

Students Sometimes Ask...
What is a haboob?

A haboob is a type of local wind that occurs in arid regions. The name was originally applied to strong dust storms in the African Sudan, where one city experiences an average of 24 per year. (The name comes form the Arabic word *habb*, meaning "wind.") Haboobs generally occur when downdrafts from large thunderstorms swiftly move across the desert. Tons of silt, sand, and dust are lifted, forming a whirling wall of debris hundreds of meters high. These dense, dark "clouds" can completely engulf desert towns and deposit enormous quantities of sediment. The deserts of the southwestern United States occasionally experience dust storms produced in this manner.

Single-Cell Circulation Model

One of the first contributions to the classical model of global circulation came from George Hadley in 1735. Hadley was well aware that solar energy drives the winds. He proposed that the large temperature contrast between the poles and the equator creates one large *convection cell* in each hemisphere (Northern and Southern), as shown in Figure 7–6.

In Hadley's model, intensely heated equatorial air rises until it reaches the tropopause, where it begins to spread toward the poles. Eventually, this upper-level flow would reach the poles, where cooling would cause it to sink and spread out at the surface as equatorward-moving winds. As this cold polar air approached the equator, it would be reheated and rise again. Thus, the circulation proposed by Hadley has upper-level air flowing poleward and surface air moving equatorward.

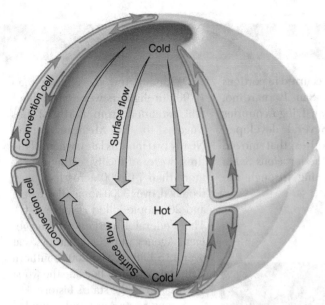

FIGURE 7-6 Global circulation on a nonrotating Earth. A simple convection system is produced by unequal heating of the atmosphere on a nonrotating Earth.

Although correct in principle, Hadley's model does not take into account the fact that Earth rotates on its axis. (Hadley's model would better approximate the circulation of a *nonrotating* planet.) As Earth's pressure and wind patterns became better known, it was clear that the single-cell model (in each hemisphere) could not create the global circulation that was actually observed. Consequently, the Hadley model was replaced by a model that better fit observations.

Three-Cell Circulation Model

In the 1920s a three-cell circulation model (for each hemisphere) was proposed. Although this model has been modified to fit upper-air observations, it remains a useful way to examine global circulation. Figure 7–7 illustrates the idealized three-cell model and the surface winds that result.

In the zones between the equator and roughly 30° latitude north and south, the circulation closely resembles the model used by Hadley for the whole Earth. Consequently, the name **Hadley cell** is generally applied. Near the equator, the warm rising air that releases latent heat during the formation of cumulus towers is believed to provide the energy to drive the Hadley cells. The clouds also provide the rainfall that maintains the lush vegetation of the rain forests of southeast Asia, equatorial Africa, and South America's Amazon Basin.

As the flow aloft in Hadley cells moves poleward, it begins to subside in a zone between 20° and 35° latitude. Two factors contribute to this general subsidence: (1) As upper-level flow moves away from the stormy equatorial region, where the release of latent heat of condensation keeps the air warm and buoyant, radiation cooling increases the density of the air. Satellites that monitor radiation emitted in the upper troposphere record considerable outward-emitted radiation over the tropics. (2) Because the Coriolis force becomes stronger with increasing distance from the equator, the poleward-moving upper air is deflected into a nearly west-to-east flow by the time it reaches 25° latitude. Thus, a restricted poleward flow of air ensues. Stated another way, the Coriolis force causes a general pileup of

FIGURE 7-7 Idealized global circulation proposed for the three-cell circulation model of a rotating Earth.

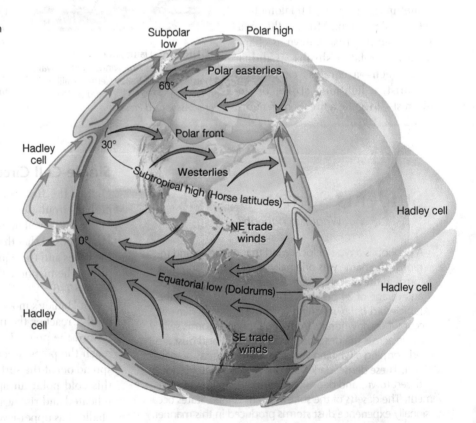

air (convergence) aloft. As a result, general subsidence occurs in the zones located between 20° and 35° latitude.

This subsiding air is relatively dry, because it has released its moisture near the equator. In addition, the effect of adiabatic heating during descent further reduces the relative humidity of the air. Consequently, this zone of subsidence is the site of the world's subtropical deserts. The Sahara Desert of North Africa and the Great Australian Desert are located in these regions of sinking air.

Because winds are generally weak and variable near the center of this zone of descending air, this region is popularly called the **horse latitudes.** The name is believed to have been coined by Spanish sailors, who, while crossing the Atlantic, were sometimes becalmed in these waters and reportedly were forced to throw horses overboard when they could no longer water or feed them.

From the center of the horse latitudes, the surface flow splits into a poleward branch and an equatorward branch. The equatorward flow is deflected by the Coriolis force to form the reliable **trade winds,** so called because they enabled early sailing ships to trade between continents. In the Northern Hemisphere, the trades blow from the northeast, where they provided the sail power for exploration of the New World in the sixteenth and seventeenth centuries. In the Southern Hemisphere, the trades are from the southeast. The trade winds from both hemispheres meet near the equator in a region that has a weak pressure gradient. This region is called the **doldrums.** Here light winds and humid conditions provide the monotonous weather that is the basis for the expression "down in the doldrums."

In the three-cell model the circulation between 30° and 60° latitude (north and south) is more complicated than that within the Hadley cells (Figure 7–7). The net surface flow is poleward, and because of the Coriolis force, the winds have a strong westerly component. These **prevailing westerlies** were known to Benjamin Franklin, perhaps the first American weather forecaster, who noted that storms migrated from west to east across the colonies. Franklin also observed that the westerlies were much more sporadic and, therefore, less reliable than the trade winds for sail power. We now know that it is the migration of cyclones and anticyclones across the midlatitudes that disrupts the general westerly flow at the surface. Because of the importance of the midlatitude circulation in producing our daily weather, we will consider the westerlies in more detail in a later section.

Relatively little is known about the circulation in high (polar) latitudes. It is generally understood that subsidence near the poles produces a surface flow that moves equatorward and is deflected into the **polar easterlies** of both hemispheres. As these cold polar winds move equatorward, they eventually encounter the warmer westerly flow of the midlatitudes. The region where the flow of warm air clashes with cold air has been named the **polar front.** The significance of this region will be considered later.

Observed Distribution of Pressure and Winds

As you might expect, Earth's global wind patterns are associated with a distinct distribution of surface air pressure. To simplify this discussion, we will first examine the idealized pressure distribution that would be expected if Earth's surface were uniform, that is, composed of all sea or all smooth land.

Idealized Zonal Pressure Belts

If Earth had a uniform surface, two latitudinally oriented belts of high and two of low pressure would exist (Figure 7–8a). Near the equator, the warm rising branch of the Hadley cells is associated with the pressure zone known as the **equatorial low.** This region of ascending moist, hot air is marked by abundant precipitation. Because it is the region where the trade winds converge, it is also referred to as the **intertropical convergence zone (ITCZ).** In Figure 7–9, the ITCZ is visible as a band of heavy precipitation north of the equator.

In the belts about 20° to 35° on either side of the equator, where the westerlies and trade winds originate and go their separate ways, are the pressure zones known as the **subtropical highs.** These zones of high pressure are caused mainly by the Coriolis deflection, which restricts the poleward movement of the upper-level branch of the Hadley cells. As a result, a high-level pileup of air occurs around 20° to 35° latitude. Here a subsiding air column and diverging winds at the surface result in warm and clear weather. Recall that many large deserts lie near 30° latitude, within this zone of sinking air. Generally the rate at which air accumulates in the upper troposphere exceeds the rate at which the air descends and spreads out at the surface. Thus, the subtropical highs exist throughout most of the year and are regarded as *semipermanent* features of the general circulation.

Another low-pressure region is situated at about 50° to 60° latitude, in a position corresponding to the polar front. Here the polar easterlies and westerlies clash to form a convergent zone known as the **subpolar low.** As you will see later, this zone is responsible for much of the stormy weather in the middle latitudes, particularly in the winter.

Finally, near Earth's poles are the **polar highs,** from which the polar easterlies originate (Figure 7–8a). The high-pressure centers that develop over the cold polar areas are generated by entirely different processes than those that create the subtropical highs. Recall that the high-pressure zones in the subtropics result because the rate at which air piles up aloft exceeds the rate at which it spreads out at the surface. Stated another way, more air accumulates near 30° latitude than leaves these air columns. By contrast, the polar highs exhibit high surface pressure mainly because of surface cooling. Because air near the poles is cold and dense, it exerts a higher than average pressure.

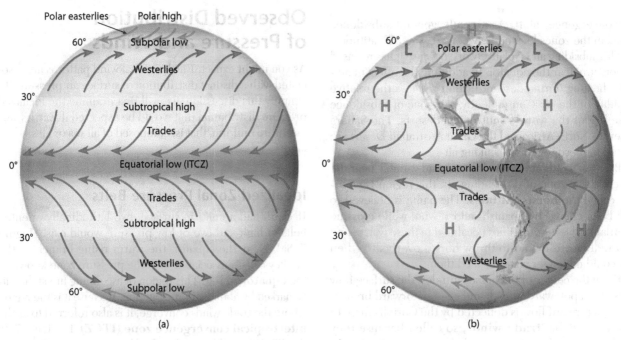

FIGURE 7-8 (a) An imaginary uniform Earth with idealized zonal (continuous) pressure belts. (b) The real Earth with disruptions of the zonal pattern caused by large landmasses. These disruptions break up pressure zones into semipermanent high- and low-pressure cells.

Semipermanent Pressure Systems: The Real World

Up to this point, we have considered the global pressure systems as if they were continuous belts around Earth. However, because Earth's surface is not uniform, the only true zonal distribution of pressure exists along the subpolar low in the Southern Hemisphere, where the ocean is continuous. To a lesser extent, the equatorial low is also continuous. At other latitudes, particularly in the Northern Hemisphere, where there is a higher proportion of land compared to ocean, the zonal pattern is replaced by semipermanent cells of high and low pressure.

The idealized pattern of pressure and winds for the "real" Earth is illustrated in Figure 7–8b. Although representative, the pattern shown is always in a state of flux because of seasonal temperature changes, which serve to either strengthen or weaken these pressure cells. In addition, the latitudinal position of these pressure systems moves either poleward or equatorward along with the seasonal migration of the zone of maximum solar heating. This is particularly true of the low-pressure belt associated with the intertropical convergence zone. The position of this thermally produced belt of low pressure is highly dependent on solar heating. As a consequence of these factors, Earth's pressure patterns vary in strength or

FIGURE 7-9 The Intertropical Convergence Zone (ITCZ) is seen as the band of heavy rainfall shown in reds and yellows, which extends east–west just north of the equator. *(Courtesy of NOAA)*

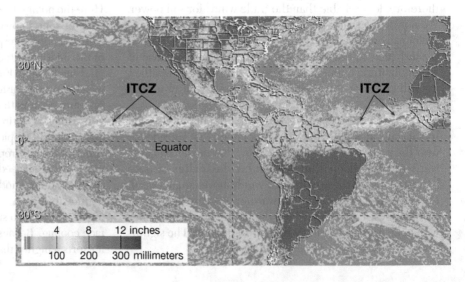

location during the course of the year. A view of the average global pressure patterns and resulting winds for the months of January and July are shown in Figure 7–10. Notice on these pressure maps that, for the most part, the observed pressure regimes are cellular (or elongated) instead of zonal. The most prominent features on both

maps are the subtropical highs. These systems are centered between 20° and 35° latitude over all the larger subtropical oceans.

When we compare Figures 7–10a (January) and 7–10b (July), we see that some pressure cells are more or less year-round features, like the subtropical highs. Others, however,

FIGURE 7-10 Average surface pressure and associated global circulation for (a) January and (b) July.

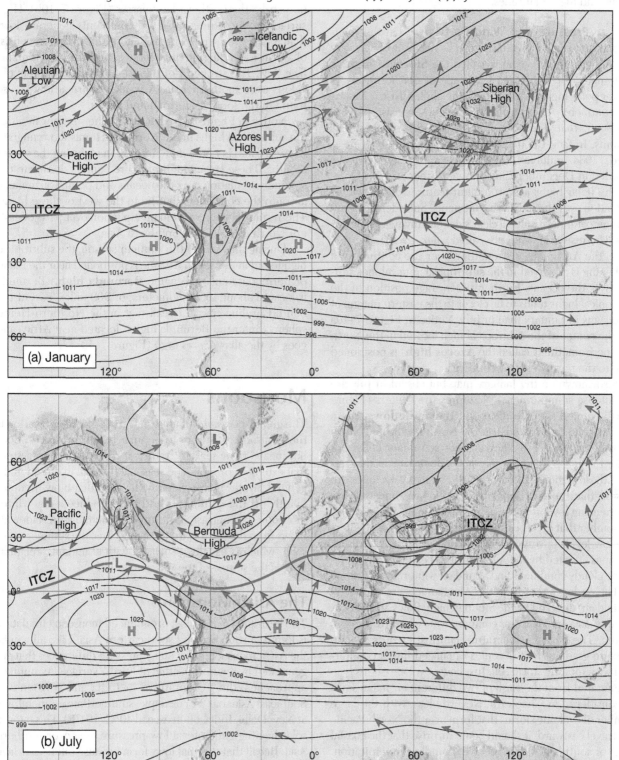

are seasonal, such as the low over the southwestern United States in the summer, which appears on only the July map. Relatively little pressure variation occurs from midsummer to midwinter in the Southern Hemisphere, a fact we attribute to the dominance of water in that hemisphere. Numerous departures from the idealized zonal pattern are evident in the Northern Hemisphere. The main cause of these variations is the seasonal temperature fluctuations experienced over the landmasses, especially those in the middle and higher latitudes.

January Pressure and Wind Patterns. On the January pressure map shown in Figure 7–10a, note that a very strong high-pressure center, called the **Siberian high,** is positioned over the frozen landscape of northern Asia. A weaker polar high is located over the chilled North American continent. These cold anticyclones consist of very dense air that accounts for the weight of these air columns. In fact, the highest sea-level pressure ever measured, 1084 millibars (32.01 inches of mercury) was recorded in December 1968 at Agata, Siberia.

The polar highs are prominent features of the winter circulation over the northern continents. Subsidence within these air columns results in clear skies and divergent surface flow. The resulting winds are called *polar easterlies.*

As the Arctic highs strengthen over the continents, a weakening is observed in the subtropical anticyclones situated over the oceans. Further, the average position of the subtropical highs tends to be closer to the eastern margin of the oceans in January than in July. Notice in Figure 7–10a that the center of the subtropical high located in the North Atlantic (sometimes called the **Azores high**) is positioned close to the northwest coast of Africa.

Also shown on the January map but absent in July are two intense semipermanent low-pressure centers (Figure 7–10). Named the **Aleutian** and **Icelandic lows,** these cyclonic cells are situated over the North Pacific and North Atlantic, respectively. They are not stationary cells, but rather the composite of numerous cyclonic storms that traverse these regions. In other words, so many cyclones are present that these regions of the globe are almost always experiencing low pressure, hence the term *semipermanent.* Remember that cyclones are traveling low-pressure centers with low-level convergence and an upward flow. As a result, the areas affected by the Aleutian and Icelandic lows experience cloudy conditions and abundant winter precipitation.

The cyclones that form the Aleutian low are produced as frigid air, directed by the Siberian high, flows off the continent of Asia and overruns comparatively warm air over the Pacific. The strong temperature contrast creates a steep pressure gradient that becomes organized into a counterclockwise rotating storm cell. Just how a cyclone of this type is generated from the clash of two different air masses will be considered in Chapter 9. Nevertheless, with the large number of cyclonic storms that form over the North Pacific and travel eastward, it should be no surprise that the coastal areas of southern Alaska receive abundant precipitation. This fact is exemplified by the climate data for Sitka, Alaska,

a coastal town that receives 215 centimeters (85 inches) of precipitation each year, over five times that received in Churchill, Manitoba, Canada. Although both towns are situated at roughly the same latitude, Churchill is located in the continental interior far removed from the influence of the Aleutian low.

July Pressure and Wind Patterns. The pressure pattern over the Northern Hemisphere changes dramatically with the onset of summer as increased amounts of radiation strike the northern landmasses (Figure 7–10b). High surface temperatures over the continents generate lows that replace the winter highs. These thermal lows consist of warm ascending air that induces inward directed surface flow. The strongest of these low-pressure centers develops over southern Asia. A weaker thermal low is also found in the southwestern United States.

Notice in Figure 7–10 that during the summer months, the subtropical highs in the Northern Hemisphere migrate westward and become more intense than during the winter months. These strong high-pressure centers dominate the summer circulation over the oceans and pump warm moist air onto the continents that lie to the west of these highs. This results in an increase in precipitation over parts of eastern North America and Southeast Asia.

During the peak of the summer season, the subtropical high found in the North Atlantic is positioned near the island of Bermuda, hence the name **Bermuda high.** (Bermuda is located about 1500 kilometers, or 900 miles, east of the South Carolina coast.) Recall that in the Northern Hemisphere winter the Bermuda high is located near Africa and goes by the alias *Azores high* (Figure 7–10).

Monsoons

The greatest *seasonal* change in Earth's global circulation is the monsoon. Contrary to popular belief, **monsoon** does not mean "rainy season"; rather, it refers to a wind system that exhibits a pronounced seasonal reversal in direction. In general, winter is associated with winds that blow predominantly off the continents and that produce a dry winter monsoon. By contrast, in summer, warm moisture-laden air blows from the sea toward the land. Thus, the summer monsoon, which usually associated with abundant precipitation, is the source of the misconception.

The Asian Monsoon

The best-known and most pronounced monsoon circulation is found in southern and southeastern Asia. Like all winds, the Asian monsoon is driven by pressure differences that are generated by unequal heating of Earth's surface. As summer approaches, the temperatures in India and surrounding Southeast Asia soar. For example, summertime temperatures at New Delhi, India, often exceed 40°C (104°F). This intense solar heating generates a low-pressure area over southern Asia. Recall that thermal lows form because intense surface heating causes expansion of the overlying air column. This in turn generates outflow aloft that encourages inward flow at the surface. With the development of the low-pressure center over India, moisture-laden air from the Indian Ocean flows landward, thereby generating a pattern of precipitation typical of the summer monsoon.

One of the world's rainiest regions is found on the slopes of the Himalayas where orographic lifting of moist air from the India Ocean produces copious precipitation. Cherrapunji, India, once recorded an annual rainfall of 25 meters (82.5 feet), most of which fell during the four months of the summer monsoon (Figure 7–11b).

As winter approaches, long nights and low sun angles result in the accumulation of frigid air over the vast landscape of northern Russia. This generates a cold anticyclone called the *Siberian high*, which begins to dominate the winter circulation over Asia. The subsiding dry air of the Siberian high produces surface flow that moves across southern Asia producing predominantly offshore winds (Figure 7–11a). By the time this flow reaches India, it has warmed considerably but remains extremely dry. For example, Bombay, India, receives less than 1 percent of its annual precipitation in the winter. The remainder comes in the summer, with the vast majority falling from June through September.

The Asian monsoon is complex and is strongly influenced by the seasonal change in the amount of solar heating received by the vast Asian continent. However, another factor, related to the annual migration of the Sun, also contributes to the pronounced monsoon circulation of southeastern Asia. As shown in Figure 7–11, the Asian monsoon is associated with a larger than average seasonal migration of the intertropical convergence zone (ITCZ). With the onset of summer the ITCZ moves northward over the continent and is accompanied by peak rainfall. The opposite occurs in the Asian winter as the ITCZ moves south of the equator. (Recall the ITCZ is a belt of low pressure and rising air that drives the Hadley cells.)

The migration of the ITCZ is accompanied by a dramatic change in pressure. The strong high-pressure system and subsidence that dominates the winter flow is replaced by low pressure and convergence during the summer months. This significant shift in pressure is thought to aid the northward movement of the ITCZ.

Of major importance are the Himalaya Mountains and the huge Tibetan Plateau, which have an *average* elevation that is higher than the highest peaks in the Colorado Rockies. During the winter months these topographic barriers contribute to the extreme temperature difference that exists between the cold continental interior and the milder coastal areas. This temperature contrast produces a strong jet stream that becomes anchored over these highlands. The role that this jet stream plays in the dry winter monsoon is not known with certainty. Nevertheless, in the summer, as the temperature differential over the continent diminishes, the jet stream breaks down. Clearly, these topographic barriers and the resulting upper airflow play a major role in the migration of the ITCZ.

Nearly half the world's population inhabits regions affected by monsoonal circulation. Further, many of these

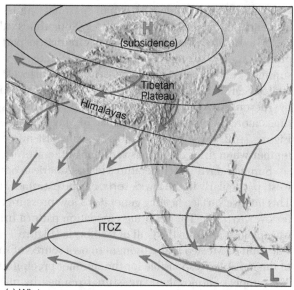

(a) Winter monsoon

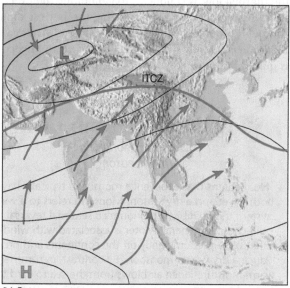

(b) Summer monsoon

FIGURE 7-11 Asia's monsoon circulation occurs in conjunction with the seasonal shift of the intertropical convergence zone (ITCZ). (a) In January a strong high pressure develops over Asia and cool, dry continental air generates the dry winter monsoon. (b) With the onset of summer, the ITCZ migrates northward and draws warm, moist air onto the continent.

people depend on subsistence agriculture for their livelihood. Therefore, the timely arrival of the monsoon rains often means the difference between adequate nutrition and widespread malnutrition.

The North American Monsoon

Many regions of the globe experience seasonal wind shifts like those associated with the Asian monsoon. Although none are as dramatic as the Asian monsoon, these smaller features are important elements of the global circulation and affect most of Earth's landmasses.

For example, a relatively small seasonal wind shift influences a portion of North America. Sometimes called the *North American monsoon,* this circulation pattern produces a dry spring followed by a comparatively rainy summer that impacts large areas of the southwestern United States and northwestern Mexico.° This is illustrated by Tucson, Arizona, which typically receives almost sixty times more precipitation in July than in May. As shown in Figure 7–12, these summer rains typically last into September when drier conditions reestablish themselves.

Summer daytime temperatures in the American Southwest, particularly in the low deserts, can be extremely hot. This intense surface heating generates a low-pressure center over Arizona. The resulting circulation pattern brings warm, moist air from the Gulf of California (Figure 7–13). The Gulf of Mexico is also thought to be a source of some of the moisture responsible for the summer precipitation. The supply of atmospheric moisture from nearby marine sources, coupled with the convergence and upward flow of the thermal low, is conducive to generating the precipitation this region experiences during the hottest months. Although often associated with the state of Arizona, this monsoon is actually strongest in northwestern Mexico and is quite pronounced in New Mexico.

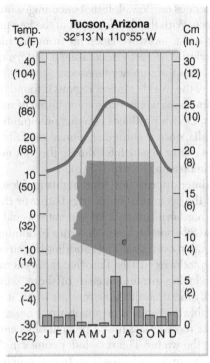

FIGURE 7-12 Climate diagram for Tucson, Arizona, showing a summer precipitation maximum produced by monsoon circulation that draws moist air in from the Gulf of California and to a lesser extent from the Gulf of Mexico.

Students Sometimes Ask...

Does monsoon mean "rainy season"?

No. Regions that experience monsoons typically have both a wet and a dry season. Monsoon refers to a wind system that exhibits a pronounced seasonal reversal in direction. In general, winter is associated with winds that blow predominantly off the continents and produce a dry winter monsoon. By contrast, in summer, warm moisture-laden air blows from the sea toward the land. Thus, the summer monsoon, which is usually associated with abundant precipitation, is the source of the misconception.

The Westerlies

Prior to World War II, upper-air observations were scarce. Since then, aircraft and radiosondes have provided a great deal of data about the upper troposphere. Among the most important discoveries was that airflow aloft in the middle latitudes has a strong west-to-east component, thus the name *westerlies.*

Why Westerlies?

Let us consider the reason for the predominance of westerly flow aloft. Recall that winds are created and maintained by pressure differences that are a result of temperature dif-

ferences. In the case of the westerlies, it is the temperature contrast between the poles and equator that drives these winds. Figure 7–14 illustrates the pressure distribution with height over the cold polar region as compared to the much

FIGURE 7-13 High summer temperatures over the southwestern United States create a thermal low that draws moisture from the Gulf of California and the Gulf of Mexico. This summer monsoon produces an increase in precipitation, which often comes in the form of thunderstorms, over the southwestern United States and northwestern Mexico.

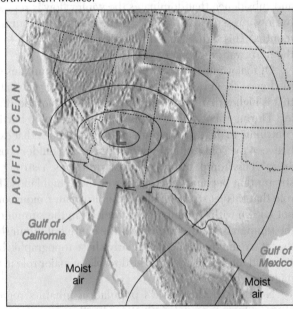

°This event is also called the *Arizona monsoon* and the *Southwest monsoon* because it has been extensively studied in this part of the United States.

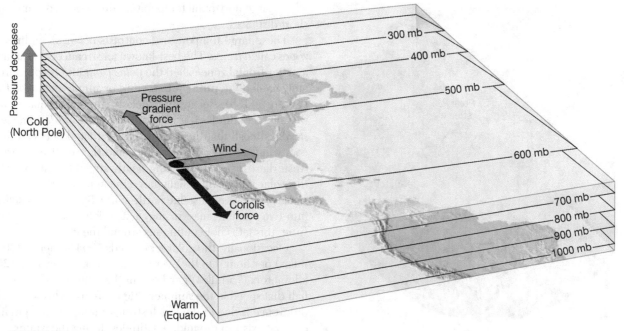

FIGURE 7-14 Idealized pressure gradient that develops aloft because of density differences between cold polar air and warm tropical air. Notice that the poleward-directed pressure-gradient force is balanced by an equatorward-directed Coriolis force. The result is a prevailing flow from west to east, which is called the *westerlies*.

warmer tropics. Because cold air is more dense (compact) than warm air, air pressure decreases more rapidly in a column of cold air than in a column of warm air. The pressure surfaces (planes) in Figure 7–14 represent a grossly simplified view of the pressure distribution we would expect to observe from pole to equator.

Over the equator, where temperatures are higher, air pressure decreases more gradually than over the cold polar regions. Consequently, at the same altitude above Earth's surface, higher pressure exists over the tropics and lower pressure is the norm above the poles. Thus, the resulting pressure gradient is directed from the equator (area of higher pressure) toward the poles (area of lower pressure).

Once the air from the tropics begins to advance poleward in response to this pressure gradient force (red arrow in Figure 7–14), the Coriolis force comes into play to change the direction of airflow. Recall that in the Northern Hemisphere the Coriolis force causes winds to be deflected to the right. Eventually, a balance is reached between the poleward-directed pressure-gradient force and the Coriolis force to generate a wind with a strong west-to-east component (Figure 7–14). Recall that such winds are called *geostrophic winds*. Because the equator-to-pole temperature gradient shown in Figure 7–14 is typical over the globe, a westerly flow aloft should be expected, and on most occasions it is observed.

It can also be shown that the pressure gradient increases with altitude; as a result, so should wind speeds. This increase in wind speed continues only to the tropopause, where it starts to decrease upward into the stratosphere.

Jet Streams

Imbedded within the westerly flow aloft are narrow ribbons of high-speed winds that meander for thousands of kilometers (Figure 7–15a). These fast streams of air once were considered analogous to jets of water and thus were named **jet streams.** These high-speed air currents have widths that vary from less than 100 kilometers (60 miles) to over 500 kilometers (300 miles) and are generally a few kilometers thick. Wind speeds are frequently in excess of 200 kilometers (120 miles) per hour but rarely exceed 400 kilometers (240 miles) per hour.

Although jet streams had been predicted earlier, their existence was first dramatically illustrated during World War II. American bombers heading westward toward Japanese-occupied islands occasionally made little headway. On abandoning their missions, the planes on their return flight experienced westerly tail winds that sometimes exceeded 300 kilometers per hour. Even today commercial aircraft use these strong tail winds to increase their speed when making eastward flights around the globe. On westward flights, of course, these fast currents of air are avoided when possible.

Origin of the Polar Jet Stream

What is the origin of these distinctive, energetic winds that exist within the slower, general westerly flow? The key is that large temperature contrasts at the surface produce steep pressure gradients aloft and hence faster upper air winds. In winter it is not unusual to have a warm balmy day

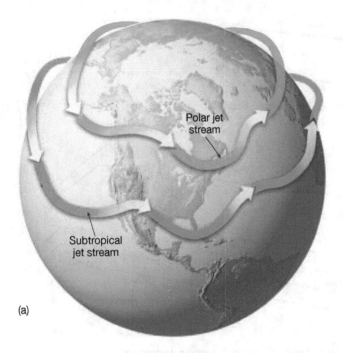

(a)

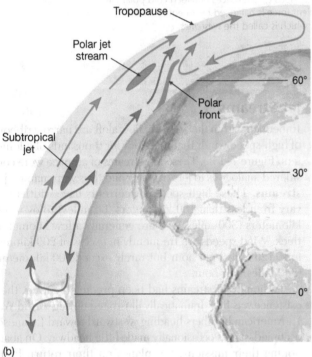

(b)

FIGURE 7-15 Jet streams. (a) Approximate positions of the polar and subtropical jet streams. Note that these fast-moving currents are generally not continuous around the entire globe. (b) A cross-sectional view of the polar and subtropical jets.

where large horizontal temperature differences occur over short distances.

These large temperature contrasts occur along linear zones called *fronts*. The best-known jet stream occurs along a major frontal zone called the *polar front* and is appropriately named the **polar jet stream,** or simply the *polar jet* (Figure 7–15b). Because this jet stream occurs mainly in the middle latitudes it is also known as the *mid-latitude jet stream.* Recall that the polar front is situated between the cool winds of the polar easterlies and the relatively warm westerlies. Instead of flowing nearly straight west-to-east, the polar jet stream usually has a meandering path. Occasionally, it flows almost due north–south. Sometimes it splits into two jets that may, or may not, rejoin. Like the polar front, this jet is not continuous around the globe.

Occasionally, the polar jet exceeds 500 kilometers (300 miles) per hour. On the average, however, it travels at 125 kilometers (75 miles) per hour in the winter and roughly half that speed in the summer (Figure 7–16). This seasonal difference is due to the much stronger temperature gradient that exists in the middle latitudes during the winter.

Because the location of the polar jet roughly coincides with that of the polar front, its latitudinal position migrates with the seasons. Thus, like the zone of maximum solar heating, the jet moves northward during summer and southward in winter. During the cold winter months, the polar jet stream may extend as far south as 30° north latitude (Figure 7–16). With the coming of spring, the zone of maximum solar heating and therefore the jet begins a gradual northward migration. By midsummer, its average position is about 50° north latitude, but it may penetrate much farther poleward.

As the polar jet shifts northward, there is a corresponding change in the region where outbreaks of severe thunderstorms and tornadoes occur. For example, in February most tornadoes occur in the states bordering the Gulf of Mexico. By midsummer the center of this activity shifts to

FIGURE 7-16 The position and speed of the polar jet stream changes with the seasons, migrating freely between about 30° and 70° latitude. Shown are flow patterns that are common for summer and winter.

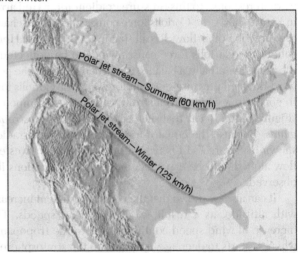

in southern Florida and near-freezing temperatures in Georgia, only a few hundred kilometers to the north. Such large wintertime temperature contrasts lead us to expect faster westerly flow at that time of year. Observations substantiate these expectations. In general, the fastest upper air winds are located above regions of the globe having large temperature contrasts across very narrow zones. Stated another way, jet streams are located in regions of the atmosphere

the northern plains and Great Lakes states. As you can see, the polar jet stream plays a very important role in the weather of the midlatitudes. In addition to supplying energy to the circulation of surface storms, it also directs their paths of movement. Consequently, determining changes in the location and flow pattern of the polar jet is an important part of modern weather forecasting.

Subtropical Jet Stream

Other jet streams are known to exist, but none have been studied in as much detail as the polar jet stream. A semi-permanent jet exists over the subtropics and as such is called the **subtropical jet** (see Figure 7–15b). The subtropical jet is mainly a wintertime phenomenon. Due to the weak summertime temperature gradient, the subtropical jet is relatively weak during the warm season. Somewhat slower than the polar jet, this west-to-east flowing current is centered at 25° latitude at an altitude of about 13 kilometers (8 miles).

Waves in the Westerlies

It is important to remember that the midlatitude jet stream is an integral part of the westerlies. It is not a dramatic anomaly like a hurricane. In fact, the jet stream can be more accurately described as the fast core of the overall westerly flow, like the fastest moving portion of a river (Figure 7–17). Studies of upper-level wind charts reveal that the westerlies follow wavy paths that have rather long wavelengths. Much of our knowledge of these large-scale motions is attributed to C. G. Rossby, who first explained the nature of

these waves. The longest wave patterns (called *Rossby waves*) have wavelengths of 4000 to 6000 kilometers, so that three to six waves will fit around the globe (Figure 7–17). Although the air flows eastward along this wavy path, these long waves tend to remain stationary or move slowly.

In addition to Rossby waves, shorter waves occur in the middle and upper troposphere. These shorter waves are often associated with cyclones at the surface and, like these storms, they travel from west to east around the globe at rates of up to 15° of longitude per day.

Although much remains to be learned about the wavy flow of the westerlies, its basic features are understood with some certainty. Among the most obvious characteristics of the flow aloft are its seasonal changes. The higher wind speeds in the cool season are depicted on upper-air charts by more closely spaced contour lines, as shown in Figure 7–18. The summer-to-winter change in wind speed is a consequence of the seasonal contrasts of the temperature gradients. The steep temperature gradient across the middle latitudes in winter corresponds to a stronger flow aloft.

In addition to seasonal changes in the strength of its flow, the position of the polar jet stream also shifts from summer to winter. With the approach of winter, the jet migrates equatorward. As summer nears, it moves back toward the poles (Figure 7–16). By midwinter the jet core may penetrate as far south as central Florida. Because the paths of cyclonic systems are guided by the flow aloft, we can expect the southern tier of states to encounter most of their severe weather in the winter. During hot summer months, the storm track is across the northern states, and some cyclones never leave Canada. In addition to seasonal changes in storm tracks, the number of cyclones generated also varies seasonally. The largest number form in the cooler months when temperature contrasts are most pronounced.

As you might expect, a close relationship exists between the location of the polar jet stream and conditions near the surface, particularly temperatures. When the midlatitude jet is situated equatorward of your location, the weather will usually be colder and stormier than normal. Conversely, when the polar jet moves poleward of your location, warmer and drier conditions are likely to prevail. Further, when the position of the jet stream remains fixed for extended periods, weather extremes can result. Thus, depending on the position of the jet stream, the weather could be hotter, colder, drier, or wetter than normal. We shall return later to this important relationship between the jet stream and middle latitude weather.

FIGURE 7-17 Idealized airflow of the westerlies at the 500-millibar level. The five long-wavelength undulations, called *Rossby waves,* compose this flow. The jet stream is the fast core of this wavy flow.

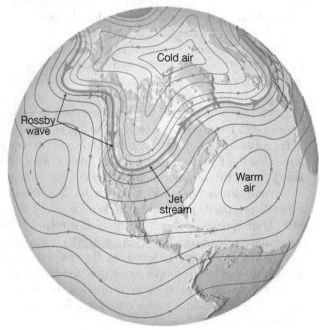

Westerlies and Earth's Heat Budget

Now let us return to the wind's function of maintaining Earth's heat budget by transporting heat from the equator toward the poles. In Chapter 2 we showed that the equator receives more solar radiation than it radiates back into space,

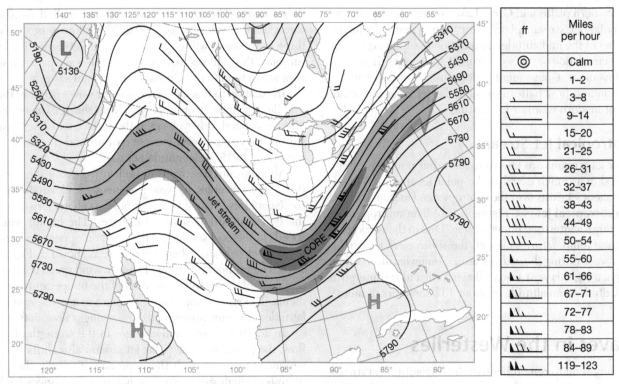

FIGURE 7-18 Simplified 500-millibar height-contour chart for January. The position of the jet-stream core is shown in dark red.

whereas the poles experience the reverse situation. Thus, the equator has excess heat, whereas the poles experience a deficit. Although the flow near the equator is somewhat *meridional* (north to south), at most other latitudes the flow is *zonal* (west to east). The reason for the zonal flow, as we have seen, is the Coriolis force. The question we now consider is: *How can wind with a west-to-east flow transfer heat from south to north?*

In addition to its seasonal migrations, the polar jet can change positions on shorter time scales as well. There may be periods of a week or more when the flow is nearly west to east, as shown in Figure 7–19a. When this condition prevails, relatively mild temperatures occur and few disturbances are experienced in the region south of the jet stream. Then without warning, the flow aloft begins to meander and produces large-amplitude waves and a general north-to-south flow (Figure 7–19b and c). Such a change allows cold air to advance southward. Because this influx intensifies the temperature gradient, the flow aloft is also strengthened. Recall that strong temperature contrasts create steep pressure gradients that organize into rotating cyclonic systems. The jet stream supports these lows by providing divergence aloft that enhances the inward flow at the surface.

During these periods, cyclonic activity dominates the weather. For a week or more, cyclonic storms redistribute large quantities of heat across the middle latitudes by moving cold air equatorward and warm air poleward. This redistribution eventually results in a weakened temperature gradient and a return to a flatter flow aloft and less intense

weather at the surface (Figure 7–19d). Cycles such as these, which consist of alternating periods of calm and stormy weather, can last from one to six weeks.

Laboratory experiments using rotating fluids to simulate Earth's circulation support the existence of waves and eddies that carry on the task of heat transfer in the middle latitudes. In these studies, called *dishpan experiments*, a large circular pan is heated around the outer edge to represent the equator and the center is cooled to duplicate a pole. Colored particles are added so that the flow can be easily observed and photographed. When the pan is heated, but not rotated, a simple convection cell forms to redistribute the heat. This cell is similar to the Hadley cell considered earlier. When the pan is rotated, however, the simple circulation breaks down and the flow develops a wavy pattern with eddies embedded between meanders, as seen in Figure 7–20. These experiments indicate that changing the rate of rotation and varying the temperature gradient largely determine the flow pattern produced. Such studies have added greatly to our understanding of global circulation.

In summary, we now understand that the wavy flow aloft is largely responsible for producing surface weather patterns. During periods when the flow aloft is relatively flat (small-amplitude waves), little cyclonic activity is generated at the surface. Conversely, when the flow exhibits large-amplitude waves having short wavelengths, vigorous cyclonic storms are created. This important relationship between the flow aloft and cyclonic storms is considered in more detail in Chapter 9.

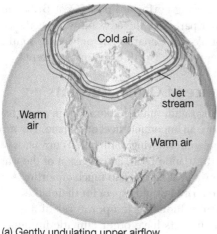

(a) Gently undulating upper airflow

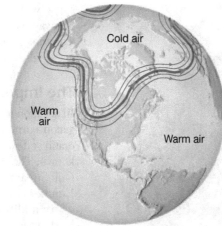

(b) Meanders form in jet stream

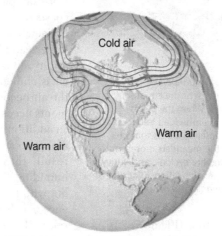

(c) Strong waves form in upper airflow

(d) Return to a period of flatter flow aloft

FIGURE 7-19 Cyclic changes that occur in the upper-level airflow of the westerlies. The flow, which has the jet stream as its axis, starts out nearly straight and then develops meanders and cyclonic activity that dominate the weather.

Students Sometimes Ask...

Why do pilots of commercial aircraft always remind passengers to keep their seat belts fastened, even in ideal flying conditions?

The reason for this request is a phenomenon known as *clear air turbulence.* Clear air turbulence occurs when airflow in two adjacent layers is moving at different velocities. This can happen when the air at one level is traveling in a different direction than the air above or below it. More often however, it occurs when air at one level is traveling faster than air in an adjacent layer. Such movements create eddies (turbulence) that can cause the plane to move suddenly up or down.

Global Winds and Ocean Currents

Where the atmosphere and ocean are in contact, energy is passed from moving air to the water through friction. As a consequence, the drag exerted by winds blowing steadily across the ocean causes the surface layer of water to move

(see Box 7–3). Thus, because winds are the primary driving force of **ocean currents,** a relationship exists between the oceanic circulation and the general atmospheric circulation. A comparison of Figures 7–21 and 7–10 illustrates this. A further clue to the influence of winds on ocean circulation is provided by the currents in the northern Indian Ocean, where there are seasonal wind shifts known as the *summer* and *winter monsoons.* When the winds change directions, the surface currents also reverse direction. North and south of the equator are two westward-moving currents, the North and South Equatorial currents, which derive their energy principally from the trade winds that blow from the northeast and southeast, respectively, toward the equator. These equatorial currents can be thought of as the backbone of the system of ocean currents. Because of the Coriolis force, these currents are deflected poleward to form clockwise spirals in the Northern Hemisphere and counterclockwise spirals in the Southern Hemisphere. These nearly circular ocean currents are found in each of the major ocean basins centered around the subtropical high-pressure systems (Figure 7–21).

In the North Atlantic, the equatorial current is deflected northward through the Caribbean, where it becomes the *Gulf Stream.* As the Gulf Stream moves along the eastern coast of the United States, it is strengthened by the prevailing westerly winds and is deflected to the east (to the right)

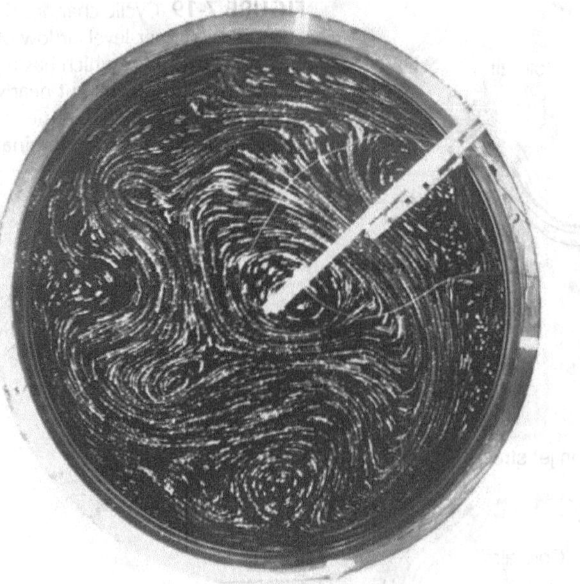

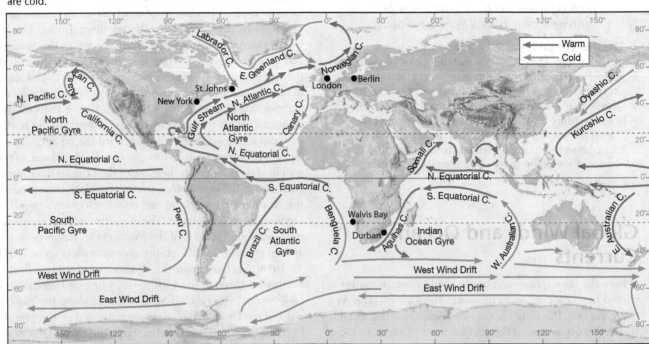

FIGURE 7-20 Photograph obtained from a *dishpan experiment*. The pan is heated around the edge to represent the equator, and the center is cooled to duplicate the poles. When the pan is rotated, a wavy flow develops with eddies embedded between meanders, as shown. This flow pattern closely parallels that produced in the "real" atmosphere, where the meanders represent the wavy flow of the westerlies and the eddies are cyclonic and anticyclonic systems embedded within this larger circulation. *(Courtesy of D. H. Fultz, University of Chicago Hydrodynamics Laboratory)*

splits, with part moving northward past Great Britain and Norway. The other part is deflected southward as the cool Canaries current. As the Canaries current moves south, it eventually merges into the North Equatorial current.

The Importance of Ocean Currents

In addition to being significant considerations in ocean navigation, currents have an important effect on climate. The moderating effect of poleward-moving warm ocean currents is well known. The North Atlantic Drift, an extension of the warm Gulf Stream, keeps Great Britain and much of northwestern Europe warmer than one would expect for their latitudes.

In addition to influencing temperatures of adjacent land areas, cold currents have other climatic influences. For example, where tropical deserts exist along the west coasts of continents, cold ocean currents have a dramatic impact. The principal west-coast deserts are the Atacama in Peru and Chile, and the Namib in southern Africa. The aridity along these coasts is intensified because the lower air is chilled by cold offshore waters. When this occurs, the air becomes very stable and resists the upward movements necessary to create precipitation-producing clouds. In addition, the presence of cold currents causes temperatures to approach and often reach the dew point. As a result, these areas are characterized by high relative humidities and much fog. Thus, not all tropical deserts are hot with low humidities and clear skies. Rather, the presence of cold currents transforms some tropical deserts into relatively cool, damp places that are often shrouded in fog.

Ocean currents also play a major role in maintaining Earth's heat balance. They accomplish this task by transferring heat from the tropics, where there is an excess of heat, to the polar regions, where a deficit exists. Ocean water

between 35° north and 45° north latitude (Figure 7–22). As it continues northeastward beyond the Grand Banks, it gradually widens and decreases speed until it becomes a vast, slowly moving current known as the North Atlantic Drift. As the North Atlantic Drift approaches Western Europe, it

FIGURE 7-21 Major ocean currents. Poleward-moving currents are warm, and equatorward-moving currents are cold.

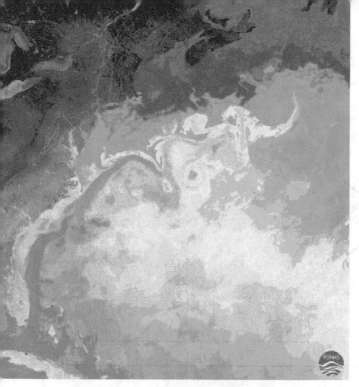

FIGURE 7-22 Enhanced satellite image of the complex flow of the Gulf Stream. Reds and yellows indicate warmer waters. Note that the Gulf Stream flows northward along the Florida coast (lower left) and then diagonally toward the upper right of the image. *(Courtesy of O. Brown, R. Evans, and M. Carle/Rosenstiel School of Marine and Atmospheric Science)*

movements account for about a quarter of this total heat transport and winds the remaining three-quarters.

Ocean Currents and Upwelling

In addition to producing surface currents, winds can also cause vertical water movements. **Upwelling,** the rising of cold water from deeper layers to replace warmer surface water, is a common wind-induced vertical movement. It is most characteristic along the eastern shores of the oceans, most notably along the coasts of California, Peru, and West Africa.

Upwelling occurs in these areas when winds blow toward the equator parallel to the coast. Because of the Coriolis force, the surface-water movement is directed away from the shore. As the surface layer moves away from the coast, it is replaced by water that "upwells" from below the surface. This slow upward flow from depths of 50 to 300 meters (165 to 1000 feet) brings water that is cooler than the original surface water and creates a characteristic zone of lower temperatures near the shore.

For swimmers who are accustomed to the waters along the mid-Atlantic shore of the United States, a dip in the Pacific off the coast of central California can be a chilling surprise. In August, when temperatures in the Atlantic are 21°C (70°F) or higher, central California's surf is only about 15°C (60°F). Coastal upwelling also brings to the ocean surface greater concentrations of dissolved nutrients, such as nitrates and phosphates. These nutrient-enriched waters from below promote the growth of plankton, which in turn supports extensive populations of fish.

El Niño and La Niña

As can be seen in Figure 7–23a, the cold Peruvian current flows equatorward along the coast of Ecuador and Peru. This flow encourages upwelling of cold nutrient-filled waters that serve as the primary food source for millions of fish, particularly anchovies. Near the end of each year, however, a warm current that flows southward along the coasts of Ecuador and Peru replaces the cold Peruvian current. During the nineteenth century the local residents named this warm countercurrent El Niño ("the child") after the Christ child because it usually appeared during the Christmas season. Normally, these warm countercurrents last for at most a few weeks when they again give way to the cold Peruvian flow. However, at irregular intervals of three to seven years, these countercurrents become unusually strong and replace normally cold offshore waters with warm equatorial waters (Figure 7–23b). Today scientists use the term **El Niño** for these episodes of ocean warming that affect the eastern tropical Pacific.

The onset of El Niño is marked by abnormal weather patterns that drastically affect the economies of Ecuador and Peru. As shown in Figure 7–23b, these unusually strong undercurrents amass large quantities of warm water that block the upwelling of colder, nutrient-filled water. As a result, the anchovies starve, devastating the fishing industry. At the same time, some inland areas that are normally arid receive an abnormal amount of rain. Here, pastures and cotton fields have yields far above the average. These climatic fluctuations have been known for years, but they were originally considered local phenomena. Today, we know that El Niño is part of the global circulation and affects the weather at great distances from Peru and Ecuador.

Two of the strongest El Niño events on record occurred between 1982–83 and 1997–98, and were responsible for weather extremes of a variety of types in many parts of the world. During the 1982–83 El Niño event, heavy rains and flooding plagued normally dry portions of Ecuador and Peru. Some locations that usually receive only 10 to 13 centimeters of rain each year had as much as 350 centimeters of precipitation. At the same time, severe drought beset Australia, Indonesia, and the Philippines. Huge crop losses, property damage, and much human suffering were recorded.

The 1997–98 El Niño brought ferocious storms that struck the California coast, causing unprecedented beach erosion, landslides, and floods. In the southern United States, heavy rains also brought floods to Texas and the Gulf states. The same energized jet stream that produced storms in the South, upon reaching the Atlantic, sheared off the northern portions of hurricanes, destroying the storms. It was one of the quietest Atlantic hurricane seasons in years.

Major El Niño events, such as the one in 1997 and 1998, are intimately related to the large-scale atmospheric circulation. Each time an El Niño occurs, the barometric pressure drops over large portions of the southeastern Pacific, whereas in the western Pacific, near Indonesia and northern Australia, the pressure rises (Figure 7–24). Then, as a major El Niño event comes to an end, the pressure difference between these two regions swings back in the opposite direction. This seesaw

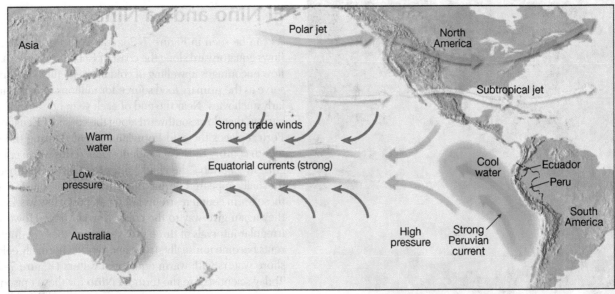

(a) Normal conditions

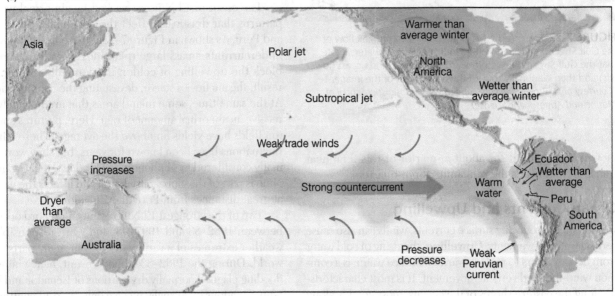

(b) El Niño

FIGURE 7-23 The relationship between the Southern Oscillation and El Niño is illustrated on these simplified maps. (a) Normally, the trade winds and strong equatorial currents flow toward the west. At the same time, the strong Peruvian current causes upwelling of cold water along the west coast of South America. (b) When the Southern Oscillation occurs, the pressure over the eastern and western Pacific flip-flops. This causes the trade winds to diminish, leading to an eastward movement of warm water along the equator. As a result, the surface waters of the central and eastern Pacific warm, with far-reaching consequences to weather patterns.

pattern of atmospheric pressure between the eastern and western Pacific is called the **Southern Oscillation.** It is an inseparable part of the El Niño warmings that occur in the central and eastern Pacific every three to seven years. Therefore, this phenomenon is often termed El Niño/Southern Oscillation, or ENSO for short.

Winds in the lower atmosphere are the link between the pressure change associated with the Southern Oscillation and the extensive ocean warming associated with El Niño (see Box 7–4). During a typical year the trade winds converge near the equator and flow westward toward Indonesia (Figure 7–24a). This steady westward flow creates a

warm surface current that moves from east to west along the equator. The result is a "piling up" of a thick layer of warm surface water that produces higher sea levels (by 30 centimeters) in the western Pacific. Meanwhile, the eastern Pacific is characterized by a strong Peruvian current, upwelling of cold water, and lower sea levels.

Then when the Southern Oscillation occurs, the normal situation just described changes dramatically. Barometric pressure rises in the Indonesian region, causing the pressure gradient along the equator to weaken or even to reverse. As a consequence, the once-steady trade winds diminish and may even change direction. This reversal creates a major change in

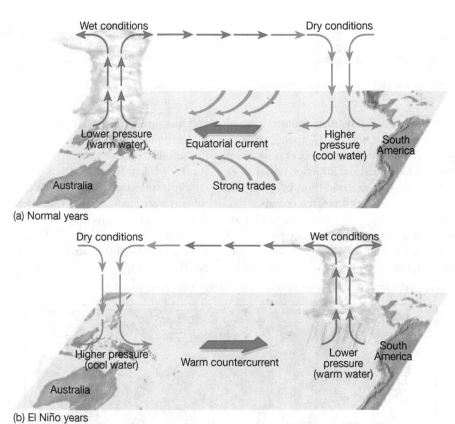

Wet conditions → → → Dry conditions

Lower pressure
(warm water)　Equatorial current　Higher pressure
(cool water)　South America

Australia　Strong trades

(a) Normal years

Dry conditions ← ← ← Wet conditions

Higher pressure
(cool water)　Warm countercurrent　Lower pressure
(warm water)　South America

Australia

(b) El Niño years

FIGURE 7-24 Simplified illustration of the seesaw pattern of atmospheric pressure between the eastern and western Pacific, called the *Southern Oscillation.* (a) During average years, high pressure over the eastern Pacific causes surface winds and warm equatorial waters to flow westward. The result is a pileup of warm water in the western Pacific, which promotes the lowering of pressure. (b) An El Niño event begins as surface pressure increases in the western Pacific and decreases in the eastern Pacific. This air pressure reversal weakens, or may even reverse the trade winds, and results in an eastward movement of the warm waters that had accumulated in the western Pacific.

the equatorial current system, with warm water flowing eastward (Figure 7–24b). With time, water temperatures in the central and eastern Pacific increase and sea level in the region rises. This eastward shift of the warmest surface water marks the onset of El Niño and sets up changes in atmospheric circulation that affect areas far outside the tropical Pacific.

When an El Niño began in the summer of 1997, forecasters predicted that the pool of warm water over the Pacific would displace the paths of both the subtropical and polar jet streams, which steer weather systems across North America (Figure 7–23). As predicted, the subtropical jet brought rain to the Gulf Coast, where Tampa, Florida, received more than three times its normal winter precipitation. Furthermore, the midlatitude jet pumped warm air far north into the continent. As a result, winter temperatures west of the Rockies were significantly above normal.

The effects of El Niño are somewhat variable depending in part on the temperatures and size of the warm pools. Nevertheless, some locales appear to be affected more consistently. In particular, during most El Niños, warmer-than-normal winters occur in the northern United States and Canada. In addition, normally arid portions of Peru and Ecuador, as well as the eastern United States, experience wet conditions. By contrast, drought conditions are generally observed in Indonesia, Australia, and the Philippines. One major benefit of the circulation associated with El Niño is a suppression of the number of Atlantic hurricanes.

The opposite of El Niño is an atmospheric phenomenon known as **La Niña** Figure 7–25. Once thought to be the normal conditions that occur between two El Niño events, mete-

orologists now consider La Niña an important atmospheric phenomenon in its own right. Researchers have come to recognize that when surface temperatures in the eastern Pacific are *colder than average,* a La Niña event is triggered that has a distinctive set of weather patterns. A typical La Niña winter blows colder than normal air over the Pacific Northwest and the northern Great Plains while warming much of the rest of the United States. Further, greater precipitation is expected in the Northwest. During the La Niña winter of 1998–99, a world record snowfall for one season occurred

FIGURE 7-25 This graph illustrates the cyclical nature of El Niño/Southern Oscillation (ENSO). Negative values (blue) represent the cold La Niña phase, while positive values (red) represent the warm El Niño phase. The graph was created by analyzing six variables, including sea-surface temperatures and sea-level pressures. *(After Wolter and Timlin/NOAA)*

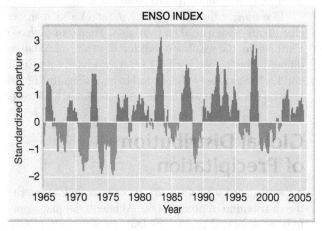

ENSO INDEX

BOX 7-3   Monitoring Winds from Space

The global ocean makes up 71 percent of Earth's surface. Winds moving over the sea surface effectively move heat and moisture from place to place, while driving ocean currents and ultimately weather and climate. Surface-based methods of monitoring winds using ships and data buoys provide only a glimpse of the wind patterns over the ocean. Today instruments aboard NASA's *QuickSCAT* spacecraft can continuously and accurately map wind speed and direction under most atmospheric conditions over 90 percent of Earth's ice-free oceans.

QuickSCAT carries the *SeaWinds* scaterometer, a specialized type of radar that operates by transmitting microwave pulses to the ocean surface and measuring the amount of energy that is bounced back (or echoed) to the satellite. Smooth ocean surfaces return weaker signals because less energy is reflected, while rough water returns a stronger signal. From such data, scientists can compute wind speed and direction (Figure 7–D). By measuring global sea-surface winds, *SeaWinds* helps researchers more

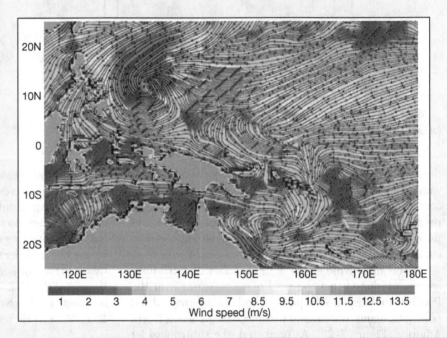

FIGURE 7-D Map produced from *SeaWinds* data showing wind patterns over a portion of the western Pacific on March 4, 2002. The strongest winds in this image (red area) are about 50 kilometers (30 miles) per hour.

in Washington State. Another La Niña impact is greater hurricane activity. A recent study concluded that the cost of hurricane damages in the United States is 20 times greater in La Niña years as compared to El Niño years.

In summary, the effects of El Niño and La Niña on world climate are widespread and variable. There is no place on Earth where the weather is indifferent to air and ocean conditions in the tropical Pacific. Events associated with El Niño and La Niña are now understood to have a significant influence on the state of weather and climate almost everywhere.

Global Distribution of Precipitation

A casual glance at Figure 7–26a reveals a complex pattern for the distribution of precipitation. Although the map appears to be complicated, the general features of the pattern can be explained using our knowledge of global winds and pressure systems. In general, regions influenced by high pressure, with its associated subsidence and divergent winds, experience dry conditions. Conversely, regions under the influence of low pressure and its converging winds and ascending air receive ample precipitation. However, if the wind-pressure regimes were the only control of precipitation, the pattern shown in Figure 7–26a would be much simpler.

The inherent nature of the air is also important in determining precipitation potential. Because cold air has a low capacity for moisture compared with warm air, we would expect a latitudinal variation in precipitation, with low latitudes receiving the greatest amounts of precipitation and high latitudes receiving the least. Figure 7–26a indeed reveals heavy precipitation in equatorial regions and meager moisture near the landmasses poleward of 60° latitude. A noticeably arid region, however, is also found in the subtropics. This situation can be explained by examining the global wind-pressure regimes.

accurately predict marine phenomena that have the potential to affect human endeavors. For example, the satellite's instruments provide meteorologists with a method to identify areas of gale-force winds over the entire ocean. These real-time data can be used to give advance warning of high waves to vessels at sea and to coastal communities.

In addition, these snapshots of ocean winds help researchers better understand and predict the development of large storm systems, such as mid-latitude cyclones and hurricanes, as well as aid in our understanding of global weather events such as El Niño (Figure 7–E).

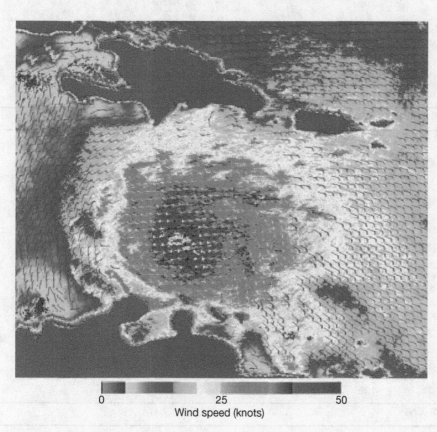

0   25   50
Wind speed (knots)

FIGURE 7-E This image shows Hurricane Ivan as it roared through the Caribbean as a deadly Category 5 storm early on September 9, 2004. Data from the *SeaWinds* scatterometer aboard NASA's *QuickSCAT* spacecraft augments traditional satellite images of clouds by providing direct measurements of surface winds to compare with observed cloud patterns in an effort to better determine a storm's structure and strength.

In addition to latitudinal variations in precipitation, the distribution of land and water complicates the precipitation pattern. Large landmasses in the middle latitudes commonly experience decreased precipitation toward their interiors. For example, central North America and central Eurasia receive considerably less precipitation than do coastal regions at the same latitude. Furthermore, the effects of mountain barriers alter the idealized precipitation regimes we would expect solely from the global wind systems. Windward mountain slopes receive abundant precipitation, whereas leeward slopes and adjacent lowlands are usually deficient in moisture.

Zonal Distribution of Precipitation

Let us first examine the zonal distribution of precipitation that we would expect on a uniform Earth, and then add the variations caused by land and water influences. Recall from our earlier discussion that on a uniform Earth, four major pressure zones emerge in each hemisphere (see Figure 7–8a). These zones include the equatorial low (ITCZ), the subtropical high, the subpolar low, and the polar high. Also, remember that these pressure belts show a marked seasonal shift toward the summer hemisphere.

The idealized precipitation regimes expected from these pressure systems are shown in Figure 7–27, in which we can see that the equatorial regime is centered over the equatorial low throughout most of the year. In this region, where the trade winds converge (ITCZ), heavy precipitation is experienced in all seasons. Poleward of the equatorial low in each hemisphere lie the belts of subtropical high pressure. In these regions, subsidence contributes to the dry conditions found there throughout the year. Between the wet equatorial regime and the dry subtropical regime lies a zone that is influenced by both pressure systems. Because the pressure systems migrate seasonally with the Sun, these transitional regions receive most of their precipitation in the summer when they are under the

FIGURE 7-26 Global distribution of precipitation: (a) annual, (b) July, and (c) January.

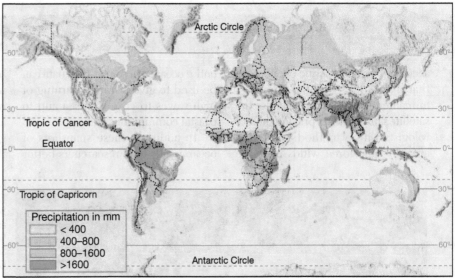

(a) Annual

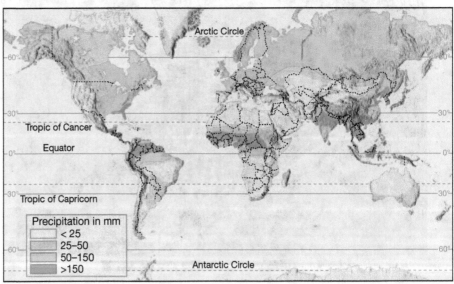

(b) July

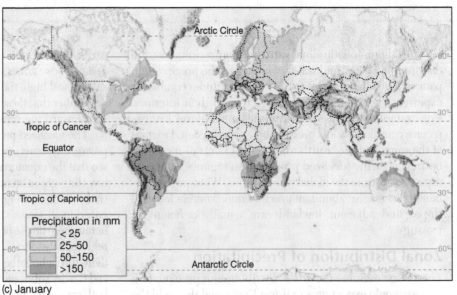

(c) January

FIGURE 7-27 Zonal precipitation patterns.

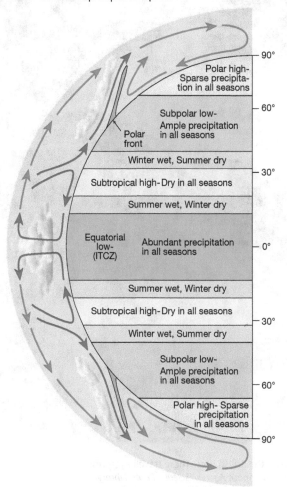

Distribution of Precipitation over the Continents

The zonal pattern outlined in the previous section roughly approximates general global precipitation. Abundant precipitation occurs in the equatorial and midlatitude regions, whereas substantial portions of the subtropical and polar realms are relatively dry. Yet numerous exceptions to this idealized zonal pattern are obvious in Figure 7–26a.

For example, several arid areas are found in the midlatitudes. The desert region of southern South America, known as Patagonia, is one example. Midlatitude deserts such as Patagonia exist mostly on the leeward (rain shadow) side of a mountain barrier or in the interior of a continent, cut off from a source of moisture. Most other departures from the idealized zonal scheme result from the distribution of continents and oceans.

The most notable anomaly in the zonal distribution of precipitation occurs in the subtropics. Here we find not only many of the world's great deserts but also regions of abundant rainfall (Figure 7–26a). This pattern results because the subtropical high-pressure centers that dominate the circulation in these latitudes have different characteristics on their eastern and western flanks (Figure 7–29). Subsidence is most pronounced on the eastern side of these oceanic highs, and a strong temperature inversion is encountered very near the surface and results in stable atmospheric conditions. The upwelling of cold water along the west coasts of the adjacent continents cools the air from below and adds to the stability on the eastern sides of these highs.

Because these anticyclones tend to crowd the eastern side of an ocean, particularly in the winter, we find that the western sides of the continents adjacent to these subtropical highs are arid (Figure 7–29). Centered at approximately 25° north or south latitude on the western side of their respective continents, we find the Sahara Desert of North Africa, the Namib of southwest Africa, the Atacama of South America, the deserts of the Baja Peninsula of North America, and the Great Desert of Australia.

On the western side of these highs, however, subsidence is less pronounced, and convergence with associated rising air appears to be more prevalent. In addition, as this air travels over a large expanse of warm water, it acquires moisture through evaporation that acts to enhance its instability. Consequently, the eastern regions of subtropical continents generally receive ample precipitation throughout the year. Southern Florida is a good example.

Precipitation Regimes on a Hypothetical Continent

When we consider the influence of land and water on the distribution of precipitation, the pattern illustrated in Figure 7–30 emerges. This figure is a highly idealized precipitation scheme for a hypothetical continent located in the Northern Hemisphere. The "continent" is shaped as it is to approximate the percentage of land found at various latitudes.

influence of the ITCZ. They experience a dry season in the winter when the subtropical high moves equatorward.

The midlatitudes receive most of their precipitation from traveling cyclonic storms (Figure 7–28). This region is the site of the polar front, the convergent zone between cold polar air and the warmer westerlies. It is along the polar front that cyclones are frequently generated. Because the position of the polar front migrates freely between approximately 30° and 70° latitude, most midlatitude areas receive ample precipitation. But the mean position of this zone also moves north and south with the Sun, so that a narrow belt between 30° and 40° latitude experiences a marked seasonal fluctuation in precipitation.

In winter, this zone receives precipitation from numerous cyclones as the position of the polar front moves equatorward. During the summer, however, this region is dominated by subsidence associated with the dry subtropical high. Compare the July and January precipitation data for the west coast of North America by referring to Figure 7–26b and c.

The polar regions are dominated by cold air that holds little moisture. Throughout the year, these regions experience only meager precipitation. Even in the summer, when temperatures rise, these areas of ice and snow are dominated by high pressure that blocks the movement of the few cyclones that do travel poleward.

FIGURE 7-28 Satellite image of a well-developed mid-latitude cyclone over the British Isles. These traveling storms produce most of the precipitation in the middle latitudes. *(Courtesy of European Space Agency/Science Photo Library/ Photo Researchers, Inc.)*

Notice that this hypothetical landmass has been divided into seven zones. Each zone represents a different precipitation regime. Stated another way, all locations within the same zone (precipitation regime) experience roughly the same precipitation pattern. As we shall see, the odd shape and size of these zones reflect the way precipitation is normally distributed across landmasses located in the Northern Hemisphere. The cities shown are representatives of the precipitation pattern of each location. With this in mind, we will now examine each precipitation regime (numbered 1 through 7) to see

FIGURE 7-29 Characteristics of subtropical high-pressure systems. Subsidence on the east side of these systems produces stable conditions and aridity. Convergence and uplifting on the western flank promote uplifting and instability.

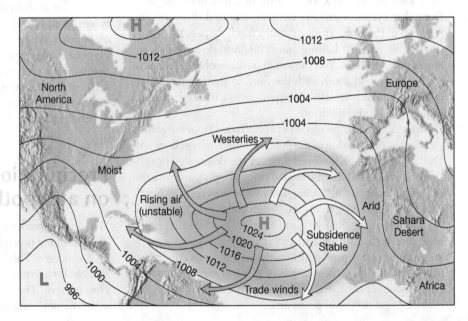

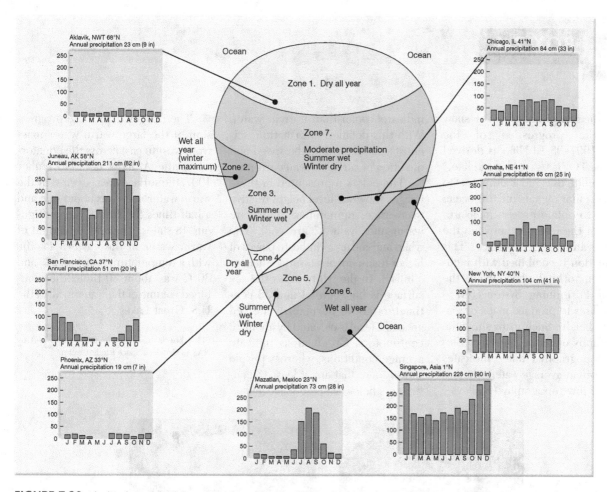

FIGURE 7-30 Idealized precipitation regimes for a hypothetical landmass in the Northern Hemisphere.

the influences of land and water on the distribution of precipitation.

First, compare the precipitation patterns for the nine cities. Notice that the precipitation regimes for west coast locations correspond to the zonal pressure and precipitation pattern shown in Figure 7–27: Zone 6 equates to the equatorial low (wet all year); Zone 4 matches the subtropical high (dry all year), and so on.

For illustration, Aklavik, Canada, which is strongly influenced by the polar high, has scant moisture, whereas Singapore, near the equator, has plentiful rain every month. Also note that precipitation varies seasonally with both latitude and each city's location with respect to the ocean.

For example, precipitation graphs for San Francisco and Mazatlan, Mexico, illustrate the marked seasonal variations found in Zones 3 and 5. Recall that it is the seasonal migration of the pressure systems that causes these fluctuations. Notice that Zone 2 shows a precipitation maximum in the fall and early winter, as illustrated by data for Juneau, Alaska. This pattern occurs because cyclonic storms over the North Pacific are more prevalent in the coolest half of the year. Further, the average path of these storms moves equatorward during the winter, impacting locations as far south as southern California.

The eastern half of the continent shows a marked contrast to the zonal precipitation pattern on the western side. Only

the dry polar regime (Zone 1) is similar in size and position on both the Eastern and Western seaboards. The most noticeable departure from the zonal pattern is the absence of the arid subtropical region from the East Coast. As noted earlier, this difference is caused by the behavior of subtropical anticyclones located over the oceans. Recall that southern Florida, which is located on the east coast of the continent, receives ample precipitation year-round, whereas the Baja Peninsula on the West Coast is arid. Moving inland from the East Coast, observe how precipitation decreases (compare total precipitation westward for New York, Chicago, and Omaha). This decrease, however, does not hold true for mountainous regions; even relatively small ranges, like the Appalachians, are able to extract a greater share of precipitation.

Another variation is seen with latitude. As we move poleward along the eastern half of our hypothetical continent, note the decrease in precipitation (compare Singapore, New York, and Aklavik). This is the decrease we would expect with cooler air temperatures and corresponding lower moisture capacities. We do not, however, find a similar decrease in precipitation in the higher middle latitudes along the West Coast. Because this region lies in the westerly wind belt, the West Coasts of midlatitude regions, such as Alaska, Canada, and Norway, receive abundant moisture from storms that originate over the adjacent oceans. In fact, some of the rainiest

BOX 7-4 Tracking El Niño from Space

The images in Figure 7–F show the progression of the 1997–98 El Niño as derived from the TOPEX/Poseidon satellite.° This satellite uses radar altimeters to bounce radar signals off the ocean surface to obtain precise measurements of the distance between the satellite and the sea surface. This information is combined with high-precision orbital data from the Global Positioning System (GPS) of satellites to produce maps of sea-surface height. Such maps show the topography of the sea surface. Elevated topography ("hills") indicates warmer-than-average water, whereas areas of low topography ("valleys")

indicate cooler-than-normal water. With this detailed information, scientists can determine the speed and direction of surface ocean currents.

The colors represented in these images show sea-level height relative to average. Remember, "hills" are warm and "valleys" are cool. The white and red areas indicate places of higher-than-normal sea-surface heights ("hills"). In the white areas the sea surface is between 14 and 32 centimeters above normal; in the red areas sea level is elevated by about 10 centimeters. Green areas indicate average conditions, whereas purple shows zones that are at least 18 centimeters below average sea level.

The images depict the progression of the large warm water mass from west to east across the equatorial Pacific. At its peak in November 1997, the surface area covered by the warm water mass was about one and a half times the size of the contiguous 48 states. The added amount of warm water in the eastern Pacific with a temperature between 21° and 30°C was about 30 times the combined volume of the water in all of the U.S. Great Lakes.

°This box is based on material published by NASA's Goddard Space Flight Center.

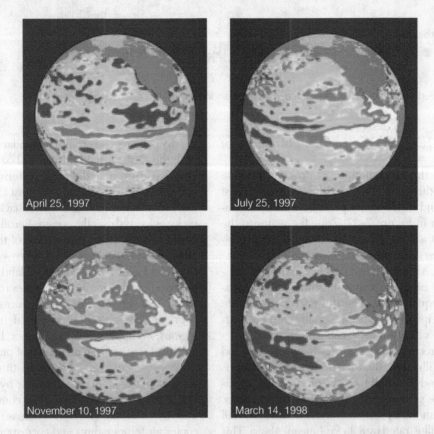

FIGURE 7-F The image for April 25, 1997, shows the Pacific on the eve of the 1997–98 El Niño event. By examining the images for July 25 and November 10, you can see the dramatic buildup of warm water (white and red areas) in the eastern Pacific and the enlarging region of cool water (purple) in the western Pacific. By the time of the March 14, 1998, image, the area of warm water in the eastern Pacific was *much* smaller. *(Courtesy of NASA Goddard Space Flight Center)*

regions on Earth are found in such settings. In contrast, the east coasts of mid-latitude locations experience temperature and moisture regimes more typical of continental locations, particularly in the winter when the airflow is off the land.

Consider next the continental interior, which shows a somewhat different precipitation pattern, especially in the middle latitudes. Because cyclones are more common in the winter, we would expect mid-latitude locations also to experience maximum precipitation in the winter. The precipitation regimes of the interior, however, are affected to a degree by a type of monsoon circulation. Cold winter temperatures and dominance of flow off the land in the winter make it the drier season (Omaha and Chicago). Although cyclonic storms frequent the continental interior in the winter, they do not become precipitation producers until they

have drawn in abundant moist air from the Gulf of Mexico. Thus, most of the winter precipitation falls in the eastern one-third of the United States. The lack of abundant winter precipitation in the Plains states, compared with the East, can be seen in the data for Omaha and New York City.

In the summer, the inflow of warm, moist air from the ocean is aided by the thermal low that develops over the land and causes a general increase in precipitation over the midcontinent. The dominance of summer monsoon-type precipitation is evident when we compare the patterns for India in summer and winter by using Figure 7–26b and c. In the United States, places in the Southeast begin their rainy season in early spring, whereas more northerly and westerly locations do not experience their peak precipitation until summer or early fall.

Chapter Summary

- The largest planetary-scale wind patterns, called *macroscale winds,* include the westerlies and trade winds. A somewhat smaller macroscale circulation is called *synoptic scale,* or *weather-map scale. Mesoscale winds,* such as thunderstorms, tornadoes, and land and sea breezes, influence smaller areas and often exhibit intense vertical flow. The smallest scale of air motion is the *microscale.* Examples of these very local, often chaotic winds include gusts and dust devils.

- All winds have the same cause: pressure differences that arise because of temperature differences that are caused by unequal heating of Earth's surface. In addition to *land* and *sea breezes* brought about by the daily temperature contrast between land and water, other mesoscale winds include *mountain* and *valley breezes, chinook (foehn)* winds, *katabatic (fall)* winds, and *country breezes.* Mountain and valley breezes develop as air along mountain slopes is heated more intensely than air at the same elevation over the valley floor. Chinooks are warm, dry winds that sometimes move down the east slopes of the Rockies. In the Alps, winds similar to chinooks are called foehns. Katabatic (fall) winds originate when cold air, situated over a highland area such as the ice sheets of Greenland and Antarctica, is set in motion under the influence of gravity. Country breezes are associated with large urban areas where the circulation pattern is characterized by a light wind blowing into the city from the surrounding countryside.

- A simplified view of global circulation is a three-cell circulation model for each hemisphere. Because the circulation patterns between the equator and roughly 30° latitude north and south closely resemble a single-cell model developed by George Hadley in 1735, the name *Hadley cell* is generally applied. According to the three-cell circulation model, in each hemisphere, atmospheric circulation cells are located between the equator and 30° latitude, 30° and 60° latitude, and 60° latitude and the pole. The areas of general subsidence in the zone between

20° and 35° are called the *horse latitudes.* In each hemisphere, the equatorward flow from the horse latitudes forms the reliable *trade winds.* Convergence of the trade winds from both hemispheres near the equator produces a region of light winds called the *doldrums.* The circulation between 30° and 60° latitude (north and south) results in the *prevailing westerlies.* Air that moves equatorward from the poles produces the *polar easterlies* of both hemispheres. The area where the cold polar easterlies clash with the warm westerly flow of the midlatitudes is referred to as the *polar front,* an important meteorological region.

- If Earth's surface were uniform, two latitudinally oriented belts of high and two of low pressure would exist. Beginning at the equator, the four belts would be the (1) *equatorial low,* also referred to as the *intertropical convergence zone (ITCZ),* because it is the region where the trade winds converge, (2) *subtropical high,* at about 20° to 35° on either side of the equator, (3) *subpolar low,* situated at about 50° to 60° latitude, and (4) *polar high,* near Earth's poles.

- In reality, the only true zonal pattern of pressure exists along the subpolar low in the Southern Hemisphere. At other latitudes, particularly in the Northern Hemisphere, where there is a higher proportion of land compared to ocean, the zonal pattern is replaced by semipermanent cells of high and low pressure. January pressure and wind patterns show a very strong high-pressure center, called the *Siberian High,* positioned over the frozen landscape of northern Asia. Also evident in January, but absent in July, are two intense semipermanent low-pressure centers, the *Aleutian* and *Icelandic lows,* situated over the North Pacific and North Atlantic, respectively. With the onset of summer the pressure pattern over the Northern Hemisphere changes dramatically and high temperatures over the continents generate lows that replace the winter highs. During the peak summer season, the subtropical high found in the North Atlantic (called the

Azores high in winter) is positioned near the island of Bermuda and is called the *Bermuda high*.

- The greatest seasonal change in Earth's global circulation is the development of *monsoons,* wind systems that exhibit a pronounced seasonal reversal in direction. The best-known and most pronounced monsoonal circulation, the *Asian monsoon* found in southern and southeastern Asia, is a complex seasonal change that is strongly influenced by the amount of solar heating received by the vast Asian continent. The *North American monsoon* (also called the *Arizona monsoon* and *Southwest monsoon*), a relatively small seasonal wind shift, produces a dry spring followed by a comparatively rainy summer that impacts large areas of southwestern United States and northwestern Mexico.

- The temperature contrast between the poles and equator drives the westerly winds (*westerlies*) located in the middle latitudes. Imbedded within the westerly flow aloft are narrow ribbons of high-speed winds, called *jet streams,* that meander for thousands of kilometers. The key to the origin of polar jet streams is found in great temperature contrasts at the surface. In the region between 30° and 70°, the *polar jet stream* occurs in association with the *polar front.*

- Studies of upper-level wind charts reveal that the westerlies follow wavy paths that have rather long wavelengths. The longest wave patterns are called *Rossby waves.* During periods when the flow aloft is relatively flat, little cyclonic activity is generated at the surface. Conversely, when the flow exhibits large-amplitude waves having short wavelengths, vigorous cyclonic storms are created. In addition to seasonal changes in the strength of its flow, the position of the polar jet also shifts from summer to winter.

- Because winds are the primary driving force of ocean currents, a relationship exists between the oceanic circulation and the general atmospheric circulation. In general, in response to the circulation associated with the subtropical highs, ocean currents form clockwise spirals in the Northern Hemisphere and counterclockwise spirals in the Southern Hemisphere. In addition to influencing temperatures of adjacent land areas, cold ocean currents also transform some subtropical deserts into relatively cool, damp places that are often shrouded in fog. Furthermore, ocean currents play a major role in main-taining Earth's heat balance. In addition to producing surface currents, winds may also cause vertical water movements, such as the *upwelling* of cold water from deeper layers to replace warmer surface water.

- *El Niño* refers to episodes of ocean warming caused by a warm countercurrent flowing southward along the coasts of Ecuador and Peru that replaces the cold Peruvian current. The events are part of the global circulation and related to a seesaw pattern of atmospheric pressure between the eastern and western Pacific called the *Southern Oscillation.* El Niño events influence weather at great distances from Peru and Ecuador. Two of the strongest El Niño events (1982–83 and 1997–98) were responsible for a variety of weather extremes in many parts of the world. When surface temperatures in the eastern Pacific are colder than average, a *La Niña* event is triggered. A typical La Niña winter blows colder than normal air over the Pacific Northwest and the northern Great Plains while warming much of the rest of the United States.

- The general features of the global distribution of precipitation can be explained by global winds and pressure systems. In general, regions influenced by high pressure, with its associated subsidence and divergent winds, experience dry conditions. On the other hand, regions under the influence of low pressure and its converging winds and ascending air receive ample precipitation.

- On a uniform Earth throughout most of the year, heavy precipitation would occur in the equatorial region, the mid-latitudes would receive most of their precipitation from traveling cyclonic storms, and polar regions would be dominated by cold air that holds little moisture. The most notable anomaly to this zonal distribution of precipitation occurs in the subtropics, where many of the world's great deserts are located. In these regions, pronounced subsidence on the eastern side of subtropical high-pressure centers results in stable atmospheric conditions. Upwelling of cold water along the west coasts of the adjacent continents further adds to the stable and dry conditions. On the other hand, the east coast of the adjacent continent receives abundant precipitation year-round due to the convergence and rising air associated with the western side of the oceanic high.

Vocabulary Review

Aleutian low (p. 210)
Azores high (p. 210)
bora (p. 204)
Bermuda high (p. 210)
chinook (p. 203)
country breeze (p. 204)
doldrums (p. 207)
El Niño (p. 219)
equatorial low (p. 207)
foehn (p. 203)
Hadley cell (p. 206)

horse latitudes (p. 207)
Icelandic low (p. 210)
intertropical convergence zone (ITCZ) (p. 207)
jet stream (p. 213)
katabatic or fall wind (p. 203)
land breeze (p. 202)
La Niña (p. 221)
macroscale winds (p. 199)
mesoscale winds (p. 199)
microscale circulation (p. 199)

mistral (p. 204)
monsoon (p. 210)
mountain breeze (p. 202)
ocean currents (p. 217)
polar easterlies (p. 207)
polar front (p. 207)
polar high (p. 207)
polar jet stream (p. 214)
prevailing westerlies (p. 207)
Santa Ana (p. 203)
sea breeze (p. 202)

Siberian high (p. 210)
Southern Oscillation (p. 221)
subpolar low (p. 207)

subtropical high (p. 207)
subtropical jet stream (p. 215)
trade winds (p. 207)

upwelling (p. 219)
valley breeze (p. 202)

Review Questions

1. Distinguish among macroscale, mesoscale, and microscale winds. Give an example of each.

2. If you were to view a weather map of the entire world for any single day of the year, would the global pattern of winds likely be visible? Explain your answer.

3. Why is the well-known Texas "norther" not a true local (mesoscale) wind?

4. The most intense sea breezes develop along tropical coasts adjacent to cool ocean currents. Explain.

5. What are katabatic (fall) winds? Name two examples.

6. Explain how cities create their own local winds.

7. Briefly describe the idealized global circulation proposed by George Hadley. What are the shortcomings of the Hadley model?

8. Which factors cause air to subside between 20° and 35° latitude?

9. If Earth rotated more rapidly, the Coriolis force would be stronger. How would a faster rate of rotation affect the location (latitude) of Earth's belts of subtropical high pressure?

10. Referring to the idealized three-cell model of atmospheric circulation, most of the United States is situated in which belt of prevailing winds?

11. Briefly explain each of the following statements that relate to the global distribution of surface pressure:
    a. The only true zonal distribution of pressure exists in the region of the subpolar low in the Southern Hemisphere.
    b. The subtropical highs are stronger in the North Atlantic in July than in January.
    c. The subpolar low in the Northern Hemisphere is represented by individual cyclonic storms that are more common in the winter.
    d. A strong high-pressure cell develops in the winter over northern Asia.

12. Explain the cause of the Asian monsoon. In which season (summer or winter) does it rain?

13. What area of North America experiences a pronounced monsoon circulation?

14. Why is the flow aloft predominantly westerly?

15. At what time of year should we expect the fastest westerly flow? Explain.

16. Describe the situation in which jet streams were first encountered.

17. Describe the manner in which pressure distribution is shown on upper-air charts. How are high- and low-pressure areas depicted on these charts?

18. What were the *dishpan experiments* and what have we learned from them?

19. Describe how a major El Niño event in the tropical Pacific might affect the weather in other parts of the globe.

20. How is La Niña different from El Niño?

21. What factors, other than global wind and pressure systems, exert an influence on the world distribution of precipitation?

Atmospheric Science Online

The Atmosphere 10e web site uses the resources and flexibility of the Internet to aid in your study of the topics in this chapter. Written and developed by meteorology instructors, this site will help improve your understanding of meteorology. Visit **http://www.prenhall.com/lutgens** and click on the cover of *The Atmosphere 10e* to find:

- **Online review quizzes**
- **Critical thinking exercises**
- **Links to chapter-specific web resources**
- **Internet-wide key term searches**

http://www.prenhall.com/lutgens

AIR MASSES

In late December 2001, a major
lake-effect snowstorm dropped about
2 meters (7 feet) of snow on the Buffalo,
New York area over a five-day period.
(AP Photo/David Duprey)

Most people living in the middle latitudes have experienced hot, "sticky" summer heat waves and frigid winter cold waves. In the first case, after several days of sultry weather, the spell may come to an abrupt end that is marked by thundershowers and followed by a few days of relatively cool relief. In the second case, thick stratus clouds and snow may replace the clear skies that had prevailed, and temperatures may climb to values that seem mild compared with what preceded them. In both examples, what was experienced was a period of generally uniform weather conditions followed by a relatively short period of change and the subsequent reestablishment of a new set of weather conditions that remained for perhaps several days before changing again.

What Is an Air Mass?

Basic Weather Patterns

▶ Air Masses

The weather patterns just described are the result of the movements of large bodies of air, called air masses. An **air mass,** as the term implies, is an immense body of air, usually 1600 kilometers (1000 miles) or more across and perhaps several kilometers thick, which is characterized by homogeneous physical properties (in particular, tempera-

ture and moisture content) at any given altitude. When this air moves out of its region of origin, it will carry these temperatures and moisture conditions elsewhere, eventually affecting a large portion of a continent (Figure 8–1).

An excellent example of the influence of an air mass is illustrated in Figure 8–2. Here a cold, dry mass from northern Canada moves southward. With a beginning temperature of −46°C (−51°F), the air mass warms 13°C (24°F), to −33°C (−27°F), by the time it reaches Winnipeg. It continues to warm as it moves southward through the Great Plains and into Mexico. Throughout its southward journey, the air mass becomes warmer, but it also brings some of the coldest weather of the winter to the places in its path. Thus, the air mass is modified, but it also modifies the weather in the areas over which it moves.

The horizontal uniformity of an air mass is not complete because it may extend through 20 degrees or more of latitude and cover hundreds of thousands to millions of square kilometers. Consequently, small differences in temperature and humidity from one point to another at the same level are to be expected. Still, the differences observed within an air mass are small in comparison to the rapid rates of change experienced across air-mass boundaries.

Because it may take several days for an air mass to traverse an area, the region under its influence will probably experience generally constant weather conditions, a situation called **air-mass weather.** Certainly, some day-to-day

FIGURE 8-1 When an air mass that forms in the desert Southwest in summer moves out from its region of origin, it will bring hot, dry conditions to other regions. This scene is in Arizona's Sonoran desert. *(Photo by Michael Collier)*

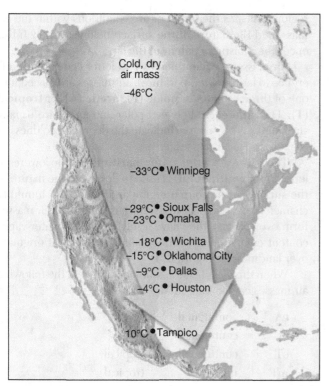

FIGURE 8-2 As this frigid Canadian air mass moved southward, it brought some of the coldest weather of the winter. *(After Tom L. McKnight,* Physical Geography, *5th ed. Upper Saddle River, NJ: Prentice Hall, 1996, p. 174)*

variations may exist, but the events will be very unlike those in an adjacent air mass.

The air-mass concept is an important one because it is closely related to the study of atmospheric disturbances. Many significant middle-latitude disturbances originate along the boundary zones that separate different air masses.

Source Regions

 **Basic Weather Patterns**

▶ Air Masses

Where do air masses form? What factors determine the nature and degree of uniformity of an air mass? These two basic questions are closely related, because the site where an air mass forms vitally affects the properties that characterize it.

Areas in which air masses originate are called **source regions.** Because the atmosphere is heated chiefly from below and gains its moisture by evaporation from Earth's surface, the nature of the source region largely determines the initial characteristics of an air mass. An ideal source region must meet two essential criteria. First, it must be an extensive and physically uniform area. A region having highly irregular topography or one that has a surface consisting of both water and land is not satisfactory.

The second criterion is that the area be characterized by a general stagnation of atmospheric circulation so that air will stay over the region long enough to come to some measure of equilibrium with the surface. In general, it means regions dominated by stationary or slow-moving anticyclones with their extensive areas of calms or light winds.

Regions under the influence of cyclones are not likely to produce air masses because such systems are characterized by converging surface winds. The winds in lows are constantly bringing air with unlike temperature and humidity properties into the area. Because the time involved is not long enough to eliminate these differences, steep temperature gradients result, and air-mass formation cannot take place.

Figure 8–3 shows the source regions that produce the air masses that most often influence North America. The waters

FIGURE 8-3 Air-mass source regions for North America. Source regions are largely confined to subtropical and subpolar locations. The fact that the middle latitudes are the site where cold and warm air masses clash, often because the converging winds of a traveling cyclone draw them together, means that this zone lacks the conditions necessary to be a source region. The differences between polar and arctic are relatively small and serve to indicate the degree of coldness of the respective air masses. By comparing the summer and winter maps, it is clear that the extent and temperature characteristics fluctuate.

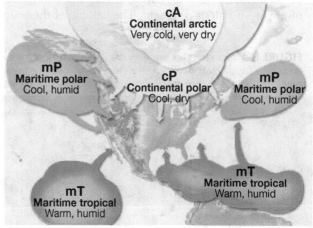

(a) Winter pattern

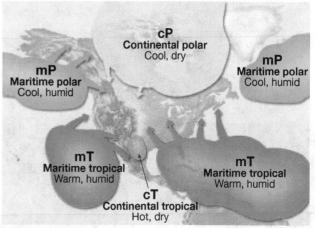

(b) Summer pattern

of the Gulf of Mexico and Caribbean Sea and similar regions in the Pacific west of Mexico yield warm air masses, as does the land area that encompasses the southwestern United States and northern Mexico. In contrast, the North Pacific, the North Atlantic, and the snow- and ice-covered areas comprising northern North America and the adjacent Arctic Ocean are major source regions for cold air masses. It is also clear that the size and intensity of the source regions change seasonally.

Notice in Figure 8–3 that major source regions are not found in the middle latitudes but instead are confined to subtropical and subpolar locations. The fact that the middle latitudes are the site where cold and warm air masses clash, often because the converging winds of a traveling cyclone draw them together, means that this zone lacks the conditions necessary to be a source region. Instead, this latitude belt is one of the stormiest on the planet.

Classifying Air Masses

 **Basic Weather Patterns**

▶ Air Masses

The classification of an air mass depends on the latitude of the source region and the nature of the surface in the area of origin—ocean or continent. The latitude of the source region indicates the temperature conditions within the air mass, and the nature of the surface below strongly influences the moisture content of the air.

Air masses are identified by two-letter codes. With reference to latitude (temperature), air masses are placed into one of three categories: **polar (P), arctic (A),** or **tropical (T).** The differences between polar and arctic are usually small and simply serve to indicate the degree of coldness of the respective air masses.

The lowercase letter *m* (for **maritime**) or the lowercase letter *c* (for **continental**) is used to designate the nature of the surface in the source region and hence the humidity characteristics of the air mass. Because maritime air masses form over oceans, they have a relatively high water-vapor content compared to continental air masses that originate over landmasses (Figure 8–4).

When this classification scheme is applied, the following air masses can be identified:

cA	continental	arctic
cP	continental	polar
cT	continental	tropical
mT	maritime	tropical
mP	maritime	polar

Notice that the list does not include mA (maritime arctic). These air masses are not listed, because they seldom,

FIGURE 8-4 Air masses acquire their properties of temperature and moisture from extensive and physically uniform areas called *source regions.* When an air mass forms over the ocean, it is called *maritime.* Such air masses are relatively humid in contrast to continental air masses, which are dry. *(Photo by Norbert Wu/Peter Arnold, Inc.)*

if ever, form. Although arctic air masses form over the Arctic Ocean, this water body is ice-covered throughout the year. Consequently, the air masses that originate here consistently have the moisture characteristics associated with a continental source region.

Air-Mass Modification

After an air mass forms, it normally migrates from the area where it acquired its distinctive properties to a region with different surface characteristics. Once the air mass moves from its source region, it not only modifies the weather of the area it is traversing, but it is also gradually modified by the surface over which it is moving. Warming or cooling from below, the addition or loss of moisture, and vertical movements all act to bring about changes in an air mass. The amount of modification can be relatively small, or as the following example illustrates, the changes can be profound enough to alter completely the original identity of the air mass.

When cA or cP air moves over the ocean in winter, it undergoes considerable change. Evaporation from the water surface rapidly transfers large quantities of moisture to the once-dry continental air. Furthermore, because the underlying water is warmer than the air above, the air is also heated from below. This factor leads to instability and vertically ascending currents that rapidly transport heat and moisture to higher levels. In a matter of days, cold, dry, and stable continental air is transformed into an unstable mP air mass.

When an air mass is colder than the surface over which it is passing, as in the preceding example, the lowercase letter *k* is added after the air-mass symbol. If, however, an air mass is warmer than the underlying surface, the lowercase letter *w* is added. It should be remembered that the *k* or *w* suffix does not mean that the air mass itself is cold or warm. It means only that the air is *relatively* cold or warm in comparison with the underlying surface over which it is traveling. For example, an mT air mass from the Gulf of Mexico is usually classified as mTk as it moves over the southeastern states in summer. Although the air mass is warm, it is still cooler than the highly heated landmass over which it is passing.

The *k* or *w* designation gives an indication of the stability of an air mass and hence the weather that might be expected. An air mass that is colder than the surface is obviously going to be warmed in its lower layers. This fact causes greater instability that favors the ascent of the heated lower air and creates the possibility of cloud formation and precipitation. Indeed, a *k* air mass is often characterized by cumulus clouds, and should precipitation occur, it will be of the shower or thunderstorm variety. Also, visibility is generally good (except in rain) because of the stirring and overturning of the air.

Conversely, when an air mass is warmer than the surface over which it is moving, its lower layers are chilled. A surface inversion that increases the stability of the air mass often develops. This condition does not favor the ascent of

air, and so it opposes cloud formation and precipitation. Any clouds that do form will be stratus, and precipitation, if any, will be light to moderate. Moreover, because of the lack of vertical movements, smoke and dust often become concentrated in the lower layers of the air mass and cause poor visibility. During certain times of the year, fogs, especially the advection type, may also be common in some regions.

In addition to modifications resulting from temperature differences between an air mass and the surface below, upward and downward movements induced by cyclones and anticyclones or topography can also affect the stability of an air mass. Such modifications are often called *mechanical* or *dynamic* and are usually independent of the changes caused by surface cooling or heating. For example, significant modification can result when an air mass is drawn into a low. Here convergence and lifting dominate and the air mass is rendered more unstable. Conversely, the subsidence associated with anticyclones acts to stabilize an air mass. Similar alterations in stability occur when an air mass is lifted over highlands or descends the leeward side of a mountain barrier. In the first case, the air's stability is reduced; in the second case, the air becomes more stable.

Properties of North American Air Masses

Air masses frequently pass over us, which means that the day-to-day weather we experience often depends on the temperature, stability, and moisture content of these large bodies of air. In this section, we briefly examine the properties of the principal North American air masses. In addition, Table 8–1 serves as a summary.

Continental Polar (cP) and Continental Arctic (cA) Air Masses

Continental polar and continental arctic air masses are, as their classification implies, cold and dry. Continental polar air originates over the often snow-covered interior regions of Canada and Alaska, poleward of the 50th parallel. Continental arctic air forms farther north, over the Arctic Basin and the Greenland ice cap (Figure 8–3).

Continental arctic air is distinguished from cP air by its generally lower temperatures, although at times the differences may be slight. In fact, some meteorologists do not differentiate between cP and cA.

During the winter, both air masses are bitterly cold and very dry. Winter nights are long, and the daytime Sun is short-lived and low in the sky. Consequently, as winter advances, Earth's surface and atmosphere lose heat that, for the most part, is not replenished by incoming solar energy. Therefore, the surface reaches very low temperatures and the air near the ground is gradually chilled to heights of 1 kilometer (0.6 mile) or more. The result is a strong and

TABLE 8-1 Weather characteristics of North American air masses

Air mass	Source region	Temperature and moisture characteristics in source region	Stability in source region	Associated weather
cA	Arctic basin and Greenland ice cap	Bitterly cold and very dry in winter	Stable	Cold waves in winter
cP	Interior Canada and Alaska	Very cold and dry in winter	Stable entire year	a. Cold waves in winter b. Modified to cPk in winter over Great Lakes bringing "lake-effect" snow to leeward shores
mP	North Pacific	Mild (cool) and humid entire year	Unstable in winter Stable in summer	a. Low clouds and showers in winter b. Heavy orographic precipitation on windward side of western mountains in winter c. Low stratus and fog along coast in summer; modified to cP inland
mP	Northwestern Atlantic	Cold and humid in winter Cool and humid in summer	Unstable in winter Stable in summer	a. Occasional "nor'easter" in winter b. Occasional periods of clear, cool weather in summer
cT	Northern interior Mexico and southwestern U.S. (summer only)	Hot and dry	Unstable	a. Hot, dry, and cloudless, rarely influencing areas outside source region b. Occasional drought to southern Great Plains
mT	Gulf of Mexico, Caribbean Sea, western Atlantic	Warm and humid entire year	Unstable entire year	a. In winter it usually becomes mTw moving northward and brings occasional widespread precipitation or advection fog b. In summer, hot and humid conditions, frequent cumulus development and showers or thunderstorms
mT	Subtropical Pacific	Warm and humid entire year	Stable entire year	a. In winter it brings fog, drizzle, and occasional moderate precipitation to N.W. Mexico and S.W. United States b. In summer this air mass occasionally reaches the western United States and is a source of moisture for infrequent convectional thunderstorms.

persistent temperature inversion with the coldest temperatures near the ground. Marked stability is, therefore, the rule. Because the air is very cold and the surface below is frozen, the mixing ratio of these air masses is necessarily low, ranging from perhaps 0.1 gram per kilogram in cA up to 1.5 grams per kilogram in some cP air.

As wintertime cP or cA air moves outward from its source region, it carries its cold, dry weather to the United States, normally entering between the Great Lakes and the Rockies. Because there are no major barriers between the high-latitude source regions and the Gulf of Mexico, cP and cA air masses can sweep rapidly and with relative ease far southward into the United States. The winter cold waves experienced in much of the central and eastern United States are closely associated with such polar outbreaks. One such cold wave is described in Box 8–1. Usually, the last freeze in spring and the first in autumn can be correlated with outbreaks of polar or arctic air.

Because cA air is present principally in the winter, only cP air has any influence on our summer weather, and this effect is considerably reduced when compared with winter. During summer months, the properties of the source region for cP air are very different from those during winter. Instead of being chilled by the ground, the air is warmed from below as the long days and higher Sun angle warm the snow-free land surface. Although summer cP air is warmer and has a higher moisture content than its wintertime counterpart, the air is still cool and relatively dry compared with areas farther south. Summer heat waves in the northern portions of the eastern and central United States are often ended by the southward advance of cP air, which for a day or two brings cooling relief and bright, pleasant weather.

Students Sometimes Ask...

When a cold air mass moves south from Canada into the United States, how rapidly can temperatures change?

When a fast-moving frigid air mass advances into the northern Great Plains, temperatures have been known to plunge 20° to 30°C (40°–50°F) in a matter of just a few hours. One notable example is a drop of 55.5°C (100°F), from 6.7°C to −48.8°C (44° to −56°F), in 24 hours at Browning, Montana, on January 23–24, 1916. Another remarkable example occurred on Christmas Eve, 1924, when the temperature at Fairfield, Montana, dropped from 17°C (63°F) at noon to −29°C (−21°F) at midnight—an amazing 46°C (83°F) change in just 12 hours.

Lake-Effect Snow: Cold Air over Warm Water

Continental polar air masses are not, as a rule, associated with heavy precipitation. Yet during late autumn and winter a unique and interesting weather phenomenon takes place along the downwind shores of the Great Lakes.° Periodically, brief, heavy snow showers issue from dark clouds that move onshore from the lakes (see Box 8–2). Seldom do these storms move more than about 80 kilometers (50 miles) inland from the shore before the snows come to an end. These highly localized storms, occurring along the leeward shores of the Great Lakes, create what are known as **lake-effect snows.**

Lake-effect storms account for a high percentage of the snowfall in many areas adjacent to the lakes. The strips of land that are most frequently affected, called *snowbelts*, are shown in Figure 8–5. A comparison of average snowfall totals at Thunder Bay, Ontario, on the north shore of Lake Superior, and Marquette, Michigan, along the southern shore, provides another excellent example. Because Marquette is situated on the leeward shore of the lake, it receives substantial lake-effect snow and therefore has a much higher snowfall total than does Thunder Bay (Table 8–2).

° Actually, the Great Lakes are just the best-known example. Other large lakes can also experience this phenomenon.

What causes lake-effect snow? The answer is closely linked to the differential heating of water and land (Chapter 3) and to the concept of atmospheric instability. During the summer months, bodies of water, including the Great Lakes, absorb huge quantities of energy from the Sun and from the warm air that passes over them. Although these water bodies do not reach particularly high temperatures, they nevertheless represent huge reservoirs of heat. The surrounding land, in contrast, cannot store heat nearly as effectively. Consequently, during autumn and winter, the temperature of the land drops quickly, whereas water bodies lose their heat more gradually and cool slowly.

From late November through late January the contrasts in average temperatures between water and land range from about 8°C in the southern Great Lakes to 17°C farther north. However, the temperature differences can be much greater (perhaps 25°C) when a very cold cP or cA air mass pushes southward across the lakes. When such a dramatic temperature contrast exists, the lakes interact with the air to produce major lake-effect storms. Figure 8–6 depicts the movement of a cP air mass across one of the Great Lakes. During its journey, the air acquires large quantities of heat and moisture from the relatively warm lake surface. By the time it reaches the opposite shore, this cPk air is humid and unstable and heavy snow showers are likely.

Students Sometimes Ask...

I know that Buffalo, New York, is famous for its lake-effect snows. Just how bad can it get?

Because of Buffalo's location along the eastern shore of Lake Erie, it does indeed receive a great deal of lake-effect snow (see Figure 8–5). One of the most memorable events took place between December 24, 2001, and January 1, 2002. This storm, which set a record as the longest-lasting lake-effect event, buried Buffalo with 207.3 centimeters (81.6 inches) of snow. Prior to this storm, the record for the *entire month* of December had been 173.7 centimeters (68.4 inches)! The eastern shore of Lake Ontario was also hard hit, with one station recording more than 317 centimeters (125 inches) of snow.

Maritime Polar (mP) Air Masses

Maritime polar air masses form over oceans at high latitudes. As the classification would indicate, mP air is cool to cold and humid, but compared with cP and cA air masses in winter, mP air is relatively mild because of the higher temperatures of the ocean surface as contrasted to the colder continents.

BOX 8-1   The Siberian Express

T he surface weather map for December 22, 1989, shows a high-pressure center covering the eastern two-thirds of the United States and a substantial portion of Canada (Figure 8–A). As is usually the case in winter, a large anticyclone such as this is associated with a huge mass of dense and bitterly cold arctic air. After

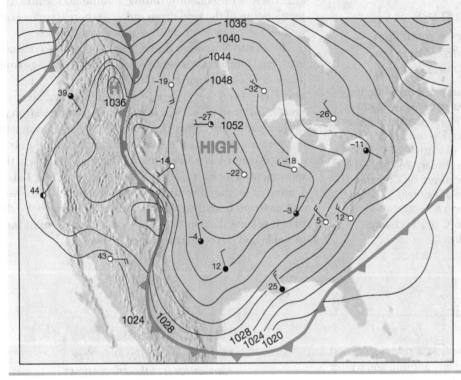

FIGURE 8-A A surface weather map for 7 A.M. EST, December 22, 1989. This simplified National Weather Service (NWS) map shows an intense winter cold wave caused by an outbreak of frigid continental arctic air. This event brought subfreezing temperatures as far south as the Gulf of Mexico. Temperatures on NWS maps are in degrees Fahrenheit.

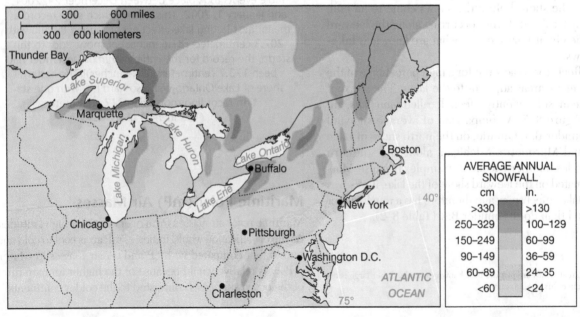

FIGURE 8-5 The snowbelts of the Great Lakes region are easy to pick out on this snowfall map. *(Data from NOAA)*

AVERAGE ANNUAL SNOWFALL	
cm	in.
>330	>130
250–329	100–129
150–249	60–99
90–149	36–59
60–89	24–35
<60	<24

such an air mass forms over the frozen expanses near the Arctic Circle, the winds aloft sometimes direct it toward the south and east. When an outbreak takes place, it is popularly called the "Siberian Express" by the news media.

November 1989 was unusually mild for late autumn. In fact, across the United States, over 200 daily high-temperature records were set. December, however, was different. East of the Rockies, the month's weather was dominated by two arctic outbreaks. The second brought record-breaking cold.

Between December 21–25, as the frigid dome of high pressure advanced southward and eastward, more than 370 record low temperatures were reported. On December 21, Havre, Montana, had an overnight low of −42.2°C (−44°F), breaking a record set in 1884. Meanwhile, Topeka's −32.2°C (−26°F) was that city's lowest temperature for any date since record keeping started 102 years earlier.

The three days that followed saw the arctic air migrate toward the south and east. By December 24, Tallahassee, Florida, had a low temperature of −10°C (14°F). In the center of the state the daily minimum at Orlando was −5.6°C (22°F). It was actually warmer in North Dakota on Christmas Eve than in central and northern Florida!

As we would expect, utility companies in many states reported record demand. When the arctic air advanced into Texas and Florida, agriculture was especially hard hit. Some Florida citrus growers lost 40 percent of their crop, and many vegetable crops were wiped out completely (Figure 8–B).

After Christmas the circulation pattern that brought this record-breaking Siberian Express from the arctic deep into the United States changed. As a result, temperatures for much of the country during January and February 1990 were well above normal. In fact, January 1990

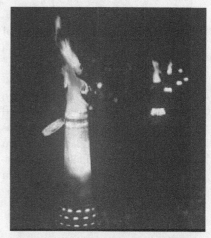

FIGURE 8-B When an arctic air mass invades the citrus regions of Florida and Texas, even modern freeze controls may not be able to prevent significant losses. *(Photo courtesy of Florida Department of Citrus)*

was the second warmest January in 96 years. Thus, despite frigid December temperatures, the winter of 1989–1990 "averaged out" to be a relatively warm one.

Two regions are important sources for mP air that influences North America: the North Pacific and the northwestern Atlantic from Newfoundland to Cape Cod (Figure 8–3). Because of the general west-to-east circulation in the middle latitudes, mP air masses from the North Pacific source region have a more profound influence on North American weather than do mP air masses generated in the northwestern Atlantic. Whereas air masses that form in the Atlantic generally move eastward toward Europe, mP air from the

FIGURE 8-6 (a) As continental polar air crosses the Great Lakes in winter, it acquires moisture and is made unstable because of warming from below. A "lake-effect" snow shower on the lee side of the lakes is often the consequence of this air-mass modification. (b) This satellite image from December 27, 2001, shows thick bands of clouds extending from the eastern tip of Lake Erie to east of Buffalo. Thick cloud bands also extend from the eastern margin of Lake Huron over southern Ontario. The arrows show the wind direction, which was blowing across the length of the lake. *(Image courtesy of NASA GOES Project Science Office)*

TABLE 8-2 Monthly snowfall at Thunder Bay, Ontario, and Marquette, Michigan

Thunder Bay, Ontario			
October	November	December	January
3.0 cm	14.9 cm	19.0 cm	22.6 cm
(1.2 in.)	(5.8 in.)	(7.4 in.)	(8.8 in.)

Marquette, Michigan			
October	November	December	January
5.3 cm	37.6 cm	56.4 cm	53.1 cm
(2.1 in.)	(14.7 in.)	(22 in.)	(20.7 in.)

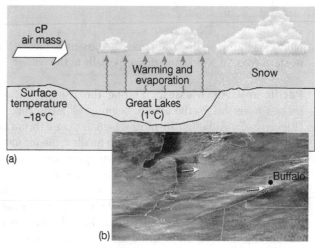

BOX 8-2 Atmospheric Hazard: An Extraordinary Lake-Effect Snowstorm

ortheastern Ohio is part of the Lake Erie snowbelt, a zone that extends eastward into northwestern Pennsylvania and western New York (see Figure 8–5). Here snowfall is enhanced when cold winds blow from the west or northwest across the relatively warm unfrozen waters of Lake Erie. Average annual snowfall in northeastern Ohio is between 200 and 280 cen-

timeters (80 to 110 inches) and increases to 450 centimeters (175 inches) in western New York.

Although residents here are accustomed to abundant snows, even they were surprised in November 1996 by an especially early and strong storm. During a six-day span, from November 9–14, northeastern Ohio experienced record-breaking lake-effect snows. Rather than raking fall

leaves, people were shoveling sidewalks and clearing snow from overloaded roofs (Figure 8–C).

Persistent snow squalls (narrow bands of heavy snow) frequently produced accumulation rates of 5 centimeters (2 inches) per hour during the six-day siege. The snow was the result of especially deep and prolonged lower atmospheric instability created by the movement of cold air

FIGURE 8-C A six-day lake-effect snowstorm in November 1996 dropped 175 centimeters (nearly 69 inches) of snow on Chardon, Ohio, setting a new state record. *(Photo by Tony Dejak/AP/Wide World Photos)*

North Pacific has a strong influence on the weather along the western coast of North America, especially in the winter.

Pacific mP Air Masses. During the winter, mP air masses from the Pacific usually begin as cP air in Siberia (Figure 8–7). Although air rarely stagnates over this area, the source region is extensive enough to allow the air moving across it to acquire its characteristic properties. As the air advances eastward over the relatively warm water, active evaporation and heating occur in the lower levels. Consequently, what was once a very cold, dry, and stable air mass is changed into one that is mild and humid near the surface and relatively unstable. As this mP air arrives

at the western coast of North America, it is often accompanied by low clouds and shower activity. When the mP air advances inland against the western mountains, orographic uplift produces heavy rain or snow on the windward slopes of the mountains (see Figure 15–12).

Maritime Polar Air from the North Atlantic. As is the case for mP air from the Pacific, air masses forming in the northwestern Atlantic source region were originally cP air masses that moved from the continent and were transformed over the ocean. However, unlike air masses from the North Pacific, mP air from the Atlantic only occasionally affects the weather of North America. Nevertheless,

across a relatively warm Lake Erie. The surface temperature of the lake was 12°C (54°F), several degrees above normal. The air temperature at a height of 1.5 kilometers (nearly 5000 feet) was −5°C (23°F).

The northwest flow of cold air across Lake Erie and the 17°C lapse rate generated lake-effect rain and snow almost immediately.[*] During some periods loud thunder accompanied the snow squalls!

Data from the Cleveland National Weather Service Snow Spotters Network show 100 to 125 centimeters (39 to 49 inches) of snow through the core of the Ohio snowbelt (Figure 8–D). The deepest accumulation was

measured near Chardon, Ohio. Here the six-day total of 175 centimeters (68.9 inches) far exceeded the previous Ohio record of 107 centimeters (42 inches) set in 1901. In addition, the November 1996 snowfall total of 194.8 centimeters (76.7 inches) at the same site set a new monthly snowfall record for Ohio. The previous one-month record had been 176.5 centimeters (69.5 inches).

The impact of the storm was considerable. Ohio's governor declared a state of emergency on November 12, and National Guard troops were dispatched to assist in snow removal and aid in the rescue of snowbound residents. There was widespread damage

to trees and shrubs across northeastern Ohio because the snow was particularly wet and dense and readily clung to objects. Press reports indicated that about 168,000 homes were without electricity, some for several days. Roofs of numerous buildings collapsed under the excessive snow loads. Although residents of the northeast Ohio snowbelt are winter storm veterans, the six-day storm in November 1996 will be long remembered as an extraordinary event.

[*]Thomas W. Schmidlin and James Kasarik, "A Record Ohio Snowfall during 9–14 November 1996," *Bulletin of the American Meteorological Society*, Vol. 80, No. 6, June 1999, p. 1109.

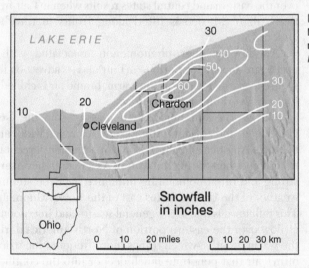

FIGURE 8-D Snowfall totals (in inches) for northeastern Ohio for the November 9–14, 1996, lake-effect storm. The deepest accumulation, nearly 69 inches (175 centimeters), occurred near Chardon. *(After National Weather Service)*

this air mass does have an effect when the northeastern United States is on the northern or northwestern edge of a passing low-pressure center. On these occasions, cyclonic winds draw mP air into the region. Its influence is generally confined to the area east of the Appalachians and north of Cape Hatteras, North Carolina. The weather associated with an invasion of mP air from the Atlantic is known locally as a **nor'easter.** Strong northeast winds, freezing or near freezing temperatures, high relative humidity, and the likelihood of precipitation make this weather phenomenon an unwelcome event.

Summer brings a change in the characteristics of mP air masses from the North Pacific. During the warm season, the

FIGURE 8-7 During winter, maritime polar (mP) air masses in the North Pacific usually begin as continental polar (cP) air masses in Siberia. The cP air is modified to mP as it slowly crosses the ocean.

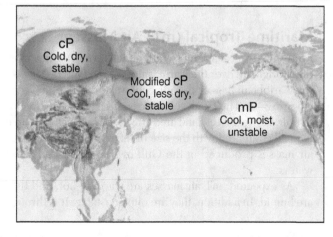

ocean is cooler than the surrounding continents. In addition, the Pacific high lies off the western coast of the United States (see Figure 7–10). Consequently, there is almost continuous southward flow of air having moderate temperatures. Although the air near the surface may often be conditionally unstable, the presence of the Pacific high means that there is subsidence and stability aloft. Thus, low stratus clouds and summer fogs characterize much of the western coast. Once summer mP air from the Pacific moves inland, it is heated at the surface over the hot and dry interior. The heating and resulting turbulence act to reduce the relative humidity in the lower layers, and the clouds dissipate.

Although mP air masses from the Atlantic may produce an occasional unwelcome nor'easter during the winter, summertime incursions of this air mass often bring pleasant weather. Like the Pacific source region, the northwestern Atlantic is dominated by high pressure during the summer (see Figure 7–10). Thus, the upper air is stable because of subsidence and the lower air is essentially stable because of the chilling effect of the relatively cool water. As the circulation on the southern side of the anticyclone carries this stable and relatively dry mP air into New England, and occasionally as far south as Virginia, the region enjoys clear, cool weather and good visibility.

Students Sometimes Ask…

I once heard a weather report refer to some storms in California as being associated with the "Pineapple Express." What were they talking about?

Much of the precipitation along the western margin of North America occurs in winter when unstable mP air originating in the vicinity of the Gulf of Alaska is drawn into a cyclonic system and/or lifted orographically. Occasionally, however, storms approach the West Coast from the subtropical Pacific in the vicinity of the Hawaiian Islands. Because these storms advance from the direction of Hawaii, they are sometimes called the "Pineapple Express." These systems, with their associated mT air, sometimes yield torrential flood-producing rains.

Maritime Tropical (mT) Air Masses

Maritime tropical air masses affecting North America most often originate over the warm waters of the Gulf of Mexico, the Caribbean Sea, or the adjacent western Atlantic Ocean (Figure 8–3). The tropical Pacific is also a source region for mT air. However, the land area affected by this latter source is small compared with the size of the region influenced by air masses produced in the Gulf of Mexico and adjacent waters.

As expected, mT air masses are warm to hot, and they are humid. In addition, they are often unstable. It is through invasions of mT air masses that the subtropics export much heat and moisture to the cooler and drier areas to the north. Consequently, these air masses are important to the weather whenever present because they are capable of contributing significant precipitation.

North Atlantic mT Air. Maritime tropical air masses from the Gulf–Caribbean–Atlantic source region greatly affect the weather of the United States east of the Rocky Mountains. Although the source region is dominated by the North Atlantic subtropical high, the air masses produced are not stable but are neutral or unstable because the source region is located on the weak western edge of the anticyclone where pronounced subsidence is absent.

During winter, when cP air dominates the central and eastern United States, mT air only occasionally enters this part of the country. When an invasion does occur, the lower portions of the air mass are chilled and stabilized as it moves northward. Its classification is changed to mTw. As a result, the formation of convective showers is unlikely. Widespread precipitation does occur, however, when a northward-moving mT air mass is pulled into a traveling cyclone and forced to ascend. In fact, much of the wintertime precipitation over the eastern and central states results when mT air from the Gulf of Mexico is lifted along fronts in traveling cyclones.

Another weather phenomenon associated with a northward-moving wintertime mT air mass is advection fog. Dense fogs can develop as the warm, humid air is chilled as it moves over the cold land surface.

During the summer, mT air masses from the Gulf, Caribbean, and adjacent Atlantic affect a much wider area of North America and are present for a greater percentage of the time than during the winter. As a result, they exert a strong and often dominating influence over the summer weather of the United States east of the Rocky Mountains. This influence is due to the general sea-to-land (monsoonal) airflow over the eastern portion of North America during the warm months, which brings more frequent incursions of mT air that penetrate much deeper into the continent than during the winter months. Consequently, these air masses are largely responsible for the hot and humid conditions that prevail over the eastern and central United States.

Initially, summertime mT air from the Gulf is unstable. As it moves inland over the warmer land, it becomes an mTk air mass as daytime heating of the surface layers further increases the air's instability. Because the relative humidity is high, only modest lifting is necessary to bring about active convection, cumulus development, and thunderstorm or shower activity (Figure 8–8). This is, indeed, a common warm-weather phenomenon associated with mT air.

It should be also noted here that air masses from the Gulf–Caribbean–Atlantic region are the primary source of much, if not most, of the precipitation received in the eastern two-thirds of the United States. Pacific air masses con-

FIGURE 8-8 As mT air from the Gulf of Mexico moves over the heated land in the summer, cumulus development and afternoon showers frequently result. *(Photo by Rod Planck/Photo Researchers, Inc.)*

tribute little to the water supply east of the Rockies because the western mountains effectively "drain" the moisture from the air by numerous episodes of orographic uplift.

Figure 8–9, which shows the distribution of average annual precipitation for the eastern two-thirds of the United States by using **isohyets** (lines connecting places having equal rainfall), illustrates this situation nicely. The pattern of isohyets shows the greatest rainfall in the Gulf region and a decrease in precipitation with increasing distance from the mT source region.

FIGURE 8-9 Average annual precipitation for the eastern two-thirds of the United States. Note the general decrease in yearly precipitation totals with increasing distance from the Gulf of Mexico, the source region for mT air masses. Isohyets are labeled in inches. *(Courtesy of Environmental Data Service, NOAA)*

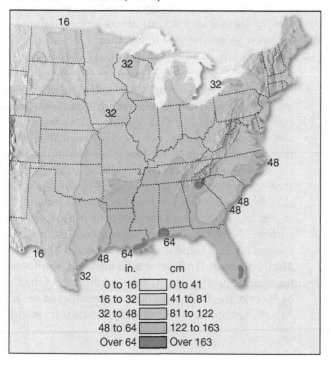

North Pacific mT Air. Compared to mT air from the Gulf of Mexico, mT air masses from the Pacific source region have much less of an impact on North American weather. In winter, only northwestern Mexico and the extreme southwestern United States are influenced by air from the tropical Pacific. Because the source region lies along the eastern side of the Pacific anticyclone, subsidence aloft produces upper-level stability. When the air mass moves northward, cooling at the surface also causes the lower layers to become more stable, often resulting in fog or drizzle. If lifted along a front or forced over mountains, moderate precipitation results.

For many years the summertime influence of air masses from the tropical Pacific source region on the weather of the southwestern United States and northern Mexico was believed to be minimal. It was thought that the moisture for the infrequent summer thunderstorms that occur in the region came from occasional westward thrusts of mT air from the Gulf of Mexico. However, the Gulf of Mexico is no longer believed to be the primary supplier of moisture for the area west of the Continental Divide. Rather, it has been demonstrated that the tropical North Pacific west of central Mexico is a more important source of moisture for this area.

In summer the mT air moves northward from its Pacific source region up the Gulf of California and into the interior of the western United States. This movement, which is confined largely to July and August, is essentially monsoonal in character. That is, the inflow of moist air is a response to the thermally produced low pressure that develops over the heated landmass. The July–August rainfall maximum for Tucson is a response to this incursion of Pacific mT air (Figure 8–10).

Continental Tropical (cT) Air Masses

North America narrows as it extends southward through Mexico; therefore, the continent has no extensive source region for continental tropical air masses. By checking the maps in Figure 8–3, you can see that only in summer do northern interior Mexico and adjacent parts of the arid

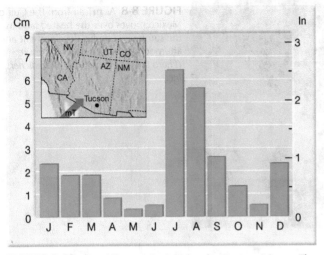

FIGURE 8-10 Monthly precipitation data for Tucson, Arizona. The July–August rainfall maximum in the desert Southwest results from the monsoonal flow of Pacific mT air into the region.

southwestern United States produce hot, dry cT air. Because of the intense daytime heating at the surface, both a steep environmental lapse rate and turbulence extending to considerable heights are found. Nevertheless, although the air is unstable, it generally remains nearly cloudless because of extremely low humidity. Consequently, the prevailing weather is hot, with an almost complete lack of rainfall. Large daily temperature ranges are the rule. Although cT air masses are usually confined to the source region, occasionally they move into the southern Great Plains. If the cT air persists for long, drought may occur.

Chapter Summary

- In the middle latitudes many weather events are associated with the movements of air masses. An *air mass* is a large body of air, usually 1600 kilometers (1000 miles) or more across and perhaps several kilometers thick, that is characterized by homogeneous physical properties (in particular temperature and moisture content) at any given altitude. A region under the influence of an air mass will probably experience generally constant weather conditions, a situation referred to as *air-mass weather.*

- Areas in which air masses originate are called *source regions.* An ideal source region must meet two criteria. First, it must be an extensive and physically uniform area. The second criterion is that the area is characterized by a general stagnation of atmospheric circulation so that air will stay over the region long enough to come to some measure of equilibrium with the surface.

- The classification of an air mass depends on (1) the latitude of the source region, and (2) the nature of the surface in the area of origin—ocean or continent. Air masses are identified by two-letter codes. With reference to latitude (temperature), air masses are placed into one of three categories: *polar (P), arctic (A),* or *tropical (T).* A lowercase letter (*m,* for *maritime,* or *c* for *continental*) is placed in front of the uppercase letter to designate the nature of the surface in the source region and therefore the humidity characteristics of the air mass. Using this classification scheme, the following air masses are identified: cA, cP, cT, mT, and mP.

- Once an air mass moves from its source region, it not only modifies the weather of the area it is traversing, but it is also gradually modified by the surface over which it is moving. Changes to the stability of an air mass can result from temperature differences between an air mass and the surface and/or vertical movements induced by cyclones, anticyclones or topography.

- The day-to-day weather we experience depends on the temperature, stability, and moisture content of the air mass we are experiencing. *Continental polar* (cP) and *continental arctic* (cA) air masses are, as their classification implies, cold and dry. Although cP air masses are not, as a rule, associated with heavy precipitation, those that cross the Great Lakes during late autumn and winter sometimes bring *lake-effect snows* to the leeward shores. *Maritime polar* air masses (mP) form over oceans at high latitudes and are cool to cold and humid. The stormy winter weather associated with an invasion of mP air from the Atlantic into an area east of the Appalachians and north of Cape Hatteras is known as a *nor'easter.* *Maritime tropical* (mT) air masses affecting North America most often originate over the warm water of the Gulf of Mexico, the Caribbean Sea, or the adjacent western Atlantic Ocean. As expected, mT air masses are warm to hot, and they are humid. During winter, when cP air dominates the central and eastern United States, mT air only occasionally enters this part of the country. However, during the summer, mT air masses from the Gulf, Caribbean, and adjacent Atlantic are more common and cover a much wider area of the continent. The mT air masses from the Gulf–Caribbean–Atlantic source region are also the source of much, if not most, of the precipitation received in the eastern two-thirds of the United States. *Isohyets,* lines of equal rainfall drawn on a map, show that the greatest rainfall occurs in the Gulf region and decreases with increasing distance from the mT source region. Hot and dry *continental tropical* (cT) air is produced only in the summer in northern interior Mexico and adjacent parts of the arid southwestern United States.

Vocabulary Review

air mass (p. 234)
air-mass weather (p. 324)
arctic (A) air mass (p. 326)
continental (c) air mass (p. 326)

isohyet (p. 245)
lake-effect snow (p. 239)
maritime (m) air mass (p. 236)
nor'easter (p. 242)

polar (P) air mass (236)
source region (p. 235)
tropical (T) air mass (p. 236)

Review Questions

1. Define the terms *air mass* and *air-mass weather.*
2. What two criteria must be met for an area to be an air-mass source region?
3. Why are regions that have a cyclonic circulation generally not conducive to air-mass formation?
4. On what bases are air masses classified? Compare the temperature and moisture characteristics of the following air masses: cP, mP, mT, and cT.
5. Why is mA left out of the air-mass classification scheme?
6. What do the lowercase letters k and w indicate about an air mass? List the general weather conditions associated with k and w air masses.
7. During winter, polar air masses are cold. Which should be coldest, a wintertime mP air mass or a wintertime cP air mass? Explain your choice.
8. How might vertical movements induced by a pressure system or topography act to modify an air mass?
9. What two air masses are most important to the weather of the United States east of the Rocky Mountains? Explain your choice.
10. What air mass influences the weather of the Pacific Coast more than any other?
11. Why do cA and cP air masses often sweep so far south into the United States?
12. Describe the modifications that occur as a cP air mass moves across one of the Great Lakes in the winter.
13. Why do mP air masses from the North Atlantic source region seldom affect the eastern United States?
14. What air mass and source region provide the greatest amount of moisture to the eastern and central United States?
15. For each statement below, indicate which air mass is most likely involved and from what source region it came:
    a. summer drought in the southern Great Plains
    b. wintertime advection fog in the Midwest
    c. heavy winter precipitation in the western mountains
    d. summertime convectional showers in the Midwest and East
    e. a nor'easter

Problems

1. Figure 8–11 shows the distribution of air temperatures (top number) and dew-point temperatures (lower number) for a December morning. Two well-developed air masses are influencing North America at this time. The air masses are separated by a broad zone that is not affected by either air mass. Draw lines on the map that show the boundaries of each air mass. Label each air mass with the proper classification.

2. The Great Lakes are not the only water bodies associated with lake-effect snow. For example, large lakes in Canada also experience this phenomenon. Shown here are snowfall data (in centimeters) for two Canadian stations that receive significant lake-effect snow. Fort Resolution is on the southeastern shore of Great Slave Lake, and Norway House is at the northern end of Lake Winnipeg. During what month does each station have its snowfall maximum? Suggest an explanation as to why the maximum occurs when it does.

	Sept.	Oct.	Nov.	Dec.	Jan.
Fort Resolution	2.5	13.7	36.6	19.6	15.4
Norway House	3.8	6.9	29.5	20.1	16.3

3. Refer to Figure 8–5. Notice the narrow, north–south-oriented zone of relatively heavy snowfall east of Pittsburgh and Charleston. This region is too far from the Great Lakes to receive lake-effect snows. Speculate on a likely reason for the higher snowfalls here. Does your explanation explain the shape of this snowy zone?

4. Albuquerque, New Mexico, is situated in the desert Southwest. Its annual precipitation is just 21.2 centimeters (8.3 inches). Month-by-month data (in centimeters) are as follows:

J	F	M	A	M	J	J	A	S	O	N	D
1.0	1.0	1.3	1.3	1.3	1.3	3.3	3.8	2.3	2.3	1.0	1.3

What are the two rainiest months? The pattern here is similar to other southwestern cities, including Tuscon, Arizona. Briefly explain why the rainiest months occur when they do.

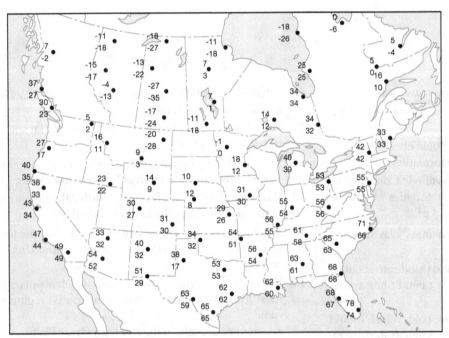

FIGURE 8-11 Map to accompany Problem 1.

Atmospheric Science Online

The Atmosphere 10e web site uses the resources and flexibility of the Internet to aid in your study of the topics in this chapter. Written and developed by meteorology instructors, this site will help improve your understanding of meteorology. Visit **http://www .prenhall.com/lutgens** and click on the cover of *The Atmosphere 10e* to find:

- **Online review quizzes**
- **Critical thinking exercises**
- **Links to chapter-specific web resources**
- **Internet-wide key term searches**

http://www.prenhall.com/lutgens

WEATHER PATTERNS

Storm clouds over Tucson, Arizona.
(Photo by A. T. Willett/Alamy)

The winter of 1992–1993 came to a stormy conclusion in eastern North America during a weekend in mid-March. The daffodils were already out across the South, and people were thinking about spring when the Blizzard of '93 struck on March 13 and 14. The huge storm brought record-low temperatures, record-low barometric-pressure readings, and record-high snowfalls to an area that stretched from Alabama to the Maritime Provinces of eastern Canada (Table 9–1). The monster storm, with its driving winds and heavy snow, combined the attributes of both hurricane and blizzard as it moved up the spine of the Appalachians, lashing and burying a huge swatch of territory (Figure 9–1). Although the atmospheric pressure at the storm's center was lower than the pressures at the centers of some hurricanes and the winds were frequently as strong as those in a hurricane, this was definitely not a tropical storm but a classic winter cyclone (Figure 9–2).

The event quickly earned the title Storm of the Century. The name was well deserved. Although many notable storms occurred during the twentieth century, none could match the extreme dimensions of this event. A famous nineteenth-century storm known as the Blizzard of '88 was equally severe but affected a much smaller area.

TABLE 9-1 A look at the Storm of the Century

Snowfall totals		
City	(CM)	(IN.)
Mount LeConte, Tenn.	140	56
Mount Mitchell, N.C.	125	50
Syracuse, N.Y.	108	43
Lincoln, N.H.	88	35
Mountain City, Ga.	60	24
Chattanooga, Tenn.	50	20
Asheville, N.C.	48	19
Record-low temperatures in the south		
City	(°C)	(°F)
Mount LeConte, Tenn.	−23	−10
Waynesville, N.C.	−20	−4
Birmingham, Ala.	−17	2
Knoxville, Tenn.	−14	6
Atlanta, Ga.	−8	18
Daytona Beach, Fla.	−0.6	31
Strong wind gusts		
City	(KPH)	(MPH)
Mount Washington, N.H.	232	144
Flattop Mountain, N.C.	163	101
South Marsh Island, La.	148	92
Myrtle Beach, S.C.	145	90
Fire Island, N.Y.	143	89
Boston, Mass.	130	81

FIGURE 9-1 One of the heaviest snowstorms to hit New York City since the Blizzard of '93, occurred on February 17, 2003. *(Photo by Benjamin Lowy/CORBIS)*

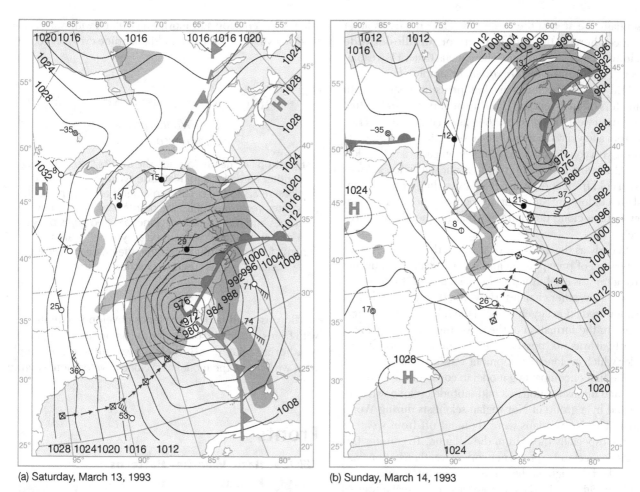

(a) Saturday, March 13, 1993

(b) Sunday, March 14, 1993

FIGURE 9-2 These simplified weather maps show the positions of an enormous cyclonic storm on March 13 and 14, 1993. After the storm formed in the Gulf of Mexico, it moved northeastward, spawning tornadoes in Florida and dumping huge quantities of snow from Alabama to Canada's Maritime Provinces. The closely spaced isobars depict the steep pressure gradient that generated hurricane-force winds in many places. The strong winds caused extreme drifting of snow and created storm waves in the Atlantic that pounded the coast, causing much beach erosion and damage to shoreline homes. The shaded areas indicate regions where precipitation occurred.

Despite excellent forecasts that permitted timely warnings, at least 270 people died as a result of the storm, more than three times the combined death tolls of hurricanes Hugo and Andrew. In Florida severe weather that included 27 tornadoes killed 44 people. At one time or another, every major airport on the U.S. East Coast was closed, as were most highways. Hundreds of hikers were stranded in the mountains by the record snowfalls, and thousands of others were stranded away from home in a variety of settings. At one point, 3 million people were without electricity. As the blizzard buried the region, hundreds of roofs collapsed under the wet, heavy snow. The National Weather Service office in Asheville, North Carolina, reported an extraordinary snow-to-water ratio of 4.2 to 1. A general ratio of 10 units of snow to 1 unit of water is common. Meanwhile, storm-generated waves pounded the coast. About 200 homes along the Outer Banks of North Carolina were damaged, with many left uninhabitable, and on Long Island 18 houses succumbed to the surf.

In the aftermath of the storm, temperatures plunged to record low levels as a frigid continental arctic air mass spilled into the region. On Sunday, March 14, some 70 cities in the East and South experienced record low temperatures. The next day 75 more record-low daily minimums were established. Freezing temperatures that reached as far south as Orlando, Florida, and Birmingham, Alabama, set a new March record of −17°C (2°F). The Storm of the Century was truly an awesome event that inhabitants of eastern North America will not soon forget.

Polar-Front Theory (Norwegian Cyclone Model)

In previous chapters we examined the basic elements of weather as well as the dynamics of atmospheric motions. We are now ready to apply our knowledge of these diverse phenomena to an understanding of day-to-day weather patterns in the middle latitudes. For our purposes, *middle latitudes* refers to the region between southern Florida and Alaska, essentially the area of the westerlies. The primary weather producer here is the **mid-latitude** or **middle-latitude cyclone**°. These are the same phenomena that a TV weather reporter calls a *low-pressure system* or simply a *low*.

Mid-latitude cyclones are low-pressure systems with diameters often exceeding 1000 kilometers (600 miles) that travel from west to east across the planet (Figure 9–3). Lasting from a few days to more than a week, these weather systems have a counterclockwise circulation pattern with a flow inward toward their centers. Most mid-latitude cyclones have a cold front and a warm front extending from the central area of low pressure. Surface convergence and upward flow initiate cloud development that frequently produces precipitation.

As early as the 1800s, it was known that cyclones were the bearers of precipitation and severe weather. Thus, the barometer was established as the main tool in "forecasting" day-to-day weather changes. However, this early method of weather prediction largely ignored the role of air-mass interactions in the formation of these weather systems. Consequently, it was not possible to determine the conditions under which cyclone development was favorable.

The first encompassing model to consider the development and intensification of a mid-latitude cyclone was constructed by a group of Norwegian scientists during World War I. The Norwegians were then cut off from weather reports, especially those from the Atlantic. To counter this deficiency, a closely spaced network of weather stations was established throughout the country. Using this network, several Norwegian-trained meteorologists made great advances in broadening our understanding of the weather and in particular our understanding of the middle-latitude cyclone. Included in this group were Vilhelm Bjerknes (pronounced *Bee-YURK-ness*), his son Jacob Bjerknes, Jacob's fellow student Halvor Solberg, and Swedish meteorologist Tor Bergeron (see Box 5–3). In 1921 the work of these scientists resulted in a publication outlining a compelling model of how mid-latitude cyclones progress through stages of birth, growth, and decay. These insights, which marked a turning point in atmospheric science, became known as the **polar-front theory**—also referred to as the **Norwegian cyclone model.** Even without the benefit of upper-air charts, these skilled meteorologists presented a working model that remains remarkably accurate to this day.

In the Norwegian cyclone model, middle-latitude cyclones develop in conjunction with the polar front. Recall that the polar front separates cold polar air from warm subtropical air (Chapter 7). During cool months the polar front is generally well defined and forms a nearly continuous band around Earth that can be recognized on upper-air charts. At the surface, this frontal zone is often broken into distinct segments. These frontal segments are separated by regions of more gradual temperature change. It is along frontal zones

where cold, equatorward-moving air collides with warm, poleward-moving air that most middle-latitude cyclones form.

Students Sometimes Ask...

What is an extratropical cyclone?

Extratropical means "outside the tropics," so this is just another name for a mid-latitude cyclone. The term cyclone refers to the circulation around any low-pressure center, regardless of its size or intensity. Hence, hurricanes and mid-latitude cyclones are two types of cyclones. Whereas "extratropical cyclone" is another name for a mid-latitude cyclone, the name "tropical cyclone" is often used to describe a hurricane.

Because mid-latitude cyclones develop in conjunction with fronts, we will first consider the nature of fronts and the weather associated with their movement and then apply what we learn to the model of cyclone development (Figure 9–3).

Fronts

GEODe **Basic Weather Patterns**
▶ Fronts

Fronts are boundary surfaces that separate air masses of different densities. One air mass is usually warmer and often contains more moisture than the other. However, fronts can form between any two contrasting air masses. When the vast sizes of air masses are considered, these 15- to 200-kilometer- (9- to 120-mile-) wide bands of discontinuity are relatively narrow. On the scale of a weather map, they are normally thin enough to represent as a broad line.

Above the ground the frontal surface slopes at a low angle so that warmer air overlies cooler air, as shown in Figure 9–4. In the ideal case the air masses on both sides of the front would move in the same direction and at the same speed. Under this condition the front would act simply as a barrier that travels along with the air masses. Generally, however, the distribution of pressure across a front is such that one air mass moves faster relative to the frontal boundary than does the other. Thus, one air mass actively advances into another and "clashes" with it. The Norwegian meteorologists visualized these zones of airmass interactions as analogous to battle lines and tagged them "fronts," like battlefronts. It is along these zones of conflict that mid-latitude cyclones develop and produce much of the precipitation and severe weather in the belt of the westerlies.

As one air mass moves into another, limited mixing occurs along the frontal surface, but for the most part, the air masses retain their identity as one is displaced upward over the other. No matter which air mass is advancing, it is always the

°Mid-latitude cyclones go by a number of different names, including wave cyclones, frontal cyclones, extratropical cyclones, low-pressure systems, and, simply, lows.

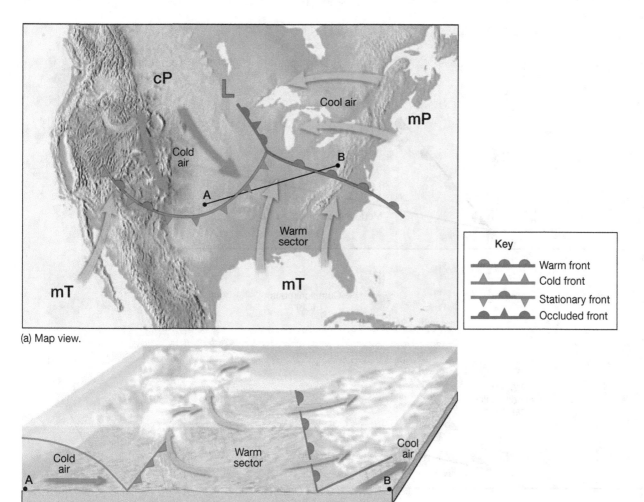

(a) Map view.

(b) Three-dimentional view from points A to B.

FIGURE 9-3 Idealized structure of a mid-latitude cyclone. (a) Map view showing fronts, air masses, and surface flow. (b) Three-dimensional view of the warm and cold fronts along a line from point A to point B.

warmer, less dense air that is forced aloft, whereas the cooler, denser air acts as a wedge on which lifting takes place. The term **overrunning** is generally applied to warm air gliding up along a cold air mass. We now shall look at five types of fronts—*warm, cold, stationary, occluded*, and *drylines*.

Warm Fronts

When the surface (ground) position of a front moves so that warm air occupies territory formerly covered by cooler air, it is called a **warm front** (Figure 9–4). On a weather map, the surface position of a warm front is shown by a red line with red semicircles protruding into the cooler air. East of the Rockies, maritime tropical (mT) air often enters the United States from the Gulf of Mexico and overruns receding cool air. As the colder air retreats, friction with the ground greatly slows the advance of the surface position of the front compared to its position aloft. Stated another way, less dense, warm air has a hard time displacing heavier, cold air. Consequently, the boundary separating these air masses acquires a very gradual slope. The slope of a warm front (height compared to horizontal distance) averages only

about 1:200. This means that if you traveled 200 kilometers (120 miles) ahead of the surface location of a warm front, the frontal surface would be only 1 kilometer (0.6 miles) overhead.

As warm air ascends the retreating wedge of cold air, it expands and cools adiabatically, causing moisture in the ascending air to condense into clouds that often produce precipitation. The cloud sequence in Figure 9–4a typically precedes a warm front. The first sign of the approaching warm front is cirrus clouds. These high clouds form where the overrunning warm air has ascended high up the wedge of cold air, 1000 kilometers (600 miles) or more ahead of the surface front. Another indication of an approaching warm front is provided by aircraft contrails. On a clear day, when these condensation trails persist for several hours, you can be fairly certain that comparatively warm, moist air is ascending overhead.

As the front nears, cirrus clouds grade into cirrostratus that gradually blend into denser sheets of altostratus. About 300 kilometers (180 miles) ahead of the front, thicker stratus and nimbostratus clouds appear and precipitation commences.

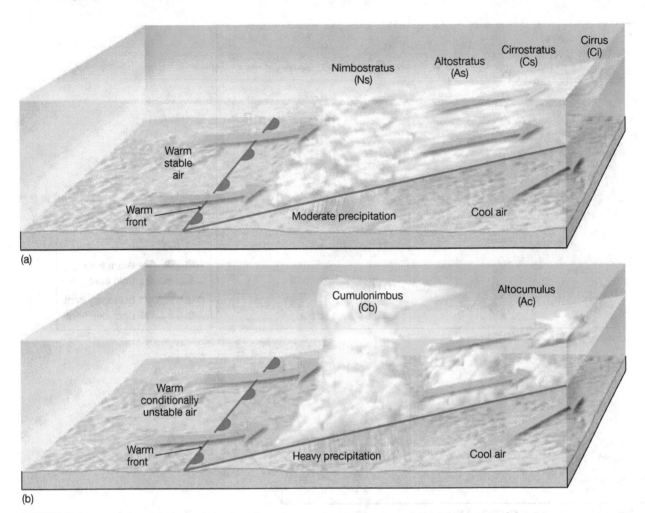

(a)

(b)

FIGURE 9-4 Warm fronts. (a) Idealized clouds and weather associated with a warm front. During most of the year, warm fronts produce light-to-moderate precipitation over a wide area. (b) During the warm season, when conditionally unstable air is forced aloft, cumulonimbus clouds and thunderstorms often arise.

Because of their slow rate of advance and very gentle slope, lifting associated with warm fronts has a large horizontal component. As a result, warm fronts tend to produce light-to-moderate precipitation over a wide area for an extended period (Figure 9–5). But this is not always the case. If, for example, the overriding air mass is relatively dry (low dew-point temperatures), there will be minimal cloud development, and no precipitation. By contrast, during the hot summer months, very moist air is commonly associated with an approaching warm front. If this conditionally unstable air is lifted sufficiently it will freely rise on its own, producing towering cumulonimbus clouds and thunderstorms (Figure 9–4b).

As you can see from Figure 9–4, the precipitation associated with a warm front occurs ahead of the surface position of the front. Some of the rain that falls through the cool air below the clouds evaporates. As a result, the air directly beneath the cloud base often becomes saturated and a stratus cloud deck develops. These clouds occasionally grow rapidly downward, which can cause problems for pilots of small aircraft that require visual landings. One minute pilots may have adequate visibility and the next be in a cloud mass (frontal fog) that has the landing strip "socked in." Occasionally during the winter, a relatively warm air mass is forced over a body of subfreezing air. When this occurs, it can create hazardous driving conditions. Raindrops become supercooled as they fall through the subfreezing air. Upon colliding with the road surface they flash-freeze to produce the icy layer called *glaze*.

When a warm front passes, temperatures gradually rise. As you would expect, the increase is most apparent when a large contrast exists between adjacent air masses. Moreover, a wind shift from the east to the southwest is generally noticeable. (The reason for this shift will become evident later.) The moisture content and stability of the encroaching warm air mass largely determine the time period required for clear skies to return. During the summer, cumulus and occasionally cumulonimbus clouds are embedded in the warm unstable air mass that follows the front. These clouds may produce precipitation, which can be heavy but is usually scattered and of short duration.

Cold Fronts

When cold, continental polar air actively advances into a region occupied by warmer air, the zone of discontinuity is called a **cold front** (Figure 9–6). As with warm fronts, friction slows the surface position of a cold front compared to its position aloft. Thus, the cold front steepens as it moves. On the average, cold fronts are about twice as steep as warm fronts, having a slope of perhaps 1:100. In addition, cold fronts advance at speeds around 35 to 50 kilometers (20 to 35 miles) per hour compared to 25 to 35 kilometers (15 to 20 miles) per hour for warm fronts. These two differences, steepness of slope and rate of movement, largely account for the more violent nature of cold-front weather, compared to the weather generally accompanying a warm front.

The arrival of a cold front is sometimes preceded by altocumulus clouds. As the front approaches, generally from the west or northwest, towering clouds can often be seen in the distance. Near the front, a dark band of ominous clouds foretells the ensuing weather. The forceful lifting of warm, moist air along a cold front is often so rapid that the released latent heat increases the air's buoyancy. The heavy downpours and vigorous wind gusts associated with mature cumulonimbus clouds frequently result. Because a cold front produces roughly the same amount of lifting as a warm front, but over a shorter distance, the precipitation intensity is greater but of shorter duration (Figure 9–7).

In addition, a marked temperature drop and wind shift from the southwest to the northwest usually accompany frontal passage. The reason for this shift will be explained later in this chapter. The sharp temperature contrast and sometimes violent weather along cold fronts are symbolized on a weather map by a blue line with blue triangular points extending into the warm air mass (Figure 9–6).

FIGURE 9-6 Fast-moving cold front and cumulonimbus clouds. Thunderstorms often occur if the warm air is unstable.

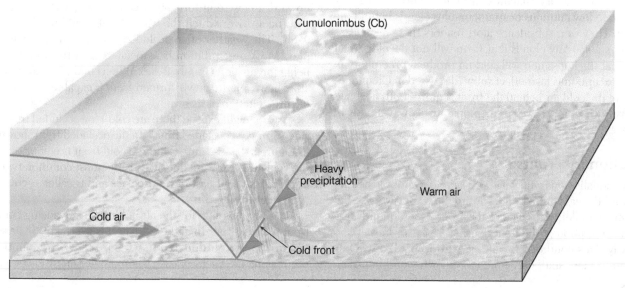

FIGURE 9-7 Thunderstorm development along a cold front over the Great Plains. *(Photo by A. and J. Verkaik/CORBIS)*

Most often the weather behind a cold front is dominated by subsiding air within a continental polar air mass. Thus, the drop in temperature is accompanied by clearing that begins soon after the front passes. Although subsidence causes adiabatic heating aloft, the effect on surface temperatures is minor. In winter the long, cloudless nights that often follow the passage of a cold front allow for abundant radiation cooling that reduces surface temperatures.

When a cold front moves over a relatively warm surface, radiation emitted from Earth can heat the lower atmosphere enough to produce shallow convection. This in turn may generate low cumulus or stratocumulus clouds behind the front. However, subsidence aloft renders these air masses quite stable. Any clouds that form will not develop great vertical thickness and will seldom produce precipitation. One exception is lake-effect snow (discussed in Chapter 8) where the cold air behind the front acquires both heat and moisture when it traverses a comparatively warm body of water.

Stationary Fronts

Occasionally, the airflow on both sides of a front is neither toward the cold air mass nor toward the warm air mass, but almost parallel to the line of the front. Consequently, the surface position of the front does not move, or moves very slowly. This condition is called a **stationary front.** On a weather map, stationary fronts are shown with blue trian-

gular points on one side of the line and red semicircles on the other. Because overrunning usually occurs along stationary fronts, gentle to moderate precipitation is likely. Stationary fronts may remain over an area for several days, in which case flooding is possible.

Occluded Fronts

The fourth type of front is the **occluded front.** Here a rapidly moving cold front overtakes a warm front, as shown in Figure 9–8a. As the cold air wedges the warm front upward, a new front forms between the advancing cold air and the air over which the warm front is gliding (Figure 9–8b). The weather of an occluded front is generally complex. Most precipitation is associated with the warm air being forced aloft (Figure 9–8c). When conditions are suitable, however, the newly formed front is capable of initiating precipitation of its own.

As you might expect, there are cold-type occluded fronts and warm-type occluded fronts. In the occluded front shown in Figure 9–9a, the air behind the cold front is colder than the cool air it is overtaking. This is the most common type of occluded front east of the Rockies and is called a **cold-type occluded front.**

It is also possible for the air behind the advancing cold front to be warmer than the cold air it is overtaking. These **warm-type occluded fronts** (Figure 9–9b) frequently occur along the Pacific Coast, where milder maritime polar

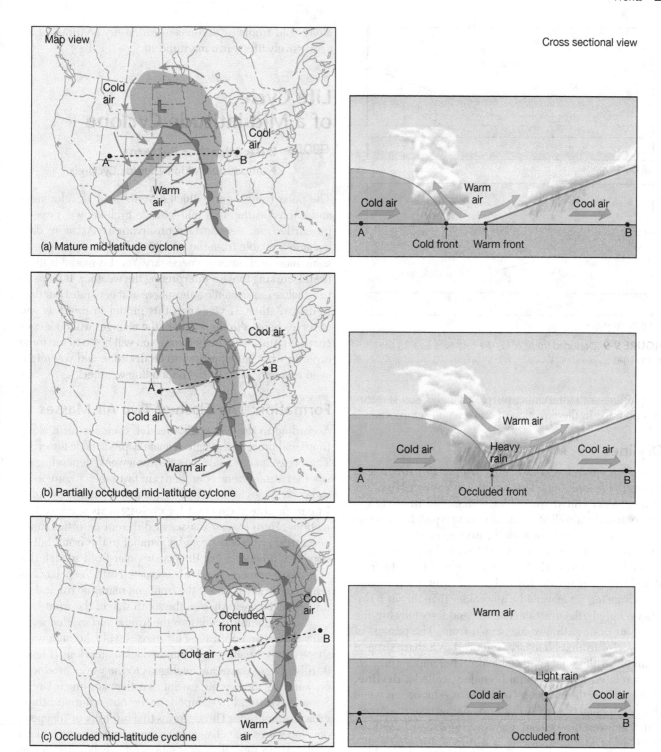

FIGURE 9-8 Stages in the formation of an occluded front and its relationship to a developing mid-latitude cyclone. After the warm air has been forced aloft, the system begins to dissipate. The shaded areas indicate regions where precipitation is most likely to occur.

air invades more frigid polar air that had its origin over the continent.

Notice in Figure 9–9 that in the warm-type occluded front, the warm air aloft (and hence the precipitation) often precedes the arrival of the surface front. This situation is reversed for the cold-type occluded front, where the front aloft (and its associated precipitation) lags behind the sur-

face front. Also note that cold-type occluded fronts frequently resemble cold fronts in the type of weather generated.

Because of the complex nature of occluded fronts, they are often drawn on weather maps as either warm or cold fronts, depending on what kind of air is the aggressor. In those cases when they are drawn as an occluded front, a

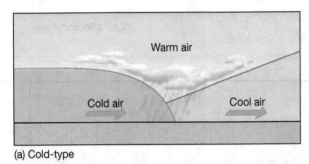

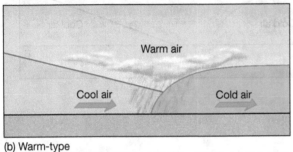

(a) Cold-type

(b) Warm-type

FIGURE 9-9 Occluded fronts of (a) the cold type and (b) the warm type.

purple line with alternating purple triangles and semicircles pointing in the direction of movement is employed.

Drylines

Classifying fronts based only on the temperature differences across the frontal boundary can be misleading. Humidity also influences the density of air, with humid air being less dense than dry air, all other factors being equal. In the summer it is not unusual for a southeastward moving air mass that originated over the northern Great Plains to displace warm, humid air over the lower Mississippi Valley. The front that develops is usually labeled a cold front, even though the advancing air may not be any colder than the air it displaces. Simply, the drier air is denser and forcefully lifts the moist air in its path, just like a cold front. The passage of this type of frontal boundary is noticed as a sharp drop in humidity, without an appreciable drop in temperature.

A related type of frontal boundary, called a **dryline,** develops over the southern Great Plains. This occurs when dry, continental tropical (cT) air originating over the American Southwest meets moist, maritime tropical (mT) air from the Gulf of Mexico. Basically a spring and summer phenomenon, drylines most often generate a band of severe thunderstorms along a line extending from Texas to Nebraska that moves eastward across the Great Plains. A dryline is easily identified by comparing the dew point temperatures of the cT air west of the front with the dew points of the mT air mass to the east (see Figure 10–12, p. 296).

In summary, because cold fronts are the aggressor, the lifting associated along a cold front tends to be more concentrated and forceful than that along a warm front. Hence, the precipitation associated with a cold front usually occurs along a narrow zone and is heavier than that associated with a warm front. Further, most severe weather occurs along cold fronts or drylines in which dry continental air aggressively lifts warm maritime air.

Life Cycle of a Mid-latitude Cyclone

 Basic Weather Patterns
▶ Introducing Middle-Latitude Cyclones

The polar-front theory, which describes the development and intensification of a mid-latitude cyclone, was created primarily from near-surface observations. As more data became available from the middle and upper troposphere, some modifications were necessary. Yet this model is still a useful working tool for interpreting the weather. It helps us to visualize our dynamic atmosphere as it generates our day-to-day weather. If you keep this model in mind as you observe changes in the weather, the changes will no longer come as a surprise. Furthermore, you will begin to see some order in what had appeared to be disorder, and you might even correctly forecast the impending weather!

Formation: The Clash of Two Air Masses

According to the Norwegian model, cyclones form along fronts and proceed through a generally predictable life cycle. This cycle can last a few days to over a week, depending on whether atmospheric conditions are favorable. Figure 9–10 shows six stages in the life of a typical mid-latitude cyclone. In part (a), the stage is set for **cyclogenesis** (cyclone formation). Here two air masses of different densities (temperatures) are moving roughly parallel to the front, but in opposite directions. (In the classic polar-front model, this would be continental polar air associated with the polar easterlies on the north side of the front and maritime tropical air driven by the westerlies on the south side of the front.)

Under suitable conditions the frontal surface that separates these two contrasting air masses will take on a wave shape that is usually several hundred kilometers long (Figure 9–10b). These waves are analogous to the waves produced on water by moving air, except that they are much larger. Some waves tend to dampen, or die out, whereas others grow in amplitude. Those storms that intensify or "deepen" develop waves that change in shape over time, much like a gentle ocean swell does as it moves into shallow water and becomes a tall, breaking wave (see Figure 9–10c).

Development of Cyclonic Flow

As the wave develops, warm air advances poleward invading the area formerly occupied by colder air, while cold air moves equatorward. This change in the direction of the surface flow is accompanied by a readjustment in the pressure pattern that results in nearly circular isobars, with the low pressure centered at the crest of the wave. The resulting flow is a counterclockwise cyclonic circulation that can be seen clearly on the weather map shown in Figure 9–11. Once the

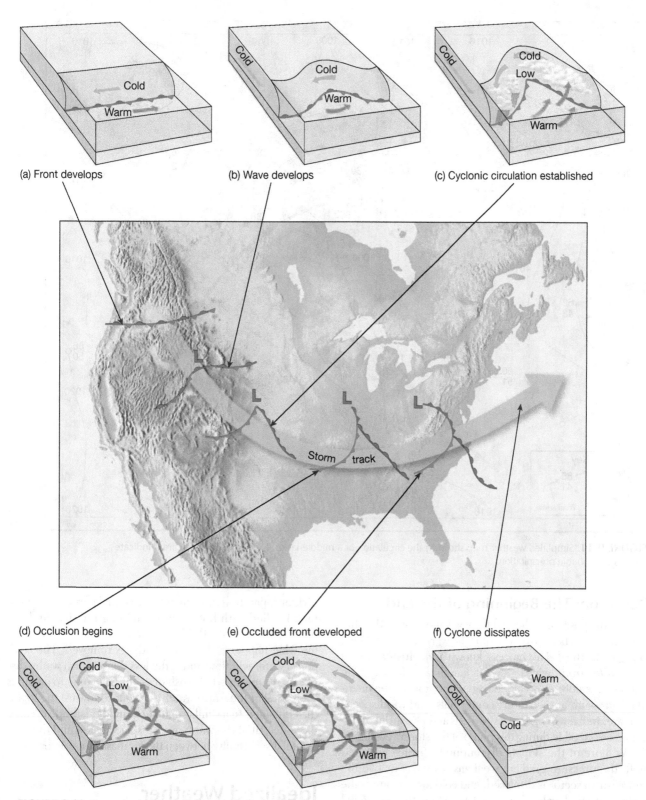

(a) Front develops

(b) Wave develops

(c) Cyclonic circulation established

(d) Occlusion begins

(e) Occluded front developed

(f) Cyclone dissipates

FIGURE 9-10 Stages in the life cycle of a middle-latitude cyclone, as proposed by J. Bjerknes.

cyclonic circulation develops, we would expect general convergence to result in lifting, especially where warm air is overrunning colder air. You can see in Figure 9–11 that the air in the warm sector (over the southern states) is flowing northeastward toward colder air that is moving toward the northwest. Because the warm air is moving in a direction perpendicular to this front, we can conclude that the warm air is invading a region formerly occupied by cold air. Therefore, this must be a warm front. Similar reasoning indicates that to the left (west) of the cyclonic disturbance, cold air from the northwest is displacing the air of the warm sector and generating a cold front.

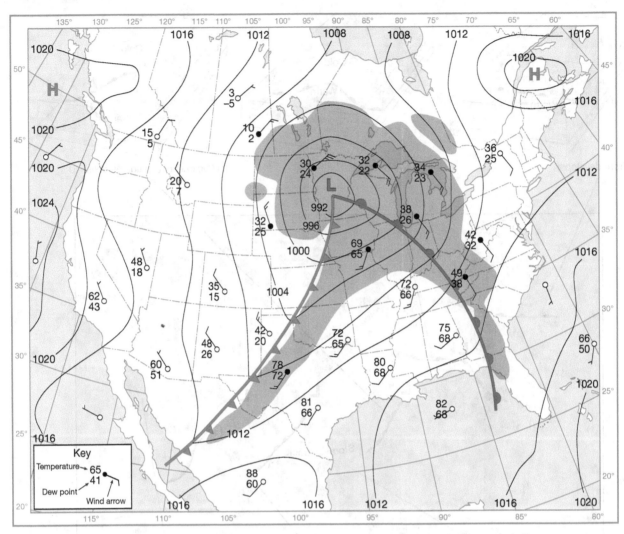

FIGURE 9-11 Simplified weather map showing the circulation of a middle-latitude cyclone. The gray areas indicate regions of probable precipitation.

Occlusion: The Beginning of the End

Usually, the position of the cold front advances faster than the warm front and begins to close (lift) the warm front, as shown in Figure 9–10c,d. This process, known as **occlusion,** forms an *occluded front,* which grows in length as it displaces the warm sector aloft. As occlusion begins, the storm often intensifies. Pressure at the storm's center falls, and wind speeds increase. In the winter, heavy snowfalls and blizzardlike conditions are possible during this phase of the storm's evolution.

As more of the sloping discontinuity (front) is forced aloft, the pressure gradient weakens. In a day or two the entire warm sector is displaced, and cold air surrounds the cyclone at low levels (Figure 9–10f). Thus, the horizontal temperature (density) difference that existed between the two contracting air masses has been eliminated. At this point the cyclone has exhausted its source of energy. Friction slows the surface flow, and the once highly organized counterclockwise flow ceases to exist.

A simple analogy may help you visualize what is happening to the cold and warm air masses in the preceding discussion. Imagine a large water trough that has a vertical divider separating the tank into two equal parts. Half of the tank is filled with hot water containing red dye, and the other half is filled with blue-colored ice water. Now imagine what happens when the divider is removed. The cold, dense water will flow under the less dense warm water, displacing it upward. This rush of water will come to a halt as soon as all of the warm water is displaced toward the top of the container. In a similar manner a middle-latitude cyclone dies once all of the warm air is displaced aloft and the horizontal discontinuity between the air masses no longer exists.

Idealized Weather of a Mid-latitude Cyclone

 Basic Weather Patterns

▶ Introducing Middle-Latitude Cyclones

As stated earlier, the Norwegian model is a useful tool for examining weather patterns of the middle latitudes. Figure 9–12 illustrates a mature mid-latitude cyclone; note the

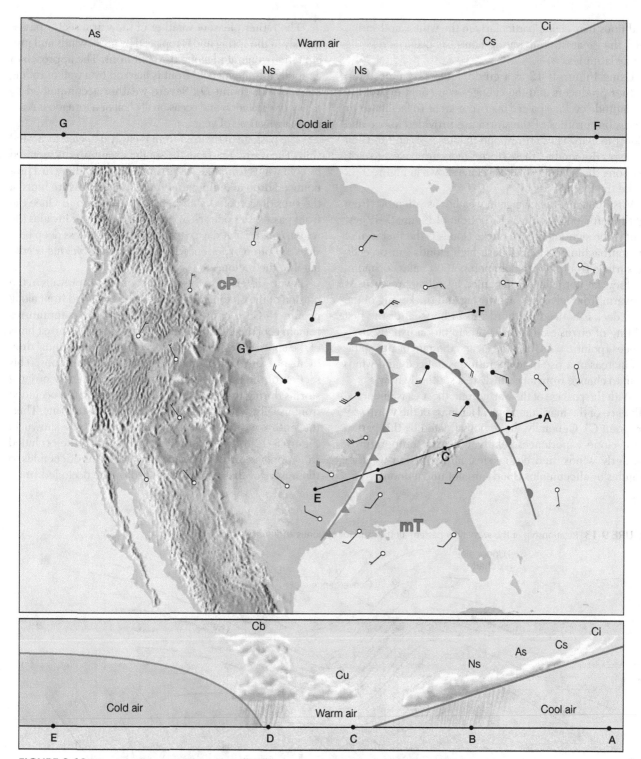

FIGURE 9-12 Cloud patterns typically associated with a mature middle-latitude cyclone. The middle section is a map view. Note the cross-section lines (F–G, A–E). Above the map is a vertical cross section along line F–G. Below the map is a section along A–E. For cloud abbreviations, refer to Figures 9–4 and 9–6.

distribution of clouds and thus the regions of possible precipitation. Compare this map to the satellite image of a cyclone in Figure 9–25 (p. 280). It is easy to see why we often refer to the cloud pattern of a cyclone as having a "comma" shape.

Guided by the westerlies aloft, cyclones generally move eastward across the United States. Therefore, we can expect

the first signs of a cyclone's arrival to appear in the western sky. In the region of the Mississippi Valley, however, cyclones often begin a more northeasterly trajectory and occasionally move directly northward. Typically, a mid-latitude cyclone requires two to four days to pass completely over a region. During that period, abrupt changes in atmospheric conditions may occur, particularly in the winter and spring when the greatest temperature contrasts occur across the middle latitudes.

Using Figure 9–12 as a guide, let us examine these weather producers and the changes you could expect if a mid-latitude cyclone passed over your area. To facilitate our discussion, profiles of the storm are provided above and below the map. They correspond to lines A–E and F–G on the map. (Remember, these storms move from west to east; therefore, the right side of the cyclone shown in Figure 9–12 will be the first to pass by.)

First, imagine the change in weather as you move from right to left along profile A–E (bottom of Figure 9–12). At point *A* the sighting of high cirrus clouds is the first sign of the approaching cyclone. These high clouds can precede the surface front by 1000 kilometers (600 miles) or more, and they are normally accompanied by falling pressure. As the warm front advances, a lowering and thickening of the cloud deck is noticed. Within 12 to 24 hours after the first sighting of cirrus clouds, light precipitation usually commences (point *B*). As the front nears, the rate of precipitation increases, a rise in temperature is noticed, and winds begin to change from an easterly to a southerly flow.

With the passage of the warm front, the area is under the influence of the maritime tropical air mass of the warm sector (point *C*). Generally, the region affected by this part of the cyclone experiences relatively warm temperatures, southerly winds, and clear skies, although fair-weather cumulus or altocumulus clouds are not uncommon.

The rather pleasant weather of the warm sector passes quickly in the spring and is replaced by gusty winds and precipitation generated along the cold front. The approach of a rapidly advancing cold front is marked by a wall of rolling black clouds (point *D*). Severe weather accompanied by heavy precipitation and occasionally hail or a tornado is common at this time of year.

The passage of the cold front is easily detected by a wind shift. The warm flow from the south or southwest is replaced by cold winds from the west to northwest, resulting in a pronounced drop in temperature. Also, rising pressure hints of the subsiding cool, dry air behind the cold front. Once the front passes, the skies clear quickly as cooler air invades the region (point *E*). A day or two of almost cloudless deep blue skies are often experienced, unless another cyclone is edging into the region.

A very different set of weather conditions prevails in the portion of the cyclone that contains the occluded front along profile F–G (top of Figure 9–12). Here temperatures remain cool during the passage of the storm. The first hints of the approaching low-pressure center are a continual drop in air pressure and increasingly overcast conditions. This section of the cyclone most often generates snow or icing storms during the coldest months. Moreover, the occluded front usually moves more slowly than the other fronts. Thus, the entire wishbone-shaped frontal structure shown in Figure 9–12 rotates counterclockwise so that the occluded front appears to "bend over backward." This effect adds to the misery of the region influenced by the occluded front,

FIGURE 9-13 Relationship of the wavy flow pattern aloft to surface cyclones and anticyclones.

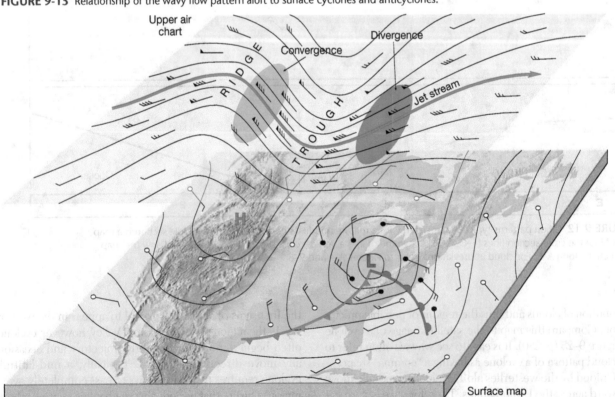

for it remains over the area longer than the other fronts (see Box 9–1).

Cyclone Formation

The polar-front model shows that cyclogenesis (cyclone formation) occurs where a frontal surface is distorted into a wave-shaped discontinuity. Several surface factors are thought to produce this wave in a frontal zone. Topographic irregularities (such as mountains), temperature contrasts (as between sea and land), or ocean-current influences can disrupt the general zonal flow sufficiently to produce a wave along a front. In addition, an intensification of the flow aloft frequently precedes the formation of a surface cyclone. This fact strongly suggests that upper-level flow contributes to the formation of these rotating storm systems.

When the earliest studies of cyclones were made, little data were available on airflow in the middle and upper troposphere. Since then, a close relationship has been established between surface disturbances and the flow aloft. Whenever the winds aloft exhibit a relatively straight zonal flow—that is, from west to east—little cyclonic activity occurs at the surface. However, when the upper air begins to meander widely from north-to-south, forming high-amplitude waves of alternating troughs (lows) and ridges (highs), cyclonic activity intensifies (Figure 9–13). Moreover, when surface cyclones form, almost invariably they are centered

below the jet-stream axis and downwind from an upper-level trough (Figure 9–13).

Cyclonic and Anticyclonic Circulation

Before discussing how surface cyclones are generated and supported by the flow aloft, let us review the nature of cyclonic and anticyclonic winds. Recall that airflow about a surface low is inward, a fact that leads to mass convergence (coming together). Because accumulation of air is accompanied by a corresponding increase in surface pressure we might expect a surface low-pressure center to "fill" rapidly and be eliminated, just as the vacuum in a coffee can is quickly equalized when we open it. However, cyclones often exist for a week or longer. For this to happen, surface convergence must be offset by outflow aloft (Figure 9–14). As long as divergence (spreading out) aloft is equal to or greater than the surface inflow, the low pressure can be sustained.

Because cyclones are bearers of stormy weather, they have received far more attention than their counterparts, anticyclones. Yet the close relationship between them makes it difficult to totally separate a discussion of these two pressure systems. The surface air that feeds a cyclone, for example, generally originates as air flowing out of an anticyclone (Figure 9–14). Consequently, cyclones and anticyclones are typically found adjacent to one another. Like the cyclone, an anticyclone depends on the flow aloft to maintain its circulation. In the anticyclone, divergence at the surface is

FIGURE 9-14 Idealized depiction of the support that divergence and convergence aloft provide to cyclonic and anticyclonic circulation at the surface.

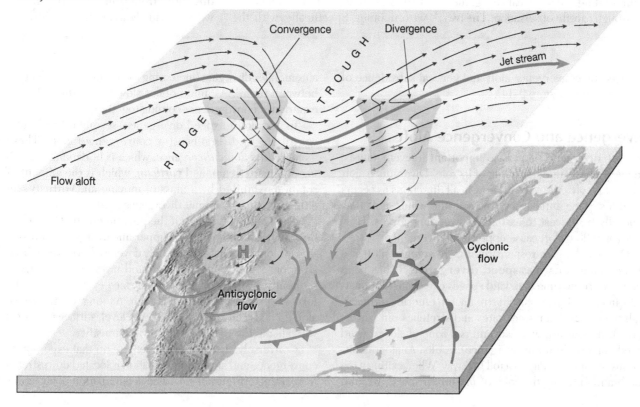

BOX 9-1   Winds As a Forecasting Tool

Every wind has its weather.

Francis Bacon

People living in the middle latitudes know well that during the winter, northerly winds can chill you to the bone. Conversely, a sudden change to a southerly flow can bring welcome relief from these frigid conditions. If you are more observant, you might have noticed that when the winds switch from a southerly flow to a more easterly direction, foul weather often follows. By contrast, a change in wind direction from the southwest to the northwest is usually accompanied by clearing conditions. Just how are the winds and the forthcoming weather related?

Modern weather forecasts require the processing capabilities of high-speed computers as well as the expertise of people with considerable professional training. Nevertheless, some reasonable insights into the impending weather can be gained through careful observation. The two most significant elements for this purpose are barometric pressure and wind direction. Recall that anticyclones (high-pressure cells) are associated with clear skies, and that cyclones (low-pressure cells) frequently bring clouds and precipitation. Thus, by noting whether the barometer is rising, falling, or steady, we have some indication of the forthcoming weather. For example, rising pressure indicates the approach of a high-pressure system and generally clearing conditions.

The use of winds in weather forecasting is also quite straightforward. Because cyclones are the "'villains" in the weather game, we are most concerned with the circulation around these storm centers. In particular, changes in wind direction that occur with the passage of warm and cold fronts are useful in predicting the impending weather. Notice in Figure 9–12, that with the passage of both the warm and cold fronts, the wind arrows change positions in a clockwise manner. Specifically, with the passage of the cold front, the wind shifts from southwest to northwest. From nautical terminology, the word *veering* is applied to this clockwise wind shift. Because clearing conditions normally occur with the passage of either front, veering winds are indicators that the weather will improve.

In contrast, the area in the northern portion of the cyclone will experience winds that shift in a counterclockwise direction, as can be seen in Figure 9–12. Winds that shift in this manner are said to be *backing*. With the approach of a mid-latitude cyclone, backing winds indicate cool temperatures and continued foul weather.

A summary of the relationship among barometer readings, winds, and the impending weather is provided in Table 9–A. Although this information is applicable in a very general way to much of the United States, local influences must be taken into account. For example, a rising barometer and a change in wind direction, from southwest to northwest, is usually associated with the

---

balanced by convergence aloft and general subsidence of the air column (Figure 9–14).

Divergence and Convergence Aloft

Because divergence aloft is so important to cyclogenesis, we need a basic understanding of its role. Divergence aloft does not involve the outward flow in all directions as occurs about a surface anticyclone. Instead, the winds aloft flow generally from west to east along sweeping curves. How does zonal flow aloft cause upper-level divergence?

One mechanism responsible for divergence aloft is a phenomenon known as **speed divergence.** It has been known for some time that wind speeds can change dramatically in the vicinity of the jet stream. On entering a zone of high wind speed, air accelerates and stretches out (divergence). In contrast, when air enters a zone of slower wind speed, an air pile-up (convergence) results. Analogous situations occur every day on a toll highway. When exiting a toll booth and entering the zone of maximum speed, we find automobiles diverging (increasing the number of car lengths between them). As automobiles slow to pay the toll, they experience convergence (coming together).

In addition to speed divergence, several other factors contribute to divergence (or convergence) aloft. These include *directional divergence,* which is horizontal spreading of an air stream, and *vorticity,* which is the amount of rotation exhibited by a mass of moving air. Vorticity can either enhance or inhibit divergence aloft.

The combined effect of the phenomena that influence flow aloft is that an area of upper-air divergence and surface cyclonic circulation generally develop downstream from an upper-level trough, as illustrated in Figure 9–14. Consequently, in the United States surface cyclones generally form east of an upper-level trough. As long as divergence aloft exceeds convergence at ground level, surface pressures will fall and the cyclonic storm will intensify.

Conversely, the zone in the jet stream that experiences convergence and anticyclonic rotation is located downstream from a ridge (Figure 9–14). The accumulation of air in this

TABLE 9-A Wind, barometric pressure, and impending weather

Changes in wind direction	Barometric pressure	Pressure tendency	Impending weather
Any direction	1023 mb and above (30.20 in.)	Steady or rising	Continued fair with no temperature change
SW to NW	1013 mb and below (29.92 in.)	Rising rapidly	Clearing within 12 to 24 hours and colder
S to SW	1013 mb and below (29.92 in.)	Rising slowly	Clearing within a few hours and fair for several days
SE to SW	1013 mb and below (29.92 in.)	Steady or slowly falling	Clearing and warmer, followed by possible precipitation
E to NE	1019 mb and above (30.10 in.)	Falling slowly	In summer, with light wind, rain may not fall for several days; in winter, rain within 24 hours
E to NE	1019 mb and above (10.10 in.)	Falling rapidly	In summer, rain probable within 12 to 24 hours; in winter, rain or snow with strong winds likely
SE to NE	1013 mb and below (29.92 in.)	Falling slowly	Rain will continue for 1 to 2 days
SE to NE	1013 mb and below (29.92 in.)	Falling rapidly	Stormy conditions followed within 36 hours by clearing and, in winter, colder temperatures

Source: Adapted from the National Weather Service.

passage of a cold front and indicates that clearing conditions should follow. However, in the winter, residents of the southeast shore of one of the Great Lakes may not be so lucky. As cold, dry northwest winds cross large expanses of open water, they acquire heat and moisture from the relatively warm lake surface. By the time this air reaches the leeward shore, it is often humid and unstable enough to produce heavy lake-effect snow (see Chapter 8).

region of the jet stream leads to subsidence and increased surface pressure. Hence, this is a favorable site for the development of a surface anticyclone.

Because of the significant role that the upper-level flow has on cyclogenesis, it should be evident that any attempt at weather prediction must take into account the airflow aloft. This is why television weather reporters frequently illustrate the flow within the jet stream.

In summary, the flow aloft contributes to the formation and intensification of surface low- and high-pressure systems. Areas of upper-level convergence and divergence are located in the vicinity of jet stream, where dramatic changes in wind speeds cause air either to pile up (converge) or spread out (diverge). Upper-level convergence is favored downstream (east) of a ridge, whereas divergence occurs downstream of an upper-level trough. Below regions of upper-level convergence are areas of high pressure (anticyclones), whereas upper-level divergence supports the formation and development of cyclonic systems (lows).

Traveling Cyclones

Cyclone development does not occur uniformly over Earth but tends to favor certain locations, such as the leeward sides of mountains and coastal regions. In general, cyclones form in areas where large temperature contrasts occur in the lower troposphere. Figure 9–15 shows areas of greatest cyclone development over North America and adjacent oceans. Notice that the main sites for cyclone formation occur along the lee side of the Rocky Mountains and along the Atlantic Coast east of the Appalachian Mountains. Other important sites are in the North Pacific and the North Atlantic.

Patterns of Movement

Once formed, cyclones tend to first travel in an easterly direction across North America and then follow a more northeasterly path into the North Atlantic (Figure 9–16). However, numerous exceptions to this general trend occur.

FIGURE 9-15 Major sites of cyclone formation.

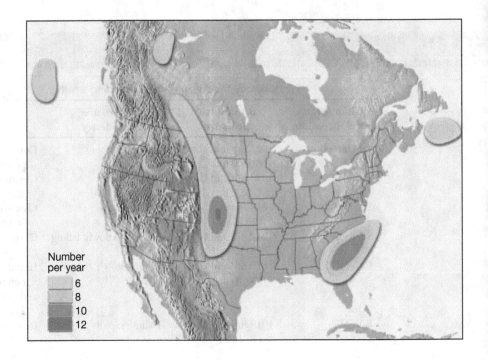

One well-known example is a storm that goes by the name of *Panhandle Hook*. The "Hook" describes the curved path these storms follow (Figure 9–16). Developing in southern Colorado near the Texas and Oklahoma panhandles, these cyclones first travel toward the southeast and then bend sharply northward traveling across Wisconsin and into Canada.

Cyclones that influence western North America originate over the North Pacific. Many of these systems move northeastward toward the Gulf of Alaska. However, during the winter months these storms travel farther southward and often reach the coast of the contiguous 48 states, occasionally traveling as far south as southern California. These cyclonic systems provide the winter rainy season that affects much of the West Coast.

Most Pacific storms do not cross the Rockies intact but may redevelop on the lee (eastward) side of these mountains. A favorite site for redevelopment is Colorado, but other common sites of formation exist as far south as Texas and as far north as Alberta. The cyclones that form in Canada tend to move southeastward toward the Great Lakes and then turn northeastward and move out into the Atlantic. Cyclones that redevelop over the Great Plains generally migrate eastward until they reach the central United States, where a northeastward or even northward trajectory is followed. Many of these cyclones traverse the Great Lakes region, making it the most storm-ridden portion of the country. Another area where cyclogenesis occurs is east of the southern Appalachians. These storms tend to move northward with the warm Gulf Stream and bring stormy conditions to the entire East Coast.

FIGURE 9-16 Typical paths of cyclonic storms that affect the lower 48 states.

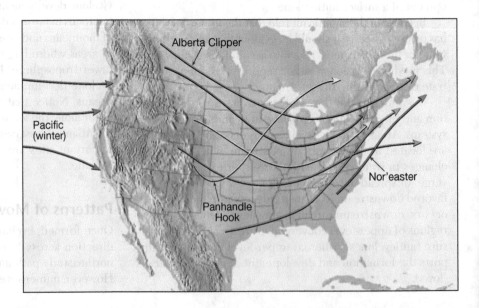

Alberta Clipper.   An *Alberta Clipper* is a cold, windy cyclonic storm that forms on the eastern side of the Canadian Rockies in the province of Alberta (Figure 9–16). Noted for their speed, they are called "clippers" because in Colonial times the fastest vehicles were small ships by the same name. The average Alberta Clipper dives southeastward into Montana or the Dakotas and than tracks across the Great Lakes where it brings dramatically lower temperatures. Winds associated with Clippers frequently exceed 50 kilometers (30 miles) per hour. Because clippers move rapidly and remain a long way from the mild waters of the Gulf of Mexico they tend to be moisture deprived. As a result they do not drop large amounts of snow. Instead, they may leave a few inches in a narrow band from the Dakotas to New York over a span as short as two days. However, because these winter storms are relatively frequent occurrences, they make a significant contribution to the total winter snowfall in the northern tier of states.

Nor'easter.   From the Mid-Atlantic Coast to New England, the classic storm is called a *nor'easter* (Figure 9–16). They are called nor'easters because the winds preceding the passage of these storms in coastal areas are from the northeast. They are most frequent and violent between September and April when cold air pouring south from Canada meets relatively warm humid air from the Atlantic. Once formed, nor'easters follow the coast often bringing rain, sleet, and heavy snowfall to the Northeast. Because the circulation produces strong onshore winds, these storms can cause considerable coastal erosion, flooding, and property damage. The popular book and movie *The Perfect Storm* was based on a true story of a fishing boat that was caught in an intense nor'easter in October 1991.

Flow Aloft and Cyclone Migration

Recall that the wavy flow aloft is important to the development and evolution of a surface cyclonic storm. In addition, the flow in the middle and upper troposphere appears to strongly influence the rate at which these pressure systems advance and the direction they follow. As a general rule of thumb, surface cyclones move in the same direction as the 500-millibar wind, but at about half the speed. Normally these systems travel at 25 to 50 kilometers (15 to 30 miles) per hour so that distances of roughly 600 to 1200 kilometers (400 to 800 miles) are traversed each day. The faster speeds occur during the coldest months when temperature gradients are greatest.

One of the most exacting tasks in weather forecasting is predicting the paths of cyclonic storms. We have already seen that the flow aloft tends to steer developing pressure systems. Let us examine an example of this steering effect by seeing how changes in the upper-level flow correspond to changes in the path taken by a cyclone.

Figure 9–17a illustrates the changing position of a middle-latitude cyclone over a four-day period. Notice in Figure 9–17b that on March 21, the 500-millibar contours are relatively flat. Also notice that for the following two days, the cyclone moves in a rather straight southeasterly direction. By March 23 the 500-millibar contours make a sharp bend northward on the eastern side of a trough situated over Wyoming (Figure 9–17c). Likewise, the next day the path of the cyclone makes a similar northward migration.

Although this is an oversimplified example, it illustrates the "steering" effect of upper-level flow. Here we have examined the influence of upper airflow on cyclonic movement after the fact. To make useful predictions of future positions of cyclones, accurate appraisals of changes in the westerly flow aloft are required. For this reason, predicting the behavior of the wavy flow in the middle and upper troposphere is an important part of modern weather forecasting.

Anticyclonic Weather and Blocking Highs

Owing to the gradual subsidence within them, anticyclones generally produce clear skies and calm conditions. Because these high-pressure systems are not associated with stormy weather, both their development and movement have not been studied as extensively as that of mid-latitude cyclones. This does not imply, however, that anticyclones always bring desirable weather. Large anticyclones often develop over the Arctic during the winter. These cold high-pressure centers are known to migrate as far south as the Gulf Coast where they can impact the weather over as much as two-thirds of the United States (Figure 9–18). This dense frigid air often brings record-breaking cold temperatures (Figure 9–19).

Approximately one to three times each winter, and occasionally during other seasons, large anticyclones form and persist over the middle latitudes for nearly two weeks and sometimes longer than a month. These large highs deflect the nearly zonal west-to-east flow and send it poleward. Thus, they are sometimes called *blocking highs*. Once in place, these stagnant anticyclones block the eastward migration of cyclones. As a result, one section of the nation is kept dry for a week or more while another region remains continually under the influence of cyclonic storms. Such a situation prevailed during the summer of 1993 when a strong high-pressure system became anchored over the southeastern United States and caused migrating storms to stall over the Midwest. The result was the most devastating flooding on record for the central and upper Mississippi Valley (see Box 9–2). At the same time, the Southeast experienced severe drought.

Large stagnant anticyclones can also contribute to air-pollution episodes. The subsidence within an anticyclone can produce a temperature inversion that acts like a lid to trap pollutants. (For more on this, see Chapter 13.) Further, the light winds associated with the center of an anticyclone do little to disperse polluted air. Both Los Angeles and Mexico City experience air pollution episodes when

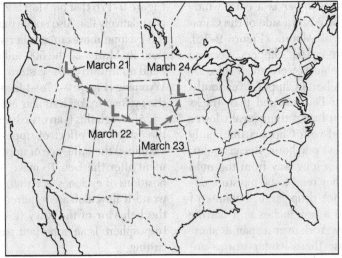

(a) Movement of cyclone
from March 21-24

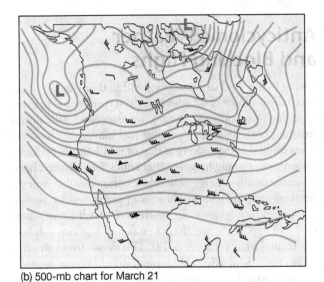

(b) 500-mb chart for March 21

(c) 500-mb chart for March 23

FIGURE 9-17 Steering of mid-latitude cyclones. (a) Notice that the cyclone (low) moved almost in a straight southeastward direction on March 21 and March 22. On the morning of March 23, it abruptly turned northward. This change in direction corresponds to the change from (b) rather straight contours on the upper-air chart for March 21 to (c) curved contours on the chart for March 23.

strong, stagnant high-pressure systems dominate their circulation for extended periods.

Case Study
of a Mid-latitude Cyclone

 Basic Weather Patterns

▶ In the Lab: Examining a Mature Middle-
   Latitude Cyclone

To give you a picture of the weather one might expect from a strong late-winter cyclonic storm we are going to look at an actual event. Our sample storm was one of three cyclones to migrate across the United States during the latter half of March. This cyclone reached the U.S. West Coast on March 21 a few hundred kilometers northwest of Seattle, Wash-

ington. Like many Pacific storms, this one rejuvenated over the western United States and moved eastward into the Plains states. By the morning of March 23, it was centered over the Kansas–Nebraska border (Figure 9–20). At this time, the central pressure had reached 985 millibars, and its well-developed cyclonic circulation exhibited a warm front and a cold front.

During the next 24 hours, the forward motion of the storm's center became sluggish. It curved slowly northward through Iowa, and the pressure deepened to 982 millibars (Figure 9–21). Although the storm center advanced slowly, the associated fronts moved vigorously toward the east and somewhat northward. The northern sector of the cold front overtook the warm front and generated an occluded front, which by the morning of March 24 was oriented nearly east-west (Figure 9–21).

This period in the storm's history marked one of the worst blizzards ever to hit the north-central states. While

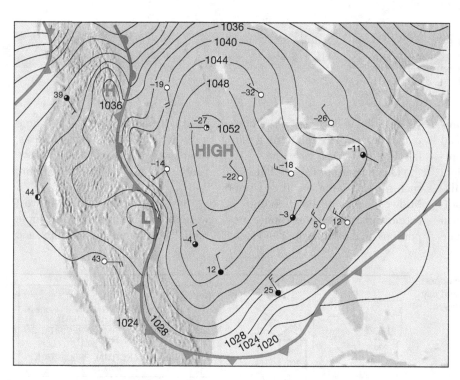

FIGURE 9-18 A cold anticyclone associated with an outbreak of frigid arctic air impacts the eastern two-thirds of North America. Temperatures are shown in degrees Fahrenheit.

FIGURE 9-19 Cold outbreak of arctic air invades New England, bringing subzero temperatures and mostly clear skies. *(Photo by Karen Thomas/Stock Boston Inc./PictureQuest)*

BOX 9-2   Atmospheric Hazard: The Great Flood of 1993

by Steven Hilberg*

Unprecedented rainfall produced the wettest spring and early summer of the twentieth century for the Upper Mississippi River basin (upstream of Quincy, Illinois), according to rainfall data gathered by the Midwestern Regional Climate Center at the Illinois State Water Survey. Portions of the basin received over twice the normal rainfall (Figure 9–A).

The magnitude of rainfall over such a vast area of the Upper Midwest resulted in flooding of extraordinary and catastrophic proportions on the Mississippi and many of its tributaries, affecting large portions of Illinois, Iowa, Kansas, Minnesota, Missouri, Nebraska, South Dakota, and Wisconsin (Figure 9–B).

Soils throughout the Midwest were already saturated from ample rainfall in summer and fall 1992, and

FIGURE 9-A Precipitation data for the upper Mississippi River basin between April 1 and July 31, 1993. *(Data from the Illinois State Water Survey)*

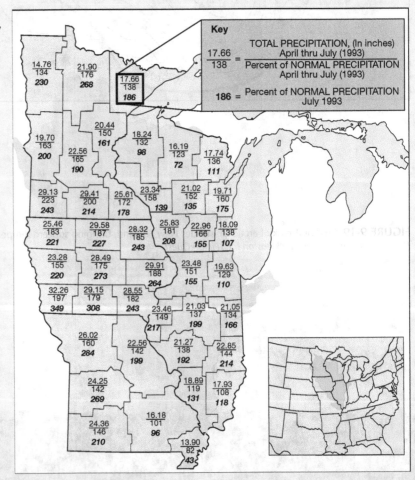

Key

$$\frac{17.66}{138} = \frac{\text{TOTAL PRECIPITATION, (In inches)}}{\text{Percent of NORMAL PRECIPITATION}}$$
April thru July (1993)

$186 = $ Percent of NORMAL PRECIPITATION July 1993

the winter storm was brewing in the north, the cold front marched from northwestern Texas (on March 23) to the Atlantic Ocean (March 25). During its two-day trek to the ocean, this violent cold front generated numerous severe thunderstorms and 19 tornadoes.

By March 25 the low pressure had diminished in intensity (1000 millibars) and had split into two centers (Figure 9–22). Although the remnant low from this system, which was situated over the Great Lakes, generated some snow for the remainder of March 25, by the following day it had completely dissipated.

Violent Spring Weather

Now that you have read an overview of this storm, let us revisit this cyclone's passage in detail using the weather charts for March 23 through March 25 (Figures 9–20 to 9–22). The weather map for March 23 depicts a classic developing cyclone. The warm sector of this system, as exemplified by Fort Worth, Texas, is under the influence of a warm, humid air mass having a temperature of 70°F and a dew-point temperature of 64°F. Notice in the warm sector that winds are from the south and are overrunning cooler

FIGURE 9-B Water rushes through a break in an artificial levee in Monroe County, Illinois. During the record-breaking 1993 Midwest floods, many artificial levees could not withstand the force of the floodwaters. Sections of many weakened structures were overtopped or simply collapsed. *(Photo by James A. Finley/AP/Wide World Photos)*

soils remained moist as winter began. This pattern continued into spring and summer 1993.

Compared to the long-term average, rainfall in the Upper Mississippi River basin during April and May was 40 percent higher than average, and June rainfall was double the average. As the deluge continued through July, much of the basin received rainfall between two and three times the norm.

A stationary weather pattern over the United States was responsible for the Midwest's persistent, drenching rains. Most of the showers and thunderstorms developed in the boundary area between cooler air over the Northern Plains and warm, very humid air over the South. This front oscillated north and south over the Midwest during much of June and July. Meanwhile, a strong high-pressure system (the "Bermuda High") became anchored over the southeastern United States, blocking the progression of weather systems through the eastern half of the nation.

Some of the individual station reports were nothing short of astounding. In northwestern Missouri, Skidmore reported 25.35 inches of rain in July, and Worth County reported 30.30 inches through July 25. Normal July rainfall for this area is about 4 inches, while the average annual rainfall is 35 inches. Alton (northwestern Iowa) had a July rainfall total of 20.41 inches, and Leon (southcentral Iowa) reported 20.68 inches.

July rainfall in Illinois was also much above normal in most areas, but maximum amounts were in the 10- to 15-inch range: 10.65 inches at the Quincy Memorial Bridge, 11.45 inches at Monmouth, 11.83 inches at Galesburg, and 13.88 inches at Flora. Rainfall totals such as these leave no doubt that the record-breaking flooding on the Mississippi and other rivers in the Midwest was directly related to the exceptional rainfall during the spring and early summer.

*Steven Hilberg is Meteorologist and Director, Office of Extension Services and Operations, Illinois State Water Survey.

air situated north of the warm front. In contrast, the air behind the cold front is 20° to 40°F cooler than the air of the warm sector and is flowing from the northwest, as depicted by the data for Roswell, New Mexico.

Prior to March 23, this system had generated some precipitation in the Northwest and as far south as California. On the morning of March 23, little activity was occurring along the fronts. As the day progressed, however, the storm intensified and changed dramatically. The map for March 24 illustrates the highly developed cyclone that evolved during the next 24 hours. The extent and spacing of the isobars indicate a strong system that affected the circulation of the entire eastern two-thirds of the United States. A glance at the winds reveals a robust counterclockwise flow converging on the low.

The activity in the cold sector of the storm just north of the occluded front produced one of the worst March blizzards ever to affect the northcentral United States. In the Duluth–Superior area of Minnesota and Wisconsin, winds of up to 81 miles per hour were measured. Unofficial estimates

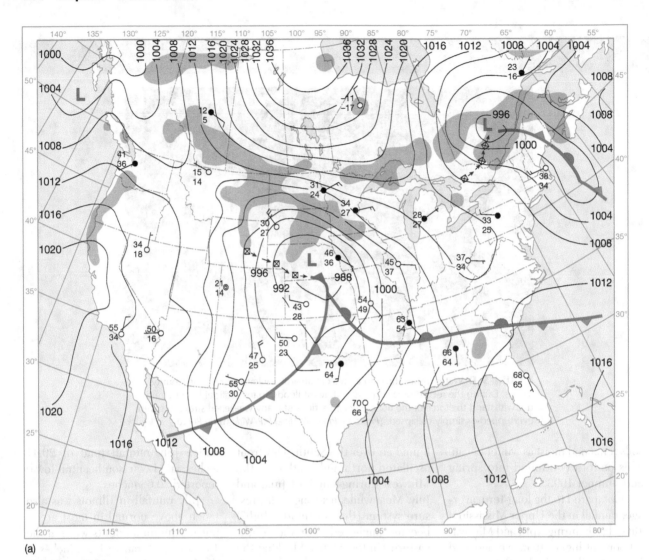

(a)

(b)

FIGURE 9-20 (a) Surface weather map for March 23. (b) Satellite image showing the cloud patterns for March 23. *(Courtesy of NOAA/Seattle)*

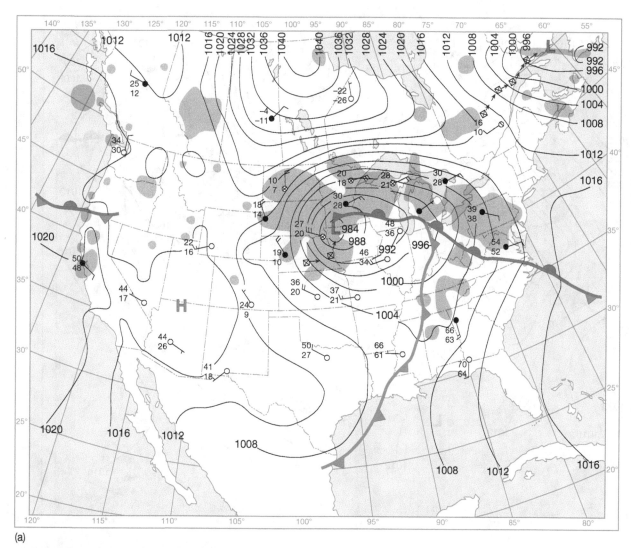

(a)

(b)

FIGURE 9-21 (a) Surface weather map for March 24. (b) Satellite image showing the cloud patterns on that day. *(Courtesy of NOAA/Seattle)*

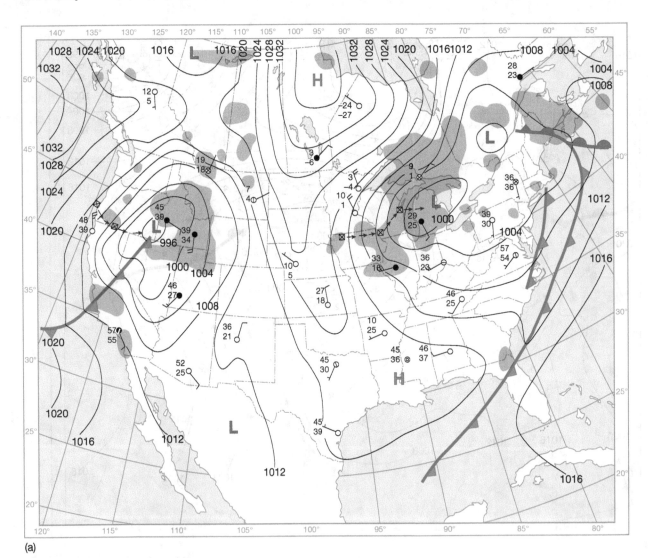

(a)

(b)

FIGURE 9-22 (a) Surface weather map for March 25. (b) Satellite image showing the cloud patterns on that day. *(Courtesy of NOAA/Seattle)*

of wind speeds in excess of 100 miles per hour were made on the aerial bridge connecting these cities. Winds blew 12 inches of snow into 10- to 15-foot drifts, and some roads were closed for three days (Figure 9–23). One large supper club in Superior was destroyed by fire because drifts prevented fire-fighting equipment from reaching the blaze.

At the other extreme was the weather produced by the cold front as it closed in on the warm, humid air flowing into the warm sector. By the late afternoon of March 23, the cold front had generated a hailstorm in parts of eastern Texas. As the cold front moved eastward, it affected all of the southeastern United States except southern Florida. Throughout this region, numerous thunderstorms were spawned. Although high winds, hail, and lightning triggered extensive damage, the 19 tornadoes generated by the storm caused even greater death and destruction.

The path of the front can be easily traced from the reports of storm damage. By the evening of March 23, hail and wind damage were reported as far east as Mississippi and Tennessee. Early on the morning of March 24, golf ball size hail was reported in downtown Selma, Alabama. About 6:30 A.M. that day the "Governor's Tornado" struck Atlanta, Georgia. Here the storm displayed its worst temper. Damage was estimated at over $50 million, three lives were lost, and 152 people were injured. The 12-mile path of the "Governor's Tornado" cut through an affluent residential area of Atlanta that included the governor's mansion (hence the name). (The official report on this tornado notes than no mobile homes lay in the tornado's path. Why was this fact

worth noting?) The final damage along the cold front was reported at 4:00 A.M. on March 25 in northeastern Florida. Here hail and a small tornado caused minor damage. Thus, a day and a half and some 1200 kilometers (about 750 miles) after the cold front became active in Texas, it left the United States to vent its energy harmlessly over the Atlantic Ocean.

By the morning of March 24, you can see that cold polar air had penetrated deep into the United States behind the cold front (Figure 9–21). Fort Worth, Texas, which just the day before was in the warm sector, now experienced cool northwest winds. Subfreezing temperatures had moved as far south as northern Oklahoma. Notice, however, that by March 25, Fort Worth was again experiencing a southerly flow. We can conclude that this was a result of the decaying cyclone that no longer dominated the circulation in the region. We can also safely assume that a warming trend was experienced in Fort Worth over the next day or so. Also notice on the map for March 25 that a high was situated over southwestern Mississippi. The clear skies and weak surface winds associated with the center of a subsiding air mass are well illustrated here.

You may have already noticed another cyclone moving in from the Pacific on March 25 as our storm exited to the east. This storm developed in a similar manner, but was centered somewhat farther north. As you might guess, another blizzard hammered the northern Plains states and a few tornadoes spun through Texas, Arkansas, and Kentucky, while precipitation dominated the weather in the central and eastern United States.

FIGURE 9-23 Paralyzing blizzard strikes the north-central United States. *(Photo by Mike McCleary/Bismarck Tribune)*

Weather in Peoria

Having examined the general weather associated with the passage of this cyclone from March 23 through March 25, let us now look at the weather experienced at a single location during this time. We have selected Peoria, a city in central Illinois located just north of the Springfield station shown on the weather charts.

Before you read the description of Peoria's weather, try to answer the following questions by using Table 9–2, which provides weather observations at three-hour intervals during this time period. Also use the three weather charts (Figures 9–20 through 9–22) and recall the general wind and temperature changes expected with the passage of fronts.

1. What type of clouds were probably present in Peoria during the early morning hours of March 23?
2. At approximately what time did the warm front pass through Peoria?

3. List two lines of evidence indicating that a warm front did pass through Peoria.
4. How did the wind and temperature changes during the early morning hours of March 23 indicate the approach of a warm front?
5. Explain the slight temperature increases experienced between 6:00 P.M. and 9:00 P.M. on March 23.
6. By what time had the cold front passed through Peoria?
7. List some changes that indicate the passage of the cold front.
8. The cold front had already gone through Peoria by noon on March 24, so how do you account for the snow shower that occurred during the next 24 hours?
9. Did the thunderstorms in Peoria occur with the passage of the warm front, the cold front, or the occluded front?

TABLE 9-2 Weather data for Peoria, Illinois, March 23 to 25

	Temperature (°F)	Wind direction	Cloud coverage (tenths)	Visibility (miles)	Weather and precipitation
March 23					
00:00	43	ENE	5	15	
3:00 A.M.	43	ENE	8	15	
6:00 A.M.	42	E	5	12	
9:00 A.M.	50	ESE	10	10	
12:00 P.M.	61	SE	10	12	
3:00 P.M.	64	SE	10	10	Thunderstorm with rain showers
6:00 P.M.	64	SE	10	6	Haze
9:00 P.M.	65	S	10	10	Thunderstorm with rain
March 24					
00:00	57	WSW	10	15	
3:00 A.M.	47	SW	2	15	
6:00 A.M.	42	SW	6	15	
9:00 A.M.	39	SW	8	15	
12:00 P.M.	37	SSW	10	15	Snow showers
3:00 P.M.	33	SW	10	10	Snow showers
6:00 P.M.	30	WSW	10	10	Snow showers
9:00 P.M.	26	WSW	10	6	Snow showers
March 25					
00:00	26	WSW	10	15	
3:00 A.M.	25	WSW	10	8	Snow shower
6:00 A.M.	24	WSW	10	1	Snow
9:00 A.M.	26	W	10	3	Snow
12:00 P.M.	25	W	10	12	Snow
3:00 P.M.	27	WNW	10	12	Snow
6:00 P.M.	25	NW	9	12	
9:00 P.M.	24	NW	4	15	

10. Basing your answer on the apparent clearing skies late on March 25, would you expect the low temperature on March 26 to be lower or higher than on March 25? Explain.

Now read the following discussion to obtain a more complete description of the weather you just reviewed.

We begin our weather observations in Peoria just after midnight on March 23 (Table 9–2). The sky contains cirrus and cirrocumulus clouds, and cool winds from the ENE dominate. As the early morning hours pass, we observe a slight wind shift toward the southeast and a very small drop in temperature. Three hours after sunrise, altocumulus clouds are replaced by stratus and nimbostratus clouds that darken the sky, yet the warm front passes without incident. The 20°F increase in temperature and the wind shift from an easterly to a southeasterly flow mark the passage of the warm front as the warm sector moves over Peoria. The pleasant 60°F temperatures are welcome in Peoria, which enjoys a day 14°F above normal.

But the mild weather is short-lived because the part of the cyclone that passed Peoria was near the apex of the storm, where the cold front is generally close behind the warm front. By afternoon the cold front generates numerous thunderstorms from cumulonimbus clouds embedded in the warm sector just ahead of the cold front. Strong winds, half-inch hail, and a tornado cause local damage. The temperature remains unseasonably warm during the thunderstorm activity.

Early on the morning of March 24 the passage of the cold front is marked by a wind shift, rapidly clearing skies, and a temperature drop of nearly 20°F, all in less than four hours. Throughout March 24 southwesterly winds bring cold air around the back (west) side of the intensifying storm (see Figure 9–22). Although the surface fronts have passed, this intense cyclone, with its occluded front aloft, is generating snowfall over a wide area. This is not unusual behavior. Occluding cyclones often slow their movement as this one did. For about 24 hours, snow flurries dominate Peoria's weather picture.

By noon on March 25 the storm has lost its punch and the pressure begins to climb. The skies start clearing and the winds become northwesterly as the once tightly wound storm weakens. The mean temperature on March 25 is 16°F below normal, and the ground is covered with snow.

This example demonstrates the effect of a spring cyclone on the weather of a mid-latitude location. Within just three days, Peoria's temperatures changed from unseasonably warm to unseasonably cold. Thunderstorms with hail were followed by snow showers. You can see how the north–south temperature gradient, which is most pronounced in the spring, generates these intense storms. Recall that it is the role of these storms to transfer heat from the tropics poleward. Because of Earth's rotation, however, this latitudinal heat exchange is complex, for the Coriolis force gives the winds a zonal (west-to-east) orientation. If Earth rotated more slowly or not at all, a more leisurely north-south flow would exist that might reduce the temperature gradient. Thus, the tropics would be cooler and the poles warmer, and the mid-latitudes would not be as stormy.

A Modern View: The Conveyor Belt Model

The Norwegian cyclone model has proven to be a valuable tool for describing the formation and development of mid-latitude cyclones. Although modern ideas have not replaced this model, a great deal more has been learned about the structure and evolution of these storm systems as a result of upper-air and satellite data. Armed with this additional information, meteorologists have developed another model to describe the circulation of a mid-latitude cyclone.

Along with this new way of describing the flow within a cyclone comes a new analogy. Recall that the Norwegian model describes cyclone development in terms of the interactions of air masses along frontal boundaries, similar to armies clashing along battlefronts. By contrast, the new model employs an example from industry—conveyor belts. Just as conveyor belts transport goods (or at airports, people) from one location to another, these atmospheric conveyor belts transport air with distinct characteristics from one location to another.

The modern view of cyclogenesis, called the **conveyor belt model,** provides a good picture of the airflow within a cyclonic system. It consists of three interacting airstreams: two that originate near the surface and ascend, and a third that originates in the uppermost troposphere. A schematic representation of these airstreams is shown in Figure 9–24.

The *warm conveyor belt* (shown in red) carries warm, moist air from the Gulf of Mexico into the warm sector of the mid-latitude cyclone (Figure 9–24). As this airstream flows northward, convergence causes it to slowly ascend. When it reaches the sloping boundary of the warm front, it rises even more rapidly over the cold air that lies beyond (north of) the front. During its ascent, the warm, humid air cools adiabatically and produces a wide band of clouds and precipitation. Depending on atmospheric conditions, drizzle, rain, freezing rain (glaze), and snow are possible. When this airstream reaches the middle troposphere, it begins to turn right (eastward) and eventually joins the general west-to-east flow aloft. The warm conveyor belt is the main precipitation producing air stream in a mid-latitude cyclone.

The *cold conveyor belt* (blue arrow) is airflow that starts at the surface ahead (north of) of the warm front and flows westward toward the center of the cyclone (Figure 9–24). Flowing beneath the warm conveyor belt, this air is moistened by the evaporation of raindrops falling through it. (Near the Atlantic Ocean this conveyor belt has a marine origin and feeds significant moisture into the storm.) Convergence causes this air stream to rise as it nears the center

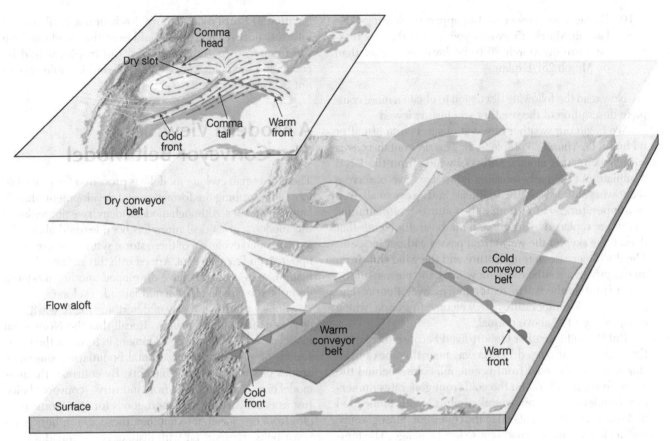

FIGURE 9-24 Schematic drawing of the circulation of a mature mid-latitude cyclone, showing the warm conveyor belt (red), cold conveyor belt (blue), and dry conveyor belt (yellow). The inset shows the cloud cover produced by the warm and cold conveyor belts and the dry slot produced by the dry conveyor belt.

FIGURE 9-25 Satellite view of a mature mid-latitude cyclone over the eastern half of the United States. It is easy to see why we often refer to the cloud pattern of a cyclone as having a "comma" shape. *(Courtesy of John Jensenius/National Weather Service)*

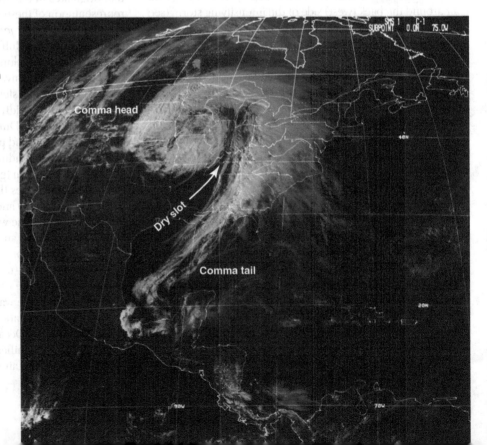

of the cyclone. During its ascent, this air becomes saturated and contributes to the cyclone's precipitation. Upon reaching the middle troposphere, some of the flow rotates cyclonically around the low to produce the distinctive "comma head" of the mature storm system (Figure 9–25). The remaining flow turns right (clockwise) and becomes incorporated into the general westerly flow. Here it parallels the flow of the warm conveyor belt and may generate precipitation.

The third airstream, called the *dry conveyor belt*, is shown as a yellow arrow in Figure 9–24. Whereas the warm and cold conveyor belts begin at the surface, the dry airstream originates in the uppermost troposphere. Being part of the upper-level westerly flow, the dry conveyor belt

is relatively cold and dry. As this air stream enters the cyclone, it splits. One branch descends behind the cold front. The result is the clear, cool conditions normally associated with the passage of a cold front. In addition, this flow maintains the strong temperature contrast observed across the cold front. The other branch of the dry conveyor belt maintains its westerly flow and forms the *dry slot* (cloudless area) that separates the head and tail of a comma cloud pattern (Figure 9-25).

In summary, the conveyor belt model of the mid-latitude cyclone provides a three dimensional picture of the major circulation of these storm systems. It also accounts for distribution of precipitation and the comma-shaped cloud pattern characteristic of mature cyclonic storms.

Chapter Summary

- The primary weather producer in the middle latitudes (for our purposes, the region between southern Florida and Alaska, essentially the area of the westerlies) is the *middle-latitude* or *mid-latitude cyclone*. Mid-latitude cyclones are large low pressure systems with diameters often exceeding 1000 kilometers (600 miles) that generally travel from west to east. They last a few days to more than a week, have a counterclockwise circulation pattern with a flow inward toward their centers, and have a cold front and frequently a warm front extending from the central area of low pressure. In the *polar front theory* (also called the *Norwegian cyclone model*), mid-latitude cyclones develop in conjunction with the *polar front*.

- *Fronts* are boundary surfaces that separate air masses of different densities, one usually warmer and more moist than the other. As one air mass moves into another, the warmer, less dense air mass is forced aloft in a process called *overrunning*. The five types of fronts are (1) *warm front*, which occurs when the surface (ground) position of a front moves so that warm air occupies territory formerly covered by cooler air, (2) *cold front*, where cold continental polar air actively advances into a region occupied by warmer air, (3) *stationary front*, which occurs when the airflow on both sides of a front is neither toward the cold air mass nor toward the warm air mass, (4) *occluded front*, which develops when an active cold front overtakes a warm front and wedges the warm front upward, and (5) a *dryline*, a boundary between denser dry, air and less dense humid air often associated with severe thunderstorms during the spring and summer. The two types of occluded fronts are the *cold-type occluded front*, where the air behind the cold front is colder than the cool air it is overtaking, and the *warm-type occluded front*, where the air behind the advancing cold front is warmer than the cold air it overtakes.

- According to the polar front model, mid-latitude cyclones form along fronts and proceed through a generally predictable life cycle. Along the polar front, where two air masses of different densities are moving parallel to the

front and in opposite directions, *cyclogenesis* (cyclone formation) occurs and the frontal surface takes on a wave shape that is usually several hundred kilometers long. Once a wave forms, warm air advances poleward invading the area formerly occupied by colder air. This change in the direction of the surface flow causes a readjustment in the pressure pattern that results in almost circular isobars, with the low pressure centered at the apex of the wave. Usually, the position of the cold front advances faster than the warm front and gradually closes the warm sector and lifts the warm front. This process, known as *occlusion*, creates an occluded front. Eventually all the warm sector is forced aloft and cold air surrounds the cyclone at low levels. At this point, the cyclone has exhausted its source of energy and the once highly organized counterclockwise flow ceases to exist.

- Guided by the westerlies aloft, cyclones generally move eastward across the United States. As an idealized mid-latitude cyclone moves over a region, the passage of a warm front places the area under the influence of a maritime tropical air mass and its generally warm temperatures, southerly winds, and clear skies. The passage of a cold front is easily detected by a wind shift, the replacement of south or southwesterly winds with winds from the west or northwest. There is also a pronounced drop in temperature. A passing occluded front is often associated with cool, overcast conditions, and snow or glaze during the cool months.

- Airflow aloft (divergence and convergence) plays an important role in maintaining cyclonic and anticyclonic circulation. In a cyclone, divergence aloft does not involve the outward flow of air in all directions. Instead, the winds flow generally from west to east, along sweeping curves. Also, at high altitudes, speed variations within the jet stream cause air to converge in areas where the velocity slows, and to diverge where air is accelerating. In addition to *speed divergence, directional divergence* (the horizontal spreading of an air stream) and *vorticity* (the amount of rotation exhibited by a mass of moving air) also contribute to divergence (or convergence) aloft.

- During the colder months, when temperature gradients are steepest, cyclonic storms advance at their fastest rate. Furthermore, the westerly airflow aloft tends to steer these developing pressure systems in a general west-to-east direction. Cyclones that influence western North America originate over the Pacific Ocean. Although most Pacific storms do not cross the Rockies intact, many redevelop on the lee (eastern) side of these mountains. Some cyclones that affect the United States form over the Great Plains and are associated with an influx of maritime tropical air from the Gulf of Mexico. Another area where cyclogenesis occurs is east of the southern Appalachians. These cyclones tend to migrate toward the northeast, impacting the Eastern Seaboard.

- Due to the gradual subsidence within them, anticyclones generally produce clear skies and calm conditions. One

to three times each winter, large highs, called *blocking highs*, persist over the middle latitudes and deflect the nearly zonal west-to-east flow poleward. These stagnant anticyclones block the eastward migration of cyclones, keeping one section of the nation dry for a week or more while another region experiences one cyclonic storm after another. Also due to subsidence, large stagnant anticyclones can produce a temperature inversion that contributes to air pollution episodes.

- In the spring, Earth's pronounced north–south temperature gradient can generate intense cyclonic storms. At a mid-latitude location, as a spring cyclone with its associated fronts passes, temperatures can change quickly from unseasonably warm to unseasonably cold, and thunderstorms with hail can be followed by snow showers.

Vocabulary Review

cold front (p. 257)
cold-type occluded front (p. 258)
conveyor belt model (p. 279)
cyclogenesis (p. 260)
dryline (p. 260)
front (p. 254)

middle-latitude (mid-latitude) cyclone (p. 252)
Norwegian cyclone model (p. 253)
occluded front (p. 258)
occlusion (p. 262)
overrunning (p. 255)

polar-front theory (p. 253)
speed divergence (p. 266)
stationary front (p. 258)
warm front (p.256)
warm-type occluded front (p. 258)

Review Questions

1. How did the early Norwegian meteorologists describe fronts?
2. If you were located 400 kilometers ahead of the surface position of a typical warm front, how high would the frontal surface be above you?
3. Compare the weather of a warm front with that of a cold front.
4. Why is cold-front weather usually more severe than warm-front weather?
5. Explain the basis for the following weather proverb:

   Rain long foretold, long last;

   Short notice, soon past.
6. How does a stationary front produce precipitation when its position does not change, or changes very slowly?
7. Distinguish between cold-type and warm-type occluded fronts.
8. Describe the initial stage in the formation of a mid-latitude cyclone.
9. Mid-latitude cyclones are sometimes called *wave cyclones*. Why do you think this is so?
10. Although the formation of an occluded front often represents a period of increased intensity for a mid-latitude cyclone, it also marks the beginning of the end of the system. Explain why such is the case.
11. For each of the weather elements listed here, describe the changes that an individual experiences when a

middle-latitude cyclone passes with its center *north* of the observer. (*Hint:* See Figures 9–11 and 9–12)
   a. wind direction
   b. pressure tendency
   c. cloud type
   d. cloud cover
   e. precipitation
   f. temperature
12. Describe the weather conditions that an observer would experience if the center of a mid-latitude cyclone passed to the south.
13. Distinguish between veering and backing winds (see Box 9–1).
14. Briefly explain how the flow aloft maintains cyclones at the surface.
15. What is speed divergence? Speed convergence?
16. Given an upper air chart, where do forecasters usually look to find favorable sites for cyclogenesis? Where do anticyclones usually form in relation to the upper-level flow?
17. What are two possible ways a blocking high might influence the weather?
18. Briefly describe the various weather phenomena that could be associated with a strong springtime cyclonic storm traveling across the United States.

Atmospheric Science Online

The Atmosphere 10e web site uses the resources and flexibility of the Internet to aid in your study of the topics in this chapter. Written and developed by meteorology instructors, this site will help improve your understanding of meteorology. Visit **http://www.prenhall.com/lutgens** and click on the cover of *The Atmosphere 10e* to find:

- **Online review quizzes**
- **Critical thinking exercises**
- **Links to chapter-specific web resources**
- **Internet-wide key term searches**

http://www.prenhall.com/lutgens

THUNDERSTORMS
and
TORNADOES

This lightning display occurred near Colorado Springs, Colorado. *(Photo by Sean Cayton/The Image Works)*

The subject of this and the following chapter, is severe weather. In this chapter we will examine the severe local weather produced in association with cumulonimbus clouds—namely, thunderstorms and tornadoes (Figure 10–1). In Chapter 11 the focus will turn to the large tropical storms we call hurricanes.

Occurrences of severe weather have a fascination that ordinary weather phenomena cannot provide. The lightning display generated by a thunderstorm can be a spectacular event that elicits both awe and fear. Of course, hurricanes and tornadoes also attract a great deal of much deserved attention. A single tornado outbreak or hurricane can cause billions of dollars in property damage as well as many deaths.

What's in a Name?

In Chapter 9 we examined the middle-latitude cyclones that play such an important role in causing day-to-day weather changes. Yet the use of the term "cyclone" is often confusing. For many people the term implies only an intense storm, such as a tornado or a hurricane. When a hurricane unleashes its fury on India or Bangladesh, for example, it is usually reported in the media as a cyclone (the term denoting a hurricane in that part of the world).

Similarly, tornadoes are referred to as cyclones in some places. This custom is particularly common in portions of the Great Plains of the United States. Recall that in the *Wizard of Oz,* Dorothy's house was carried from her Kansas farm to the land of Oz by a cyclone. Indeed, the nickname for the athletic teams at Iowa State University is the *Cyclones*. Although hurricanes and tornadoes are, in fact, cyclones, the vast majority of cyclones are not hurricanes or tornadoes. The term "cyclone" simply refers to the circulation around any low-pressure center, no matter how large or intense it is.

Tornadoes and hurricanes are both smaller and more violent than middle-latitude cyclones. Middle-latitude cyclones may have a diameter of 1600 kilometers (1000 miles) or more. By contrast, hurricanes average only 600 kilometers (375 miles) across, and tornadoes, with a diameter of just 0.25 kilometer (0.16 mile), are much too small to show up on a weather map.

The thunderstorm, a much more familiar weather event, hardly needs to be distinguished from tornadoes, hurricanes, and midlatitude cyclones. Unlike the flow of air about these storms, the circulation associated with thunderstorms is characterized by strong up-and-down movements. Winds in the vicinity of a thunderstorm do not follow the inward spiral of a cyclone, but they are typically variable and gusty.

FIGURE 10-1 This tornado occurred over south central Kansas in May 2004. *(Photo by Weatherstock/Peter Arnold, Inc.)*

Although thunderstorms form "on their own" away from cyclonic storms, they also form in conjunction with cyclones. For instance, thunderstorms are frequently spawned along the cold front of a midlatitude cyclone, where on rare occasions a tornado may descend from the thunderstorm's cumulonimbus tower. Hurricanes also generate widespread thunderstorm activity. Thus, thunderstorms are related in some manner to all three types of cyclones mentioned here.

Thunderstorms

Almost everyone has observed various small-scale phenomena that result from the vertical movements of relatively warm, unstable air. Perhaps you have seen a dust devil over an open field on a hot day whirling its dusty load to great heights (see Box 7–1) or maybe you have seen a bird glide effortlessly skyward on an invisible thermal of hot air. These examples illustrate the dynamic thermal instability that occurs during the development of a *thunderstorm*. A **thunderstorm** is simply a storm that generates lightning and thunder. It frequently produces gusty winds, heavy rain, and hail. A thunderstorm may be produced by a single cumulonimbus cloud and influence only a small area, or it may be associated with clusters of cumulonimbus clouds covering a large area.

Thunderstorms form when warm, humid air rises in an unstable environment. Various mechanisms can trigger the upward air movement needed to create thunderstorm-producing cumulonimbus clouds. One mechanism, the unequal heating of Earth's surface, significantly contributes to the formation of *air-mass thunderstorms*. These storms are associated with the scattered puffy cumulonimbus clouds that commonly form *within* maritime tropical air masses and produce scattered thunderstorms on summer days. Such storms are usually short-lived and seldom produce strong winds or hail.

In contrast, thunderstorms in a second category not only benefit from uneven surface heating but are associated with the lifting of warm air, as occurs along a front or a mountain slope. Moreover, diverging winds aloft frequently contribute to the formation of these storms because they tend to draw air from lower levels upward beneath them. Some of the thunderstorms in this second category may produce high winds, damaging hail, flash floods, and tornadoes. Such storms are described as *severe*.

At any given time there are an estimated 2000 thunderstorms in progress. As we would expect, the greatest proportion occurs in the tropics, where warmth, plentiful moisture, and instability are always present. About 45,000 thunderstorms take place each day, and more than 16 million occur annually around the world. The lightning from these storms strikes Earth 100 times each second (Figure 10–2).

Annually the United States experiences about 100,000 thunderstorms and millions of lightning strikes. A glance at Figure 10–3 shows that thunderstorms are most frequent in Florida and the eastern Gulf Coast region, where activity is recorded between 70 and 100 days each year. The region on the east side of the Rockies in Colorado and New Mexico is next, with thunderstorms occurring 60 to 70 days annually. Most of the rest of the nation experiences thunderstorms 30 to 50 days a year. Clearly, the western margin of the United States has little thunderstorm activity. The same is true for the northern tier of states and for Canada, where warm, moist, unstable mT air seldom penetrates.

Air-Mass Thunderstorms

In the United States **air-mass thunderstorms** frequently occur in maritime tropical (mT) air that moves northward from the Gulf of Mexico. These warm, humid air masses contain abundant moisture in their lower levels and can be rendered unstable when heated from below or lifted along a front. Because mT air most often becomes unstable in spring and summer, when it is warmed from below by the heated land surface, it is during these seasons that air-mass thunderstorms are most frequent. They also have a strong preference for midafternoon, when surface temperatures are highest. Because local differences in surface heating aid the growth of air-mass thunderstorms, they generally occur as scattered, isolated cells instead of being organized in relatively narrow bands or other configurations.

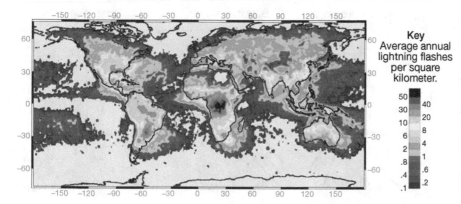

FIGURE 10-2 Data from space-based optical sensors show the worldwide distribution of lightning, with color variations indicating the average annual number of lightning flashes per square kilometer. The map includes data obtained from April 1995 to March 2000 from NASA's Optical Transient Detector, and from December 1997 to November 2000 from NASA's Lightning Imaging Sensor. Both are satellite-based sensors that use high-speed cameras capable of detecting brief lightning flashes even under daytime conditions. *(NASA image)*

Key
Average annual lightning flashes per square kilometer.

50
30
10
6
2
.8
.4
.1

40
20
8
4
1
.6
.2

FIGURE 10-3 Average number of days each year with thunderstorms. The humid subtropical climate that dominates the southeastern United States receives much of its precipitation in the form of thunderstorms. Most of the Southeast averages 50 or more days each year with thunderstorms. *(Source: Environmental Data Service, NOAA)*

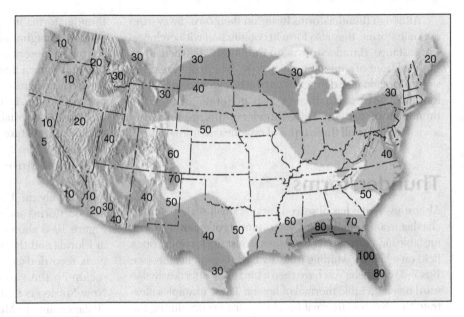

Stages of Development

Important field experiments that were conducted in Florida and Ohio in the late 1940s probed the dynamics of air-mass thunderstorms. This pioneering work, known as the *Thunderstorm Project,* was prompted by a number of thunderstorm-related airplane crashes. It involved the use of radar, aircraft, radiosondes, and an extensive network of surface instruments. The research produced a three-stage model of the life cycle of an air-mass thunderstorm that remains basically unchanged after more than 50 years. The three stages are depicted in Figure 10–4.

Cumulus Stage. Recall that an air-mass thunderstorm is largely a product of the uneven heating of the surface, which leads to rising currents of air that ultimately produce a cumulonimbus cloud. At first the buoyant thermals produce fair weather cumulus clouds that may exist for just minutes before evaporating into the drier, surrounding air (Figure 10–5a). This initial cumulus development is important because it moves water vapor from the sur-

face to greater heights. Ultimately, the air becomes sufficiently humid that newly forming clouds do not evaporate, but instead continue to grow vertically.

The development of a cumulonimbus tower requires a continuous supply of moist air. The release of latent heat allows each new surge of warm air to rise higher than the last, adding to the height of the cloud (Figure 10–5b). This phase in the development of a thunderstorm, called the **cumulus stage,** is dominated by updrafts (Figure 10–4a).

Once the cloud passes beyond the freezing level, the Bergeron process begins producing precipitation. Eventually, the accumulation of precipitation in the cloud is too great for the updrafts to support. The falling precipitation causes drag on the air and initiates a downdraft.

The creation of the downdraft is further aided by the influx of cool, dry air surrounding the cloud, a process termed **entrainment.** This process intensifies the downdraft because the air added during entrainment is cool and therefore heavy; possibly of greater importance, it is dry. It thus causes some of the falling precipitation to evaporate

FIGURE 10-4 Stages in the development of a thunderstorm. During the cumulus stage, strong updrafts act to build the storm. The mature stage is marked by heavy precipitation and cool downdrafts in part of the storm. When the warm updrafts disappear completely, precipitation becomes light and the cloud begins to evaporate.

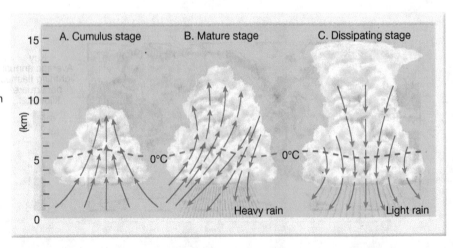

(b)

FIGURE 10-5 (a) At first, buoyant thermals produce fair weather cumulus clouds that soon evaporate into the surrounding air, making it more humid. As this process of cumulus development and evaporation continues, the air eventually becomes sufficiently humid so that newly forming clouds do not evaporate but continue to grow. *(Photo by Henry Lansford/Photo Researchers, Inc.)* (b) This developing cumulonimbus cloud became a towering August thunderstorm over central Illinois. *(Photo by E. J. Tarbuck)*

(a cooling process), thereby cooling the air within the down-draft.

Mature Stage. As the downdraft leaves the base of the cloud, precipitation is released, marking the beginning of the cloud's **mature stage** (Figure 10–4b). At the surface the cool downdrafts spread laterally and can be felt before the actual precipitation reaches the ground. The sharp, cool gusts at the surface are indicative of the downdrafts aloft. During the mature stage, updrafts exist side by side with downdrafts and continue to enlarge the cloud. When the cloud grows to the top of the unstable region, often located at the base of the stratosphere, the updrafts spread laterally and produce the characteristic anvil top. Generally, ice-laden cirrus clouds make up the top and are spread downwind by strong winds aloft. The mature stage is the most active period of a thunderstorm. Gusty winds, lightning, heavy precipitation, and sometimes small hail are experienced.

Dissipating Stage. Once downdrafts begin, the vacating air and precipitation encourage more entrainment of the cool, dry air surrounding the cell. Eventually, the downdrafts dominate throughout the cloud and initiate the **dissipating stage** (Figure 10–4c). The cooling effect of falling precipitation and the influx of colder air aloft mark the end of the thunderstorm activity. Without a supply of moisture from updrafts, the cloud will soon evaporate. An interesting fact is that only a modest portion—on the order of 20 percent—of

the moisture that condenses in an air-mass thunderstorm actually leaves the cloud as precipitation. The remaining 80 percent evaporates back into the atmosphere.

It should be noted that within a single air-mass thunderstorm there may be several individual *cells*—that is, zones of adjacent updrafts and downdrafts. When you view a thunderstorm, you may notice that the cumulonimbus cloud consists of several towers (Figure 10–5b). Each tower may represent an individual cell that is in a somewhat different part of its life cycle.

To summarize, the stages in the development of an air-mass thunderstorm are as follows:

1. The *cumulus stage,* in which updrafts dominate throughout the cloud, and growth from a cumulus to a cumulonimbus cloud occurs.
2. The *mature stage,* the most intense phase, with heavy rain and possibly small hail, in which downdrafts are found side by side with updrafts.
3. The *dissipating stage,* dominated by downdrafts and entrainment, causing evaporation of the structure.

Occurrence

Mountainous regions, such as the Rockies in the West and the Appalachians in the East, experience a greater number of air-mass thunderstorms than do the Plains states. The air near the mountain slope is heated more intensely than air at the same elevation over the adjacent lowlands. A general upslope movement then develops during the daytime that can sometimes generate thunderstorm cells. These cells may remain almost stationary above the slopes below.

Although the growth of thunderstorms is aided by high surface temperatures, many thunderstorms are not generated solely by surface heating. For example, many of Florida's thunderstorms are triggered by the convergence associated with sea-to-land airflow (see Figure 4–22, p. 117). Many thunderstorms that form over the eastern two-thirds of the United States occur as part of the general convergence and frontal wedging that accompany passing mid-latitude cyclones. Near the equator, thunderstorms commonly form in association with the convergence along the equatorial low. Most of these thunderstorms are not severe, and their life cycles are similar to the three-stage model described for air-mass thunderstorms.

Severe Thunderstorms

Severe thunderstorms are capable of producing heavy downpours and flash flooding as well as strong, gusty straight-line winds, large hail, frequent lightning, and perhaps tornadoes (see Box 10–1). For a thunderstorm to be officially classified as *severe* by the National Weather Service, it must have winds in excess of 93 kilometers (58 miles) per hour (50 knots) or produce hailstones with diameters larger than 1.9 centimeters (0.75 inch) or generate a tornado. Of the estimated 100,000 thunderstorms that occur annually in the United States, about 10 percent (10,000 storms) reach severe status.

As you learned in the preceding section, air-mass thunderstorms are localized, relatively short-lived phenomena that dissipate after a brief, well-defined life cycle. They actually extinguish themselves because downdrafts cut off the supply of moisture necessary to maintain the storm. For this reason, air-mass thunderstorms seldom if ever produce severe weather. By contrast, other thunderstorms do not quickly dissipate but instead may remain active for hours. Some of these larger, longer-lived thunderstorms attain severe status.

Why do some thunderstorms persist for many hours? A key factor is the existence of strong vertical wind shear—that is, changes in wind direction and/or speed between different heights. When such conditions prevail, the updrafts that provide the storm with moisture do not remain vertical, but become tilted. Because of this, the precipitation that forms high in the cloud falls into the downdraft rather than into the updraft as occurs in air-mass thunderstorms. This allows the updraft to maintain its strength and continue to build upward. Sometimes the updrafts are sufficiently strong that the cloud top is able to push its way into the stable lower stratosphere, a situation called *overshooting* (Figure 10–6).

Beneath the cumulonimbus tower, where downdrafts reach the surface, the denser cool air spreads out along the ground. The leading edge of this outflowing downdraft acts like a wedge, forcing warm, moist surface air into the thunderstorm. In this way, the downdrafts act to maintain the updrafts, which in turn sustain the thunderstorm.

By examining Figure 10–6, you can see that the outflowing cool air of the downdraft acts as a "mini cold front" as it advances into the warmer surrounding air. This outflow boundary is called a **gust front.** As the gust front moves across the ground, the very turbulent air sometimes picks up loose dust and soil, making the advancing boundary visible. Frequently a *roll cloud* may form as warm air is lifted along the leading edge of the gust front (Figure 10–7). The

FIGURE 10-6 Diagram of a well-developed cumulonimbus tower showing updrafts, downdrafts, and an overshooting top. Precipitation forming in the tilted updraft falls into the downdraft. Beneath the cloud, the denser cool air of the downdraft spreads out along the ground. The leading edge of the outflowing downdraft acts to wedge moist surface air into the cloud. Eventually the outflow boundary may become a gust front that initiates new cumulonimbus development.

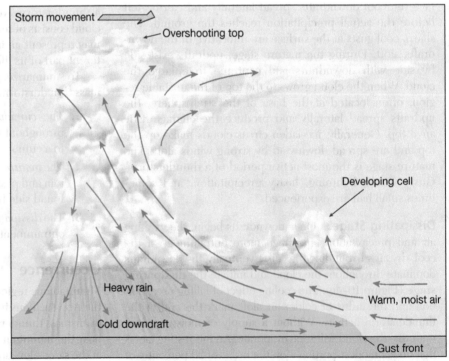

Storm movement
Overshooting top
Developing cell
Heavy rain
Warm, moist air
Cold downdraft
Gust front

FIGURE 10-7 Roll clouds, like this one at Miles City, Montana, are sometimes produced along a gust front in an eddy between the inflow and the downdraft. *(Photo by National Science Foundation/National Center for Atmospheric Research)*

advance of the gust front can provide the lifting needed for the formation of new thunderstorms many kilometers away from the initial cumulonimbus clouds.

Supercell Thunderstorms

Some of our most dangerous weather is caused by a type of thunderstorm called a **supercell.** Few weather phenomena are as awesome (Figure 10–8). An estimated 2000 to 3000 supercell thunderstorms occur annually in the United States. They represent just a small fraction of all thunderstorms, but they are responsible for a disproportionate share of the deaths, injuries, and property damage associated with severe weather. Less than half of all supercells produce tornadoes, yet virtually all of the strongest and most violent tornadoes are spawned by supercells.

A supercell consists of a single, very powerful cell that at times can extend to heights of 20 kilometers (65,000 feet) and that persists for many hours. These massive clouds have diameters ranging between about 20 and 50 kilometers (12 and 30 miles).

Despite the single-cell structure of supercells, these storms are remarkably complex. The vertical wind profile may cause the updraft to rotate. For example, this could occur if the surface flow is from the south or southeast and the winds aloft increase in speed and become more westerly with height. If a thunderstorm develops in such a wind environment, the updraft is made to rotate. It is within this column of cyclonically rotating air, called the **mesocyclone,** that tornadoes often form.°

°More on mesocyclones can be found in the section on "Tornado Development."

The huge quantities of latent heat needed to sustain a supercell require special conditions that keep the lower troposphere warm and moisture-rich. Studies suggest that the existence of an inversion layer a few kilometers above the surface helps to provide this basic requirement. Recall that temperature inversions represent very stable atmospheric conditions that restrict vertical air motions. The presence of an inversion seems to aid the production of a few very large thunderstorms by inhibiting the formation of many smaller ones (Figure 10–9). The inversion prevents the mixing of warm, humid air in the lower troposphere with cold, dry air above. Consequently, surface heating continues to increase the temperature and moisture content of the layer of air trapped below the inversion. Eventually, the inversion is locally eroded by strong mixing from below. The unstable air below "erupts" explosively at these sites, producing unusually large cumulonimbus clouds. It is from such clouds, with their concentrated, persistent updrafts, that supercells form.

Squall Lines and Mesoscale Convective Complexes

Because the atmospheric conditions favoring the formation of severe thunderstorms often exist over a broad area, they frequently develop in groups that consist of many individual storms clustered together. Sometimes these clusters occur as elongate bands called *squall lines.* At other times the storms are organized into roughly circular clusters known as *mesoscale convective complexes.* No matter how the cells are arranged, they are not simply clusters of unrelated individual storms. Rather, they are related by a common origin, or they occur in a situation in which some cells lead to the formation of others.

BOX 10-1 Atmospheric Hazard: Flash Floods—The Number One Thunderstorm Killer

Tornadoes and hurricanes are nature's most awesome storms. Because of this status, they are logically the focus of much well-deserved attention. Yet, surprisingly, in most years these dreaded events are not responsible for the greatest number of storm-related deaths. That distinction is reserved for flash floods. For the nine-year period 1995–2004, the number of storm-related deaths in the United States from flooding averaged 84 per year. By contrast, tornado fatalities averaged 65 annually and hurricanes, 15 (Figure 10–A).

Flash floods are local floods of great volume and short duration. The rapidly rising surge of water usually occurs with little advance warning and can destroy roads, bridges, homes, and other substantial structures (Figure 10–B). Discharges quickly reach a maximum and diminish almost as rapidly. Flood flows often contain large quantities of sed-

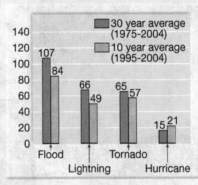

FIGURE 10-A Average annual storm-related deaths in the United States for two time spans. *(Data from National Weather Service)*

iment and debris as they sweep channels clean.

Several factors influence flash flooding. Among them are rainfall intensity and duration, surface conditions, and topography. Urban areas are susceptible to flash floods because a high percentage of the

surface area is composed of impervious roofs, streets, and parking lots, where runoff is very rapid (Figure 10–C).

Frequently, flash floods result from the torrential rains associated with a slow-moving severe thunderstorm or take place when a series of thunderstorms repeatedly pass over the same location. Sometimes they are triggered by heavy rains from hurricanes and tropical storms. Occasionally, floating debris or ice can accumulate at a natural or artificial obstruction and restrict the flow of water. When such temporary dams fail, torrents of water can be released as a flash flood.

Flash floods can take place in almost any area of the country. They are particularly common in mountainous terrain, where steep slopes can quickly channel runoff into narrow valleys. The hazard is most acute

FIGURE 10-B Debris piled around the sign for a campground in Spain's Pyrenees Mountains on August 8, 1996, after a flash flood flowed through the campground killing at least 67 people and injuring another 180. *(AP Photo/Christophe Ena)*

when the soil is already nearly saturated from earlier rains or consists of impermeable materials. A disaster in Shadydale, Ohio, demonstrates what can happen when even moderately heavy rains fall on saturated ground with steep slopes.

On the evening of 14 June 1990, 26 people lost their lives as rains estimated to be in the range of 3 to 5 inches fell on saturated soil, which generated flood waves in streams that reached tens of feet in height, destroying near-bank residences and businesses. Preceding months of above-normal rainfall had generated soil moisture contents of near saturation. As a result,

moderate amounts of rainfall caused large amounts of surface and near-surface runoff. Steep valleys with practically vertical walls channeled the floods, creating very fast, high, and steep wave crests.[*]

Why do so many people perish in flash floods? Aside from the factor of surprise (many are caught sleeping), people do not appreciate the power of moving water. A glance at Figure 10–B helps illustrate the force of a

[*]"Prediction and Mitigation of Flash Floods: A Policy Statement of the American Meteorological Society." *Bulletin of the American Meteorological Society*, Vol. 74, No. 8 (Aug. 1993), p. 1586.

flood wave. Just 15 centimeters (6 inches) of fast-moving flood water can knock a person down. Most automobiles will float and be swept away in only 0.6 meter (2 feet) of water. *More than half of all U.S. flash-flood fatalities are auto related!* Clearly, people should never attempt to drive over a flooded road. The depth of water is not always obvious. Also, the road bed may have been washed out under water. Present-day flash floods are calamities with potential for very high death tolls and huge property losses. Although efforts are being made to improve observations and warnings, flash floods remain elusive natural killers.

FIGURE 10-C Urban areas are susceptible to flash floods because runoff following heavy rains is rapid due to the high percentage of the surface that is impervious. Flash flooding in Las Vegas, Nevada, in August 2003. Parts of the city received nearly half the average annual rainfall in a matter of hours. Here firefighters are rescued from a fire truck that was caught in a torrent of water. *(Phot by John Locher/Las Vegas Review-Journal)*

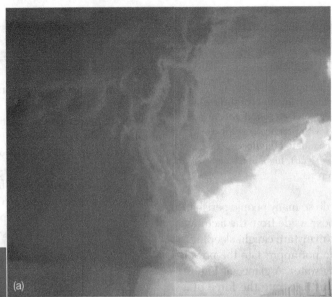

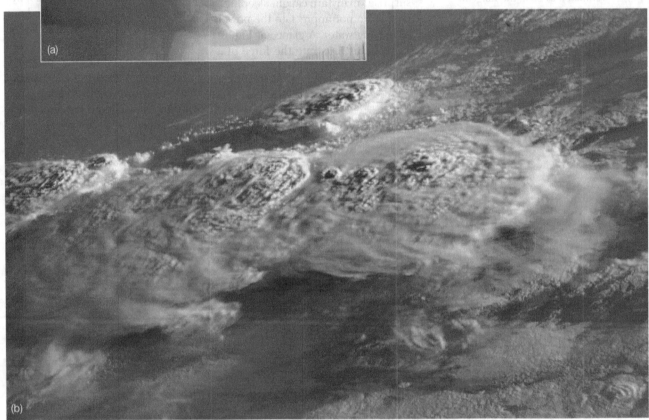

FIGURE 10-8 (a) A supercell thunderstorm. *(Photo © Howard B. Bluestein, Professor of Meteorology)* (b) This photo of a cluster of supercell thunderstorms along the Manitoba–Minnesota border in September 1994 was taken from space by an astronaut. *(NASA photo)*

Squall Lines. A **squall line** is a relatively narrow band of thunderstorms, some of which may be severe, that develops in the warm sector of a middle-latitude cyclone, usually 100 to 300 kilometers (60 to 180 miles) in advance of the cold front. The linear band of cumulonimbus development might stretch for 500 kilometers (300 miles) or more and consists of many individual cells in various stages of development. An average squall line can last for 10 hours or more, and some have been known to remain active for more than a day. Sometimes the approach of a squall line is preceded by a *mammatus sky* consisting of dark cloud rolls that have downward pouches (Figure 10–10).

Most squall lines are not the product of forceful lifting along a cold front. Some develop from a combination of warm, moist air near the surface and an active jet stream aloft. The squall line forms when the divergence and resulting lift created by the jet stream is aligned with a strong, persistent low-level flow of warm, humid air from the south.

A squall line with severe thunderstorms can also form along a boundary called a **dryline,** a narrow zone along which there is an abrupt change in moisture. It forms when continental tropical (cT) air from the southwestern United States is pulled into the warm sector of a middle-latitude cyclone, as shown in Figure 10–11. The denser cT air acts to lift the less dense mT air with which it is converging.* By contrast, both cloud formation and storm development along

*Warm, dry air is more dense than warm, humid air, because the molecular weight of water vapor (H_2O) is only about 62 percent as great as the molecular weight of the mixture of gases that make up dry air.

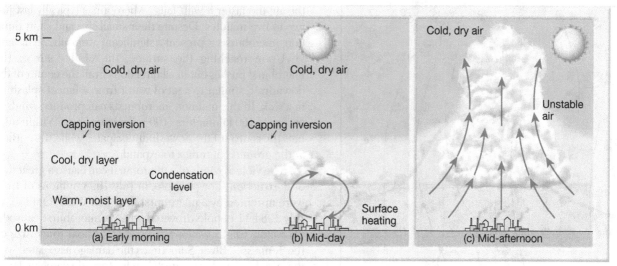

FIGURE 10-9 The formation of severe thunderstorms can be enhanced by the existence of a temperature inversion located a few kilometers above the surface.

the cold front are minimal because the front is advancing into dry cT air.

Drylines most frequently develop in the western portions of Texas, Oklahoma, and Kansas. Such a situation is illustrated by Figure 10–12. The dryline is easily identified by comparing the dew-point temperatures on either side of the squall line. The dew points in the mT air to the east are 30° to 45°F higher than those in the cT air to the west. Much severe weather was generated as this extraordinary squall line moved eastward, including 55 tornadoes over a six-state region.

Mesoscale Convective Complexes.

A **mesoscale convective complex (MCC)** consists of many individual thunderstorms organized into a large oval to circular cluster. A typ-

ical MCC is large, covering an area of at least 100,000 square kilometers (39,000 square miles). The usually slow-moving complex may persist for 12 hours or more (Figure 10–13).

MCCs tend to form most frequently in the Great Plains. When conditions are favorable, an MCC develops from a group of afternoon air-mass thunderstorms. In the evening, as the local storms decay, the MCC starts developing. The transformation of afternoon air-mass thunderstorms into an MCC requires a strong low-level flow of very warm and moist air. This flow enhances instability, which in turn spurs convection and cloud development. As long as favorable conditions prevail, MCCs remain self-propagating as gust fronts from existing cells lead to the formation of new powerful cells nearby. New thunderstorms tend to develop near

FIGURE 10-10 The dark overcast of a mammatus sky, with its characteristic downward bulging pouches, sometimes precedes a squall line. When a mammatus formation develops, it is usually after a cumulonimbus cloud reaches its maximum size and intensity. Its presence is generally a sign of an especially vigorous thunderstorm. (*Photo by Annie Griffiths/DRK Photo*)

FIGURE 10-11 Squall-line thunderstorms frequently develop along a dryline, the boundary separating warm, dry continental tropical air and warm, moist maritime tropical air.

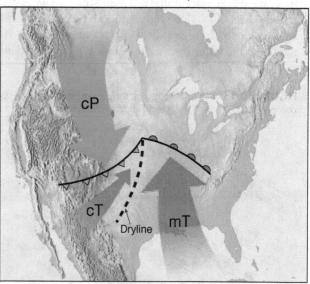

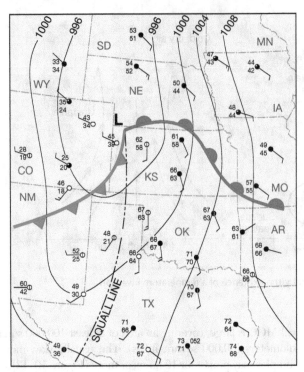

FIGURE 10-12 The squall line of this middle-latitude cyclone was responsible for a major outbreak of tornadoes. The squall line separates dry (cT) and very humid (mT) air. The dryline is easily identified by comparing dew-point temperatures on either side of the squall line. Dew point (°F) is the lower number at each station.

the side of the complex that faces the incoming low-level flow of warm, moist air.

Although mesoscale convective complexes sometimes produce severe weather, they are also beneficial because they provide a significant portion of the growing-season rainfall to the agricultural regions of the central United States.

Microbursts

Beneath some thunderstorms, strong localized downdrafts known as *downbursts* sometimes occur. When downbursts are small—that is, less than 4 kilometers (2.5 miles) across—they are called **microbursts.** These straight-line concentrated bursts of wind are often produced when downdrafts are accelerated by a great deal of evaporative cooling. (Remember, the colder the air, the denser it is, and the denser

FIGURE 10-13 This satellite image shows a mesoscale convective complex (MCC) over the eastern Dakotas. *(NOAA)*

the air, the faster it will "fall.") Microbursts typically last just two to five minutes. Despite their small size and short duration, microbursts represent a significant atmospheric hazard.

Upon reaching the surface, the chilled air of the microburst pushes out in all directions from the center of the downdraft, similar to a jet of water from a faucet splashing in a sink. In this manner, microbursts can produce winds in excess of 160 kilometers (100 miles) per hour. Within minutes the source of the downdraft dissipates while the outflow at the ground continues to expand.

The violent winds of a microburst can cause a great deal of destruction. For example, in July 1993 millions of trees were uprooted by a microburst near Pak Wash, Ontario. In July 1984 11 people drowned when a microburst caused a 28-meter- (90-foot-) long sternwheeler boat to capsize on the Tennessee River. Sometimes the damage associated with these violent outflows is mistaken for tornado damage. However, wind damage from microbursts occurs in straight lines, whereas a rotational circulation pattern is usually detectable along the damage path created by a tornado.

The wind shear associated with microbursts has been responsible for a number of airplane crashes. Imagine an aircraft attempting to land and being confronted by a microburst, as in Figure 10–14. As the airplane flies into the microburst, it initially encounters a strong headwind, which tends to carry it upward. To reduce the lift, the pilot points the nose of the aircraft downward. Then, just seconds later, a tailwind is encountered on the opposite side of the microburst. Here, because the wind is moving with the airplane, the amount of air flowing over the wings and providing lift is dramatically reduced, causing the craft to suddenly lose altitude and crash.

The number of aviation deaths due to microbursts has declined significantly as understanding of the event has increased. Systems to detect the wind shifts associated with microbursts have been installed at most major airports in the United States. Moreover, pilots now receive training on how to handle microbursts during takeoffs and landings.

Lightning and Thunder

A storm is classified as a thunderstorm only after thunder is heard. Because thunder is produced by lightning, lightning must also be present (see chapter-opening photo and Figure 10–15). **Lightning** is similar to the electrical shock you may have experienced on touching a metal object on a very dry day. Only the intensity is different.

During the formation of a large cumulonimbus cloud, a separation of charge occurs, which simply means that part of the cloud develops an excess negative charge, whereas another part acquires an excess positive charge. The object of lightning is to equalize these electrical differences by producing a negative flow of current from the region of excess negative charge to the region with excess positive charge or vice versa. Because air is a poor conductor of electricity (good insulator), the electrical potential (charge difference) must be very high before lightning will occur.

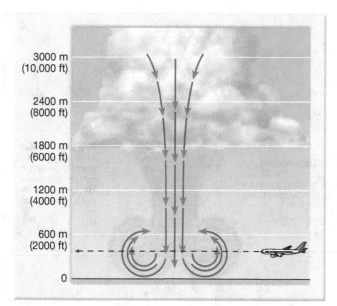

FIGURE 10-14 The arrows in this sketch represent the movement of air in a microburst, a concentrated intense downdraft formed by extraordinary evaporative cooling that creates an outward wind burst at the surface. If you could see it leave the cloud and strike the ground, it might resemble a narrow stream of water "splashing" into a sink. Because of the extremely abrupt changes in wind direction within microbursts, they are a threat to aircraft during landings and takeoffs.

The most common type of lightning occurs between oppositely charged zones *within* a cloud or between clouds. About 80 percent of all lightning is of this type. It is often called *sheet lightning* because it produces a bright but diffuse illumination of those parts of the cloud in which the flash occurred. Sheet lightning is not a unique form; rather, it is ordinary lightning in which the flash is obscured by the clouds. The second type of lightning, in which the electrical discharge occurs between the cloud and Earth's surface, is often more dramatic (see chapter-opening photo). This *cloud-to-ground lightning* represents about 20 percent of lightning strokes and is the most damaging and dangerous form.

What Causes Lightning?

The origin of charge separation in clouds, although not fully understood, must hinge on rapid vertical movements within, because lightning occurs primarily in the violent mature stage of a cumulonimbus cloud. In the midlatitudes the formation of these towering clouds is chiefly a summertime phenomenon, which explains why lightning is seldom observed there in the winter. Furthermore, lightning rarely occurs before the growing cloud penetrates the 5-kilometer level, where sufficient cooling begins to generate ice crystals.

Some cloud physicists believe that charge separation occurs during the formation of ice pellets. Experimentation shows that as droplets begin to freeze, positively charged ions are concentrated in the colder regions of the droplets, whereas negatively charged ions are concentrated in the warmer regions. Thus, as the droplets freeze from the outside in, they develop a positively charged ice shell and a negatively charged interior. As the interior begins to freeze, it expands and shatters the outside shell. The small positively charged ice fragments are carried upward by turbulence, and the relatively heavy droplets eventually carry their negative charge toward the cloud base. As a result, the upper part of the cloud is left with a positive charge, and the lower portion of the cloud maintains an overall negative charge with small positively charged pockets (Figure 10–16).

As the cloud moves, the negatively charged cloud base alters the charge at the surface directly below by repelling negatively charged particles. Thus, the surface beneath the cloud acquires a net positive charge. These charge differences build to millions and even hundreds of millions of volts before a lightning stroke acts to discharge the negative region of the cloud by striking the positive area of the ground below, or, more frequently, the positively charged portion of that cloud, or a nearby cloud.

FIGURE 10-15 Multiple lightning stroke of a single flash as recorded by a moving-film camera. *(Courtesy of E. J. Tarbuck)*

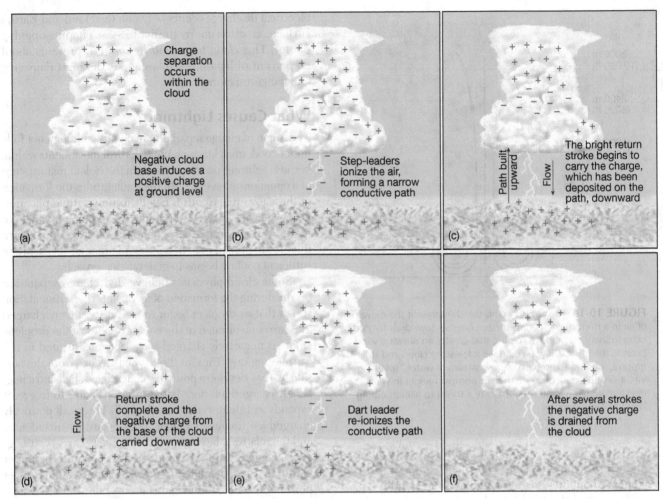

Charge separation occurs within the cloud

Negative cloud base induces a positive charge at ground level

(a)

Step-leaders ionize the air, forming a narrow conductive path

(b)

Path built upward Flow

The bright return stroke begins to carry the charge, which has been deposited on the path, downward

(c)

Flow

Return stroke complete and the negative charge from the base of the cloud carried downward

(d)

Dart leader re-ionizes the conductive path

(e)

After several strokes the negative charge is drained from the cloud

(f)

FIGURE 10-16 Discharge of a cloud via cloud-to-ground lightning. Examine this drawing carefully while reading the text.

The Lightning Stroke

Cloud-to-ground strokes are of most interest and have been studied in detail (see Box 10-2). Moving-film cameras have greatly aided in these studies (see Figure 10–15). They show that the lightning we see as a single flash is really several very rapid strokes between the cloud and the ground. We will call the total discharge—which lasts only a few tenths of a second and appears as a bright streak—the **flash.** Individual components that make up each flash are termed **strokes.** Each stroke is separated by roughly 50 milliseconds, and there are usually three to four strokes per flash.° When a lightning flash appears to flicker, it is because your eyes discern the individual strokes that make up this discharge. Moreover, each stroke consists of a downward propagating leader that is immediately followed by a luminous return stroke.

Each stroke is believed to begin when the electrical field near the cloud base frees electrons in the air immediately below, thereby ionizing the air (Figure 10–16). Once ionized, the air becomes a conductive path having a

°One millisecond equals one one-thousandth ($\frac{1}{1000}$) of a second.

radius of roughly 10 centimeters and a length of 50 meters. This path is called a **leader.** During this electrical breakdown, the mobile electrons in the cloud base begin to flow down this channel. This flow increases the electrical potential at the head of the leader, which causes a further extension of the conductive path through further ionization. Because this initial path extends itself earthward in short, nearly invisible bursts, it is called a **step leader.** Once this channel nears the ground, the electrical field at the surface ionizes the remaining section of the path. With the path completed, the electrons that were deposited along the channel begin to flow downward. The initial flow begins near the ground.

As the electrons at the lower end of the conductive path move earthward, electrons positioned successively higher up the channel begin to migrate downward. Because the path of electron flow is continually being extended upward, the accompanying electric discharge has been appropriately named a **return stroke.** As the wave front of the return stroke moves upward, the negative charge that was deposited on the channel is effectively lowered to the ground. It is this intense return stroke that illuminates the conductive path and discharges the lowest

BOX 10-2 Atmospheric Hazard: Lightning Safety*

In the United States, lightning ranks second only to floods in the number of storm-related deaths each year. Although the number of reported lightning deaths in the United States annually averages about 70, many go unreported. About 100 people are estimated to be killed and more than 500 injured by lightning every year in the United States.

Warnings, statements, and forecasts are routinely issued for floods, tornadoes, and hurricanes, but not for lightning. Why is this the case? The answer relates to the wide geographic occurrence and frequency of lightning.

The magnitude of the cloud-to-ground lightning hazard is understood better today than ever before. Lightning occurs in the United States every day in summer and nearly every day during the rest of the year. Because lightning is so widespread and strikes the ground with such great frequency, it is not possible to warn each person of every flash. For this reason, lightning can be considered the most dangerous weather hazard that many people encounter each year.

Being aware of and following proven safety guidelines can greatly reduce the risk of injury or death. Individuals are ultimately responsible for their personal safety and should take appropriate action when threatened by lightning.

No place is absolutely safe from the threat of lightning, but some places are safer than others.

• Large enclosed structures (substantially constructed buildings) tend to be much safer than smaller or open structures. The risk for lightning injury depends on whether the structure incorporates lightning protection, the types of construction materials used, and the size of the structure.

• In general, fully enclosed metal vehicles, such as cars, trucks, buses, vans, and fully enclosed farm vehicles, etc., with the windows rolled up, provide good shelter from lightning. Avoid contact with metal or conducting surfaces outside or inside the vehicle.

• Avoid being in or near high places and open fields, isolated trees, unprotected gazebos, rain or picnic shelters, baseball dugouts, communications towers, flagpoles, light poles, bleachers (metal or wood), metal fences, convertibles, golf carts, and water (ocean, lakes, swimming pools, rivers, etc.).

• When inside a building, avoid use of the telephone, taking a shower, washing your hands, doing dishes, or any contact with conductive surfaces with exposure to the outside, such as metal doorframes or window frames, electrical wiring, telephone wiring, cable TV wiring, plumbing, and so forth.

Safety guidelines for individuals include the following:

• Generally speaking, if individuals can see lightning and/or hear thunder, they are already at risk. Louder or more frequent thunder indicates that lightning activity is approaching, thus increasing the risk for lightning injury or death. If the time delay between seeing the flash (lightning) and hearing the bang (thunder) is less than 30 seconds, the individual should be in, or seek, a safer location. Be aware that this method of ranging has severe limitations, in part due to the difficulty of associating the proper thunder to the corresponding flash.

• High winds, rainfall, and cloud cover often act as precursors to actual cloud-to-ground strikes, and these should motivate individuals to take action. Many lightning casualties occur in the beginning, as the storm approaches, because people ignore these precursors. Also, many lightning casualties occur after the perceived threat has passed. Generally, the lightning threat diminishes with time after the last sound of thunder but may persist for more than 30 minutes. When thunderstorms are in the area but not overhead, the lightning threat can exist even when it is sunny, not raining, or when clear sky is visible.

• When available, pay attention to weather-warning devices such as NOAA (National Oceanic and Atmospheric Administration) weather radio and/or credible lightning-detection systems; however, do not let this information override good common sense.

*Material in this box is based on "Updated Recommendations for Lightning Safety—1998," in *Bulletin of the American Meteorological Society*, Vol. 80, No. 10, October 1999, pp. 2035–39.

kilometer or so of the cloud. During this phase, tens of coulombs of negative charge are lowered to the ground.*

The first stroke is usually followed by additional strokes that apparently drain charges from higher areas within the cloud. Each subsequent stroke begins with a **dart leader** that once again ionizes the channel and carries the cloud potential toward the ground. The dart leader is continuous and less branched than the step leader. When the current between strokes has ceased for periods greater than 0.1 second, further strokes will be preceded by a step leader whose path is different from that of the initial stroke. The total time of each flash consisting of three or four strokes is about 0.2 second.

Students Sometimes Ask...

About how many people who are struck by lightning are actually killed?

According to the National Weather Service, only about 10 percent are killed, leaving 90 percent with various injuries. Lightning tends to injure the nervous system. When the brain is affected, the person may have difficulty with short-term memory, coding new information and accessing old information, multitasking, and being easily distracted. Lightning victims may also suffer personality changes because of frontal lobe damage and become irritable and easy to anger. In addition, some survivors complain of becoming more easily exhausted than before being struck.

Thunder

The electrical discharge of lightning superheats the air immediately around the lightning channel. In less than a second the temperature rises by as much as 33,000°C. When air is heated this quickly, it expands explosively and produces the sound waves we hear as **thunder.** Because lightning and thunder occur simultaneously, it is possible to estimate the distance to the stroke. Lightning is seen instantaneously, but the relatively slow sound waves, which travel approximately 330 meters (1000 feet) per second, reach us a little later. If thunder is heard five seconds after the lightning is seen, the lightning occurred about 1650 meters away (approximately 1 mile).

The thunder that we hear as a rumble is produced along a long lightning path located at some distance from the observer. The sound that originates along the path nearest the observer arrives before the sound that originated farthest away. This factor lengthens the duration of the thunder. Reflection of the sound waves by mountains or buildings further delays their arrival and adds to this effect. When lightning occurs more than 20 kilometers (12 miles) away, thunder is rarely heard. This type of lightning, popularly called *heat lightning*, is no different from the lightning that we associate with thunder.

Tornadoes

Tornadoes are local storms of short duration that must be ranked high among nature's most destructive forces. Their sporadic occurrence and violent winds cause many deaths each year. The nearly total destruction in some stricken areas has led many to liken their passage to bombing raids during war (Box 10–3).

Such was the case when devastating tornadoes hit parts of Oklahoma and Kansas on Monday evening, May 3, 1999 (Figure 10–17a). The estimated death toll was 49 people— 44 in Oklahoma and five in the Wichita, Kansas, area. Altogether, 76 tornadoes occurred during this outbreak. Oklahoma officials estimated that nearly 8100 homes and businesses were damaged or destroyed. In Kansas the figure exceeded 1100. The insurance industry incurred losses that exceeded $1 billion. Oklahoma and Kansas are well known for tornadoes, but Maryland is not. Nevertheless, on April 28, 2002, towering thunderstorms spawned several tornadoes. The most powerful created a 39-kilometer (24-mile) path of destruction across southern Maryland (Figure 10-17b). Three people died and damages exceeded $100 million. It may have been the strongest tornado ever recorded along the eastern seaboard.

Tornadoes, sometimes called *twisters* or *cyclones*, are violent windstorms that take the form of a rotating column of air, or *vortex*, that extends downward from a cumulonimbus cloud. Pressures within some tornadoes have been estimated to be as much as 10 percent lower than immediately outside the storm. Drawn by the much lower pressure in the center of the vortex, air near the ground rushes into the tornado from all directions. As the air streams inward, it is spiraled upward around the core until it eventually merges with the airflow of the parent thunderstorm deep in the cumulonimbus tower.

Because of the rapid drop in pressure, air sucked into the storm expands and cools adiabatically. If the air cools below its dew point, the resulting condensation creates a pale and ominous-appearing cloud that may darken as it moves across the ground, picking up dust and debris (Figure 10–18). Occasionally, when the inward spiraling air is relatively dry, no condensation funnel forms because the drop in pressure is not sufficient to cause the necessary adiabatic cooling. In such cases, the vortex is only made visible by the material that it vacuums from the surface and carries aloft.

Some tornadoes consist of a single vortex, but within many stronger tornadoes are smaller intense whirls called *suction vortices* that orbit the center of the larger tornado circulation (Figure 10–19). The tornadoes in this latter category are called **multiple vortex tornadoes.** Suction vortices have diameters of only about 10 meters (30 feet) and usually form and die out in less than a minute. They can occur in all sorts of tornado sizes, from huge "wedges" to narrow "ropes." Suction vortices are responsible for most

---

*A coulomb is a unit of electrical charge equal to the quantity of charge transferred in 1 second by a steady current of 1 ampere.

BOX 10-3   Atmospheric Hazard: Surviving a Violent Tornado

About 11 A.M. on Tuesday, July 13, 2004, much of northern and central Illinois was put on a tornado watch.* A large supercell had developed in the northwestern part of the state and was moving southeast into a very unstable environment (Figure 10–D). A few hours later, as the supercell entered Woodford County, rain began to fall and the storm showed signs of becoming severe. The National Weather Service (NWS) issued a *severe thunderstorm warning* at 2:29 P.M. CDT. Minutes afterward a tornado developed. Twenty-three minutes later, the quarter-mile-wide twister had carved a 9.6-mile-long path across the rural Illinois countryside.

What, if anything, made this storm special or unique? After all, it was just one of a record-high 1819 tornadoes that were reported in the United States in 2004. For one, this tornado attained F4 status for a portion of its life.** The NWS estimated that maximum winds reached 240 miles per hour. Fewer than 1 percent of tornadoes attain this level of severity. However, what was most remarkable is that no one was killed or

*Watches and warnings are discussed later in this chapter on p. 308.

**F4 is a reference to the Fujita Scale of tornado intensity. See Table 10–1, p. 308.

FIGURE 10-D On July 13, 2004, an F4 tornado cut a 23-mile path through the rural countryside near the Woodford County town of Roanoke, Illinois. The Parsons Manufacturing plant was just west of town.

injured when the Parsons Manufacturing facility west of the small town of Roanoke took a direct hit while the storm was most intense. At the time, 150 people were in three buildings that comprised the plant. The 250,000-square-foot facility was flattened, cars were twisted into gnarled masses, and debris was strewn for miles (Figure 10–E).

How did 150 people escape death or injury? The answer is foresight and planning. More than 30 years earlier, company owner Bob Parsons was inside his first factory when a small tornado passed close enough to blow windows out. Later, when he built a new plant, he made sure that the restrooms were constructed to dou-

ble as tornado shelters with steel-reinforced concrete walls and eight-inch-thick concrete ceilings. In addition, the company developed a severe weather plan. When the severe thunderstorm warning was issued at 2:29 P.M. on July 13, the emergency response team leader at the Parsons plant was immediately notified. A few moments later he went outside and observed a rotating wall cloud with a developing funnel cloud. He radioed back to the office to institute the company's severe weather plan. Employees were told to immediately go to their designated storm shelter. Everyone knew where to go and what to do because the plant conducted semi-annual tornado drills. All 150 people reached a shelter in less than four minutes. The emergency response team leader was the last person to reach shelter, less than two minutes before the tornado destroyed the plant at 2:41 P.M.

The total number of tornado deaths in 2004 for the entire United States was just 36. The toll could have been much higher. The building of tornado shelters and the development of an effective severe storm plan made the difference between life and death for 150 people at Parsons Manufacturing.

FIGURE 10-E The quarter-mile-wide tornado had wind speeds reaching 240 miles per hour. The destruction at Parsons Manufacturing was devastating. *(Photos courtesy of NOAA)*

(a)

(b)

FIGURE 10-17 (a) Aftermath of a violent (F5) tornado that struck Oklahoma City on May 3, 1999. The largest and most destructive of the 76 tornadoes formed about 72 kilometers (45 miles) southwest of Oklahoma City and cut a path about 0.8 kilometer (0.5 mile) wide as it moved north and east across the Oklahoma City area, staying on the ground for nearly four hours. The death toll was relatively low because of repeated warnings broadcast throughout the late afternoon and early evening. Yet, even with up to a half hour warning, many could not find adequate shelter from the tremendous power of the strongest storm. *(Photo by Sue Ogrocki/Reuters)* (b) This satellite image shows the path of a tornado that struck Maryland on April 28, 2002. It was the strongest tornado ever recorded in the state and perhaps the strongest ever recorded along the Eastern Seaboard. The storm flattened everything in its 39-kilometer-(24-mile-) long path, including the historic downtown in the community of LaPlata. In all, nearly 1100 homes and businesses were damaged or destroyed, and damages exceeded $100 million. *(NASA image)*

of the narrow, short swaths of extreme damage that sometimes are through tornado tracks. It is now believed that most reports of several tornadoes at once—from news accounts and early-twentieth-century tornado tales—actually were multiple vortex tornadoes.

Because of the tremendous pressure gradient associated with a strong tornado, maximum winds can sometimes exceed 480 kilometers (300 miles) per hour. For example, using Doppler radar observations, scientists measured wind speeds of 510 kilometers (310 miles) per hour in one of the May 3, 1999, Oklahoma City tornadoes. Reliable wind-speed measurements using traditional anemometers are lacking. The changes that occur in atmospheric pressure with the passage of a tornado are largely estimates and are based on a few storms that happened to pass a nearby weather station. Thus, meteorologists have had to base their tornado models on a relatively scant observational foundation. Although additional data might be gathered if shelters and instruments capable of withstanding the fury of a tornado were placed in an area, such an effort would probably not be worthwhile. Tornadoes are highly localized and randomly distributed, and the probability of placing instruments at the right site would thus be infinitesimally small.

For instance, the probability of a tornado striking a given point in the region most frequently subject to tornadoes is about once in 250 years. The development of Doppler radar, however, has increased our ability to study tornado-producing thunderstorms. As we shall see, the development of this technology is allowing meteorologists to gather important new data from a safe distance.

Students Sometimes Ask...
What does a tornado sound like?

That depends on what it is hitting, its size, intensity, closeness, and other factors. The most common tornado sound is a continuous rumble, like a nearby train. Sometimes a tornado produces a loud whooshing sound, like that of a waterfall or of open car windows while driving very fast. Tornadoes that are tearing through densely populated areas may be producing all kinds of loud noises at once, which collectively may make a tremendous roar. Remember that just because you may have heard a loud roar during a damaging storm does not necessarily mean it was a tornado. Any intense thunderstorm wind can produce damage and cause a roar.

The Development and Occurrence of Tornadoes

Tornadoes form in association with severe thunderstorms that produce high winds, heavy (sometimes torrential) rainfall, and often damaging hail. Although hail may or may not precede a tornado, the portion of the thunderstorm adjacent to large hail is often the area where strong tornadoes are most likely to occur.

Fortunately, less than 1 percent of all thunderstorms produce tornadoes. Nevertheless, a much higher number must be monitored as potential tornado producers. Although meteorologists are still not sure what triggers tornado formation, it is apparent that they are the product of the interaction between strong updrafts in a thunderstorm and the winds in the troposphere.

Tornado Development

Tornadoes can form in any situation that produces severe weather, including cold fronts, squall lines, and tropical cyclones (hurricanes). Usually the most intense tornadoes are those that form in association with supercells. An important precondition linked to tornado formation in severe thunderstorms is the development of a mesocyclone. A *mesocyclone* is a vertical cylinder of rotating air, typically about 3 to 10 kilometers (2 to 6 miles) across, that develops in the updraft of a severe thunderstorm. The formation of this large vortex often precedes tornado formation by 30 minutes or so.

Mesocyclone formation depends on the presence of vertical wind shear. Moving upward from the surface, winds change direction from southerly to westerly and the wind speed increases. The speed wind shear (that is, stronger winds aloft and weaker winds near the surface) produces a rolling motion about a horizontal axis as shown in Figure 10–20a. If conditions are right, strong updrafts in the storm tilt the horizontally rotating air to a nearly vertical alignment (Figure 10–20b). This produces the initial rotation within the cloud interior.

At first the mesocyclone is wider, shorter, and rotating more slowly than will be the case in later stages. Subsequently, the mesocyclone is stretched vertically and narrowed horizontally causing wind speeds to accelerate in an inward vortex (just as ice skaters accelerate while spinning or as a sink full of water accelerates when it spirals down a drain).* Next, the narrowing column of rotating air stretches downward until a portion of the cloud protrudes below the cloud base to produce a very dark, slowly rotating *wall cloud*. Finally, a slender and rapidly spinning vortex emerges from the base of the wall cloud to form a *funnel cloud*. If the funnel cloud makes contact with the surface, it is then classified as a *tornado* (Figure 10–20).

The formation of a mesocyclone does not necessarily mean that tornado formation will follow. Only about half of all mesocyclones produce tornadoes. The reason for this is not understood. Because this is the case, forecasters cannot determine in advance which mesocyclones will spawn tornadoes.

Tornado Climatology

Severe thunderstorms—and hence tornadoes—are most often spawned along the cold front or squall line of a middle-latitude cyclone or in association with supercell thunderstorms.

*For more on this concept, see Box 11–1 on the conservation of angular momentum.

FIGURE 10-18 A tornado is a violently rotating column of air in contact with the ground. The air column is visible when it contains condensation or when it contains dust and debris. Often the appearance is the result of both. When the column of air is aloft and does not produce damage, the visible portion is properly called a *funnel cloud*. This tornado in New Mexico near the Texas Panhandle touched down out of a rotating supercell thunderstorm. *(Photo by A.T. Willett/Alamy)*

FIGURE 10-19 Some tornadoes have multiple suction vortices. These small and very intense vortices are roughly 10 meters (30 feet) across and move in a counterclockwise path around the tornado center. Because of this multiple vortex structure, one building might be heavily damaged and another one, just 10 meters away, might suffer little damage. *(After Fujita)*

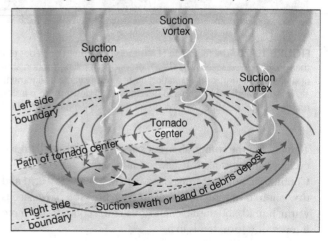

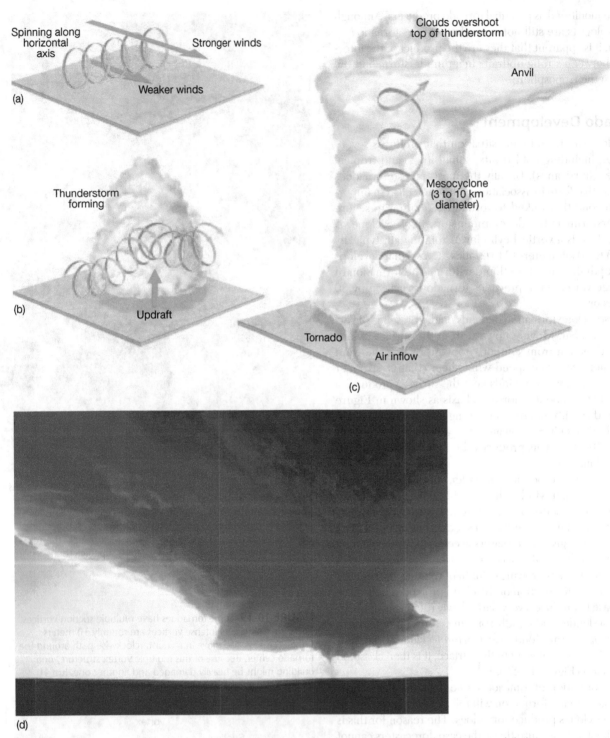

FIGURE 10-20 The formation of a mesocyclone often precedes tornado formation. (a) Winds are stronger aloft than at the surface (called *speed wind shear*), producing a rolling motion about a horizontal axis. (b) Strong thunderstorm updrafts tilt the horizontally rotating air to a nearly vertical alignment. (c) The mesocyclone, a vertical cylinder of rotating air, is established. (d) If a tornado develops it will descend from a slowly rotating wall cloud in the lower portion of the mesocyclone. This supercell tornado hit the Texas Panhandle in May 1996. *(Photo by Warren Faidley/Weatherstock)*

Throughout the spring, air masses associated with midlatitude cyclones are most likely to have greatly contrasting conditions. Continental polar air from Canada may still be very cold and dry, whereas maritime tropical air from the Gulf of Mexico is warm, humid, and unstable. The greater the contrast, the more intense the storm tends to be.

These two contrasting air masses are most likely to meet in the central United States because there is no significant natural barrier separating the center of the country from the arctic or the Gulf of Mexico. Consequently, this region generates more tornadoes than any other part of the country or, in fact, the world. Figure 10–21, which depicts the

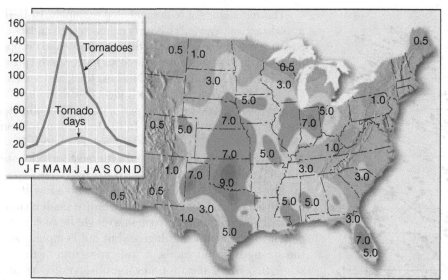

FIGURE 10-21 The map shows average annual tornado incidence per 10,000 square miles (26,000 square kilometers) for a 27-year period. The graph shows average number of tornadoes and tornado days each month in the United States for a 27-year period. *(After NOAA)*

average annual tornado incidence in the United States over a 27-year period, readily substantiates this fact.

An average of about 1200 tornadoes were reported annually in the United States between 1990 and 2004. Still, the actual numbers that occur from one year to the next vary greatly. During the 15-year span just mentioned, for example, yearly totals ranged from a low of 941 in the year 2002 to a high of 1819 in 2004. Tornadoes occur during every month of the year. April through June is the period of greatest tornado frequency in the United States, and December and January are the months of lowest activity. Of the nearly 40,522 confirmed tornadoes reported over the contiguous 48 states during the 50-year period 1950–1999, an average of almost six per day occurred during May. At the other extreme, a tornado was reported only about every other day in December and January.

More than 40 percent of all tornadoes take place during the spring. Fall and winter, by contrast, together account for only 19 percent (Figure 10–21). In late January and February, when the incidence of tornadoes begins to increase, the center of maximum frequency lies over the central Gulf states. During March this center moves eastward to the southeastern Atlantic states, with tornado frequency reaching its peak in April.

During May and June the center of maximum frequency moves through the southern Great Plains and then to the northern Plains and Great Lakes area. This drift is due to the increasing penetration of warm, moist air while contrasting cool, dry air still surges in from the north and northwest. Thus, when the Gulf states are substantially under the influence of warm air after May, there is no cold-air intrusion to speak of, and tornado frequency drops. Such is the case across the country after June. Winter cooling permits fewer and fewer encounters between warm and cold air masses, and tornado frequency returns to its lowest level by December.

Students Sometimes Ask…
What is "Tornado Alley"?

Tornado Alley is a nickname used by the popular media and others that refers to the broad swath of high tornado occurrence in the central United States (see Figure 10–21). The heart of Tornado Alley stretches from the Texas Panhandle through Oklahoma and Kansas to Nebraska. It's important to remember that violent (killer) tornadoes occur outside of Tornado Alley every year. Tornadoes can occur almost anywhere in the United States.

Profile of a Tornado

The average tornado has a diameter of between 150 and 600 meters (500 to 2000 feet), travels across the landscape at approximately 45 kilometers (30 miles) per hour, and cuts a path about 26 kilometers (16 miles) long. Because many tornadoes occur slightly ahead of a cold front, in the zone of southwest winds, most move toward the northeast. The Illinois example demonstrates this fact nicely (Figure 10–22). The figure also shows that many tornadoes do not fit the description of the "average" tornado.

Of the hundreds of tornadoes reported in the United States each year, over half are comparatively weak and short-lived. Most of these small tornadoes have lifetimes of three minutes or less and paths that seldom exceed 1 kilometer (0.6 mile) in length and 100 meters (330 feet) wide. Typical wind speeds are on the order of 150 kilometers (96 miles) per hour or less. On the other end of the tornado spectrum are the infrequent and often long-lived violent tornadoes. Although large tornadoes constitute only a small percentage of the total reported, their effects are often devastating. Such tornadoes may exist for periods in excess of three hours

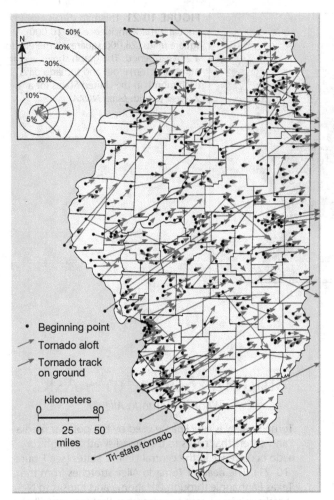

FIGURE 10-22 Paths of Illinois tornadoes (1916–1969). Because most tornadoes occur slightly ahead of a cold front, in the zone of southwest winds, they tend to move toward the northeast. Tornadoes in Illinois verify this. Over 80 percent exhibited directions of movement toward the northeast through east. *(After John W. Wilson and Stanley A. Changnon, Jr., Illinois Tornadoes, Illinois State Water Survey Circular 103, 1971, pp. 10, 24)*

and produce an essentially continuous damage path more than 150 kilometers (90 miles) long and perhaps a kilometer or more wide. Maximum winds range beyond 500 kilometers (310 miles) per hour (Figure 10–23).

Tornado Destruction

Because tornadoes generate the strongest winds in nature, they have accomplished many seemingly impossible tasks, such as driving a piece of straw through a thick wooden plank and uprooting huge trees (Figure 10–24). Although it may seem impossible for winds to cause some of the fantastic damage attributed to tornadoes, tests in engineering facilities have repeatedly demonstrated that winds in excess of 320 kilometers (200 miles) per hour are capable of incredible feats.

There is a long list of documented examples. In 1931 a tornado actually carried an 83-ton railroad coach and its 117 passengers 24 meters (80 feet) through the air and dropped them in a ditch. A year later, near Sioux Falls, South Dakota, a steel beam 15 centimeters (6 inches) thick and 4 meters (13 feet) long was ripped from a bridge, flew more than 300 meters (nearly 1000 feet), and perforated a 35-centimeter- (14-inch-) thick hardwood tree. In 1970 an 18-ton steel tank was carried nearly 1 kilometer (0.6 mile) at Lubbock, Texas. Fortunately, the winds associated with most tornadoes are not this strong.

Most tornado losses are associated with a few storms that strike urban areas or devastate entire small communities. The amount of destruction wrought by such storms depends to a significant degree (but not completely) on the strength of the winds. A wide spectrum of tornado strengths, sizes, and lifetimes are observed. One commonly used guide to tornado intensity was developed by the late T. Theodore Fujita at the University of Chicago and is appropriately called the **Fujita Intensity Scale**, or simply the **F-scale** (Table 10–1). Because tornado winds cannot be measured directly, a rating on the F-scale is determined by assessing the worst damage produced by a storm. Although widely used, the F-scale is not perfect. Estimating tornado intensity based on damage alone does not take into account the structural integrity of the objects hit by a tornado. A well-constructed building can withstand very high winds, whereas a poorly built structure can suffer devastating damage from the same or even weaker winds.

The drop in atmospheric pressure associated with the passage of a tornado plays a minor role in the damage process. Most structures have sufficient venting to allow for the sudden drop in pressure. Opening a window, once thought to be a way to minimize damage by allowing inside and outside atmospheric pressure to equalize, is no longer recommended. In fact, if a tornado gets close enough to a structure for the pressure drop to be experienced, the strong winds probably will have already caused significant damage.

Although the greatest part of tornado damage is caused by violent winds, most tornado injuries and deaths result from flying debris. On the average, tornadoes cause more deaths each year than any other weather events except lightning and flash floods. For the United States, the average annual death toll from tornadoes is about 75 people. However, the actual number of deaths each year can depart significantly from the average. On April 3–4, 1974, for example, an outbreak of 148 tornadoes brought death and destruction to a 13-state region east of the Mississippi River. More than 300 people died and nearly 5500 people were injured in this worst tornado disaster in half a century (see Box 10–4).

In one statistical study that examined a 29-year period, there were 689 tornadoes that caused loss of life. This figure represented slightly less than 4 percent of the total 19,312 reported storms. Although the percentage of tornadoes that result in death is small, every tornado is poten-

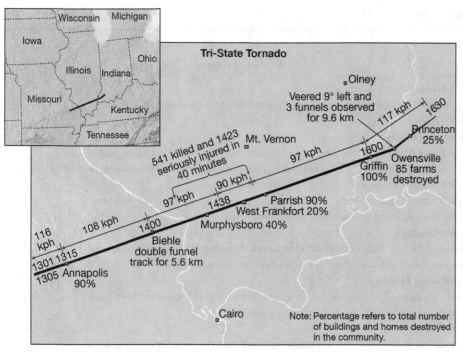

Tri-State Tornado

Olney

Veered 9° left and
3 funnels observed
for 9.6 km

117 kph

1630

Princeton
25%

541 killed and 1423
seriously injured in
40 minutes

Mt. Vernon

97 kph

1600

Owensville
85 farms
destroyed

Griffin
100%

97 kph

90 Kph

Parrish 90%
West Frankfort 20%

1438

Murphysboro 40%

116
kph

108 kph

1400

Biehle
double funnel
track for 5.6 km

1301 1315

1305 Annapolis
90%

Cairo

Note: Percentage refers to total number
of buildings and homes destroyed
in the community.

Wisconsin Michigan

Iowa

Ohio

Illinois Indiana

Missouri

Kentucky

Tennessee

FIGURE 10-23 "One tornado among the more than 13,000 which have occurred in the United States since 1915 easily ranks above all others as the single most devastating storm of this type. Shortly after its occurrence on 18 March 1925, the famed Tri-State tornado was recognized as the worst on record, and it still ranks as the nation's greatest tornado disaster. The tornado remained on the ground for 219 miles. The resulting losses included 695 dead, 2027 injured, and damages equal to $43 million in 1970 dollars. This represents the greatest death toll ever inflicted by a tornado and one of the largest damage totals." *(Map and description from John W. Wilson and Stanley A. Changnon, Jr., Illinois Tornadoes, Illinois State Water Survey Circular 103, 1971, p. 32)*

tially lethal. If you examine Figure 10–25, which compares tornado fatalities with storm intensities, the results are quite interesting. It is clear from this graph that the majority (63 percent) of all tornadoes are weak and that the number of storms decreases as tornado intensity increases. The distribution of tornado fatalities, however, is just the opposite. Although only 2 percent of tornadoes are classified as violent, they account for nearly 70 percent of the deaths.

If there is some question about the causes of tornadoes, there certainly is none about the destructive effects of these violent storms. A severe tornado leaves the affected area stunned and disorganized and may require a response of the magnitude demanded in war.

Students Sometimes Ask...

*How common are the most
violent F5 tornadoes?*

These strongest of all tornadoes are rare. During the 30-year span, 1970–1999, only 26 out of a total of 28,913 tornadoes were classified in the F5 category. That is just 0.09% (nine one-hundredths of one percent)! In many years, there were no F5 tornadoes reported. Nevertheless, during a single 16-hour span, April 3–4, 1974, there were seven F5 storms (for more on this, see Box 10–4).

FIGURE 10-24 The force of the wind during a tornado near Wichita, Kansas, in April 1991 was enough to drive this piece of metal into a utility pole. *(Photo by John Sokich/NOAA)*

TABLE 10-1 Fujita Intensity Scale

Scale	Wind speed (KPH)	(MPH)	Expected damage
F0	<116	<72	**Light Damage** Damage to chimneys and billboards; broken branches; shallow-rooted trees pushed over.
F1	116–180	72–112	**Moderate Damage** The lower limit is near the beginning of hurricane wind speed. Surfaces peeled off roofs; mobile homes pushed off foundations or overturned; moving autos pushed off the road.
F2	181–253	113–157	**Considerable Damage** Roofs torn off frame houses; mobile homes demolished; boxcars pushed over; large trees snapped or uprooted; light-object missiles generated.
F3	254–332	158–206	**Severe Damage** Roofs and some walls torn off well-constructed houses; trains overturned; most trees in forest uprooted; heavy cars lifted off ground and thrown.
F4	333–419	207–260	**Devastating Damage** Well-constructed houses leveled; structures with weak foundations blown some distance; cars thrown and large missiles generated.
F5	>419	>260	**Incredible Damage** Strong frame houses lifted off foundations and carried considerable distance to disintegrate; automobile-sized missiles fly through the air farther than 100 m; trees debarked; incredible phenomena occur.

Tornado Forecasting

Because severe thunderstorms and tornadoes are small and short-lived phenomena, they are among the most difficult weather features to forecast precisely. Nevertheless, the prediction, the detection, and the monitoring of such storms are among the most important services provided by profes-

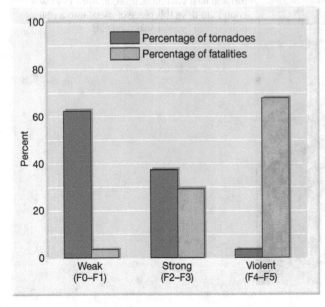

FIGURE 10-25 Percentage of tornadoes in each intensity category (blue) and percentage of fatalities associated with each category (red). *(From Joseph T. Schaefer et al., "Tornadoes—When, Where and How Often," Weatherwise, 33, no. 2 (1980), 57)*

sional meteorologists. The timely issuance and dissemination of watches and warnings are both critical to the protection of life and property.

The Storm Prediction Center (SPC) located in Norman, Oklahoma, is part of the National Weather Service (NWS) and the National Centers for Environmental Prediction (NCEP). Its mission is to provide timely and accurate forecasts and watches for severe thunderstorms and tornadoes.

Severe thunderstorm outlooks are issued several times daily. *Day 1* outlooks identify those areas likely to be affected by severe thunderstorms during the next six to 30 hours, and *day 2* outlooks extend the forecast through the following day. Both outlooks describe the type, coverage, and intensity of the severe weather expected. Many local NWS field offices also issue severe weather outlooks that provide a more local description of the severe weather potential for the next 12 to 24 hours.

Tornado Watches and Warnings

Tornado watches alert the public to the possibility of tornadoes over a specified area for a particular time interval. Watches serve to fine-tune forecast areas already identified in severe weather outlooks. A typical watch covers an area of about 65,000 square kilometers (25,000 square miles) for a four- to six-hour period. A tornado watch is an important part of the tornado alert system because it sets in motion the procedures necessary to deal adequately with detection, tracking, warning, and response. Watches are generally reserved for organized severe weather events where the tornado threat will affect at least 26,000 square kilometers

BOX 10-4   Atmospheric Hazard: The April 1974 Super Tornado Outbreak

The dates April 3–4, 1974, are important in the tornado history of the United States. In a span of just 16 hours, 148 tornadoes hit 13 states and Canada—the largest and costliest outbreak ever recorded (Figure 10–F). The storms killed 315 people and injured about 5500 more. Damages exceeded $600 million. Forty-eight tornadoes were killers, with seven rated F5 (the maximum possible on the Fujita Intensity Scale) and an additional 23 rated F4. The town of Xenia, in southwestern Ohio, was especially hard hit—more than 1000 homes were destroyed, 34 people were killed, and 1100 were injured. Property damages exceeded $100 million.

Following this record-breaking event, extensive studies and surveys were conducted. The results of this work provided meteorologists with the evidence they needed to demonstrate that many of the notions about tornadoes held by the general public were incorrect. Here are some of the myths that were disproved:

Myth: A tornado won't touch down at the confluence of major rivers. Fact: The town of Cairo, IL, located at the confluence of the Ohio and Mississippi Rivers was hit by a tornado that day.

Myth: Tornadoes don't go up and down steep or high hills. Fact: A tornado that hit Guin, AL, stayed on the ground as it climbed the 1640-foot Monte Sano Mountain and grew in intensity as it descended the northeast slope. The Blue Ridge tornado of that day formed in the mountains at 1800 feet just east of Mulberry Gap and crossed a 3000-foot ridge before moving down to the bottom of the canyon. The tornado finally climbed to the 3300-foot top of Rich Nob before dissipating.

Myth: Tornadoes will not follow terrain into steep valleys. Fact: The tornado that wiped out three schools in Monticello, IN, descended a 60-foot bluff over the Tippecanoe River as it moved out of the town and damaged homes at its base.[*]

Engineering studies of damaged schools provided information that was later incorporated into construction designs that ensured greater safety. Evidence from damaged buildings showed that interior hallways provide the safest place and that classrooms with outside walls and gymnasiums with wide roof span were most dangerous.

What is the risk of another outbreak like the April 1974 event? We know such an occurrence is rare because it has only happened once since tornado records have been kept. However, there is no way to know if the odds are once in 50 years or once in 1000 years because we do not have a long enough record of accurate tornado statistics.

[*]NOAA "Tornado Outbreak 1974: The Worst in U.S. History." This publication was prepared to mark the twenty-fifth anniversary of the April 3–4, 1974, super tornado outbreak. http://www.publicaffairs.noaa.gov/storms/

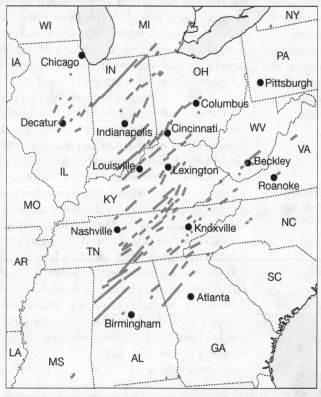

FIGURE 10-F Tracks of the 148 tornadoes that struck a 13-state area in the "super outbreak" of April 3–4, 1974. *(After NOAA)*

(10,000 square miles) and/or persist for at least three hours. Watches typically are not issued when the threat is thought to be isolated and/or short-lived.

Whereas a tornado watch is designed to alert people to the possibility of tornadoes, a **tornado warning** is issued by local offices of the National Weather Service when a tornado has actually been sighted in an area or is indicated by weather radar. It warns of a high probability of imminent danger. Warnings are issued for much smaller areas than watches, usually covering portions of a county or counties. In addition, they are in effect for much shorter periods, typically 30 to 60 minutes. Because a tornado warning may be based on an actual sighting, warnings are occasionally issued after a tornado has already developed. However, most warnings are issued prior to tornado formation, sometimes by several tens of minutes, based on Doppler radar data and/or spotter reports of funnel clouds or cloud-base rotation.

If the direction and the approximate speed of the storm are known, an estimate of its most probable path can be made. Because tornadoes often move erratically, the warning area is fan-shaped downwind from the point where the tornado has been spotted. Improved forecasts and advances in technology have contributed to a significant decline in tornado deaths over the last 50 years. Figure 10–26 illustrates this trend. During a span when the United States population grew rapidly, tornado deaths trended downward.

As noted earlier, the probability of one place being struck by a tornado, even in the area of greatest frequency, is slight. Nevertheless, although the probabilities may be small, tornadoes have provided many mathematical exceptions. For example, the small town of Codell, Kansas, was hit three years in a row—1916, 1917, and 1918—and each time on the same date, May 20! Needless to say, tornado watches and warnings should never be taken lightly.

FIGURE 10-26 Number of tornado deaths in the United States by decade 1950–1999. Even though the population has risen sharply since 1950, there has been a general downward trend in tornado deaths. *(Data from NOAA)*

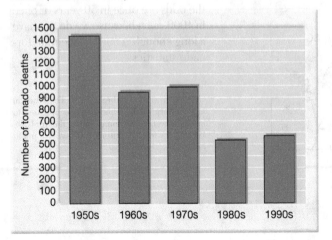

Doppler Radar

The installation of **Doppler radar** across the United States has significantly improved our ability to track thunderstorms and issue warnings based on their potential to produce tornadoes (Figure 10–27). Conventional weather radar works by transmitting short pulses of electromagnetic energy. A small fraction of the waves that are sent out is scattered by a storm and returned to the radar. The strength of the returning signal indicates rainfall intensity, and the time difference between the transmission and return of the signal indicates the distance to the storm.

However, to identify tornadoes and severe thunderstorms, we must be able to detect the characteristic circulation patterns associated with them. Conventional radar cannot do so except occasionally when spiral rain bands occur in association with a tornado and give rise to a hook-shaped echo.

Doppler radar not only performs the same tasks as conventional radar but also has the ability to detect motion directly (Figure 10–28). The principle involved is known as the *Doppler effect* (see Box 10–5). Air movement in clouds is determined by comparing the frequency of the reflected signal to that of the original pulse. The movement of precipitation toward the radar increases the frequency of reflected pulses, whereas motion away from the radar decreases the frequency. These frequency changes are then interpreted in terms of speed toward or away from the Doppler radar unit. It is this same principle that allows police radar to determine the speed of moving cars. Unfortunately, a single Doppler radar unit cannot detect air movements that occur parallel to it. Therefore, when a more complete picture of the winds within a cloud mass is desired, it is necessary to use two or more Doppler units.

Doppler radar can detect the initial formation and subsequent development of the mesocyclone within a severe thunderstorm that frequently precedes tornado development. Almost all (96 percent) mesocyclones produce damaging hail, severe winds, or tornadoes. Those that produce tornadoes (about 50 percent) can sometimes be distinguished by their stronger wind speeds and their sharper gradients of wind speeds. Mesocyclones can sometimes be identified within parent storms 30 minutes or more before tornado formation, and if a storm is large, at distances up to 230 kilometers (140 miles). In addition, when close to the radar, individual tornado circulations may sometimes be detected. Ever since the implementation of the national Doppler network, the average lead time for tornado warnings has increased from less than 5 minutes in the late 1980s to nearly 11 minutes today.

Doppler radar is not without problems. One concern relates to the weak tornadoes that rank at or near the bottom of the Fujita Intensity Scale. The nature of this problem has been summarized as follows:

> Presently, all tornadoes are treated in the same manner by the NWS (National Weather Service); a tornado warning is issued, and local governments usually respond by

(a)

(b)

(c)

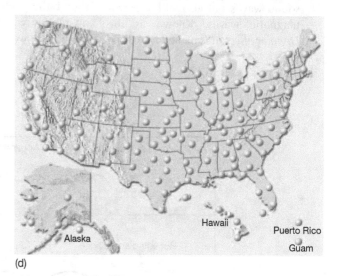

(d)

FIGURE 10-27 By using advanced Doppler radars, scientists are better able to estimate when and where thunderstorms will form, even in areas of seemingly clear air. Doppler radar installation (a) and advanced weather interactive processing system (b) at Sterling, Virginia, near Dulles International Airport. This is one of 115 state-of-the-art National Weather Service facilities shown on the map in (d). The equipment shown in (c), called *Doppler Radar on Wheels,* is scanning the skies of the Texas Panhandle on May 15, 2003. Portable units like this one are used by researchers to study severe weather events. *(Photos (a) and (b) by Brownie Harris/The Stock Market; map after National Weather Service; photo (c) © University Corporation for Atmospheric Research)*

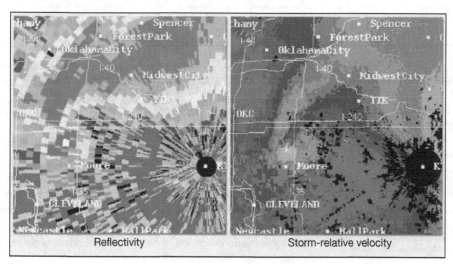

Reflectivity

Storm-relative velocity

FIGURE 10-28 This is a dual Doppler radar image of an F5 tornado near Moore, Oklahoma, on May 3, 1999. The left image (reflectivity) shows precipitation in the supercell thunderstorm. The right image shows motion of the precipitation along the radar beam, that is, how fast rain or hail are moving toward or away from the radar. In this example, the radar was unusually close to the tornado—close enough to make out the signature of the tornado itself (most of the time only the weaker and larger mesocyclone is detected). *(After NOAA)*

BOX 10-5 The Doppler Effect

We have all heard the changes in the sounds that a car, truck, or train makes as it approaches and then passes by. As the vehicle moves toward us, the sound has a higher pitch, and after the vehicle passes, the pitch drops. The faster the car, truck, or train is moving, the more the pitch drops (Figure 10–G). This phenomenon occurs not only in association with sound waves but also with electromagnetic waves. Known as the *Doppler effect*, it is named for Chris-tian Johannn Doppler, the Austrian physicist who first explained it in 1842.

Why does the wave frequency appear to shift when the wave source is moving? Figure 10–Ha shows the pattern of wave crests generated by a source that is not moving. The distance between wave crests (the wavelength) is identical for each successive wave. If this were a source emitting sound, the pitch would be the same no matter where the listener was located. However, if the source were moving, the wave crests would no longer make a concentric pattern. Rather, they would become more closely spaced in the direction the source was advancing. Therefore, the wave frequency would be greater ahead of the source and lower behind the source. Figure 10–Hb illustrates this pattern.

Astronomers apply this principle when they wish to determine whether a light source such as a star is approaching or retreating relative to Earth. When the lines in the star's

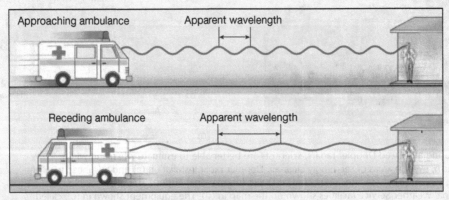

FIGURE 10-G This everyday example of the Doppler effect illustrates the apparent lengthening and shortening of wavelengths caused by the relative movement between a source and an observer.

activating their emergency procedures. Doppler radar makes forecasting and detection of these tornadoes possible in real-time operations. Thus, the potential exists for numerous warnings being issued for tornadoes which do little or no damage. This could desensitize the public to the dangers of more rare, life-threatening tornadoes. A future research goal should be the development of techniques that enable forecasting of tornado intensity.*

It should also be pointed out that not all tornado-bearing storms have clear-cut radar signatures and that other storms can give false signatures. Detection, therefore, is sometimes a subjective process and a given display could be interpreted in several ways. Consequently, trained observers will continue to form an important part of the warning system in the foreseeable future.

Although some operational problems exist, the benefits of Doppler radar are many. As a research tool, it is not only providing data on the formation of tornadoes but is also helping meteorologists gain new insights into thunderstorm development, the structure and dynamics of hurricanes, and air-turbulence hazards that plague aircraft. As a practical tool for tornado detection, it has significant advantages over a system that uses conventional radar.

*Lawrence B. Dunn, "Two Examples of Operational Tornado Warnings Using Doppler Radar Data," *Bulletin of the American Meteorological Society,* 71, no. 2 (February 1990), 152.

spectrum are shifted toward wavelengths that are shorter than those observed when such a source is at rest, the star is approaching. If the star is moving away from the observer, all of the spectral lines are shifted toward longer wavelengths. In meteorology, the new generation of weather radars use the Doppler principle to probe the circulation within a cloud by monitoring the movements of raindrops.

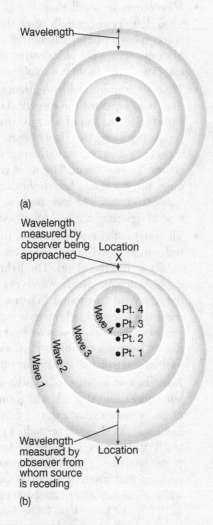

Wavelength

(a)

Wavelength measured by observer being approached

Location X

Wave 4
Wave 3
Wave 2
Wave 1

• Pt. 4
• Pt. 3
• Pt. 2
• Pt. 1

Wavelength measured by observer from whom source is receding

Location Y

(b)

FIGURE 10-H The Doppler effect is the change in the observed frequency of waves produced by the motion of the wave source and/or the wave receiver. In both parts of the diagram, the circles represent wave crests that travel at a constant speed. (a) When the wave source is stationary, the distance between waves is identical for all waves that are produced. The wave frequency (the pitch of the sound) at any point in this diagram is the same. (b) Here the source is moving toward the top of the page. Whenever the source (or the receiver) moves, the wave pattern becomes distorted. Wave 1 was produced when the source was at point 1; wave 2 was created when the source was at point 2; and wave 3 was emitted at point 3. Notice that even though the frequency emitted by the source remains the same as in part (a), a listener at location X would experience a higher frequency (higher-pitched sound) because each wave has a shorter distance to travel and therefore arrives at location X more frequently than would occur if the source were not moving. Conversely, a listener at location Y would experience a lower frequency.

Chapter Summary

- Although tornadoes and *hurricanes* are, in fact, cyclones, the vast majority of cyclones are not hurricanes or tornadoes. The term "cyclone" simply refers to the circulation around any low-pressure center, no matter how large or intense it is. *Thunderstorms,* storms containing lightning and thunder, are related in some manner to tornadoes, hurricanes, and mid-latitude cyclones.

- Dynamic thermal instability occurs during the development of thunderstorms, which form when warm, humid air rises in an unstable environment. A number of mechanisms, such as unequal heating of Earth's surface or lift-ing of warm air along a front or mountain slope, can trigger the upward air movement needed to create thunderstorm-producing cumulonimbus clouds. Severe thunderstorms produce high winds, damaging hail, flash floods, and tornadoes.

- In the United States, *air-mass thunderstorms* frequently occur in maritime tropical (mT) air that moves northward from the Gulf of Mexico. During the spring and summer, when the air is heated from below by the warmer land surface, the warm, humid air mass becomes unstable and thunderstorms develop. Generally, three stages are involved in the development of a thunderstorm. The *cumulus stage* is dominated by rising currents of air (updrafts) and the formation of a towering cumulonimbus cloud. Falling precipitation within the cloud causes drag on the air and initiates a downdraft that is further aided by the influx of cool, dry air surrounding the cloud, a process termed *entrainment*. The beginning of the *mature stage* is marked by the downdraft leaving the base of the cloud and the release of precipitation. With gusty winds, lightning, heavy precipitation, and sometimes hail, the mature stage is the most active period of a thunderstorm. Marking the end of the storm, the *dissipating stage* is dominated by downdrafts and entrainment. Without a supply of moisture from updrafts, the cloud soon evaporates. It should be noted that within a single air-mass thunderstorm there may be several individual *cells*—that is, zones of adjacent updrafts and downdrafts.

- Mountainous regions, such as the Rockies in the West and the Appalachians in the East, experience a greater number of air-mass thunderstorms than do the Plains states. Many thunderstorms that form over the eastern two-thirds of the United States occur as part of the general convergence and frontal wedging that accompany passing midlatitude cyclones.

- *Severe thunderstorms* are capable of producing heavy downpours and flash flooding as well as strong, gusty straight-line winds. They are influenced by strong vertical wind shear—that is, changes in wind direction and/or speed between different heights, and updrafts that become tilted and continue to build upward. Downdrafts from the thunderstorm cells reach the surface and spread out to produce an advancing wedge of cold air, called a *gust front*, which may form a *roll cloud* as warm air is lifted along its leading edge.

- Some of the most dangerous weather is produced by a type of thunderstorm called a *supercell*, a single, very powerful thunderstorm cell that at times may extend to heights of 20 kilometers (65,000 feet) and persist for many hours. The vertical wind profile of these cells may produce a *mesocyclone*, a column of cyclonically rotating air, within which tornadoes sometimes form. Supercells appear to form as inversion layers are eroded locally and unstable air "erupts" from below to form unusually large cumulonimbus clouds with concentrated, persistent updrafts.

- *Squall lines* are relatively narrow, elongated bands of thunderstorms that develop in the warm sector of a middle-latitude cyclone, usually in advance of a cold front. Some develop when divergence and lifting created by an active jet stream aloft is aligned with a strong, persistent low-level flow of warm, humid air from the south. A squall line with severe thunderstorms can also form along a boundary called a *dryline*, a narrow zone along which there is an abrupt change in moisture.

- A *mesoscale convective complex* (MCC) consists of many individual thunderstorms that are organized into a large oval to circular cluster. They form most frequently in the Great Plains from groups of afternoon air-mass thunderstorms. Although MCCs sometimes produce severe weather, they also provide a significant portion of the growing-season rainfall to the agricultural regions of the central United States.

- *Microbursts* are small, short-lived localized downdrafts of wind that occur beneath some thunderstorms and can reach speeds of 160 kilometers (100 miles) per hour. Microbursts are not only destructive, but the wind shear associated with them is a significant airport hazard.

- *Thunder* is produced by *lightning*. The object of lightning is to equalize the electrical difference associated with the formation of a large cumulonimbus cloud by producing a negative flow of current from the region of excess negative charge to the region with excess positive charge, or vice versa. The most common type of lightning, often called *sheet lightning*, occurs within and between clouds. The less common, but more dangerous, type of lightning is *cloud-to-ground lightning*.

- The origin of charge separation in clouds, although not fully understood, must hinge on rapid vertical movements within the cloud. The lightning we see as some single flashes are really several very rapid strokes between the cloud and the ground. When air is heated by the electrical discharge of lightning, it expands explosively and produces the sound waves we hear as thunder. The thunder we hear as a rumble is produced by a long lightning flash at some distance from the observer.

- *Tornadoes*, sometimes called twisters, or cyclones, are violent windstorms that take the form of a rotating column of air, or *vortex*, that extends downward from a cumulonimbus cloud. Some tornadoes consist of a single vortex. Within many stronger tornadoes, called *multiple vortex tornadoes*, are smaller intense whirls called *suction vortices* that rotate within the main vortex. Pressures within some tornadoes have been estimated to be as much as 10 percent lower than immediately outside the storm. Because of the tremendous pressure gradient associated with a strong tornado, maximum winds approach 480 kilometers (300 miles) per hour.

- Tornadoes form in association with severe thunderstorms that produce high winds, heavy rainfall, and often damaging hail. They form in any situation that produces severe weather including cold fronts, squall lines, and tropical cyclones (hurricanes). An important precondition linked to tornado formation in severe thunderstorms is the development of a mesocyclone that forms in the updraft of the thunderstorm. As the narrowing column of rotating air stretches downward, a rapidly spinning *funnel cloud* may emerge from a slowly rotating *wall cloud*. If the funnel cloud makes contact with the surface, it is then classified as a tornado.

- Severe thunderstorms, and hence tornadoes, are most often spawned along the cold front or squall line of a middle-latitude cyclone or in association with supercell thunderstorms. Although April through June is the period of greatest tornado activity, tornadoes occur during every month of the year. The average tornado has a diameter of between 150 and 600 meters, travels across the landscape toward the northeast at approximately 45 kilometers per hour, and cuts a path about 26 kilometers long.

- Most tornado damage is caused by tremendously strong winds. One commonly used guide to tornado intensity is the *Fujita Intensity Scale,* or simply *F-scale*. A rating on the F-scale is determined by assessing the worst damage produced by a storm. Whereas most tornado damage is done by violent winds, most tornado injuries and deaths result from flying debris.

- Because severe thunderstorms and tornadoes are small and short-lived phenomena, they are among the most difficult weather features to forecast precisely. When necessary, the Storm Prediction Center of the National Weather Service issues severe thunderstorm outlooks several times daily. When weather conditions favor the formation of tornadoes, a *tornado watch* is issued to alert the public to the possibility of tornadoes over a specified area for a particular time interval. A *tornado warning* is issued by local offices of the National Weather Service when a tornado has been sighted in an area or is indicated by weather radar. With its ability to detect the movement of precipitation within a cloud, *Doppler radar* technology has greatly advanced the accuracy of tornado warnings. Using the principle known as the *Doppler effect,* Doppler radar can identify the initial formation and subsequent development of the mesocyclone within a thunderstorm that frequently precedes tornado development.

Vocabulary Review

air-mass thunderstorm (p. 287)
cumulus stage (p. 288)
dart leader (p. 300)
dissipating stage (p. 289)
Doppler radar (p. 310)
dryline (p. 294)
entrainment (p. 288)
flash (p. 298)
Fujita Intensity Scale (F-scale) (p. 306)

gust front (p. 290)
leader (p. 298)
lightning (p. 296)
mature stage (p. 289)
mesocyclone (p. 291)
mesoscale convective complex (MCC) (p. 295)
microburst (p. 296)
multiple vortex tornado (p. 300)
return stroke (p. 298)

severe thunderstorm (p. 290)
squall line (p. 294)
step leader (p. 298)
stroke (p. 298)
supercell (p. 291)
thunder (p. 300)
thunderstorm (p. 287)
tornado (p. 300)
tornado warning (p. 308)
tornado watch (p. 308)

Review Questions

1. If you hear that a cyclone is approaching, should you immediately seek shelter?

2. Compare the wind speeds and the sizes of middle-latitude cyclones, tornadoes, and hurricanes.

3. Although tornadoes and hurricanes are dangerous storms, in most years they are not responsible for the greatest number of storm-related deaths in the United States. What is the deadliest storm phenomenon? (See Box 10–1.)

4. What are the primary requirements for the formation of thunderstorms?

5. Where would you expect thunderstorms to be most common on Earth? In the United States?

6. During what season and at what time of day is air-mass thunderstorm activity greatest? Why?

7. Why does entrainment intensify thunderstorm downdrafts?

8. Describe how downdrafts in a severe thunderstorm act to maintain updrafts. What is a *gust front*?

9. Briefly describe the formation of a squall line along a dry line.

10. How is thunder produced?

11. Which is more common, sheet lightning or cloud-to-ground lightning?

12. What is heat lightning?

13. Why do tornadoes have such high wind speeds?

14. What general atmospheric conditions are most conducive to the formation of tornadoes?

15. When is the "tornado season"? Can you explain why it occurs when it does? Why does the area of greatest tornado frequency migrate?

16. Violent (F4–F5) tornadoes are only about 2 percent of the total. What percentage of tornado fatalities is associated with these strongest storms? (See Figure 10–25.)

17. Distinguish between a tornado watch and a tornado warning.

18. A vehicle with its horn sounding moves away from an observer at point *A* and toward an observer at point *B*. Should the pitch of the horn at point *B* be higher or lower than at point *A*? What effect explains the difference in pitch experienced at points *A* and *B*? (See Box 10–5.)

19. What advantages does Doppler radar have over conventional radar?

Problems

1. If thunder is heard 15 seconds after lightning is seen, about how far away was the lightning stroke?

2. Examine the upper left portion of Figure 10–22 and determine the percentage of tornadoes that exhibited directions of movement toward the E through NNE.

3. Figures 10–29 and 10–30 represent two common ways that United States tornado statistics are graphically presented to the public. Which four states experience the greatest number of tornadoes? Are these the states with the greatest tornado threat? Which map is most useful for depicting the tornado hazard in the United States? Does the map in Figure 10–21 have an advantage over either or both of these maps?

4. Table 10–2 lists the total number of tornadoes reported in the United States by decade. Propose a reason that might explain why the total for the 1990s was so much higher than for the 1950s.

TABLE 10-2 Number of U.S. tornadoes reported by decade*	
1950–59	4796
1960–69	6813
1970–79	8579
1980–89	8196
1990–99	12,138

*Data from Storm Prediction Center, NOAA

5. Figure 10–26 shows that the number of tornado deaths in the United States in the 1990s was less than half the number that occurred in the 1950s, even though there was a significant rise in the population during that span. To what can you attribute this decline in the death toll?

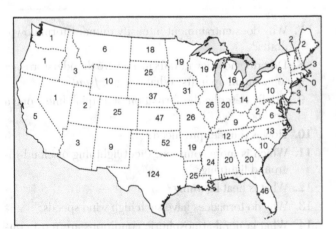

FIGURE 10-29 Annual average number of tornadoes by state for a 45-year period.

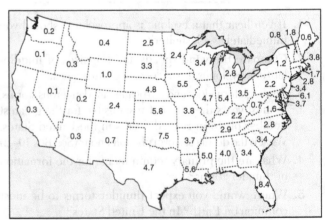

FIGURE 10-30 Annual average number of tornadoes per 10,000 square miles by state for a 45-year period.

Atmospheric Science Online

The Atmosphere 10e web site uses the resources and flexibility of the Internet to aid in your study of the topics in this chapter. Written and developed by meteorology instructors, this site will help improve your understanding of meteorology. Visit **http://www .prenhall.com/lutgens** and click on the cover of *The Atmosphere 10e* to find:

- **Online review quizzes**
- **Critical thinking exercises**
- **Links to chapter-specific web resources**
- **Internet-wide key term searches**

http://www.prenhall.com/lutgens

HURRICANES

Profile of a Hurricane

Hurricane Rita became a Category 5
hurricane late on September 21, 2005,
with sustained winds of 275 kilometers
(170 miles) per hour and a central
pressure of 897 millibars, making it the
third most powerful Atlantic basin storm
ever measured. When this image was
taken about mid-day on September 22, the
storm was slightly weaker. *(NASA image)*

The whirling tropical cyclones that occasionally have wind speeds exceeding 300 kilometers (185 miles) per hour are known in the United States as **hurricanes**—the greatest storms on Earth. Hurricanes are among the most destructive of natural disasters. When a hurricane reaches land, it is capable of annihilating coastal areas and killing tens of thousands of people. On the positive side, however, these storms provide essential rainfall over many areas they cross. Consequently, a resort owner along the Florida coast may dread the coming of hurricane season, but a farmer in Japan may welcome its arrival.

The vast majority of hurricane-related deaths and damage are caused by relatively infrequent yet powerful storms. Table 11–1 lists the deadliest hurricanes to strike the United States between 1900 and 2005. The storm that pounded an unsuspecting Galveston, Texas, in 1900 was not just the deadliest U.S. hurricane ever, but the deadliest natural disaster *of any kind* to affect the United States. Of course, the deadliest and most costly storm in recent memory occurred in August 2005, when Hurricane Katrina devastated the Gulf Coast of Louisiana, Mississippi, and Alabama (Figure 11–1). Although hundreds of thousands fled before the storm made landfall, thousands of others were caught by the storm. In addition to the human suffering and tragic loss of life that were left in the wake of Hurricane Katrina, the financial losses caused by the storm are practically incalcu-lable. Up until August 2005, the $25 billion in damages associated with Hurricane Andrew in 1992 represented the costliest natural disaster in U.S. history. This figure will be exceeded many times over when Katrina's economic impact is finally calculated. Although imprecise, some suggest that the final accounting could reach or exceed $300 billion.

The devastating hurricane season of 2005 came on the heels of an extraordinary 2004 season. Storms claimed more than 3100 lives (mostly in Haiti), and property losses in the United States topped $44 billion. The most notable storms were hurricanes Charley, Frances, Ivan, and Jeanne, all of which struck the state of Florida in August and September. Three of the storm tracks (Charley, Frances, and Jeanne) intersected in central Florida, whereas Hurricane Ivan struck the state's panhandle as it made landfall along the Gulf Coast (Figure 11–2). The Bahamas and many Caribbean islands were also hit hard. Each hurricane season, storms like those just described remind us of our vulnerability to these great forces of nature.

Profile of a Hurricane

Most of us view the weather in the tropics with favor. Places like Hawaii and the islands of the Caribbean are known for their lack of significant day-to-day variations. Warm breezes,

TABLE 11-1 The 20 deadliest U.S. hurricanes, 1900–2005				
Ranking	**Hurricane**	**Year**	**Category**	**Deaths**
1.	Texas (Galveston)	1900	4	8000*
2.	Florida (Lake Okeechobee)	1928	4	1836
3.	Katrina	2005	4	1300**
4.	Florida (Keys)/S. Texas	1919	4	600†
5.	New England	1938	3	600
6.	Florida (Keys)	1935	5	408
7. (tie)	Audrey (SW Louisiana/Texas)	1957	4	390
7. (tie)	NE United States	1944	3	390‡
9.	Louisiana (Grand Isle)	1909	4	350
10. (tie)	Louisiana (New Orleans)	1915	4	275
10. (tie)	Texas (Galveston)	1915	4	275
12.	Camille (Mississippi/Louisiana)	1969	5	256
13.	Florida (Miami)/Mississippi/Alabama/ Florida (Pensacola)	1926	4	243
14.	Diane (NE United States)	1955	1	184
15.	SE Florida	1906	2	164
16.	Mississippi/Alabama/Florida (Pensacola)	1906	3	134
17.	Agnes (NE United States)	1972	1	122
18.	Hazel (North Carolina/South Carolina)	1954	4	95
19. (tie)	Betsy (SE Florida/SE Louisiana)	1965	3	75
19. (tie)	Floyd (North Carolina)	1999	2	75

* May actually have been as high as 10,000 to 12,000.

** Estimated figure.

† Over 500 of these lost on ships at sea; 600 to 900 estimated deaths.

‡ Some 344 of these lost on ships at sea.

FIGURE 11-1 An estimated 80 percent of New Orleans was flooded after several levees failed in the wake of Hurricane Katrina. The storm surge caused the level of Lake Pontchartrain to rise, straining the levee system protecting the city. *(AP Photo/David J. Phillip)*

steady temperatures, and rains that come as heavy but brief tropical showers are expected. It is ironic that these relatively tranquil regions sometimes produce the most violent storms on Earth.

Most hurricanes form between the latitudes of 5° and 20° over all the tropical oceans except the South Atlantic and the eastern South Pacific (Figure 11–3). The North Pacific has the greatest number of storms, averaging 20 per year. Fortunately for those living in the coastal regions of the southern and eastern United States, fewer than five hurricanes, on the average, develop each year in the warm sector of the North Atlantic.

These intense tropical storms are known in various parts of the world by different names. In the western Pacific, they are called *typhoons,* and in the Indian Ocean, including the Bay of Bengal and Arabian Sea, they are simply called *cyclones.* In the following discussion, these storms will be referred to as hurricanes. The term *hurricane* is derived from Huracan, a Carib god of evil.

Although many tropical disturbances develop each year, only a few reach hurricane status. By international agreement a hurricane has sustained wind speeds of at least 119 kilometers (74 miles) per hour and a rotary circulation.° Mature hurricanes average about 600 kilometers (375 miles) across, although they can range in diameter from 100 kilometers (60 miles) up to about 1500 kilometers (930 miles). From the outer edge of the hurricane to the center, the barometric pressure has sometimes dropped 60 millibars, from 1010 to 950 millibars. The lowest pressures ever recorded in the Western Hemisphere are associated with these storms.

A steep pressure gradient like that shown in Figure 11–4 generates the rapid, inward spiraling winds of a hurricane. As the air moves closer to the center of the storm, its velocity increases. This acceleration is explained by the law of conservation of angular momentum (see Box 11–1).

As the inward rush of warm, moist surface air approaches the core of the storm, it turns upward and ascends in a ring of cumulonimbus towers (Figure 11–5). This doughnut-shaped wall of intense convective activity surrounding the center of the storm is called the **eye wall.** It is here that the greatest wind speeds and heaviest rainfall occur. Surrounding

---

°*Sustained winds* are defined as the wind averaged over a one-minute interval.

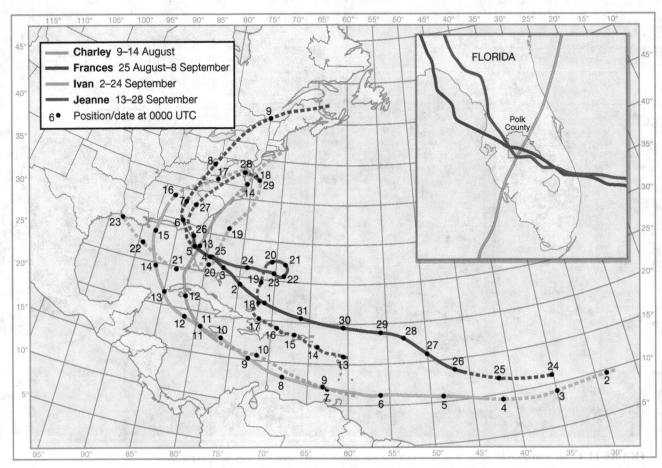

FIGURE 11-2 Tracks of the four major hurricanes to hit Florida in 2004. Hurricanes Charley, Frances, and Jeanne intersected over Polk County, Florida (see inset). Ivan made landfall near Mobile, Alabama, but greatly affected Florida's western panhandle. Each solid line shows the path of a storm when it had hurricane status. The dashed portion of each line traces the storm's path before and after hurricane stage. *(After National Hurricane Center)*

FIGURE 11-3 This world map shows the regions where most hurricanes form as well as their principal months of occurrence and the most common tracks they follow. Hurricanes do not develop within about 5° of the equator because the Coriolis force is too weak. Because warm surface ocean temperatures are necessary for hurricane formation, they seldom form poleward of 20° latitude nor over cool waters of the South Atlantic and the eastern South Pacific.

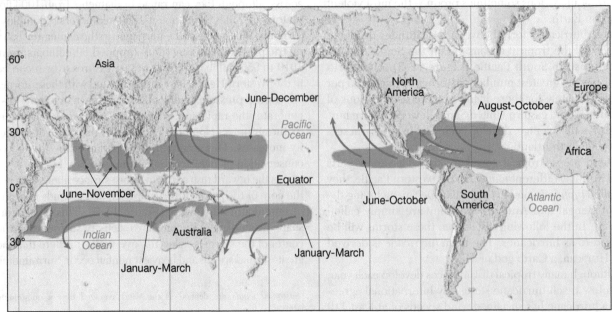

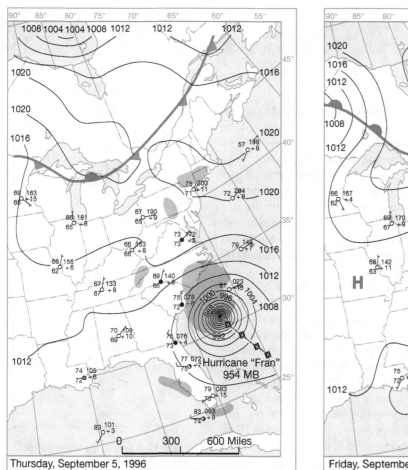

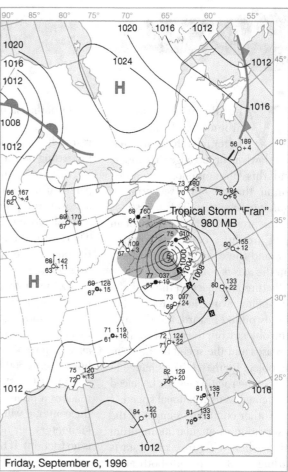

FIGURE 11-4 Weather maps showing Hurricane Fran at 7 A.M., EST, on two successive days, September 5 and 6, 1996. On September 5, winds exceeded 190 kph. As the storm moved inland, heavy rains caused flash floods, killed 30 people, and caused more than $3 billion in damages. The station information plotted off the Gulf and Atlantic coasts is from data buoys, which are remote floating instrument packages.

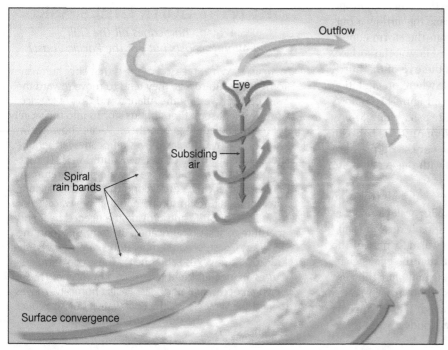

FIGURE 11-5 Cross section of a hurricane. Note that the vertical dimension is greatly exaggerated. The eye, the zone of relative calm at the center of the storm, is a distinctive hurricane feature. Sinking air in the eye warms by compression. Surrounding the eye is the eye wall, the zone where winds and rain are most intense. Tropical moisture spiraling inward creates rain bands that pinwheel around the storm center. Outflow of air at the top of the hurricane is important because it prevents the convergent flow at lower levels from "filling in" the storm. *(After NOAA)*

BOX 11-1   The Conservation of Angular Momentum

Why do winds blowing around a storm move faster near the center and more slowly near the edge? To understand this phenomenon, we must examine the *law of conservation of angular momentum*. This law states that the product of the velocity of an object around a center of rotation (axis) and the distance of the object from the axis is constant.

Picture an object on the end of a string being swung in a circle. If the string is pulled inward, the distance of the object from the axis of rotation decreases and the speed of the spinning object increases. The change in radius of the rotating mass is balanced by a change in its rotational speed.

Another common example of the conservation of angular momentum occurs when a figure skater starts whirling on the ice with both arms extended (Figure 11–A). Her arms are traveling in a circular path about an axis (her body). When the skater pulls her arms inward, she decreases the

radius of the circular path of her arms. As a result, her arms go faster and the rest of her body must follow, thereby increasing her rate of spinning.

In a similar manner, when a parcel of air moves toward the center of a storm, the product of its distance and velocity must remain unchanged. Therefore, as air moves inward from the outer edge, its rotational velocity must increase.

Let us apply the law of conservation of angular momentum to the horizontal movement of air in a hypothetical hurricane. Assume that air with a velocity of 5 kilometers per hour begins 500 kilometers from the center of the storm. By the time it reaches a point 100 kilometers from the center, it will have a velocity of 25 kilometers per hour (assuming there is no friction). If this same parcel of air were to continue to advance toward the storm's center until its radius was just 10 kilometers, it would be traveling at 250 kilometers per hour. Friction reduces these values somewhat.

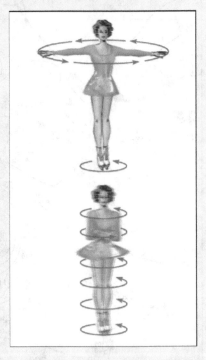

FIGURE 11-A When the skater's arms are extended, she spins slowly. When her arms are pulled in, she spins much faster.

the eye wall are curved bands of clouds that trail away in spiral fashion. Near the top of the hurricane the airflow is outward, carrying the rising air away from the storm center, thereby providing room for more inward flow at the surface.

At the very center of the storm is the **eye** of the hurricane. This well-known feature is a zone where precipitation ceases and winds subside. The graph in Figure 11–6 shows changes in wind speed and air pressure as Cyclone Monty came ashore at Mardie Station in Western Australia between February 29 and March 2, 2004. The very steep pressure gradient and strong winds associated with the eye wall are evident, as is the relative calm of the eye.

The eye offers a brief but deceptive break from the extreme weather in the enormous curving wall clouds that surround it. The air within the eye gradually descends and heats by compression, making it the warmest part of the storm. Although many people believe that the eye is characterized by clear blue skies, this is usually not the case because the subsidence in the eye is seldom strong enough to produce cloudless conditions. Although the sky appears much brighter in this region, scattered clouds at various levels are common.

Students Sometimes Ask...

Why do hurricanes hit the Gulf and Atlantic coasts but not the Pacific Coast?

There are two main reasons. One is that after hurricanes form in the subtropics, they tend to move toward the west or northwest. In the Atlantic and Gulf of Mexico, this movement sometimes brings storms into the vicinity of the mainland. In the northeast Pacific, however, a west or northwest track moves hurricanes farther offshore, away from the coast (see Figure 11–3). The second factor is the difference in water temperatures between America's coasts. Along the Gulf and Atlantic, water temperatures in summer and fall are warm (more than 27°C or 80°F) and provide the needed heat and moisture to sustain hurricanes. By contrast, along the U.S. West Coast, ocean temperatures rarely exceed the low 20s Celsius (70s Fahrenheit). These cool temperatures are not sufficient to sustain a hurricane. Thus, when an occasional northeast Pacific hurricane moves toward the West Coast, the cool waters quickly reduce the storm's strength.

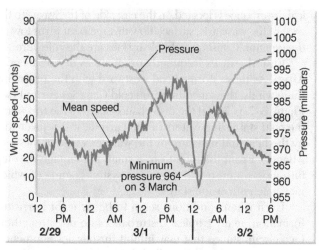

FIGURE 11-6 Measurements of surface pressure and wind speed during the passage of Cyclone Monty at Mardie Station in Western Australia between February 29 and March 2, 2004. The strongest winds are associated with the eye wall, and the weakest winds and lowest pressure are found in the eye. *(Data from World Meteorological Organization)*

Hurricane Formation and Decay

A hurricane is a heat engine that is fueled by the latent heat liberated when huge quantities of water vapor condense. The amount of energy produced by a typical hurricane in just a single day is truly immense. The release of latent heat warms the air and provides buoyancy for its upward flight. The result is to reduce the pressure near the surface, which in turn encourages a more rapid inflow of air. To get this engine started, a large quantity of warm, moist air is required, and a continuous supply is needed to keep it going.

Hurricanes develop most often in the late summer when ocean waters have reached temperatures of 27°C (80°F) or higher and are thus able to provide the necessary heat and moisture to the air. This ocean-water temperature requirement accounts for the fact that hurricanes do not form over the relatively cool waters of the South Atlantic and the eastern South Pacific (Figure 11–7). For the same reason, few hurricanes form poleward of 20 degrees of latitude (see Figure 11–3). Although water temperatures are sufficiently high, hurricanes do not form within 5 degrees of the equator, because the Coriolis force is too weak to initiate the necessary rotary motion.

FIGURE 11-7 Since the beginning of the satellite era in the mid-1960s, no hurricane had ever been observed in the South Atlantic—that is, until March 2004. On the morning of March 28, 2004, a Category 1 hurricane, with winds between 121–129 kilometers (75–80 miles) per hour, struck the east coast of Brazil. (For an explanation of hurricane categories, see Table 11–2, p. 329.) Although there was minimal loss of life, coastal property damage approached $330 million. The clouds show the clockwise spiral associated with Southern Hemisphere storms. *(NASA image)*

Hurricane Formation

Many tropical storms achieve hurricane status in the western parts of oceans, but their origins often lie far to the east. There disorganized arrays of clouds and thunderstorms, called **tropical disturbances,** sometimes develop and exhibit weak pressure gradients and little or no rotation. Most of the time these zones of convective activity die out. However, occasionally tropical disturbances grow larger and develop a strong cyclonic rotation.

Several different situations can trigger tropical disturbances. They are sometimes initiated by the powerful convergence and lifting associated with the intertropical convergence zone (ITCZ). Others form when a trough from the middle latitudes intrudes into the tropics. Tropical disturbances that produce many of the strongest hurricanes that enter the western North Atlantic and threaten North America often begin as large undulations or ripples in the trade winds known as **easterly waves,** so named because they gradually move from east to west.

Figure 11–8 illustrates an easterly wave. The lines on this simple map are not isobars. Rather, they are *streamlines,* lines drawn parallel to the wind direction used to depict surface airflow. When middle-latitude weather is analyzed, isobars are usually drawn on the weather map. By contrast, in the tropics the differences in sea-level pressure are quite small, so isobars are not always useful. Streamlines are helpful because they show where surface winds converge and diverge.

To the east of the wave axis the streamlines move poleward and get progressively closer together, indicating that the surface flow is convergent. Convergence, of course, encourages air to rise and form clouds. Therefore, the trop-

ical disturbance is located on the east side of the wave. To the west of the wave axis, surface flow diverges as it turns toward the equator. Consequently, clear skies are the rule here.

Easterly waves frequently originate as disturbances in Africa. As these storms head westward with the prevailing trade winds, they encounter the cold Canaries current (see Figure 3–7, p. 73). If the disturbance survives the trip across the cold stabilizing waters of the current, it is rejuvenated by the heat and moisture of the warmer water of the mid-Atlantic. From this point on, a small percentage develop into more intense and organized systems, some of which may reach hurricane status.

Even when conditions seem to be right for hurricane formation, many tropical disturbances do not strengthen. One circumstance that may inhibit further development is a temperature inversion called the *trade wind inversion.* It forms in association with the subsidence that occurs in the region influenced by the subtropical high.[†] A strong inversion diminishes air's ability to rise and thus inhibits the development of strong thunderstorms. Another factor that works against the strengthening of tropical disturbances is strong upper-level winds. When present, a strong flow aloft disperses the latent heat released from cloud tops, heat that is essential for continued growth and development.

What happens on those occasions when conditions favor hurricane development? As latent heat is released from the clusters of thunderstorms that make up the tropical disturbance, areas within the disturbance get warmer. As a consequence, air density lowers and surface pressure drops, creating a region of weak low pressure and cyclonic circulation. As pressure drops at the storm center, the pressure gradient steepens. In response, surface wind speeds increase and bring additional supplies of moisture to nurture storm growth. The water vapor condenses, releasing latent heat, and the heated air rises. Adiabatic cooling of rising air triggers more condensation and the release of more latent heat, which causes a further increase in buoyancy. And so it goes.

Meanwhile, higher pressure develops at the top of the developing tropical depression.[‡] This causes air to flow outward (diverge) from the top of the storm. Without this outward flow up top, the inflow at lower levels would soon raise surface pressures and thwart further storm development.

Although many tropical disturbances occur each year, only a few develop into full-fledged hurricanes. Recall that tropical cyclones are called hurricanes only when their winds reach 119 kilometers (74 miles) per hour. By international agreement, lesser tropical cyclones are given different names based on the strength of their winds. When a cyclone's strongest winds do not exceed 61 kilometers (37 miles) per hour, it is called a **tropical depression.** When sustained

FIGURE 11-8 Easterly wave in the subtropical Atlantic. Streamlines show low-level airflow. To the east of the wave axis, winds converge as they move slightly poleward. To the west of the axis, flow diverges as it turns toward the equator. Tropical disturbances are associated with the convergent flow of the easterly wave. Easterly waves extend for 2000 to 3000 kilometers (1200 to 1800 miles) and move from east to west with the trade winds at rates between 15 and 35 kilometers (10 and 20 miles) per hour. At this rate, it takes an imbedded tropical disturbance a week or 10 days to move across the North Atlantic.

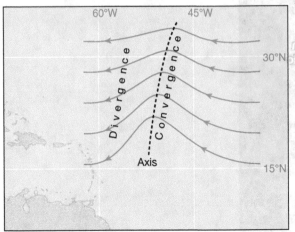

[†]In the troposphere, a temperature inversion exists when temperatures in a layer of air increase with an increase in altitude rather than by decreasing with height, which is usually the case. For more on how subsidence can produce an inversion, see the section on "Inversions Aloft" in Chapter 13, p. 392–93.

[‡]See Figure 6–11 and the discussion of the sea–land breeze in the section on "Pressure Gradient Force" in Chapter 6.

winds are between 61 and 119 kilometers (37 and 74 miles) per hour, the cyclone is termed a **tropical storm.** It is during this phase that a name is given (Andrew, Fran, Opal, etc.). Should the tropical storm become a hurricane, the name remains the same (see Box 11–2). Each year between 80 and 100 tropical storms develop around the world. Of them, usually half or more eventually reach hurricane status.

Students Sometimes Ask...
When is hurricane season?

Hurricane season is different in different parts of the world. People in the United States are usually most interested in Atlantic storms. The Atlantic hurricane season officially extends from June through November. More than 97 percent of tropical activity in that region occurs during this six-month span. The "heart" of the season is August through October. During these three months, 87 percent of the minor hurricane (category 1 and 2) days and 96 percent of the major hurricane (category 3, 4, and 5) days occur. Peak activity is in early to mid-September.

Hurricane Decay

Hurricanes diminish in intensity whenever they (1) move over ocean waters that cannot supply warm, moist tropical air, (2) move onto land, or (3) reach a location where the large-scale flow aloft is unfavorable. Richard Anthes describes the possible fate of hurricanes in the first category as follows:

> Many hurricanes approaching the North American or Asian continents from the southeast are turned toward the northeast, away from the continents, by the steering effect of an upper-level trough. This recurvature carries the storms toward higher latitudes where the ocean temperatures are cooler and an encounter with cool, dry polar air masses is more likely. Often the tropical cyclone and a polar front interact, with cold air entering the tropical cyclone from the west. As the release of latent heat is diminished, the upper-level divergence weakens, mean temperatures in the core fall and the surface pressure rises.*

Whenever a hurricane moves onto land, it loses its punch rapidly. For example, in Figure 11–4 notice how the isobars show a much weaker pressure gradient on September 6 after Hurricane Fran moved ashore than on September 5 when it was over the ocean. The most important reason for this rapid demise is the fact that the storm's source of warm, moist air is cut off. When an adequate supply of water vapor does not exist, condensation and the release of latent heat must diminish.

*Tropical Cyclones: Their Evolution, Structure, and Effects, Meteorological Monographs, Vol. 19, no. 41 (1982), p. 61. Boston: American Meteorological Society.

In addition, the increased surface roughness over land results in a rapid reduction in surface wind speeds. This factor causes the winds to move more directly into the center of the low, thus helping to eliminate the large pressure differences.

Hurricane Destruction

Although the amount of damage caused by a hurricane depends on several factors, including the size and population density of the area affected and the nearshore bottom configuration, certainly the most significant factor is the strength of the storm itself.

Based on the study of past storms, the **Saffir–Simpson scale** was established to rank the relative intensities of hurricanes (Table 11–2). Predictions of hurricane severity and damage are usually expressed in terms of this scale. When a tropical storm becomes a hurricane, the National Weather Service assigns it a scale (category) number. Category assignments are based on observed conditions at a particular stage in the life of a hurricane and are viewed as estimates of the amount of damage a storm would cause if it were to make landfall without changing size or strength. As conditions change, the category of a storm is reevaluated so that public-safety officials can be kept informed. By using the Saffir–Simpson scale, the disaster potential of a hurricane can be monitored and appropriate precautions can be planned and implemented.

A rating of 5 on the scale represents the worst storm possible, and a 1 is least severe. Storms that fall into Category 5 are rare. Only three storms this powerful are known to have hit the continental United States: Andrew struck Florida in 1992, Camille pounded Mississippi in 1969, and a Labor Day hurricane struck the Florida Keys in 1935. Damage caused by hurricanes can be divided into three classes: (1) storm surge, (2) wind damage, and (3) inland freshwater flooding.

Students Sometimes Ask...
Are larger hurricanes stronger than smaller hurricanes?

Not necessarily. Actually, there is very little correlation between intensity (either measured by maximum sustained winds or by central pressure) and size (either measured by the radius of gale force winds or the radius of the outer closed isobar). Hurricane Andrew is a good example of a very intense storm (recently reevaluated and upgraded to the most intense category 5 level) that was also relatively small (gale-force winds extended only 150 kilometers/90 miles from the eye). Research has shown that changes in intensity and size are essentially independent of one another.

BOX 11-2 Naming Tropical Storms and Hurricanes

Tropical storms are named to provide ease of communication between forecasters and the general public regarding forecasts, watches, and warnings. Tropical storms and hurricanes can last a week or longer, and two or more storms can be occurring in the same region at the same time. Thus, names can reduce the confusion about what storm is being described.

During World War II, tropical storms were informally assigned women's names (perhaps after wives and girlfriends) by U.S. Army Corps and Navy meteorologists who were monitoring storms over the Pacific. From 1950 to 1952, tropical storms in the North Atlantic were identified by the phonetic alphabet—Able, Baker, Charlie, and so forth. In 1953

the U.S. Weather Bureau (now the National Weather Service) switched to women's names.

The practice of using feminine names continued until 1978, when a list containing both male and female names was adopted for tropical cyclones in the eastern Pacific. In the same year a proposal that both male and female names be adopted for Atlantic hurricanes, beginning with the 1979 season, was accepted by the World Meteorological Organization (WMO).

The WMO has created six lists of names for tropical storms over ocean areas. The names used for Atlantic, Gulf of Mexico, and Caribbean hurricanes are shown in Table 11–A. The names are ordered alphabetically and do not contain names that begin with

the letters Q, U, X, Y, and Z because of the scarcity of names beginning with those letters. When a tropical depression reaches tropical storm status, it is assigned the next unused name on the list. At the beginning of the next hurricane season, names from the next list are selected even though many names may not have been used the previous season.

The names for Atlantic storms are used over again at the end of each six-year cycle unless a hurricane was particularly noteworthy. This is to avoid confusion when storms are discussed in future years. For example, the names of the four hurricanes that struck Florida in 2004 (Charley, Frances, Ivan, and Jeanne) were replaced by Colin, Fiona, Igor, and Julia on the list for the year 2010.

TABLE 11-A Tropical storm and hurricane names for the Atlantic, Gulf of Mexico, Caribbean Sea*

2005	2006	2007	2008	2009	2010
Arlene	Alberto	Andrea	Arthur	Ana	Alex
Bret	Beryl	Barry	Bertha	Bill	Bonnie
Cindy	Chris	Chantal	Cristobal	Claudette	Colin
Dennis	Debby	Dean	Dolly	Danny	Danielle
Emily	Ernesto	Erin	Edouard	Erika	Earl
Franklin	Florence	Felix	Fay	Fred	Fiona
Gert	Gordon	Gabrielle	Gustav	Grace	Gaston
Harvey	Helene	Humberto	Hanna	Henri	Hermine
Irene	Isaac	Ingrid	Ike	Ida	Igor
Jose	Joyce	Jerry	Josephine	Joaquin	Julia
Katrina	Kirk	Karen	Kyle	Kate	Karl
Lee	Leslie	Lorenzo	Laura	Larry	Lisa
Maria	Michael	Melissa	Marco	Mindy	Matthew
Nate	Nadine	Noel	Nana	Nicholas	Nicole
Ophelia	Oscar	Olga	Omar	Odette	Otto
Philippe	Patty	Pablo	Paloma	Peter	Paula
Rita	Rafael	Rebekah	Rene	Rose	Richard
Stan	Sandy	Sebastien	Sally	Sam	Shary
Tammy	Tony	Tanya	Teddy	Teresa	Tomas
Vince	Valerie	Van	Vicky	Victor	Virginie
Wilma	William	Wendy	Wilfred	Wanda	Walter

*If the entire alphabetical list of names for a given year is exhausted, the naming system moves on to using letters of the Greek alphabet (alpha, beta, gamma, etc). This issue never arose until the record-breaking 2005 hurricane season when Tropical Storm Alpha, Hurricane Beta, tropical storms Gamma and Delta, Hurricane Epsilon, and Tropical Storm Zeta occurred after Hurricane Wilma.

TABLE 11-2 Saffir–Simpson hurricane scale

Scale number (category)	Central pressure (millibars)	Wind speed (kph)	Wind speed (mph)	Storm surge (meters)	Storm surge (feet)	Damage
1	980	119–153	74–95	1.2–1.5	4–5	*Minimal.* No real damage to building structures. Damage primarily to unanchored mobile homes, shrubbery, and trees. Also, some coastal-road flooding and minor pier damage.
2	965–979	154–177	96–110	1.6–2.4	6–8	*Moderate.* Some roofing material, door, and window damage to buildings. Some trees blown down. Considerable damage to mobile homes. Coastal and low-lying escape routes flood 2 to 4 hours before arrival of the hurricane center. Small craft in unprotected anchorages break moorings.
3	945–964	178–209	111–130	2.5–3.6	9–12	*Extensive.* Some structural damage to small residences and utility buildings. Large trees blown down. Mobile homes are destroyed. Flooding near the coast destroys smaller structures with larger structures damaged by battering of floating debris. Terrain lower than 2 meters above sea level may be flooded inland 13 km or more. Evacuation of low-lying residences within several blocks of the shoreline may be required.
4	920–944	210–250	131–155	3.7–5.4	13–18	*Extreme.* Some complete roof structure failures on small residences. Extensive damage to doors and windows. Low-lying escape routes may be cut by rising water 3 to 5 hours before arrival of the hurricane center. Major damage to lower floors of structures near the shore. Terrain lower than 3 meters above sea level may be flooded, requiring massive evacuation of residential areas as far inland as 10 km.
5	<920	>250	>155	>5.4	>18	*Catastrophic.* Complete roof failure on many residences and industrial buildings. Some complete building failures. Severe window and door damage. Low-lying escape routes are cut by rising water 3 to 5 hours before arrival of the hurricane center. Major damage to lower floors of all structures located less than 5 meters above sea level and within 500 meters of the shoreline. Massive evacuation of residential areas on low ground within 8 to 16 km of the shoreline may be required.

Storm Surge

Without question, the most devastating damage in the coastal zone is caused by the storm surge. It not only accounts for a large share of coastal property losses but is also responsible for 90 percent of all hurricane-caused deaths. A **storm surge** is a dome of water 65 to 80 kilometers (40 to 50 miles) wide that sweeps across the coast near the point where the eye makes landfall. If all wave activity were smoothed out, the storm surge would be the height of the water above normal tide level (Figure 11–9). In addition, tremendous wave activity is superimposed on the surge. We can easily imagine the damage that this surge of water could inflict on low-lying coastal areas (Figure 11–10). The worst surges occur in places like the Gulf of Mexico, where the continental shelf is very shallow and gently sloping. In addition, local features such as bays and rivers can cause the surge height to double and increase in speed.

In the delta region of Bangladesh, for example, most of the land is less than 2 meters (6.5 feet) above sea level. When a storm surge superimposed on normal high tide inundated that area on November 13, 1970, the official death toll was 200,000; unofficial estimates ran to 500,000. It was one of the worst natural disasters of modern times. In May 1991 a similar event again struck Bangladesh. This time the storm took the lives of at least 135,000 people and devastated coastal towns in its path.

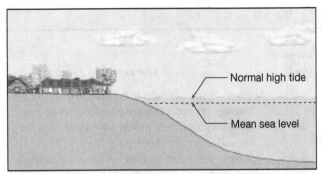
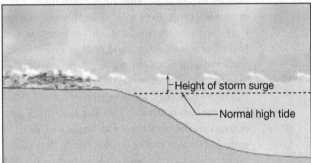

(a)

FIGURE 11-9 Superimposed upon high tide, a storm surge can devastate a coastal area. The worst storm surges occur in coastal areas where there is a very shallow and gently sloping continental shelf extending from the beach. The Gulf Coast is such a place.

A common misconception about the cause of hurricane storm surges is that the very low pressure at the center of the storm acts as a partial vacuum that allows the ocean to rise up in response. However, this effect is relatively insignificant. The most important factor responsible for the development of a storm surge is the piling up of ocean water by strong onshore winds. Gradually the hurricane's winds push water toward the shore, causing sea level to elevate while also churning up violent wave activity.

As a hurricane advances toward the coast in the Northern Hemisphere, storm surge is always most intense on the right side of the eye where winds are blowing *toward* the shore. In addition, on this side of the storm the forward movement of the hurricane also contributes to the storm surge. In Figure 11–11, assume a hurricane with peak winds of 175 kilometers (109 miles) per hour is moving toward the shore at 50 kilometers (31 miles) per hour. In this case, the net wind speed on the right side of the advancing storm is 225 kilometers (140 miles) per hour. On the left side, the hurricane's winds are blowing opposite the direction of storm movement, so the net winds are *away* from the coast at 125 kilometers (78 miles) per hour. Along the shore facing the left side of the oncoming hurricane, the water level may actually decrease as the storm makes landfall.

Wind Damage

Destruction caused by wind is perhaps the most obvious of the classes of hurricane damage. Debris such as signs, roofing materials, and small items left outside become dangerous flying missiles in hurricanes. For some struc-

(b)

FIGURE 11-10 Storm surge damage along the Mississippi coast caused by Hurricane Katrina. At some locations the surge exceeded 7.5 meters (25 feet). (a) This concrete slab is all that remains of an apartment house in Biloxi. *(Photo by Barry Williams/Getty Images)* (b) Houses and vehicles litter the railway near Pass Christian. *(AP Photo/Phil Coale)*

FIGURE 11-11 Winds associated with a Northern Hemisphere hurricane that is advancing toward the coast. This hypothetical storm, with peak winds of 175 kilometers (109 miles) per hour, is moving toward the coast at 50 kilometers (31 miles) per hour. On the right side of the advancing storm, the 175-kilometer-per-hour winds are in the same direction as the movement of the storm (50 kilometers per hour). Therefore, the *net* wind speed on the right side of the storm is 225 kilometers (140 miles) per hour. On the left side, the hurricane's winds are blowing opposite the direction of storm movement, so the *net* winds of 125 kilometers (78 miles) per hour are away from the coast. Storm surge will be greatest along that part of the coast hit by the right side of the advancing hurricane.

tures, the force of the wind is sufficient to cause total ruin. Just read the descriptions of category 3, 4, and 5 storms in Table 11–2. Mobile homes are particularly vulnerable. High-rise buildings are also susceptible to hurricane-force winds. Upper floors are most vulnerable because wind speeds usually increase with height. Recent research suggests that people should stay below the tenth floor but remain above any floors at risk for flooding. In regions with good building codes, wind damage is usually not as catastrophic as storm-surge damage. However, hurricane-force winds affect a much larger area than storm surge and can cause huge economic losses. For example, in 1992 it was largely the winds associated with Hurricane Andrew that produced more than $25 billion of damage in southern Florida and Louisiana.

Hurricanes sometimes produce tornadoes that contribute to the storm's destructive power. Studies have shown that more than half of the hurricanes that make landfall produce at least one tornado. In 2004 the number of tornadoes associated with tropical storms and hurricanes was extraordinary. Tropical Storm Bonnie and five landfalling hurricanes—Charley, Frances, Gaston, Ivan, and Jeanne—produced nearly 300 tornadoes that affected the southeast and mid-Atlantic states (Table 11–3). Hurricane Frances produced the most tornadoes ever reported from one hurricane. The large number of hurricane-generated tornadoes in 2004 helped make this a record-breaking year—surpassing the previous record by more than 300.*

*K. L. Gleason, et al. "U.S. Tornado Records" in *Bulletin of the American Meteorological Society*, Vol. 86, No. 6, June 2005, p. 551.

Inland Flooding

The torrential rains that accompany most hurricanes represent a third significant threat—flooding. The 2004 hurricane season was very deadly, with a loss of life that exceeded 3000 people. Nearly all of the deaths occurred in Haiti as a result of flash floods and mudflows caused by the heavy rains associated with then Tropical Storm Jeanne.

Hurricane Agnes (1972) illustrates that even modest storms can have devasting results. Although it was only a category 1 storm on the Saffir–Simpson scale, it was one of the costliest hurricanes of the twentieth century, creating more than $2 billion in damage and taking 122 lives. The greatest destruction was attributed to flooding in the northeastern portion of the United States, especially in Pennsylvania, where record rainfalls occurred. Harrisburg received nearly 32 centimeters (12.5 inches) in 24 hours and western Schuykill County measured more than 48 centimeters (19 inches) during the same span. Agnes's rains were not as devastating elsewhere. Prior to reaching Pennsylvania, the storm caused some flooding in Georgia, but most farmers welcomed the rain because dry conditions had been

TABLE 11–3 Number of tornadoes spawned by hurricanes and tropical storms in the United States, 2004

Tropical Storm Bonnie	30
Hurricane Charley	25
Hurricane Frances	117
Hurricane Ivan	104
Hurricane Jeanne	16

plaguing them earlier. In fact, the value of the rains to crops in the region far exceeded the losses caused by flooding.

Another well-known example is Hurricane Camille (1969). Although this storm is best known for its exceptional storm surge and the devastation it brought to coastal areas, the greatest number of deaths associated with this storm occurred in the Blue Ridge Mountains of Virginia two days after Camille's landfall. Here many places received more than 25 centimeters (10 inches) of rain and severe flooding took more than 150 lives.

To summarize, extensive damage and loss of life in the coastal zone can result from storm surge, strong winds, and torrential rains. When loss of life occurs, it is commonly caused by the storm surge, which can devastate entire barrier islands or zones within a few blocks of the coast. Although wind damage is usually not as catastrophic as the storm surge, it affects a much larger area. Where building codes are inadequate, economic losses can be especially severe. Because hurricanes weaken as they move inland, most wind damage occurs within 200 kilometers (125 miles) of the coast. Far from the coast, a weakening storm can produce extensive flooding long after the winds have diminished below hurricane levels. Sometimes the damage from inland flooding exceeds storm-surge destruction.

Estimating the Intensity of a Hurricane

The Saffir–Simpson Hurricane Scale appears to be a straightforward tool. However, the accurate observations needed to correctly portray hurricane intensity at the surface are sometimes difficult to obtain. Estimating hurricane intensity is difficult because direct surface observations in the eye wall are rarely available. Therefore, winds in this most intense part of the storm have to be estimated. One of the best ways to estimate surface intensity is to adjust the wind speeds measured by reconnaissance aircraft.

Winds aloft are stronger than winds at the surface. Therefore, the adjustment of values determined for winds aloft to values expected at the surface involves *reducing* the measurements made aloft. However, until the late 1990s, determining the proper adjustment factor was problematic because surface observations in the eye wall were too limited to establish a broadly accepted relationship between flight-level and surface winds. In the early 1990s the reduction factors commonly used ranged from 75 to 80 percent (that is, surface wind speeds were assumed to be between 75 and 80 percent of the speed at 3000 meters/10,000 feet). Some scientists and engineers even maintained that surface winds were as low as 65 percent of flight-level winds.

Beginning in 1997 a new instrument, called a *Global Positioning System (GPS) dropwindsonde*, came into use (sometimes just called a *dropsonde*). After being released from the aircraft, this package of instruments, slowed by a small parachute, drifts downward through the storm (Figure 11–12). During the descent, it continuously transmits data on tem-

perature, humidity, air pressure, wind speed, and wind direction. The development of this technology for the first time provided a way to accurately measure the strongest winds in a hurricane from flight level all the way to the surface.

Over a span of several years, hundreds of GPS dropwindsondes were released in hurricanes. The data accumulated from these trials showed that the speed of surface winds in the eye wall averaged about 90 percent of the flight-level winds, not 75 to 80 percent. Based on this new understanding, the National Hurricane Center now uses the 90 percent figure to estimate a hurricane's maximum surface winds from flight-level observations. This means that the winds in some storms in the historical record were underestimated.

For example, in 1992 the surface winds in Hurricane Andrew were estimated to be 233 kilometers (145 miles) per hour. This was 75 to 80 percent of the value measured at 3000 meters by the reconnaissance aircraft. When scientists at the National Hurricane Center reevaluated the storm using the 90 percent value, they concluded that the maximum-sustained surface winds had been 266 kilometers (165 miles) per hour—33 kilometers (20 miles) per hour faster than the original 1992 estimate. Consequently, in August 2002 the intensity of Hurricane Andrew was officially changed from category 4 to category 5. The upgrade makes Hurricane Andrew only the third category 5 storm on record to strike the continental United States. (Recall that the other

FIGURE 11-12 The Global Positioning System (GPS) dropwindsonde is frequently just called a dropsonde. This cylindrical instrument package is roughly 7 cm (2.75 in) in diameter, 40 cm (16 in) long, and weighs about 0.4 kg (0.86 lb). The instrument package is released from the aircraft and falls through the storm via a parachute, making and transmitting measurements of temperature, pressure, winds, and humidity every half-second. *(After NASA)*

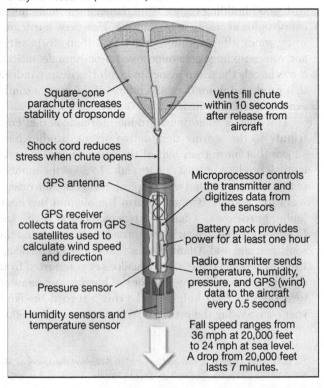

Square-cone parachute increases stability of dropsonde

Vents fill chute within 10 seconds after release from aircraft

Shock cord reduces stress when chute opens

GPS antenna

Microprocessor controls the transmitter and digitizes data from the sensors

GPS receiver collects data from GPS satellites used to calculate wind speed and direction

Battery pack provides power for at least one hour

Radio transmitter sends temperature, humidity, pressure, and GPS (wind) data to the aircraft every 0.5 second

Pressure sensor

Humidity sensors and temperature sensor

Fall speed ranges from 36 mph at 20,000 feet to 24 mph at sea level. A drop from 20,000 feet lasts 7 minutes.

two were the "Florida Keys 1935 Hurricane" and Hurricane Camille in 1969.)

Students Sometimes Ask...

If a Category 1 hurricane produces only "minimal" damage, are tropical storms any sort of significant weather threat?

The answer is a definite yes. Although tropical storm winds are less intense than winds in a hurricane, rainfall amounts can be prodigious. For example, in June 2001, Tropical Storm Allison dropped 93.95 centimeters (36.99 inches) of rain at the Port of Houston, Texas. At Houston Intercontinental Airport, 41.83 centimeters (16.47 inches) fell on June 10, 2001—roughly four times the normal June precipitation—making it the wettest June on record. The previous wettest June occurred in 1989 when 41.35 centimeters (16.28 inches) of rain fell, mostly from another tropical storm, named Allison! The 2001 storm caused nearly $5 billion in damages in the Houston area, making it the costliest tropical storm in U.S. history. In addition, the flooding, lightning, and tornadoes associated with Allison claimed more than 40 lives.

Detecting and Tracking Hurricanes

By examining Figures 11–2 and 11–3, you can see some of the typical paths followed by tropical storms and hurricanes in the North Atlantic. What determines these tracks? The storms can be thought of as being steered by the surrounding environmental flow throughout the depth of the troposphere. The movement of hurricanes has been likened to a leaf being carried along by the currents in a stream, except that for a hurricane the "stream" has no set boundaries.

In the latitude zone equatorward of about 25° north, tropical storms and hurricanes commonly move to the west with a slight poleward component. (Look at the storm tracks in Figure 11–2 and in Figure 11–G, for example.) This occurs because of the semipermanent cell of high pressure (called the *Bermuda High*) that is positioned poleward of the storm (see Figure 7–10b, p. 209). On the equatorward side of this high-pressure center, easterly winds prevail that guide the storms westward. If this high-pressure center is weak in the western Atlantic, the storm often turns northward. On the poleward side of the Bermuda High, westerly winds prevail that steer the storm back toward the east. Often it is difficult to determine whether the storm will curve back out to sea or whether it will continue straight ahead and make landfall.

A location only a few hundred kilometers from a hurricane—just a day's striking distance away—may experience clear skies and virtually no wind. Before the age of weather satellites, such a situation made it difficult to warn people of impending storms. The worst natural disaster in U.S. history came as a result of a hurricane that struck an unprepared Galveston, Texas, on September 8, 1900. The strength of the storm, together with the lack of adequate warning, caught the population by surprise and cost the lives of 6000 people in the city and at least 2000 more elsewhere (Figure 11–13).[*]

[*]For a facinating account of the Galveston storm, read *Isaac's Storm* by Erik Larson, New York: Crown Publishers, 1999.

FIGURE 11-13 Aftermath of the Galveston hurricane of 1900. Entire blocks were swept clean, while mountains of debris accumulated around the few remaining buildings. *(AP Photos)*

(a)

(b)

BOX 11-3 Atmospheric Hazard: Examining Hurricane Katrina from Space

Satellites allow us to track the formation, movement, and growth of hurricanes. In addition, their specialized instruments provide data that can be transformed into images that allow scientists to analyze the internal structure and workings of these huge storms. The images and captions in this box provide a unique perspective of Hurricane Katrina, the most devastating storm to strike the United States in more than a century.

Figures 11–B, 11–C, 11–D, and 11–E are from NASA's *Terra* satellite and are relatively "traditional" images that show Katrina at various stages of its development and dissipation.

FIGURE 11-C The storm on August 25, 2005 at 12:30 P.M. EDT, just 12 hours and 40 minutes later than the image in 11–B. By this time Katrina is a Category 1 hurricane. Because the storm moved slowly, just 10 kilometers (6 miles) per hour, heavy rainfall totals were expected. See Figure 11–H to view the rainfall pattern. *(NASA image)*

FIGURE 11-B Image of Tropical Storm Katrina on August 24, 2005, at 11:50 A.M. EDT, shortly after it became the eleventh named storm of the 2005 Atlantic hurricane season. The storm formed late on August 23 and developed quickly into a tropical storm by 11 A.M. the next morning. When this image was taken, Katrina had winds of 64 kilometers (40 miles) per hour, and was just beginning to take on the recognizable swirling shape of a hurricane. *(NASA image)*

FIGURE 11-D This image shows Katrina at 1 P.M. EDT on Sunday, August 28, 2005, as a massive storm covering much of the Gulf of Mexico. After passing over Florida as a Category 1 hurricane, Katrina entered the Gulf and intensified into a Category 5 storm with winds of 257 kilometers (160 miles) per hour and even stronger gusts. Air pressure at the center of the storm measured 902 millibars. When Katrina came ashore the next day, it was a slightly less vigorous Category 4 storm. *(NASA image)*

FIGURE 11-E In this image from 3:15 P.M. EDT on August 29, 2005, Katrina measured about 1260 kilometers (780 miles) across and is sprawled over all or part of 16 states. After coming ashore as a Category 4 storm, it was still a Category 1 after being over land for nearly 8 hours. *(NASA image)*

BOX 11-3   Atmospheric Hazard: Examining Hurricane Katrina from Space (continued)

FIGURE 11-F Color-enhanced infrared image from the *GOES-East* satellite of Hurricane Katrina several hours before making landfall on August 29, 2005. The most intense activity is associated with red and orange. *(NOAA)*

Figure 11–F is a color-enhanced infrared (IR) image from the *GOES-East* satellite. (For an explanation of infrared imaging, see Box 2–5 on p. 53). Cold cloud tops, and thus the most intense storms, are easily seen in this image of Hurricane Katrina taken a few hours before landfall. Color-enhanced imagery is a method meteorologists use to aid them with satellite interpretation. The colors enable them to easily and quickly see features that are of special interest.

Figure 11–G from NASA's *QuikSCAT* satellite is very different in appearance. It provides a detailed look at Katrina's surface winds shortly before the storm made landfall. This image depicts relative wind speeds rather than actual values. The satellite sends out high-frequency radio waves, some of which bounce off the ocean and return to the satellite. Rough, storm-tossed seas create a strong signal, whereas a smooth surface returns a weaker signal. In order to match wind speeds with the type of signal that returns to the satellite, scientists compare wind measurements taken by data buoys in the ocean to the strength of the signal received by the satellite. When there are too few data buoy measurements to compare to the satellite data, exact wind speeds cannot be determined. Instead, the image provides a clear picture of relative wind speeds.

Finally, Figure 11–H shows the *Multi-satellite Precipitation Analysis (MPA)* of the storm. This image, which also depicts the track of storm, shows the overall pattern of rainfall. It was constructed from data collected over several days by the *Tropical Rainfall Measuring Mission (TRMM)* satellite and other satellites. For yet another satellite perspective of Katrina, see Figure 11–I in Box 11–4.

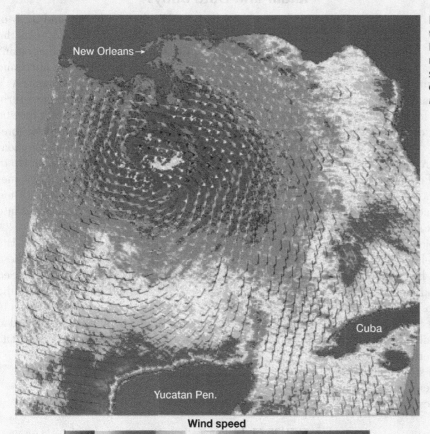

New Orleans→

Cuba

Yucatan Pen.

Wind speed

Wind speed increases

FIGURE 11-G NASA's *QuikSCAT* satellite was the source of data for this image of Hurricane Katrina on August 28, 2005. The image depicts relative wind speeds. The strongest winds, shown in shades of purple, circle a well-defined eye. The barbs show wind direction. *(NASA image)*

FIGURE 11-H Storm track and rainfall values for Hurricane Katrina for the period August 23 to 31, 2005. Rainfall amounts are derived from satellite data. The highest totals (dark red) exceeded 30 centimeters (12 inches) over northwestern Cuba and the Florida Keys. Amounts over southern Florida (green to yellow) were 12–20 centimeters (5–8 inches). Rainfall along the Mississippi coast (yellow to orange) was between 15–23 centimeters (6–9 inches). After coming ashore, Katrina moved through Mississippi, western Tennessee, and Kentucky and into Ohio. Because the storm moved rapidly, rainfall totals (green to blue) in these areas were generally less than 13 centimeters (5 inches). *(NASA image)*

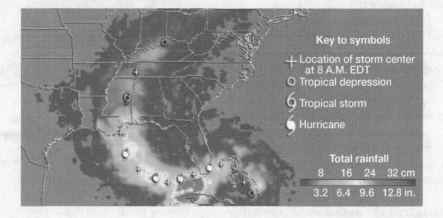

Key to symbols

+ Location of storm center at 8 A.M. EDT
◯ Tropical depression
Tropical storm
Hurricane

Total rainfall

8	16	24	32 cm
3.2	6.4	9.6	12.8 in.

In the United States, early warning systems have greatly reduced the number of deaths caused by hurricanes. At the same time, however, an astronomical rise has occurred in the amount of property damage. The primary reason for this latter trend is the rapid population growth and accompanying development in coastal areas.

The Role of Satellites

Today many different tools provide data that are used to detect and track hurricanes. This information is used to develop forecasts and to issue watches and warnings. The greatest single advancement in tools used for observing tropical cyclones has been the development of meteorological satellites.

Because the tropical and subtropical regions that spawn hurricanes consist of enormous areas of open ocean, conventional observations are limited. The needs for meteorological data from these vast regions are now met primarily by satellites. Even before a storm begins to develop cyclonic flow and the spiraling cloud bands so typical of a hurricane, it can be detected and monitored by satellites.

The advent of weather satellites has largely solved the problem of detecting tropical storms and has significantly improved monitoring (see Box 11–3, pp. 334–337). However, satellites are remote sensors, and it is not unusual for wind-speed estimates to be off by tens of kilometers per hour and for storm-position estimates to have errors. It is still not possible to precisely determine detailed structural characteristics. A combination of observing systems is necessary to provide the data needed for accurate forecasts and warnings.

Aircraft Reconnaissance

Aircraft reconnaissance represents a second important source of information about hurricanes. Ever since the first experimental flights into hurricanes were made in the 1940s, the aircraft and the instruments employed have become quite sophisticated (Figure 11–14). When a hurricane is within range, specially instrumented aircraft can fly directly into a threatening storm and accurately measure details of its position and current state of development. Data transmission can be made directly from an aircraft in the midst of a storm to the forecast center where input from many sources is collected and analyzed.

Measurements from reconnaissance aircraft are limited because they cannot be taken until the hurricane is relatively close to shore. Moreover, measurements are not taken continuously or throughout the storm. Rather, the aircraft provides sample "snapshots" of small parts of the hurricane. Nevertheless, the data collected are critical in analyzing the current characteristics needed to forecast the future behavior of the storm.

A major contribution to hurricane forecasting and warning programs has been an improved understanding of the structure and characteristics of these storms. Although advancements in remote sensing from satellites have been made, measurements from reconnaissance aircraft will be required for the foreseeable future to maintain the present level of accuracy for forecasts of potentially dangerous tropical storms.

Radar and Data Buoys

Radar is a third basic tool in the observation and study of hurricanes (Figure 11–15). When a hurricane nears the coast, it is monitored by land-based Doppler weather radar.* These radars provide detailed information on hurricane wind fields, rainfall intensity, and storm movement. As a result, local NWS offices are able to provide short-term warnings for floods, tornadoes, and high winds for specific areas. Sophisticated mathematical calculations provide forecasters with important information derived from the radar data, such as estimates of rainfall amounts. A limitation of radar is that it cannot "see" farther than about 320 kilometers (200 miles) from the coast, and hurricane watches and warnings must be issued long before the storm comes into range (see Box 11–4).

Data buoys represent a fourth method of gathering data for the study of hurricanes (see Figure 12–3, p. 349). These remote, floating instrument packages are positioned in fixed locations all along the Gulf Coast and Atlantic Coast of the United States. When you examine the weather maps in Figure 11–4, you can see data buoy information plotted at several offshore stations. Ever since the early 1970s, data

*For a more complete discussion of this important tool, see the section "Doppler Radar" in Chapter 10.

FIGURE 11-14 In the Atlantic basin, most operational hurricane reconnaissance is carried out by the U.S. Air Force Weather Reconnaissance Squadron based at Keesler AFB, Mississippi, where they maintain a fleet of 10 C-130 aircraft. Pilots fly through the hurricane to its center, measuring all basic weather elements as well as providing an accurate location of the eye. The National Oceanic and Atmospheric Administration also flies aircraft into hurricanes mostly on research missions to aid scientists in better understanding these storms. The P3 Orion aircraft shown here and state-of-the-art high-altitude jet aircraft complement the reconnaissance function of the U.S. Air Force. *(Photo by Getty Images, Inc.)*

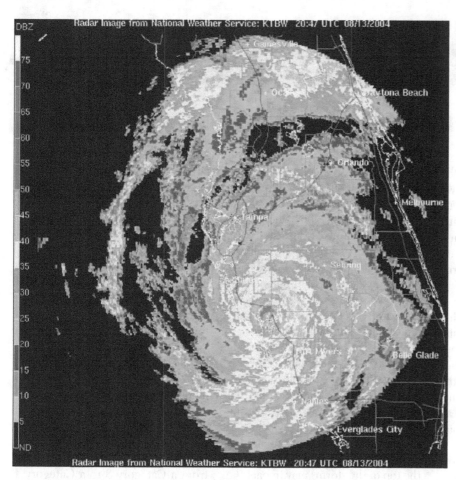

Radar Image from National Weather Service: KTBW 20:47 UTC 08/13/2004

Radar Image from National Weather Service: KTBW 20:47 UTC 08/13/2004

FIGURE 11-15 Doppler radar image of Hurricane Charley over Charlotte Harbor, Florida, just after landfall on August 13, 2004. The range of coastal radar is about 320 kilometers (200 miles). *(NOAA/National Weather Service)*

provided by these units have become a dependable and routine part of daily weather analysis as well as an important element of the hurricane warning system. The buoys represent the only means of making nearly continuous direct measurements of surface conditions over ocean areas.

Hurricane Watches and Warnings

Using input from the observational tools that were just described in conjunction with sophisticated computer models, meteorologists attempt to forecast the movements and intensity of a hurricane. The goal is to issue timely watches and warnings.

A **hurricane watch** is an announcement aimed at specific coastal areas that a hurricane poses a possible threat, generally within 36 hours. By contrast, a **hurricane warning** is issued when sustained winds of 119 kilometers (74 miles) per hour or higher are expected within a specified coastal area in 24 hours or less. A hurricane warning can remain in effect when dangerously high water or a combination of dangerously high water and exceptionally high waves continue, even though winds may be less than hurricane force.

Two factors are especially important in the watch-and-warning decision process. First, adequate lead time must be provided to protect life and, to a lesser degree, property.

Second, forecasters must attempt to keep overwarning at a minimum. This, however, is a difficult task. A policy statement from the American Meteorological Society describes the situation as follows:

Consistent with current forecast accuracy, it is necessary to issue hurricane warnings for rather large coastal areas. Warnings issued 24 hours before hurricane landfall average 300 nautical miles (560 kilometers) in length. Normally, the swath of damage encompasses about one-third of the warned area so the ratio of affected area to warned area is about one to three. In other words, approximately two-thirds of the area is, in effect, "overwarned." Such overwarning is not only costly, but also results in a loss of credibility in the warnings.[*]

Clearly, the decision to issue a warning represents a delicate balance between the need to protect the public on the one hand and the desire to minimize the degree of overwarning on the other.

---

[*]"Hurricane Detection, Tracking and Forecasting," *Bulletin of the American Meteorological Society*, 67, no. 7 (July 1993), a policy statement of an organization.

BOX 11-4 Atmospheric Hazard: A 3-D Look Inside a Hurricane

Seeing the pattern of rainfall in different parts of a hurricane is very useful to forecasters because it helps determine the strength of the storm. Scientists have developed a way to process radar data from the Tropical Rainfall Measuring Mission (TRMM) satellite within 3 hours and display it in 3-D. Because changes can occur rapidly in hurricanes, meteorologists need data as fast as possible.

TRMM is a unique satellite that is able to estimate rainfall intensity from space. In 2004, research confirmed that when cumulonimbus towers reach a certain height in the eye wall, the storm is strengthening. Images from the TRMM satellite can identify these "hot towers" of cloud development.

Because the TRMM satellite covers the tropical areas of the entire globe, the Precipitation Radar (PR)

instrument takes snapshots of storms as it passes by. Every time it passes over a named tropical cyclone anywhere in the world, the PR will send data to create a 3-D "snapshot" of the storm.

The hurricane snapshot shows forecasters information on how heavy the rain is falling in different parts of the storm, such as the eye wall versus the outer rain bands. It also gives a 3-D look at the cloud heights and "hot towers" inside the storm. Higher hot towers in the eye wall usually indicate a strengthening storm.

The snapshot also gives valuable information about how the storm is put together. For example, when scientists studying a snapshot see that the body of the hurricane may be "tilted" inward, it could give clues as to whether a wind shear (a sudden change in the direction of winds near the top of the storm) may impact the storm's strength. Normally, when a

hurricane runs into a strong wind shear, it weakens.

Figure 11–I is an image from the TRMM satellite showing Hurricane Katrina early on August 28, 2005. At the time of the image, Katrina was still a category 3 storm with maximum sustained winds of 185 kilometers (115 miles) per hour. The 3-D perspective shows the height of rain columns within the hurricane. Tall rain columns provide a clue that the storm is strengthening. Two isolated towers (in red) are visible: one in an outer rain band and the other in the northeastern part of the eye wall. The eye wall tower rises 16 kilometers (10 miles) above the surface of the ocean and is associated with an area of intense rainfall. Towers this tall near the core are often an indication the storm is intensifying. Katrina grew from a Category 3 to a Category 4 storm soon after this image was taken.

FIGURE 11-I Image from the Tropical Rainfall Measuring Mission (TRMM) satellite of Hurricane Katrina early on August 28, 2005, as the storm was gaining strength. This cutaway view of the inner portion of the storm shows cloud height on one side and rainfall rates on the other. (*NASA image*)

Chapter Summary

- The vast majority of hurricane deaths and damage are caused by relatively infrequent, yet powerful storms.

- Most hurricanes form between the latitudes of 5° and 20° over all tropical oceans except the South Atlantic and eastern South Pacific. The North Pacific has the greatest number of storms, averaging 20 per year. In the western Pacific, hurricanes are called *typhoons*, and in the Indian ocean, they are referred to as *cyclones*.

- A steep pressure gradient generates the rapid, inward spiraling winds of a hurricane. As the warm, moist air approaches the core of the storm, it turns upward and ascends in a ring of cumulonimbus towers and forms a doughnut-shaped wall called the *eye wall*. At the very center of the storm, called the *eye*, the air gradually descends, precipitation ceases, and winds subside.

- A hurricane is a heat engine fueled by the latent heat liberated when huge quantities of water vapor condense. They develop most often in late summer when ocean waters have reached temperatures of 27°C (80°F) or higher and are thus able to provide the necessary heat and moisture to the air. The initial stage of a tropical storm's life cycle, called a *tropical disturbance*, is a disorganized array of clouds that exhibits a weak pressure gradient and little or no rotation. Tropical disturbances that produce many of the strongest hurricanes that enter the western North Atlantic and threaten North America often begin as large undulations or ripples in the trade winds known as *easterly waves*.

- Each year, only a few tropical disturbances develop into full-fledged hurricanes that require minimum wind speeds of 119 kilometers per hour. When a cyclone's strongest winds do not exceed 61 kilometers per hour, it is called a *tropical depression*. When winds are between 61 and 119 kilometers per hour, the cyclone is termed a *tropical storm*. Hurricanes diminish in intensity whenever they (1) move over cool ocean waters that cannot supply warm, moist tropical air, (2) move onto land, or (3) reach a location where large-scale flow aloft is unfavorable.

- Although damages caused by a hurricane depend on several factors, including the size and population density of the area affected and the nearshore bottom configuration, the most significant factor is the strength of the storm itself. The *Saffir–Simpson* scale ranks the relative intensities of hurricanes. A 5 on the scale represents the worst storm possible, and a 1 is the least severe. Damage caused by hurricanes can be divided into three categories: (1) *storm surge*, which is most intense on the right side of the eye where winds are blowing toward the shore, occurs when a dome of water sweeps across the coast near the point where the eye makes landfall, (2) *wind damage*, and (3) *inland freshwater flooding*, which is caused by torrential rains that accompany most hurricanes.

- North Atlantic hurricanes develop in the trade winds, which generally move these storms from east to west. Today, because of early warning systems that help detect and track hurricanes, the number of deaths associated with these violent storms have been greatly reduced. Because the tropical and subtropical regions that spawn hurricanes consist of enormous areas of open oceans, meteorological data from these vast regions are provided primarily by *satellites*. Other important sources of hurricane information are *aircraft reconnaissance*, *radar*, and remote, floating instrument platforms called *data buoys*. Using data from these observational tools, meteorologists can issue an announcement, called a *hurricane watch*, aimed at specific coastal areas threatened by a hurricane, generally within 36 hours. By contrast, a *hurricane warning* is issued when sustained winds of 119 kilometers per hour or higher are expected within a specified coastal area in 24 hours or less. Two important factors in the watch and warning decision process are (1) adequate lead time and (2) attempting to keep over-warning at a minimum.

Vocabulary Review

easterly wave (p. 326)
eye (p. 324)
eye wall (p. 321)
hurricane (p. 320)

hurricane warning (p. 335)
hurricane watch (p. 335)
Saffir–Simpson scale (p. 327)
storm surge (p. 329)

tropical depression (p. 326)
tropical disturbance (p. 326)
tropical storm (p. 327)

Review Questions

1. Why might people in some parts of the world welcome the arrival of the hurricane season?

2. When a parcel of air approaches the center of a hurricane, how does its speed change? What law explains this change? (See Box 11–1.)

3. Which of these statements about the eye of a hurricane are true and which are false?
   a. It is typically the warmest part of the storm.
   b. It is usually characterized by clear, blue skies.
   c. It is in the eye that winds are strongest.

4. During what time of year do most of the hurricanes that affect North America form? Why is hurricane formation favored at this time?

5. Tropical storms that form near the equator do not acquire a rotary motion as cyclones of higher latitudes do. Why?

6. What are streamlines? How do streamlines indicate an easterly wave in the North Atlantic?

7. List two factors that inhibit the strengthening of tropical disturbances.

8. Which has the stronger winds, a tropical storm or a tropical depression?

9. Why does the intensity of a hurricane diminish rapidly when it moves onto land?

10. What is the purpose of the Saffir–Simpson scale?

11. Hurricane damage can be divided into three broad categories. Name them. Which one of the categories is responsible for the greatest percentage of hurricane-related deaths?

12. Great damage and significant loss of life can take place a day or more after a hurricane has moved ashore and weakened. When this occurs, what is the likely cause?

13. In 1992 Hurricane Andrew was classified as a Category 4 storm. Ten years later its intensity was officially changed to Category 5 by the National Hurricane Center. Why was the storm reclassified?

14. List four tools that provide data used to track hurricanes and develop forecasts.

15. A hurricane has slower wind speeds than a tornado, but a hurricane inflicts more total damage. How might this be explained?

16. Briefly describe the potential problem of "overwarning" that is related to the issuing of hurricane warnings.

17. Although observational tools and hurricane forecasts continue to improve, the potential for loss of life due to hurricanes is growing. Explain this apparent contradiction.

Problems

The questions that follow refer to the weather maps of Hurricane Fran in Figure 11–4.

1. On which of the two days were Fran's wind speeds probably highest? How were you able to determine this?

2. a. How far did the center of the hurricane move during the 24-hour period represented by these maps?
   b. At what rate did the storm move during this 24-hour span? Express your answers in miles per hour.

3. The middle-latitude cyclone shown in Figure 9–20 has an east–west diameter of approximately 1200 miles (when the 1008-mb isobar is used to define the outer boundary of the low). Measure the diameter (north–south) of Hurricane Fran on September 5. Use the 1008-mb isobar to represent the outer edge of the storm. How does this figure compare to the middle-latitude cyclone?

4. Determine the pressure gradient for Hurricane Fran on September 5. Measure from the 1008-mb isobar at Charleston, to the center of the storm. Express your answer in millibars per 100 miles.

5. The weather map in Figure 9–20 shows a well-developed middle-latitude cyclone. Calculate the pressure gradient of this storm from the 1008-mb isobar at the Wyoming–Idaho border to the center of the low. Assume the pressure at the center of the storm to be 986 mb and the distance to be 625 miles. Express your answer in millibars per 100 miles. How does this answer compare to your answer to problem 4?

Atmospheric Science Online

The Atmosphere 10e web site uses the resources and flexibility of the Internet to aid in your study of the topics in this chapter. Written and developed by meteorology instructors, this site will help improve your understanding of meteorology. Visit **http://www .prenhall.com/lutgens** and click on the cover of *The Atmosphere 10e* to find:

- **Online review quizzes**
- **Critical thinking exercises**
- **Links to chapter-specific web resources**
- **Internet-wide key term searches**

http://www.prenhall.com/lutgens

WEATHER ANALYSIS *and* FORECASTING

The Weather Business:

Predicting severe weather is one of the main tasks of the forecaster. *(Photo by Jim Brandenburg/Minden Pictures)*

Each year modern society demands more accurate weather forecasts. The desire for sound weather predictions ranges from wanting to know if the weekend's weather will permit a beach outing to NASA's need to evaluate conditions on a space shuttle launch date (Figure 12–1). Such diverse industries as airlines and fruit growers depend heavily on accurate weather forecasts. In addition, the designs of buildings, oil platforms, and many industrial facilities rely on a sound knowledge of the atmosphere in its most extreme forms, including thunderstorms, tornadoes, and hurricanes. We are no longer satisfied with short-range predictions, but instead demand accurate long-range predictions. Such a question as "Will the Northeast experience an unseasonably cold winter?" has become common.

What is a weather forecast? Simply, a **weather forecast** is a scientific estimate of the weather conditions at some future time. Forecasts are usually expressed in terms of the most significant weather variables, which include temperature, cloudiness, humidity, precipitation, wind speed, and wind direction. As the following quote illustrates, weather forecasting is a formidable task.

> Imagine a system on a rotating sphere that is 8000 miles wide, consists of different materials, different gases that have different properties (one of the most important of which, water, exists in different concentrations), heated by a nuclear reactor 93 million miles away. Then, just to make life interesting, this sphere is oriented such that, as it revolves around the nuclear reactor, it is heated differently at different times of the year. Then, someone is asked to watch the mixture of gases, a fluid only 20 miles deep, that covers an area of 250 million square miles, and to predict the state of the fluid at one point on the sphere 2 days from now. This is the problem weather forecasters face.*

The Weather Business: A Brief Overview

In the United States the governmental agency responsible for gathering and disseminating weather-related information is the **National Weather Service (NWS),** a branch of the *National Oceanic and Atmospheric Administration (NOAA).* The mission of the NWS is as follows:

> The National Weather Service (NWS) provides weather, hydrologic and climate forecasts and warnings for the United States, its territories, adjacent waters and ocean areas, for the protection of life and property and the enhancement of the national economy. NWS data and products form a national information database and infrastructure that can be used by other governmental agencies, the private sector, the public and the global community.

*Robert T. Ryan, "The Weather Is Changing . . . or Meteorologists and Broadcasters, the Twain Meet, " *Bulletin of the American Meteorological Society,* 63, no. 3 (March 1982), 308.

FIGURE 12-1 Fog can be a significant airport hazard. (*AP Photo/Natcha Pisarenko*)

Perhaps the most important services provided by the NWS are forecasts and warnings of hazardous weather including thunderstorms, flooding, hurricanes, tornadoes, winter weather, and extreme heat. According to the Federal Emergency Management Agency, 80 percent of all declared emergencies are weather related (see Box 12–1). In a similar vein, the Department of Transportation reports that more than 6000 fatalities per year can be attributed to the weather. Heat waves claim approximately 1000 lives annually in the United States. Further, 2005 was the most costly hurricane season on record. Major storms, which included Katrina, Rita, and Wilma, inflicted hundreds of billions of dollars worth of damage and killed an estimated 1300 people along the Gulf and Atlantic coasts

As global population increases, the economic impact of weather-related phenomena also escalates. During the years 1986 through 1995, for example, property damage in the United States due to wind, hail, snow, and tornadoes increased by 500 percent. As a result, the NWS is under greater pressure to provide more accurate and longer-range forecasts.

To produce even a short-range forecast is an enormous task. It involves complicated and detailed procedures, including collecting weather data, transmitting it, and compiling it on a global scale. These data must then be analyzed so that an accurate assessment of the current conditions can be made. In the United States, weather information from around the world is collected by the **National Centers for Environmental Prediction,** located in Camp Springs, Maryland, near Washington, D.C. This branch of the National Weather Service prepares weather maps, charts, and forecasts on a global and national scale. These forecasts are disseminated to regional **Weather Forecast Offices,** where they are used to produce local and regional weather forecasts.

The final phase in the weather business is the dissemination of a wide variety of forecasts. Each of the 119 Weather Forecast Offices regularly issues regional and local forecasts, aviation forecasts, and warnings covering their forecast area. The *local forecast* seen on The Weather Channel or your local TV station is derived from a forecast issued by one of the offices operated by the NWS. Further, all the data and products (maps, charts, and forecasts) provided by the NWS are available at no cost to the general public and to private forecasting services such as AccuWeather and WeatherData (Figure 12–2).

The demand for highly visual forecasts containing computer-generated graphics has grown along with the use of personal computers and the Internet. Because it is outside the mission of the National Weather Service, this publicly funded entity is not the source of the animated depictions of the weather that appear on most local newscasts. Instead, the private sector has taken over this task. In addition, private forecast services customize the NWS products to create a variety of specialized weather reports that are tailored for specific audiences. In a farming community, for example, the weather reports might include frost warnings, while winter forecasts in Denver, Colorado, include the snow conditions at ski resorts.

FIGURE 12-2 Weather broadcaster previewing graphics. *(Photo by Bob Daemmrich/Stock Boston)*

It is important to note that despite the valuable role that the private sector plays in disseminating weather-related information to the public, the NWS is the *official* voice in the United States for issuing warnings during life-threatening weather situations. Two major weather centers operated by the NWS serve critical functions in this regard. The Storm Prediction Center in Norman, Oklahoma, maintains a constant vigil for severe thunderstorms and tornadoes (see Chapter 10). Hurricane watches and warnings for the Atlantic, Caribbean, Gulf of Mexico, and eastern Pacific are issued by the National Hurricane Center/Tropical Prediction Center in Miami, Florida (see Chapter 11).

In summary, the process of providing weather forecasts and warnings throughout the United States occurs in three stages. First, to provide a picture of the current state of the atmosphere, data are collected and analyzed on a global scale. Second, the NWS employs a variety of techniques to establish the future state of the atmosphere; a process called *weather forecasting.* Third, forecasts are disseminated to the public, mainly through the private sector. The National Weather Service serves as the sole entity responsible for issuing watches and warnings of extreme weather events.

Weather Analysis

 GEODe **Introduction to the Atmosphere**
▶ In the Lab: Reading Weather Maps

Before weather can be predicted, the forecaster must have an accurate picture of current atmospheric conditions. This enormous task, called **weather analysis,** involves collecting,

BOX 12-1   Atmospheric Hazard: Debris Flows in the San Francisco Bay Region*

When prolonged, intense rain falls on steep hillsides, the saturated soils can become unstable and move rapidly downslope (see Figure 1–1c, p. 2). Such land movements, called *debris flows,* are capable of destroying homes, washing out roads and bridges, knocking down trees, and obstructing streams and roadways with thick deposits of mud and rocks (Figure 12–A). An especially destructive event occurred in 1982 when thousands of debris flows caused nearly $70 million in damages and took 25 lives. Since then, several serious but less severe events have occurred. As more and more people build in the hills around the Bay region, the potential impact of debris flows on life and property is increasing.

FIGURE 12-A On January 25, 1997, a debris flow literally buried this one-story home in Mill Valley, California. Heavy rains from a powerful Pacific storm triggered the event. *(Justin Sullivan/AP Wide World Photos)*

transmitting, and compiling millions of pieces of observational data. Because the atmosphere is ever changing, this job must be accomplished quickly. High-speed supercomputers have greatly aided the weather analyst.

Gathering Data

A vast network of weather stations is required to provide enough data for a weather chart that is useful for generating even short-range forecasts. On a global scale the **World Meteorological Organization (WMO),** an agency of the United Nations, is responsible for the international exchange of weather data. Included in this task is the oversight of observational procedures to insure the comparability of data coming from the more than 185 participating nations and territories.

Surface Observations. Worldwide, over 10,000 observation stations on land, 7000 ships at sea, and hundreds of data buoys and oil platforms report atmospheric conditions four times each day at 0000, 6000, 1200, and 1800 Greenwich Mean Time (Figure 12–3). These data are rapidly sent around the globe using a telecommunications system dedicated to weather information.

In the United States, 119 Weather Forecast Offices, in addition to their role as regional forecast centers, are responsible for gathering and transmitting weather information to a central database. The Federal Aviation Administration (FAA), in cooperation with the NWS, also operates observation stations at most metropolitan airports. Together, the NWS and the FAA operate nearly 900 **Automated Surface Observing Systems (ASOS).** These automated systems provide weather observations that include temperature, dew point, wind, visibility, sky conditions, and can even detect present weather such as rain or snow (Figure 12–4). Automation often assists or, in some cases, replaces human observers because it can provide information from inhospitable and remote areas.

Observations Aloft Because the atmosphere is three dimensional, upper-air observations are essential (see Figure 1–8, p. 9). Worldwide, nearly 900 balloon-borne instrument packages, called *radiosondes,* are launched twice daily at 0000 and 1200 Greenwich Mean Time (6:00 PM and 6:00 AM Central Standard Time). Most of the upper-air observation stations are located in the Northern Hemisphere, with 92 stations operated by the National Weather Service.

A radiosonde is a light instrument package containing sensors that measure temperature, humidity, and pressure as

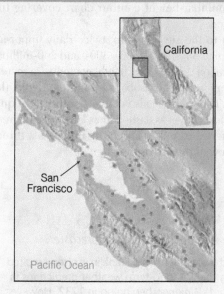

FIGURE 12-B San Francisco Bay region, showing hilly areas where debris flows are possible. Dots show locations of ALERT rain gauges. During storms, these gauges radio-transmit rainfall data to the U.S. Geological Survey and the National Weather Service. Scientists analyze the data to determine debris-flow danger. If danger is high, a Debris-Flow Watch or Warning is issued.

The Debris-Flow Warning System

Debris flows can begin suddenly, often with little warning. Loss of lives during the intense 1982 storm prompted the National Weather Service (NWS) and the U.S. Geological Survey (USGS) to develop a debris-flow warning system for the San Francisco Bay area.

During the rainy season (October through April), this warning system measures rainfall using more than 50 radio-telemetered rain gauges, called the ALERT network (Figure 12–B). Early in each rainy season, these rainfall measurements, along with measurements of soil moisture from a study site in the hills south of San Francisco, are used to estimate the moisture level of soils throughout the Bay region. Soils must reach a sufficient moisture level each year before slopes become susceptible to debris flows during intense rainstorms. Once soils reach this moisture level, the USGS monitors weather forecasts and uses up-to-the-minute

data from the ALERT network to determine the potential for imminent debris flows during each subsequent rainstorm. Warnings are then broadcast by the National Weather Service.

How Much Rain Is Needed to Trigger Debris Flows?

Once soils have reached sufficient moisture levels during a rainy season, it is the rainfall rate, rather than total rainfall amount, that is most important for determining whether debris flows will occur. For example, 4 inches of rain in 24 hours is generally not sufficient to trigger debris flows in the San Francisco Bay region. However, 4 inches of rain in 6 hours generally will trigger numerous debris flows. On burned slopes that have lost their anchoring vegetation, and altered slopes, such as road cuts, greater caution is needed because debris flows can be triggered by less severe rainfall conditions.

*Based on material prepared by the U.S. Geological Survey

---

the balloon (normall filled with hydrogen or helium) rises. Also, by tracking the radiosonde, wind speed and direction at various altitudes can be calculated. A radiosonde flight typically lasts about 90 minutes, during which it may ascend to over 35 kilometers (about 115,000 feet). Because pressure decreases with altitude, the balloon eventually stretches to its breaking point and bursts. When this occurs, a small parachute opens and the instrument package slowly descends to Earth. If you find a radiosonde, follow the mailing instructions as they can be reused.

Acquiring upper-air data over the ocean is problematic. Only a few ships launch radiosondes. Some commercial aircraft contribute upper-air information over the ocean by regularly reporting wind, temperature and, occasionally, turbulence along their flight routes.

A number of technical advances have been made that improve our ability to make observations aloft. Special radar units called **wind profilers** are used to measure wind speed and direction up to 10 kilometers (6 miles) above the surface. These measurements can be taken every six minutes in contrast to the 12-hour interval between balloon launches. In addition, satellites and weather radar have become invaluable tools for making weather observations. The

importance of these modern technologies are considered later in this chapter.

Despite the advances being made in the collection of weather data, two difficulties remain. First, observations may be inaccurate due to instrument malfunctions or data transmission errors. Second, there are some regions, particularly over oceans and in mountainous areas, where there are too few observations.

Weather Maps: Pictures of the Atmosphere

Once this large body of data has been collected, the analyst displays it in a form that can be comprehended easily by the forecaster. This step is accomplished by placing the information on a number of **synoptic weather maps** (see Box 12–2). They are called synoptic, which means "coincident in time," because they display a synopsis of the weather conditions at a given moment. These weather charts are a symbolic representation of the state of the atmosphere. Thus, to the trained eye, a weather map is a snapshot that shows the status of the atmosphere, including data on temperature, humidity, pressure, and airflow. (Forecast maps that depict the future state of the

FIGURE 12-3 Data buoy used to record atmospheric conditions over a section of the global ocean. These data are transmitted via satellite to a land-based station. *(Photo by Matthew Neal McVay/Stock Boston)*

atmosphere are also produced, a topic we will consider later in this chapter.)

Over 200 surface maps and charts covering several levels of the atmosphere are produced each day by the NWS and its forecast centers. A task once done by hand, computers are now employed to analyze and plot the data in a systematic fashion. Typically, lines and symbols are used to depict the weather patterns. Once a map is generated, an analyst fine-tunes it, correcting any errors or omissions. Figure 12–5 shows a simplified version of a surface map, as well as a 500-millibar-height contour chart covering the same time period.

In addition to the surface map, twice-daily upper-air charts are drawn at 850-, 700-, 500-, 300-, and 200-millibar levels. Recall that on these charts, height contours (in meters or tens of meters) instead of isobars are used to depict the pressure field. These charts also contain isotherms (equal temperature lines) shown as dashed lines labeled in degrees Celsius. This series of upper-air charts provides a three-dimensional view of the atmosphere.

FIGURE 12-4 Diagram of an Automated Surface Observing System (ASOS) equipped to sample the sky for cloud coverage; take temperature and dew-point measurements; determine wind speed and direction; and even detect present weather—if it is raining or snowing. Also see Figure 1–7, p. 8.

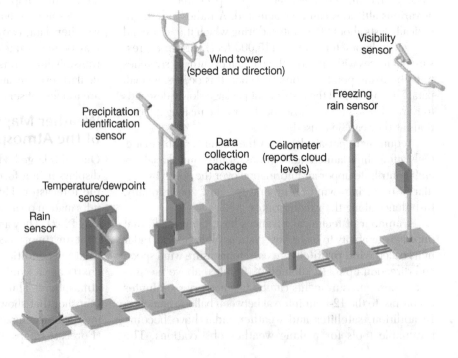

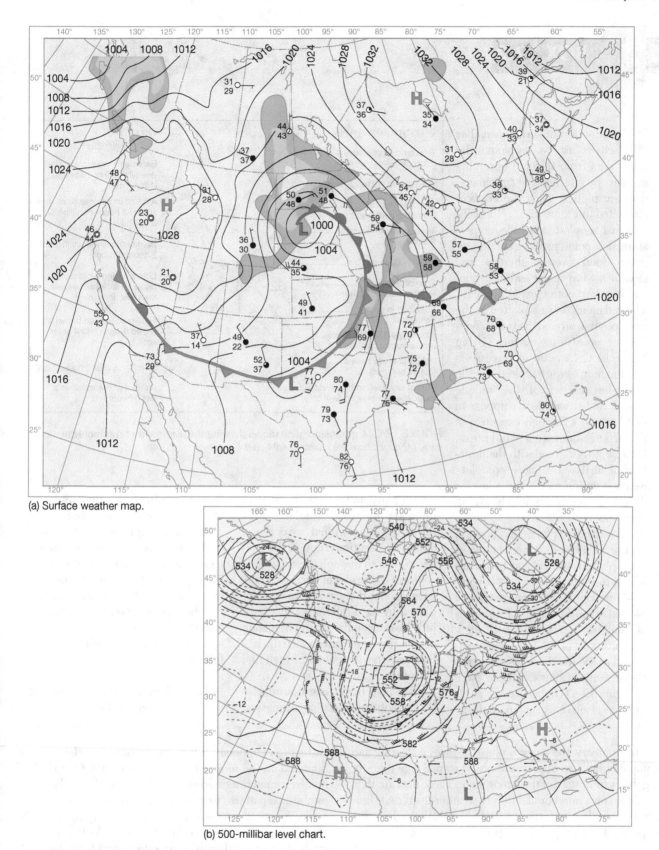

(a) Surface weather map.

(b) 500-millibar level chart.

FIGURE 12-5 Simplified synoptic weather maps. (a) Surface weather map for 7:00 A.M. Eastern Standard Time depicting a well-developed middle-latitude cyclone. (b) A 500-millibar-level map, with height contours in tens of meters, for the same time period.

BOX 12-2   Constructing a Synoptic Weather Chart

Production of surface weather charts first involves plotting the data from selected observing stations. By international agreement, data are plotted using the symbols illustrated in Figure 12–C. Normally, data that are plotted include temperature, dew point, pressure and its tendency, cloud cover (height, type, and amount), wind speed and direction, and weather, both current and past. These data are always plotted in the same position around the station symbol for consistent reading. Using Figure 12–C, for example, you can see that the temperature is plotted in the upper-left corner of the sample model, and it will always appear in that location. (The only exception to this arrangement is the wind arrow, because it is oriented with the direction of airflow.) A more complete weather station model and a key for decoding weather symbols are in Appendix B.

The data are plotted as shown in Figure 12–D (left). Once data have been plotted, isobars and fronts are added to the weather chart (Figure 12–D on right). Isobars are usually plotted on surface maps at intervals of 4 millibars (1004, 1008, 1012, etc.). The positions of the isobars are estimated as accurately as possible from the pressure readings available. Note in Figure 12–D (right) that the 1012-millibar isobar is about halfway

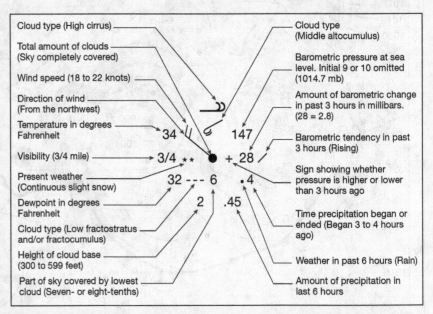

FIGURE 12-C A specimen station model showing the placement of commonly plotted data. *(Abridged from the International Code)*

between two stations that report 1010 millibars and 1014 millibars. Frequently, observational errors and other complications require the analyst to smooth the isobars so that they conform to the overall picture. Many irregularities in the pressure field are caused by local influences that have little bearing on the larger circulation depicted on the charts. Once the isobars are drawn, centers of high and low pressure are designated.

Because fronts are boundaries that separate contrasting air masses,

they can often be identified on weather charts by locating zones exhibiting abrupt changes in conditions. Because several elements change across a front, all are examined so that the frontal position is located most accurately. Some of the more easily recognized changes that can aid in identifying a front on a surface chart are as follows:

1. Marked temperature contrast over a short distance.

In summary, the analysis phase involves collecting and compiling millions of pieces of observational data describing the current state of the atmosphere. These data are then displayed on a number of different weather maps that show current weather patterns at selected levels throughout the depth of the atmosphere, not just at the surface.

Weather Forecasting

Until the late 1950s, all weather maps and charts were plotted manually and served as the primary tools for making weather forecasts. Various techniques were utilized by fore-

casters to extrapolate future conditions from the patterns depicted on the most recent weather charts. One method involved matching current conditions with similar, well-established patterns from the past. From such comparisons, meteorologists predicted how current systems might change in the hours and days to come. As this practice evolved, "rules of thumb" were established to aid forecasters. Applying these rules to current weather charts became the backbone of weather forecasting and still plays an important role in making short-range (24 hours or less) predictions.

Later, computers were used to plot data and produce surface and upper-air charts. As technologies improved,

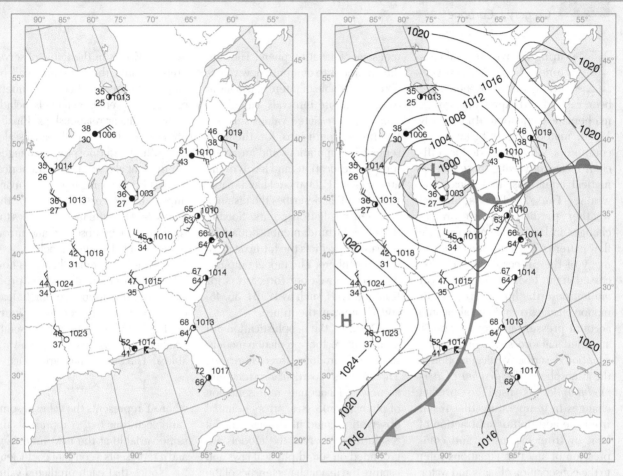

FIGURE 12-D Simplified weather charts. (left) Stations, with data for temperature, dew point, wind direction, wind speed, sky cover, and barometric pressure. (right) Same chart showing isobars and fronts.

2. Wind shift (in a clockwise direction) over a short distance by as much as 90°.

3. Humidity variations commonly occurring across a front that can be detected by examining dew-point temperatures.

4. Clouds and precipitation patterns giving clues to the position of fronts.

Notice in Figure 12–D that all the conditions listed are easily detected across the frontal zone. However, not all fronts are as easily defined as the

one on our sample map. In some cases, surface contrasts on opposite sides of the front are subdued. When this happens, charts of the upper air, where flow is less complex, become an important tool for detecting fronts.

computers eventually were used to make weather forecasts. Computers have played a key role in improving the accuracy and detail of weather forecasts, and in lengthening the period for which useful guidance can be given.

Numerical Weather Prediction: Forecasting by Computer

Numerical weather prediction is the technique used to forecast weather using numerical models designed to represent atmospheric processes. (The word "numerical" is somewhat misleading, because all types of weather forecasting are based on some quantitative data and therefore

could fit under this heading.) Numerical weather prediction relies on the fact that the behavior of atmospheric gases is governed by a set of physical principles that can be expressed as mathematical equations (see Box 12–3). If we can solve these equations, we will have a description of the future state (a forecast) of the atmosphere, derived from the current state, which we can interpret in terms of weather—temperature, moisture, cloud cover, and wind. This method is analogous to using a computer to predict the future positions of Mars, using Newton's laws of motion and knowing the planet's current position.

Highly refined computer models that attempt to mimic the behavior of the "real" atmosphere are used in numeri-

BOX 12-3 Numerical Weather Prediction

Gregory J. Carbone*

During the past several centuries, the physical laws governing the atmosphere have been refined and expressed through mathematical equations. In the early 1950s, meteorologists began using computers, which provided an efficient means of solving these mathematical equations, to forecast the weather. The goal of such numerical weather prediction is to predict changes in large-scale atmospheric flow patterns. The equations relate to many of the processes already discussed in this book. Two *equations of motion* describe how horizontal air motion changes over time, taking into account pressure gradient, Coriolis, and frictional forces. The *hydrostatic equation* describes vertical motion in the atmosphere. The *first law of thermodynamics* is used to predict changes in temperature that result from the addition or subtraction of heat or from expansion and compression of air. Two equations refer to the conservation of mass and water. Finally, the *ideal gas law* or *equation of state* shows the relationship among three fundamental variables—temperature, density, and pressure.

Weather-prediction models begin with observations describing the current state of the atmosphere. They use the equations to compute new values for each variable of interest, usually at 5- to10-minute intervals, called the *time step.* Predicted values serve as the initial conditions for the next series of computations and are made for specific locations and levels of the atmosphere. Each model has a spatial resolution that describes the distance between prediction points. Solving the model's fundamental equations repeatedly predicts the future state of the atmosphere. The model output is provided to weather forecasters for fixed intervals, such as 12, 24, 36, 48, and 72 hours in the future.

Despite the sophistication of numerical weather-prediction models, most still produce forecast errors. Three factors in particular restrict their accuracy—inadequate representation of physical processes, errors in initial observations, and inadequate model resolution. Whereas the models are grounded on sound physical laws and capture the major characteristics of the atmosphere, they necessarily simplify the workings of a very complex system. The representation of land–surface processes and topography are just two examples of features that are incompletely treated in current numerical

models. Errors in the initial observations fed into the computer will be amplified over time because numerical weather prediction models include many nonlinear relationships. Finally, physical conditions at all spatial scales can influence atmospheric changes. Yet the spatial resolution of numerical models is too coarse to capture many important processes. In fact, the atmospheric system moves at scales too small to ever be observed and incorporated explicitly into models.

A simple example illustrates how misrepresentation of physical processes or observation error might lead to inaccurate predictions. Figure 12–E is based on an equation used to predict future values of a given variable Y. The equation is written as

$$Y_t = (a \times Y_t) - Y_t^2,$$

where Y represents the value of some variable at time t, Y_{t+1} represents the same variable at the next time step, and a represents a constant coefficient.

Notice that each predicted value serves as the initial value for the next calculation, the same way in which output from a numerical weather-prediction model provides input for subsequent computations. The solid line in Figure 12–E shows the equation

cal weather prediction. All numerical simulations are based on the same governing equations but differ in the way the equations are applied and in the parameters that are used. For example, some models use a very closely spaced set of data points and cover a specific concentrated area, whereas others describe the atmosphere more broadly on a global scale. In the United States, several different numerical models are in use.

The process begins by entering current atmospheric variables (temperature, wind speed, humidity, and pressure) into a computer simulation. This set of values represents the atmosphere at the start of the forecast. After literally billions of calculations, a forecast of how these basic elements are expected to change over a short time frame (perhaps only 15 minutes) is generated. Once all the new values have been cal-

culated, the process starts over again with the next 15-minute forecast being established. By repeating this procedure many times over, a forecast for six or more days can be built.

Using mathematical models, the NWS produces a variety of generalized forecast charts at the National Centers for Environmental Predictions near Washington, D.C. Because these machine-generated maps predict atmospheric conditions at some future time, they are called **prognostic charts,** or simply **progs.** Most numerical models are designed to generate prognostic charts that predict changes in the flow pattern aloft. In addition, some models create forecasts for other conditions, including maximum and minimum temperatures, wind speeds, and precipitation probabilities. Even the simplest models require such a vast number of calculations that they could not have been

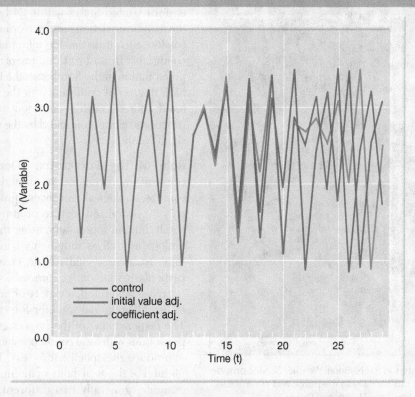

FIGURE 12-E Tiny errors may not significantly influence the early stages of a prediction, but with time, such errors amplify dramatically.

solution over a number of time steps, given an initial value of (e.g., a meteorological observation), $Y_{t=0} = 1.5$, and a coefficient value, $a = 3.75$. The graph illustrates how the precision of our equations describing the evolving state of the atmosphere may affect predictions. The blue line represents values of Y that result from the adjustment of a from 3.75 to 3.749. Similarly, we can demonstrate how a very small observation error could amplify over time by adjusting $Y_{t=0}$ from 1.5 to 1.499. The red line in the graph shows how an incremental change in the initial value affects predictions. Small errors may make very little difference in the early stages of our prediction, but such errors amplify dramatically over time. Because we cannot observe many small-scale features of the atmosphere, nor incorporate all of its processes into computer models, weather forecasts have a theoretical limit.

*Professor Carbone is a faculty member in the Department of Geography at the University of South Carolina.

used prior to the development of high-speed supercomputers.

Once generated, a statistical analysis is used to modify these machine-generated forecasts by making comparisons of how accurate previous forecasts have been. This approach, known as **Model Output Statistics (MOS,** pronounced "moss"), corrects for errors the model tends to make consistently. For example, certain forecast models may predict too much rain, overly strong winds, or temperatures that are too high or too low. MOS forecasts form the baseline that forecasters from the NWS, as well as private forecast companies, try to improve upon. This final step is performed by humans, using their knowledge of meteorology and making allowances for known model shortcomings (Figure 12–6).

To summarize, meteorologists use equations to create mathematical models of the atmosphere. Thus, by utilizing data on initial atmospheric conditions, they solve these equations to predict a future state. Of course, this is easier said than done. Earth's atmosphere is a very complex, dynamic system that can only be roughly approximated using mathematical models. Further, because of the nature of the equations, tiny differences in the data can yield huge differences in outcomes. Nevertheless, these models produce surprisingly good results—much better than those made without them.

Ensemble Forecasting. One of the most significant challenges for weather forecasters is the apparently chaotic behavior of the atmosphere. Specifically, two very

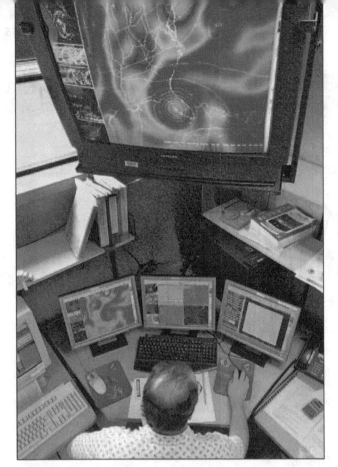

FIGURE 12-6 Forecasters at the National Weather Service provide nearly 2 million predictions annually to the public and commercial interests. *(Photo by* Florida Times-Union, *Will Dickey.)*

similar atmospheric disturbances may, over time, develop into two very different weather patterns. One may intensify, becoming a major disturbance, while the other withers and dissipates. To demonstrate this point, Edward Lorenz at the Massachusetts Institute of Technology employed a metaphor that became known as the *butterfly effect*. Lorenz described a butterfly in the Amazon rain forest fluttering its wings and setting into motion a subtle breeze that travels and gradually magnifies over time. According to Lorenz's metaphor, two weeks later this faint breeze has grown into a tornado over Kansas. Obviously, by stretching the point considerably, Lorenz tried to illustrate that a very small change in initial atmospheric conditions can dramatically affect the resulting weather pattern.

To deal with the inherent chaotic behavior of the atmosphere, forecasters rely on a technique known as **ensemble forecasting.** Simply, this method involves producing a number of forecasts using the same computer model but slightly altering the initial conditions, while remaining within an error range of the observational instruments. Essentially, ensemble forecasting attempts to assess how the inherent errors and omissions in weather measurements might affect the result.

One of the most important outcomes of ensemble forecasts is the information they provide about forecast uncer-

tainty. For example, assume that a prognostic chart that was generated using the best available weather data predicts the occurrence of precipitation over a wide area of the southeastern United States within 24 hours. Now let's say that the same calculations are performed several times in succession, each time making minor adjustments to the initial conditions. If most of these progs also predict a pattern of precipitation in the Southeast, the forecaster would place a high degree of confidence in the forecast. On the other hand, there is far less confidence in a forecast when the prognostic charts generated by the ensemble method differ significantly.

Role of the Forecaster. Despite faster computers, constant improvements in numerical models, and significant technological advances, prognostic charts provide only a generalized picture of atmospheric behavior. As a result, human forecasters, using their knowledge of meteorology as well as judgments based on experience, continue to serve a vital role in creating weather forecasts, particularly short-range forecasts.

Once generated, a variety of prognostic charts are sent to the 119 regional weather forecast offices of the NWS. The responsibility of the forecasters is to blend numerical predictions with local conditions and regional weather quirks to produce site-specific forecasts. This task is further complicated by the availability of multiple prognostic charts. For example, generally two different numerical models are employed to predict the minimum temperature for a given day. One method works better on some days than on others and performs better in some locales than in others. It is up to the forecaster to select the "best" model each day, or perhaps to blend the data from both models.

Often, forecasters add extra detail to the model forecast. Isolated summer thunderstorms, for example, are on a scale too small for the computer models to adequately resolve. In addition, weather phenomena such as tornadoes and thunderstorm microbursts cannot be predicted using available forecasting techniques (Figure 12–7). Therefore, emphasis is placed on using satellites and weather radar to detect and track these features.

In summary, computer-generated numerical models have greatly improved our ability to forecast the weather. Because the prognostic charts obtained by these techniques are somewhat general, detailed aspects of weather must still be added by an experienced human forecaster, utilizing various other forecasting methods.

Other Forecasting Methods

Although machine-generated prognostic charts form the basis of modern forecasting, other methods are available to meteorologists. These methods, which have "stood the test of time," include persistence forecasting, climatological forecasting, analog methods, and trend forecasting.

Persistence Forecasting. Perhaps the simplest forecasting technique, called **persistence forecasting,** is

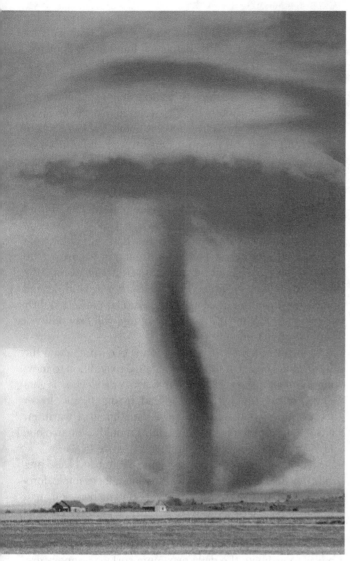

FIGURE 12-7 Mesoscale phenomena such as this tornado are too small to appear on computer-generated prognostic charts. Detection of such events relies heavily on weather radar and geostationary satellites. *(Photo by A.T. Wilett/Alamy)*

would be correct about 90 percent of the time. Nearly the opposite situation exists during December in Portland, Oregon, where forecasters would be correct about 90 percent of the time by predicting overcast skies.

Climatological forecasting is particularly useful when making agricultural business decisions. For example, in the relatively dry north-central portion of Nebraska known as the Sand Hills, the implementation of center-pivot irrigation made growing corn more feasible. However, the farmers were faced with the question of which corn hybrid to plant. A high-yield variety widely used in southeastern Nebraska (its warmest region) seemed to be the logical choice. However, review of local climatological data showed that because of the cooler temperatures in the Sand Hills, corn planted in late April would not mature until late September, when there is a 50 percent probability of an autumn frost. Farmers used this important climate information to select a hybrid that better fit the growing season in the Sand Hills.

One interesting use of climatological data is the prediction of a "White Christmas"—that is, a Christmas with one inch or more of snow on the ground. As Figure 12–8 illustrates, northern Minnesota and northern Maine have more than a 90 percent chance of experiencing a "White Christmas." By contrast, those who are in southern Florida for the holidays have a minuscule chance of experiencing snow.

Analog Method.   A somewhat more complex way to predict the weather is the **analog method,** which is based on the assumption that weather repeats itself, at least in a general way. Thus, forecasters attempt to find well-established weather patterns from the past that match (are analogous to) a current event. From such a comparison forecasters predict how the current weather might evolve.

Prior to the advent of computer modeling, the analog method was the backbone of weather forecasting. Even today, an analog method called *pattern recognition* is used to improve upon short-range machine-generated forecasts.

based on the tendency of weather to remain unchanged for several hours or even days. If it is raining at a particular location, for example, it might be reasonable to assume that it will still be raining in a few hours. Persistence forecasts do not account for changes that might occur in the intensity or direction of a weather system, nor can they predict the formation or dissipation of storms. Because of these limitations and the rapidity with which weather systems change, persistence forecasts usually diminish in accuracy within 6–12 hours, or one day at the most.

Climatological Forecasting.   Another relatively simple way of generating forecasts uses climatological data—average weather statistics accumulated over many years. This method is known as **climatological forecasting.** Consider, for example, that Yuma, Arizona, experiences sunshine approximately 90 percent of its daylight hours; thus, forecasters predicting sunshine every day of the year

FIGURE 12-8 Probability (in percent) of a "White Christmas," that is, a Christmas in which at least 1 inch of snow is on the ground. *(Data from the U.S. Department of Commerce)*

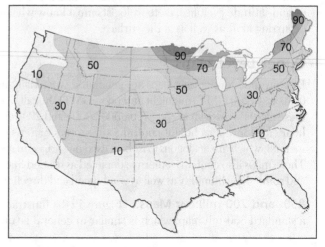

Trend Forecasting. Another related method, **trend forecasting,** involves determining the speed and direction of features such as fronts, cyclones, and areas of clouds and precipitation. Using this information, forecasters attempt to extrapolate the future position of these weather phenomena. For example, if a line of thunderstorms is moving toward the northeast at 35 miles per hour, a trend forecast would predict that the storm will reach a community located 70 miles to the northeast in about two hours.

Because weather events tend to increase or decrease in speed and intensity or change direction, trend forecasting is most effective over periods of just a few hours. Thus, it works particularly well for forecasting severe weather events that are expected to be short-lived, such as hailstorms, tornadoes, and microbursts, because warnings for such events must be issued quickly and be site-specific. The techniques used for this work, often called **nowcasting,** are heavily dependent on weather radar and geostationary satellites. These tools are important in detecting areas of heavy precipitation or clouds that are capable of triggering severe conditions. Nowcasting techniques use highly interactive computers capable of integrating data from a variety of sources. Prompt forecasting of tornadic winds is one example of the critical nature of nowcasting techniques.

In summary, weather forecasts are produced using several methods. The National Weather Service uses numerical weather prediction to generate prognostic charts for large regions. These charts are then disseminated to regional forecast centers that apply various forecasting techniques as well as the experienced judgment of meteorologists to generate area-specific forecasts.

Upper Airflow and Weather Forecasting

In Chapter 9 we demonstrated that a strong connection exists between cyclonic disturbances at the surface and the wavy flow of the westerlies aloft. The importance of this connection cannot be overstated, particularly as it applies to weather forecasting. In order to understand the development of thunderstorms or the formation and movement of mid-latitude cyclones, meteorologists must know what is occurring aloft as well as at the surface.

Upper-Level Maps

By convention, upper-air maps are generated twice daily, at 0000 and 1200 GMT (midnight and noon GMT). Recall that these charts are drawn at 850-, 700-, 500-, 300-, and 200-millibar (mb) levels as height contours (in meters or tens of meters), which are analogous to isobars used on surface maps. These maps also contain isotherms, depicted as dashed lines, and some show humidity as well as wind speed and direction.

850- and 700-millibar Maps. Figure 12–9a illustrates a standard 850-mb map, which is similar in general layout

to a 700-mb map. Both maps show height contours using solid black lines at 30-meter intervals and isotherms labeled in degrees Celsius. If relative humidity is depicted, levels above 70 percent are shown in green. Wind data is plotted using black arrows.

The 850-mb map depicts the atmosphere at an average height of about 1500 meters (1 mile) above sea level. In nonmountainous areas, this level is above the layer where daily temperature fluctuations are strongly influenced by the warming and cooling of Earth's surface. (In areas where elevations are high, such as Denver, Colorado, the 850-mb level represents surface conditions.)

Forecasters regularly examine the 850-mb map to find areas of *cold-air and warm-air advection*. Cold-air advection occurs where winds blow across isotherms from colder areas toward warmer areas. The 850-mb map in Figure 12–9b shows a blast of cold air moving south from Canada into the Mississippi Valley. Notice that the isotherms (red dashed lines) in this region of the country are packed tightly together, which means the affected area will experience a rapid drop in temperature.

By contrast, warm-air advection is occurring along the Eastern Seaboard of the United States. In addition to moving warm air into a cooler region, warm-air advection is generally associated with widespread lifting in the lower troposphere. If the humidity in the region of warm-air advection is relatively high, then lifting could result in cloud formation and possibly precipitation (Figure 12–9c).

The temperatures occurring at the 850-mb level also provide useful information. During the winter, for example, forecasters use the 0°C isotherm as the boundary between areas of rain and areas of snow or sleet. Further, because air at the 850 mb level does not experience the daily cycle of temperature changes that occurs at the surface, these maps provide a way to estimate the daily maximum surface temperature. In summer, the maximum surface temperature is usually 15°C (27°F) higher than the temperature at the 850-mb level. In winter, maximum surface temperatures tend to be about 9°C (16°F) warmer than at the 850-mb level.

In addition to serving as a proxy for the 850-mb map in areas of high elevation, the 700-mb map has other uses as well. The 700-mb flow, which occurs about 3 kilometers (2 miles) above sea level, serves as the steering mechanism for air-mass thunderstorms. Thus, winds at this level are used to predict the movement of these weather producers. One rule of thumb used with these charts is that when temperatures at the 700-mb level are 14°C (57°F) or higher, thunderstorms will not develop. A warm 700-mb layer acts as a lid inhibiting the upward movement of warm, moist surface air that might otherwise rise to generate towering cumulonimbus clouds. The cause of these warm conditions aloft is generally subsidence associated with a strong high-pressure center.

500-millibar Maps. The 500-mb level is found approximately 5.5 kilometers (18,000 feet) above sea level. Here, about half of Earth's atmosphere is below and half is

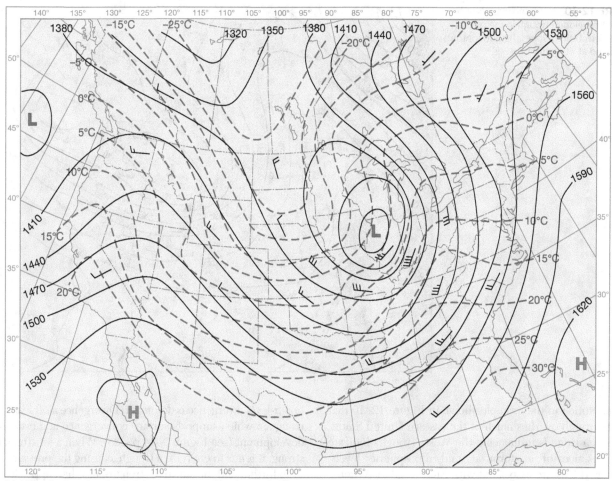

(a) 850–mb map showing height contours and isotherms in °C

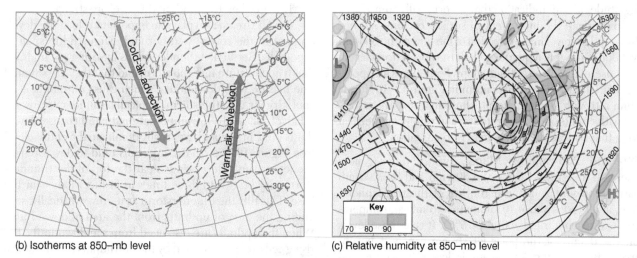

(b) Isotherms at 850–mb level

(c) Relative humidity at 850–mb level

FIGURE 12-9 A typical 850-mb map. (a) The solid lines are height contours spaced at 30-meter intervals, and the dashed lines are isotherms in degrees Celsius. (b) Areas of warm- and cold-air advection are shown with colored arrows. (c) Regions where the relative humidity is greater than 70 percent are depicted in shades of green.

FIGURE 12-10 A 500-mb map. Notice the well developed trough in the central and eastern United States. Height contours are spaced at 60 meter intervals.

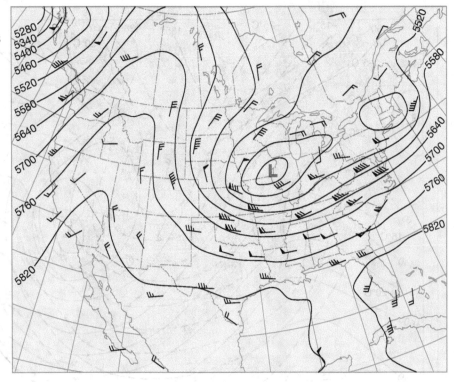

above. Notice in the example shown in Figure 12–10 that a large trough overlies much of the eastern United States, whereas a ridge is influencing the West. Troughs indicate the presence of a storm at mid-tropospheric levels, whereas ridges are associated with calm weather. When a prog (forecast chart) predicts a trough will increase in magnitude, it is an indication that a storm will intensify.

To estimate the movement of surface cyclonic storms, which tend to travel in the direction of the flow at the 500-mb level but at roughly a quarter to half the speed, forecasters find it useful to rely on 500-mb maps. Sometimes an upper-level low (shown as a closed contour in Figure 12–10) forms within a trough. When present, these features are associated with counterclockwise rotation and significant vertical lifting that typically results in heavy precipitation.

300- and 200-millibar Maps   Two of the regularly generated upper-level maps, the 300-mb and the 200-mb charts, represent zones near the top of the troposphere. Here, at altitudes above 10 kilometers (6 miles), temperatures can reach a frigid –60°C (–75°F). It is at these levels that the details of the polar jet stream can best be observed. Because the jet stream is lower in winter and higher in summer, 300-mb maps are most useful during winter and early spring, whereas the 200-mb maps are best during the warm season.

In order to show airflow aloft, these maps often plot **isotachs,** which are lines of equal wind speed. Areas exhibiting the highest wind speeds may also be colored, as shown in Figure 12–11. These segments of higher-velocity winds found within the jet stream are called **jet streaks.**

The 200- and 300-mb charts are important to forecasters for several reasons. Recall that jet streams have regions where

upper-level divergence is dominant. Divergence aloft leads to rising air, which supports surface convergence and cyclonic development (see Figure 9–14 p. 288). When a jet streak is strong, it tends to energize a trough, causing the pressure to drop further and the storm to strengthen. When upper-level winds are weak, surface cyclonic storms tend to move more slowly than when the winds at this level are strong.

The jet stream also plays an important role in the development of the severe weather and extended life span of supercells. Recall that thunderstorms have areas of updrafts that feed moisture into the storm and that they are situated side by side with downdrafts, which cause entrainment of cool, dry air into the storm. Typically, thunderstorms are relatively short-lived events that dissipate because downdrafts grow in size and eventually dominate the entire cloud (see Figure 10–4 p. 288). Supercells tend to develop near the jet stream where winds near the top of the thunderstorm may be two to three times as fast as winds near the base. This tilts the thunderstorm as it grows vertically, separating the area of updrafts from the area of downdrafts. When the updrafts are displaced from the downdrafts, the rising cells are not canceled by the downdrafts and the storm grows in intensity.

The Connection Between Upper-Level Flow and Surface Weather

Up to this point, we have considered the relationship between upper-level flow and short-lived weather phenomena—for example, how winds aloft steer and support the growth of thunderstorms. Next we will examine long-period changes that occur in the wavy flow of the westerlies and see how that behavior impacts our weather. Recall that

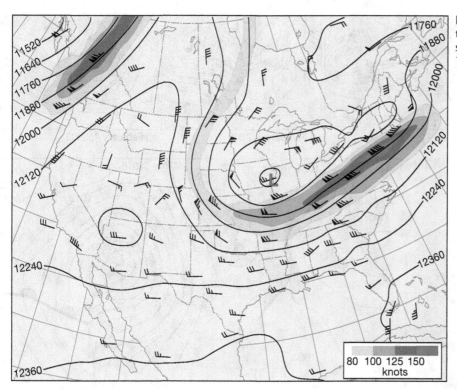

FIGURE 12-11 A 200-mb map showing the locatin of the jet stream (pink) and a jet streak (red). Height contours are spaced at 120-meter intervals.

mid-latitude winds are generated by temperature contrasts that are most extreme where warm tropical air clashes with cold, polar air. The boundary between these two contrasting air masses is the site of the polar jet stream, which is embedded in the meandering westerly flow near the top of the troposphere.

Occasionally, the flow within the westerlies is directed along a relatively straight path from west to east, a pattern referred to as *zonal*. Storms embedded in this zonal flow are quickly carried across the country, particularly in winter. This situation results in rapidly changing weather conditions in which periods of light to moderate precipitation are followed by brief periods of fair weather.

More often, however, the flow aloft consists of long-wave troughs and ridges that have large components of north–south flow, a pattern that meteorologists refer to as *meridional*. Typically, these airflow patterns slowly drift from west to east, but occasionally they stall and sometimes may even reverse direction. As this wavy pattern gradually migrates eastward, cyclonic storms embedded in the flow are carried across the country.

Figure 12–12 shows a trough that on February 1, 2003, was centered off the Pacific Coast. Over the next four days the trough grew in strength as it moved eastward into the Ohio Valley. This change in intensity is shown by the height contours, which are more closely packed around the trough on February 4 as compared to February 1. Embedded in this upper-level trough was a cyclonic system, which grew into the major storm that is shown on the surface map in Figure 12–12f. By February 5, this disturbance generated considerable precipitation over much of the eastern U.S. (Notice that the center of the surface low is located some-

what to the east of the 500-mb trough—something typical of these weather patterns.)

In general, high-amplitude patterns have the potential for generating extreme conditions. During winter, strong troughs tend to spawn large snowstorms, whereas in summer they are associated with severe thunderstorms and tornado outbreaks. By contrast, high-amplitude ridges are associated with record heat in summer and tend to bring mild conditions in winter.

Sometimes these "looped" patterns stall over an area, causing surface patterns to change very little from one day to another or, in extreme cases, from one week to another. Locations in and just east of a stationary or slow-moving trough experience extended periods of rainy or stormy conditions. By contrast, areas in and just east of a stagnant ridge experience prolonged periods of unseasonably warm, dry weather.

The strength and position of the polar jet stream fluctuate seasonally. The jet is strongest (faster wind speeds) in winter and early spring when the contrast between the warm tropics and the cold polar realm is greatest. As summer approaches and the temperature gradient diminishes, the westerlies weaken. The position of the jet stream also changes with the migration of the Sun's vertical rays. With the approach of winter, the mean position of the jet moves toward the equator. By midwinter, it may penetrate as far south as central Florida. Because the paths of mid-latitude cyclones shift with the flow aloft, we can expect the southern tier of states to encounter most of their severe weather in the winter and spring. (We are not considering the impact of hurricanes, which are tropical cyclones associated with high surface temperatures over the ocean.) During the

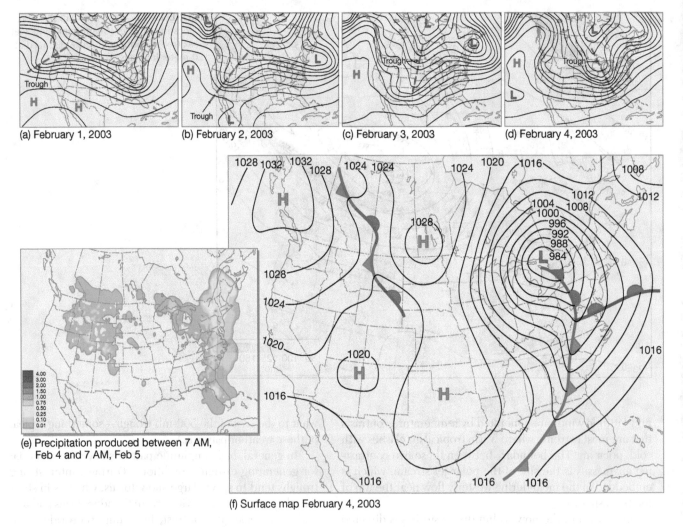

(a) February 1, 2003 (b) February 2, 2003 (c) February 3, 2003 (d) February 4, 2003

(e) Precipitation produced between 7 AM, Feb 4 and 7 AM, Feb 5

(f) Surface map February 4, 2003

FIGURE 12-12 The movement and intensification of an upper-level trough over a four-day period from February 1 to February 4, 2003. The surface map shows a strong cyclonic storm that formed and moved in conjunction with this trough.

summer, because of a poleward shift of the jet, the northern states and Canada experience an increase in the number of severe storms and tornadoes. This more northerly storm track also carries most Pacific storms toward Alaska during the warm months, producing a rather long, dry summer season for much of the Pacific Coast to the south.

The position of the jet stream relative to where you live is important for other reasons. In winter, should the jet stream move considerably south of your location, you will experience a "cold snap" as frigid air from Canada moves in. During the summer, by contrast, the core of the jet tends to be positioned over Canada, and warm, moist tropical air dominates much of the United States east of the Rockies. If, during the winter or early spring, strong cyclonic storms carried by the flow aloft pass immediately south of your location, expect cyclonic disturbances to bring heavy snowfall and cooler conditions. In summer, if the jet is overhead, periods of heavy rain, and perhaps hail and tornadic winds, may occur.

An Extreme Winter. Let us consider an example of the influence of the flow aloft for an extended period during a atypical winter. During a normal January an upper-air ridge tends to be situated over the Rocky Mountains, while a trough extends across the eastern two-thirds of the United States. In January 1977, however, the normal flow pattern was greatly accentuated, as illustrated in Figure 12–13. The greater amplitude of the upper-level flow caused an almost continuous influx of cold air into the Deep South, producing record-low temperatures throughout much of the eastern and central United States (Figure 12–14). Because of dwindling natural-gas supplies, many industries experienced layoffs. Much of Ohio was hit so hard that four-day workweeks and massive shutdowns were ordered.

While most of the East and South were in the deep freeze, the westernmost states were being influenced by a strong ridge of high pressure. Generally mild temperatures and clear skies dominated their weather. This was no

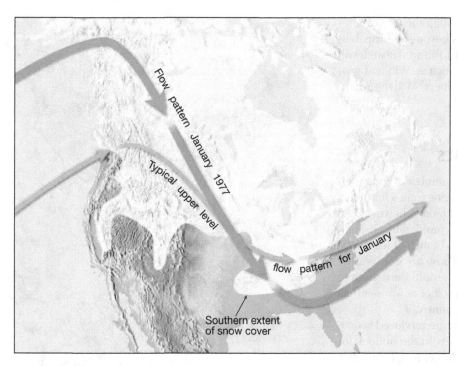

FIGURE 12-13 The unusually high amplitude experienced in the flow pattern of the prevailing westerlies during the winter of 1977 brought warmth to Alaska, drought to the west, and frigid temperatures to the central and eastern United States.

Flow pattern January 1977

Typical upper level

flow pattern for January

Southern extent of snow cover

blessing, because the ridge of high pressure blocked the movement of Pacific storms that usually provide much needed winter precipitation. The shortage of moisture was especially serious in California, where January is the middle of its three-month rainy season.

Throughout most of the western states, the winter rain and snow that supply water for summer irrigation were far below normal. This dilemma was compounded by the fact that the previous year's precipitation had also been far below normal and many reservoirs were almost empty. Although much of the country was concerned about economic disaster caused either by a lack of moisture or frigid tempera-

tures, the highly accentuated flow pattern channeled unseasonably warm air into Alaska. Even Fairbanks, which generally experiences temperatures as low as –40°C (–40°F), had a mild January, with numerous days above freezing.[*]

In summary, the wavy flow aloft governs, to a large extent, the overall magnitude and distribution of weather disturbances observed in the mid-latitudes. Thus, accurate forecasts depend on our ability to predict long- and short-term

[*]For an excellent review of the winter weather of 1976–1977, see Thomas Y. Canby, "The Year the Weather Went Wild," *National Geographic*, 152, no. 6 (1977), 798–892.

FIGURE 12-14 Arctic air invades the eastern United States. *(Photo by Seth Resnick, Stock Boston).*

changes in the upper-level flow. Although the task of forecasting long-term variations remains beyond the capabilities of meteorologists, it is hoped that future research will allow forecasters to answer questions such as: Will next winter be colder or warmer than recent winters? Will the Southwest experience a drought next year?

Long-Range Forecasts

The National Weather Service issues a number of computer-generated forecasts for time spans ranging from a few hours to more than two weeks. Beyond seven days, however, the accuracy of these forecasts diminishes considerably. In addition, the Climate Prediction Center, a branch of the NWS, produces *30- and 90-day outlooks*. These are not weather forecasts in the usual sense. Instead, they offer insights into whether it will be drier or wetter, and colder or warmer than normal in a particular region of the country.

A series of thirteen 90-day outlooks are produced in one-month increments. The series begins with the outlook for the next three months—for example, November, December, and January. Next, a separate 90-day outlook for the period beginning one month later (December, January, and February) is constructed. Figure 12–15 shows the temperature and precipitation 90-day outlooks issued for November, December, and January (2005–06). The temperature outlook for this period calls for warmer-than-usual conditions across much of the western United States. The remainder of the country is labeled "equal chance," which indicates there are not climatic signals for either above or below normal conditions during the forecast period (Figure 12–15a). As shown in Figure 12–15b, the precipitation outlook calls for wetter-than-normal conditions across most of Arkansas, Louisiana, and eastern Texas, whereas drier-than-normal conditions are expected in much of the Southwest from New Mexico to southern California.

Monthly and seasonal outlooks of this type are generated using a variety of criteria. Meteorologists consider the climatology of each region—the 30-year average of variables such as temperature. Factors such as snow and ice cover in the winter and persistently dry or wet soils in the summer are all taken into account. Forecasters also consider current patterns of temperature and precipitation. For example, over the past few years the southwestern United States has experienced below-normal levels of precipitation. Based on climatological data, the weather patterns that produce these conditions tend to gradually move toward the norm rather than making an abrupt change. Thus, forecasters predicted that this below-normal trend would continue for at least the next few months. Naturally, other climatological factors also have to be considered before a seasonal outlook is issued.

Recently, the relationship between sea-surface temperatures and patterns in the flow aloft have been shown to be particularly significant in making skillful seasonal forecasts for many parts of the world. For this reason, a great deal of

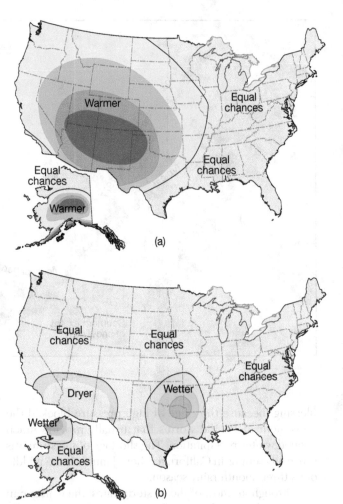

FIGURE 12-15 Extended forecast (90-day outlook) for (a) temperature and (b) precipitation for November, December, and January 2005–06. "Equal chances" means that there are not climatic signals for either above- or below-normal conditions.

emphasis is placed on monitoring and assessing oceanic conditions in the tropical Pacific, where El Niño / La Niña episodes have their roots. Although warm episodes (El Niño) have their greatest impact on Indonesia, Australia, and South America, they also influence conditions in regions outside the tropical Pacific, such as southern Africa and North America. During El Niño episodes, the westerlies increase in strength (especially during the winter) and produce above-normal precipitation over southern California and along the Gulf Coast states. In addition, warmer-than-average temperatures are the rule in the northern half of the United States. By contrast, cold (La Niña) episodes tend to result in weaker and more variable flow in the westerlies of both hemispheres.

Despite improved seasonal outlooks, the reliability of extended forecasts has been disappointing. Although some forecast skill is observed during the late winter and late summer, outlooks prepared for the "transition months," when the weather can fluctuate wildly, have shown little reliability.

Forecast Accuracy

Never, no matter what the progress of science, will honest scientific men who have a regard for their professional reputations venture to predict the weather.

Dominique François Arago

French physicist (1786–1853)

Some might argue that Arago's statement is still true! Nevertheless, a great deal of scientific and technological progress has been made in the two centuries since this observation. Today accurate weather forecasts and warnings of extreme weather conditions are provided by the U.S. National Weather Service (Figure 12–16). Their forecasts are used by government agencies to protect life and property, by electric utilities and farmers, by the construction industry, travelers, airlines—in other words, nearly everyone.

How does the NWS measure the **skill** of its forecasts? In determining the occurrence of precipitation, for example, NWS forecasts are correct more than 80 percent of the time. Does this mean the NWS is doing a great job? Not necessarily. When establishing the skill of a forecaster, we need to examine more than the percentage of accurate forecasts. For example, measurable precipitation in Los Angeles is recorded only 11 days each year, on average. Therefore, the chance of rain in Los Angeles is 11 out of 365, or about 3 percent. Knowing this, a forecaster could predict no rain for every day of the year and be correct 97 percent of the time! Although the accuracy would be high, it would not indicate skill.

Any measure of forecasting skill must consider climatic data. Thus, if a forecaster is to exhibit forecasting skill, he or she must do better than forecasts that are based simply on climatic averages. In the Los Angeles example, the forecaster must be able to predict rain on at least a few of the rainy days to demonstrate forecasting skill.

The only aspect of the weather that is predicated as a percentage probability is rainfall (see Box 12–4). Here statistical data are studied to determine how often precipitation occurred under similar conditions. Although the fact that precipitation will take place can be predicted with better than 80 percent accuracy, predictions of the amount and time of occurrence are not as reliable.

Just how skillful are the weather forecasts provided by the National Weather Service? In general, very short-range forecasts (0 to 12 hours) have demonstrated considerable skill, especially for predicting the formation and movement of large weather systems like mid-latitude cyclones. The so-called short-range forecasts (12 to 72 hours) are much better at predicting precipitation amounts than forecasts made only two decades ago. However, the exact distribution of precipitation is tied to mesoscale structures, such as individual thunderstorms, that cannot be predicted by the current numerical models.

Thus, a forecast could predict 2 inches of rain for an area, but one town might receive only a trace while a neighboring community is deluged with 4 inches. Predictions of maximum and minimum temperatures and wind, in contrast, are quite accurate. Medium-range forecasts (3 to 7 days) have also shown significant improvement in the last few decades. Large cyclonic storms, such as the 1993 East Coast blizzard described at the beginning of Chapter 9, are often predicted a few days in advance. Yet, beyond day seven, the predictability of day-to-day weather using these modern methods proves no more accurate than projections made from climatic data.

The reasons for the limited range of modern forecasting techniques are many. As noted, the network of observing stations is incomplete. Not only are large areas of Earth's land–sea surface monitored inadequately, but on a global scale data from the middle and upper troposphere is meager. Moreover, the physical laws governing the atmosphere

FIGURE 12-16
Meterologist at the National Hurricane Center, in Miami Florida examining satellite imagery of Hurricane Ivan as the eye crosses the Alabama coastline on September 16, 2004. *(Photo by Andy Newman/ Associated Press)*

BOX 12-4   Precipitation Probability Forecasts*

Many of us are satisfied with a precipitation forecast that simply tells us whether rain is likely or not (Figure 12–F). In traditional precipitation forecasts like these, the inherent uncertainty is expressed using qualifiers such as "chance" and "likely." However, such vague terminology is subject to a wide range of misinterpretations by everyone. Moreover, compared to the use of probabilities to express level of uncertainty, traditional forecast terminology is imprecise and often ambiguous. To overcome these shortcomings, the National Weather Service instituted *precipitation probability forecasts* in 1965.

Probability refers to the chance that an event will occur and is represented as a number between 0 (the probability of an impossible one) and 1 (the probability of an inevitable one). Probability can also be expressed as a percentage, so that a 0.3 chance of an event occurring is expressed as 30 percent. This expresses the idea of probability in terms that people quickly understand.

In forecasting, probability is the percentage chance that at least 0.01 inch (0.025 cm) of precipitation will fall at *any point* in the area during the time period covered by the forecast. Thus, a 70 percent probability indicates a 7 in 10 chance of precipitation, and a 3 in 10 chance of no measurable precipitation at any location in the forecast area. In general, these forecasts cover 12-hour periods and moderate-sized metropolitan areas.

Unfortunately, most people interpret this forecast to mean that there

FIGURE 12-F Umbrellas serve as safe haven in rainy weather. *(Photo by Roy Morsch/The Stock Market)*

is a 70 percent chance of precipitation somewhere in the forecast area, and a 30 percent chance that it will not occur anywhere in that area. This is not the case.

In actuality, this forecast states that at any point in the forecast area (for example, your home), there is a 70 percent chance of measurable precipitation.

Further, the chance of a shower occurring at a specific site is the product of two quantities: the probability that a precipitation-producing storm will develop or move into the area and the percent of the area that the storm is expected to cover.

For example, a forecaster can have a high degree of confidence that a storm will move into an area (say, 80 percent), but determine that

only 40 percent of the area will be affected. Under these conditions, the forecaster will call for a 30 percent chance of precipitation ($0.80 \times 0.40 = 0.32$, or about 30 percent). Although precipitation is nearly certain, the chance that it will affect you, wherever you are in the forecast area, is only 3 in 10. Consequently, in the summer, when storms are frequently isolated or scattered, the probability that your immediate area will have rain tends to be smaller than during the winter months when storms are more widespread.

*The information presented here is based on a National Weather Service publication "Precipitation Probability Forecasts" and an article by Allan H. Murphy et al., "Misinterpretations of Precipitation Probability Forecasts," *Bulletin of the American Meteorological Society*, 61, no. 6 (June), 695–700.

are not fully understood and the current models of the atmosphere remain incomplete.

Nevertheless, numerical weather prediction has greatly improved the forecaster's ability to project changes in the upper-level flow. When the flow aloft can be tied more closely to surface conditions, weather forecasts should show even greater skill.

The following abridged version of a policy statement by the American Meteorological Society summarizes the predictive skill of weather forecasts.

1. *Very short-range forecasts (0-12 hours).* These forecasts have shown considerable skill and utility, especially for predictions of the evolution and movement of large- and medium-sized weather systems. However, the accuracy of the forecasts decreases rapidly as the scale of the weather features decreases and the time range of the forecasts increases. Forecasting the evolution and movement of smaller-scale, short-lived, often intense weather phenomena such as tornadoes, hail storms, and flash floods is less mature than for predictions of larger-scale weather systems.

   Despite the difficulties in predicting these small-scale phenomena, the lead time of watches and warnings has increased. For example, the lead time for tornado warnings has more than doubled in the last decade due to the improved observing systems provided by the NWS operational Doppler radar network and satellite imagery. These warnings and watches rely heavily on observing and detecting when conditions are favorable for the development of severe convection and then monitoring each storm's evolution.

2. *Short-range forecasts (12–72 hours).* The accuracy of short-range forecasts (12–72 hours) has continued to increase during the past decade. Improvements in observing systems and in how the data are assimilated into the computer models have resulted in steady improvement in the ability to predict the evolution of major, larger-scale weather systems. Accurate predictions of the development and movement of large-scale weather systems and the associated day-to-day variations in temperature, precipitation, cloudiness, and air quality are made regularly throughout this time range.

   Forecasts of how much precipitation will fall in the 36–60-hour time frame are now more accurate than 12–36-hour predictions were during the late 1970s. However, the details of precipitation patterns are often tied to smaller-scale structures such as fronts, thunderstorm outflow boundaries, and mesoscale convective systems that are still difficult for the current generation of numerical models to simulate.

3. *Medium-range forecasts (3–7 days into the future).* Medium-range forecasts have shown significant improvement in the last two decades. Large-scale events like the East Coast blizzards of 1993 and 1996 are now often forecast days in advance of the first flake of snow, allowing emergency managers the opportunity to make plans to mitigate potential life-threatening situations that might develop. Three-day forecasts of major low-pressure systems that determine the general evolution of the weather are more skillful today than 36-hour forecasts were 15 years ago. In the late 1970s, day 5 forecasts of precipitation were no more accurate than climatology. Since then, skill of day 5 forecasts has more than doubled, with predictions of major cyclones now being as skillful as day 3 forecasts were a decade ago.

4. *Extended-range forecasts (week 2).* The predictability of the day-to-day weather for periods beyond day 7 is usually small. Operationally, forecasts at these time ranges have taken the form of 6–10 day mean temperature and occurrence of precipitation departures from normal. (see Box 12–5) The accuracy of these five-day mean temperature and precipitation forecasts has more than doubled since the 1970s. The accuracy of precipitation forecasts is less than that for temperature, even though the skill of both has increased at about the same rate.

5. *Monthly and seasonal forecasts.* As a result of research over the last decade, monthly and seasonal forecasts of mean temperature and precipitation are now useful for specialized applications in major economic sectors, such as agricultural and energy interests, if utilized over a long period. There is reason for optimism that the utility of these long-range forecasts can be improved as computer models and statistical methods become more sophisticated. These new techniques are expected to improve monthly and seasonal outlooks, especially when the relatively strong signals associated with El Niño and La Niña events are present. Notwithstanding these advances, no verifiable skill exists or is likely to exist for forecasting day-to-day weather changes beyond two weeks. Claims to the contrary should be viewed with skepticism.*

Students Sometimes Ask . . .

Why are weather forecasts so often inaccurate?

The atmosphere is a dynamic system composed of countless interacting parts. As a result, weather forecasting is an extraordinarily complex process. Nevertheless, with the advent of high-speed computers and enhanced numerical models, meteorologists are able to produce 24-hour weather forecasts that are accurate more than 80 percent of the time. Perhaps the main reason people feel forecasts are often wrong is that they are much more likely to remember the few inaccurate forecasts that have inconvenienced them.

*From the *Bulletin of the American Meteorological Society*, 79, no. 10 (October 1998), 2161–63.

BOX 12-5   What Is "Normal"?

When we watch a weather report on TV, the person making the presentation usually lists statistics for the day. Frequently, after stating the high, low, and average temperatures, the reporter indicates whether the daily mean is above or below normal. Similarly, following a report that includes the monthly or annual precipitation total, we will be told how much of a *departure from normal* the figure represents. Sometimes the weathercaster even follows up such information with a remark informing us that the daily mean temperature or the monthly rainfall total is "much" above or below normal.

Does this mean that we are experiencing abnormal conditions? Certainly, many people would assume that the statistics are unusual or even extraordinary, because most of us perceive "normal" as implying ordinary or frequent. Such a perception arises from the common usage of the word *normal:* "Conforming, adhering to, or constituting a typical or usual standard, pattern, level or type."*

If normal does not imply ordinary or frequent, just what does it mean

when applied to meteorological observations? *Normal is simply an average of a climate element over a 30-year period.* It is a standard that is used in making comparisons. A departure from normal is the difference between currently observed values and the 30-year average. The normal is usually not the most frequent value (called the *mode*) nor the value above which half the cases fall (called the median). It is safe to say that no matter what meteorological statistic is considered, experiencing a value that equals the normal is actually the exception and not the rule (Figure 12–G).

The World Meteorological Organization has established a standard definition for the 30-year span used to compute normals:

Normals are recalculated each decade in an attempt to keep up with any climatic changes that might take place. For example, on January 1, 2001, the period for computing normals changes. Prior to that date, normals represent the period January 1, 1961, through December 31, 1990. Beginning January 1,

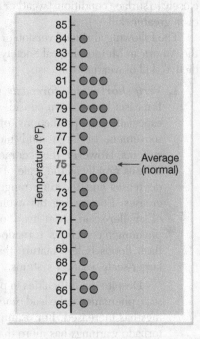

FIGURE 12-G Plot of daily mean temperatures for Peoria, Illinois, August 1993.

2001, data for the 1990s replaces the observations from the 1960s.

*From *Webster's II New Riverside University Dictionary* (Boston: Houghton Mifflin Company, 1984), p. 803.

In summary, the accuracy of weather forecasts covering short- and medium-range periods has improved steadily over the past few decades, particularly in forecasting the evolution and movement of middle-latitude cyclones. Technological developments and improved computer models, as well as an increased understanding of how the atmosphere behaves, have greatly contributed to this success. The ability to accurately predict the weather beyond day seven, however, remains poor.

Satellites in Weather Forecasting

Meteorology entered the space age on April 1, 1960, when the first weather satellite, *TIROS* 1, was launched. (*TIROS* stands for Television and Infra-Red Observation Satellite.) In its short life span of only 79 days, *TIROS* 1 transmitted

thousands of images to Earth. Nine additional *TIROS* satellites were launched by 1965. In 1964, the second-generation *Nimbus* (Latin for *cloud*) satellites had infrared sensors capable of "seeing" cloud coverage at night.

Another series of satellites was placed into polar orbits so that they circled Earth in a north-to-south direction (Figure 12–17a). These **polar satellites** orbit Earth at low altitudes (a few hundred kilometers) and require only 100 minutes per orbit. By properly orienting the orbits, these satellites drift about 15° westward over Earth's surface during each orbit. Thus, they are able to obtain images of the entire Earth twice each day and coverage of a large region in only a few hours.

By 1966 **geostationary satellites** were placed in orbit over the equator (Figure 12–17b). These satellites, as their name implies, remain fixed over a point on Earth because their rate of travel keeps pace with Earth's rate of rotation. To keep a satellite positioned over a given site, however, the

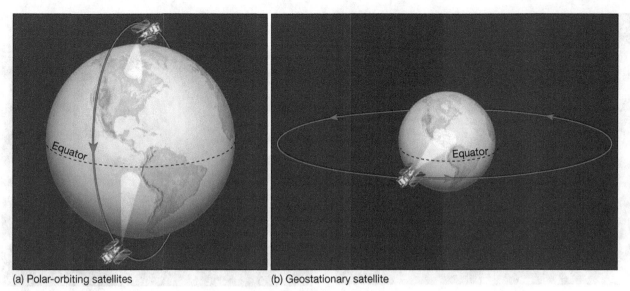

(a) Polar-orbiting satellites   (b) Geostationary satellite

FIGURE 12-17 Weather satellites. (a) Polar-orbiting satellites about 850 kilometers (530 miles) above Earth travel over the North and South poles. (b) A geostationary satellite moves west to east above the equator at a distance of 36,000 kilometers (22,300 miles) and at the same rate that Earth rotates.

satellite must orbit at a greater distance from Earth's surface (about 35,000 kilometers, or 22,000 miles). At this altitude, the speed required to keep a satellite in orbit will also keep it moving in time with the rotating Earth. However, at this distance, some detail is lost on the images.

What Weather Satellites Provide

Weather satellites greatly add to our knowledge of weather patterns and help fill gaps in observational data, especially over the oceans. For example, examine the clarity with which the clouds outline the fronts of the wave cyclone shown in Figure 9–25. These wishbone-shaped swirls are easily traced by satellites as they migrate across even the most remote portions of our planet. Moreover, as you learned in Chapter 11, satellites allow us to identify and track developing hurricanes long before they are detected by the land-based surface observational network.

Weather satellites are equipped to generate several types of images simultaneously, including visible, infrared, and water vapor images. *Visible images*, like the one shown in Figure 12–18, are views of Earth the way an astronaut would see our planet from space. The primary difference is that the satellite images are often black and white. Visible images are produced by measuring the intensity of light reflected from cloud tops and other surfaces. By contrast, *infrared images* are obtained from radiation emitted (rather than reflected) from the same objects.

Infrared images are very useful in determining regions of possible precipitation within a middle-latitude cyclone. Compare the visible image in Figure 12–18 with the infrared image in Figure 12–19. Note that in the visible image all the clouds exhibit the same intensity of white and appear very similar (Figure 12–18).

By contrast, the infrared image provides a way to determine which clouds are the most probable precipitation producers (Figure 12–19). Here, warm objects appear darker and cold objects appear lighter. Because high cloud tops are colder than low cloud tops, towering cumulonimbus clouds that may generate heavy precipitation appear very white. By contrast, the lower, thinner nimbostratus clouds that produce only medium-to-light precipitation appear darker. Thus, infrared satellite images are valuable forecasting tools. For more on this idea, see Box 2–5 "Infrared Imaging, p. 55."

Water-vapor images provide yet another way to view our planet. Most of Earth's radiation with a wavelength of 6.7 micrometers is emitted by water vapor. Therefore, satellites equipped with detectors for this narrow band of radiation are, in effect, mapping the concentration of water vapor in the atmosphere. Bright regions in Figure 12–20 translate into regions of high water-vapor concentration whereas dark areas are covered by drier air. In addition, because most fronts occur between air masses having contrasting moisture contents, water-vapor images are valuable tools for locating frontal boundaries.

The third generation of weather satellites, known as Geostationary Operational Environmental Satellites (GOES), provides visible, infrared, and water-vapor images for North America every half hour (Figure 12–21). (These are the same satellite images that often appear on The Weather Channel.) Such frequent observations allow meteorologists to track the movement of large weather systems that cannot be adequately followed by weather radar or polar-orbiting satellites. GOES has also been very important in monitoring the development and movement of tropical storms and hurricanes (Figure 12–22).

FIGURE 12-18 *GOES 8* satellite view of cloud distribution about midday on March 28, 2003. This image records visible light, much as your eyes would see it. Compare this with the infrared image in Figure 12–19. *(Courtesy of NOAA)*

FIGURE 12-19 *GOES 8* infrared image of the same cloud pattern shown in Figure 12–18. On this image, some of the clouds appear much whiter than others. These are the thicker, vertically developed clouds that have cold tops. A band of rain clouds can be seen over the north-central United States and extending into Canada. *(Courtesy of NOAA).*

Satellite Measurements

Although weather satellites are still more weather observers than weather forecasters, ingenious developments have made them more than simply TV cameras pointed at Earth from space. For example, some satellites are equipped with instruments designed to measure temperatures at various altitudes. How is this accomplished? The technique relies on the fact that different wavelengths of energy are absorbed and radiated by different layers of the atmosphere. On a clear night, for example, the atmosphere does not absorb radiation from Earth's surface that has a wavelength of 10 micrometers (recall that this is the *atmospheric window*). Thus, by measuring the radiation at 10 micrometers, we have a method of determining Earth's surface temperature. Because other wavelengths indicate the altitudes within the atmosphere from which they originate, they too can be used to measure temperatures. This method of obtaining temperature readings aloft is simpler in principle than in

FIGURE 12-20 Water-vapor image from the *GOES 10* satellite for March 19, 2003. The greater the intensity of white, the greater the atmosphere's water-vapor content. Black areas are driest. *(Courtesy of NOAA).*

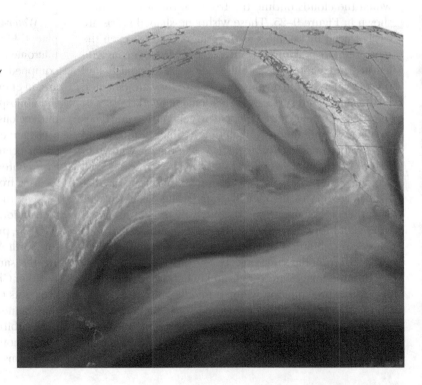

FIGURE 12-21 *GOES-N* being prepared for launch. *GOES-N* is one of three satellites that will monitor atmospheric conditions that trigger severe weather events such as tornadoes, flash floods, hailstorms, and hurricanes. *(Courtesy of NASA)*

practice, but with refinement it can supplement the limited supply of conventional radiosonde data.

Other satellites allow us to measure rainfall intensity and amounts, both at the surface and above the surface, and to monitor winds in regions where few, if any, conventional instruments are available. Images from the *Tropical Rainfall Measuring Mission (TRMM)* illustrate satellite-based precipitation measurement. For examples refer to Box 1–1, "Monitoring Earth from Space" (p. 11), and to Box 11–4, "A 3-D Look Inside a Hurricane" (p. 340). A satellite that provides data on winds is NASA's *QuickSCAT* spacecraft, which is discussed in Box 7–3, "Monitoring Winds from Space" (p. 222). It provides data that allows us to continuously map winds under most atmospheric conditions over 90 percent of Earth's ice-free oceans. Box 11–3, "Examining Hurricane Katrina from Space" (p. 334), provides excellent images from both the *TRMM* and *QuickSCAT* spacecraft.

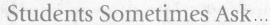

Students Sometimes Ask...

When were the first U.S. weather maps produced?

Meteorological observations were made by the U.S. Weather Bureau, the predecessor to the National Weather Service, for the first time on November 1, 1870. These observations and recordings led to the production of the first U.S. Daily Weather Map in 1871. The early maps included isobars and described the weather conditions at select locations but had little predictive value. It wasn't until the late 1930s that air-mass and frontal-analysis techniques were used by the U.S. Weather Bureau. On August 1, 1941, a new Daily Weather Map was introduced. In addition to including various types of fronts, this map made use of the station model—a group of symbols indicating weather conditions at nearly 100 locations (see Box 12–3). Although the look has changed, the basic structure of the Daily Weather Map remains largely the same today as it was over 65 year ago.

FIGURE 12-22 Weather satellites are invaluable tools for tracking storms and gathering atmospheric data. This enhanced infrared image shows Hurricane Rita approaching the Gulf Coast on September 22, 2005. *(Courtesy of NASA)*

Chapter Summary

- In the United States, the government agency responsible for gathering and disseminating weather-related information is the *National Weather Service (NWS)*. Perhaps the most important services provided by the NWS are forecasts and warnings of hazardous weather including thunderstorms, flooding, hurricanes, tornadoes, winter weather, and extreme heat.

- The process of providing weather forecasts and warnings throughout the United States occurs in three stages. First, data are collected and analyzed on a global scale. Second, a variety of techniques are used to establish the future state of the atmosphere; a process called *weather forecasting*. Finally, forecasts are disseminated to the public, mainly through the private sector.

- Assessing current atmospheric conditions, called *weather analysis*, involves collecting, transmitting, and compiling millions of pieces of observational data. On a global scale the *World Meteorological Organization* is responsible for gathering, plotting, and distributing weather data.

- Initially, weather data are displayed on a synoptic weather map. A weather map shows the status of the atmosphere and includes data on temperature, humidity, pressure, and airflow. In addition to surface maps, twice-daily upper-air charts depicting the pressure field are drawn at 850-, 700-, 500-, 300-, and 200-millibar levels.

- The methods used in weather forecasting include *numerical weather prediction, persistence forecasting, climatological forecasting*, the *analog method*, and *trend forecasting. Numerical weather prediction (NWP)* is the backbone of modern forecasting. The underlying premise of NWP is that the behavior of atmospheric gases is governed by a set of physical principals that can be expressed mathematically. Meteorologists apply current conditions to computer models that predict the future state of the atmosphere. Perhaps the simplest forecasting method, *persistence forecasting*, is based on the tendency of the weather to remain unchanged for several hours. *Climatological forecasting* uses 30-year statistical averages of weather elements, such as temperature, to make predictions. This type of forecasting is particularly useful when making agricultural decisions. Using the *analog method*, forecasters look for well-established weather patterns from the past that match a current weather event. From such comparisons meteorologists predict how the current event might evolve. *Trend forecasting* determines the speed and direction of a weather distur-

bance and, from this information, extrapolates its future position. A related technique, called *nowcasting*, uses radar and geostationary satellites to detect and track severe weather events, such as thunderstorms and tornadoes.

- For many years meteorologists have been aware of a strong correlation between cyclonic disturbances at the surface and the daily and seasonal fluctuations in the wavy flow of the westerlies aloft. Upper-air maps are generated twice daily and provide forecasters with a picture of conditions at various levels in the troposphere. These maps provide information that can be used to predict daily maximum temperature, locate areas where precipitation is likely to occur, and determine whether a thunderstorm will develop into a supercell. When the upper airflow exhibits large-amplitude waves, extreme weather is the rule. In winter strong troughs tend to spawn heavy snowstorms, whereas in summer they are associated with severe thunderstorms and tornado outbreaks. Because the position of the jet stream migrates with the Sun's vertical rays, the southern tier of states encounters most of their severe weather in winter and spring. During the summer, the northern states and Canada experience an increase in the number of strong storms and tornadoes.

- *Long-range weather forecasting* is an area that relies heavily on statistical averages obtained from past weather events, also referred to as *climatic data*. Weekly, monthly, and seasonal weather outlooks prepared by the National Weather Service are not weather forecasts in the usual sense. Rather, they indicate only whether the region will experience near-normal precipitation and temperatures or not.

- Weather forecasting relies on the validity of prognostic maps produced by computer-generated models and the skill of the forecaster. Very short-range (0–12 hours) forecasts have demonstrated considerable skill, especially for predicting the formation and movement of large weather systems. Short-range forecasts (12–72 hours) of maximum and minimum temperatures and wind speeds are quite accurate. Furthermore, predicting precipitation amounts is much better than forecasts made only two decades ago. Medium-range forecasts (3–7 days into the future) have shown significant improvement in the last 20 years. However, the accuracy of day-to-day weather forecasts for periods beyond seven days is relatively unreliable.

Vocabulary Review

analog method (p. 357)

Automated Surface Observing
 System (ASOS) (p. 348)

climatological forecasting (p. 357)

ensemble forecasting (p. 356)

geostationary satellite (p. 368)

isotachs (p. 360)

jet streaks (p. 360)

model output statistics (MOS)
 (p. 355)

National Centers for Environmental
 Prediction (p. 347)

Review Questions

1. What is the mission of the National Weather Service?
2. List the three steps involved in providing weather forecasts.
3. What is meant by *weather analysis*?
4. What information is provided by a surface weather map? (See Box 12–2.)
5. Why is the name "numerical weather forecasting" somewhat misleading?
6. Briefly describe the basis of numerical weather predictions.
7. How are prognostic charts different from synoptic weather maps?
8. What do computer-generated numerical models try to predict?
9. What is *ensemble forecasting*?
10. What additional information does an ensemble forecast provide over a traditional numerical weather prediction?
11. What method of forecasting is based on pattern recognition?
12. What term is applied to the very short-range forecasting technique that relies heavily on weather radar and satellites.
13. When forecasters predict the weather based on average weather statistics accumulated over many years, it is called _____.
14. Describe the statistical approach called the "analog method." What are its drawbacks?
15. If it is snowing today, what could be predicted for tomorrow if persistence forecasting were employed?
16. What type of weather is typically forecast using nowcasting techniques?
17. Which upper-level map is most effective for observing the polar jet stream in winter?
18. During winter, if the jet stream is considerably south of your location, will the temperatures likely be warmer or colder than normal?
19. What is a *jet streak*?
20. What are two pieces of information that forecasters can glean from 850-mb maps?
21. What elements are predicted in a long-range (monthly) weather chart?
22. Give an example of why the percent of correct forecasts is not always a good measure of forecasting skill.
23. How do satellites help identify clouds that are most likely to produce precipitation?
24. What information is provided by water-vapor images?
25. What advantage do geostationary satellites have over polar satellites? Name one disadvantage.

Problems

1. The map in Figure 12–23 has several weather stations plotted on it. Using the weather data for a typical day in March, which are given in Table 12–1, complete the following:
   a. On a copy of Figure 12–23, plot the temperature, wind direction, pressure, and sky coverage by using the international symbols given in Appendix B.
   b. Using Figure 12–D as a guide, complete this weather map by adding isobars at 4-millibar intervals, the cold front and the warm front, and the symbol for low pressure.
   c. Apply your knowledge of the weather associated with a middle-latitude cyclone in the spring of the year, and describe the weather conditions at each of the following locations:
      1. Philadelphia, Pennsylvania
      2. Quebec, Canada
      3. Toronto, Canada
      4. Sioux City, Iowa
2. Many TV weather reports include a seven-day outlook. Tune in such a report and jot down the forecast for the last (seventh) day. Then, each day thereafter, write

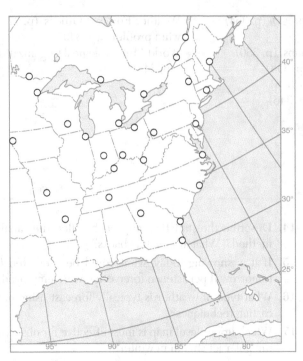

FIGURE 12-23 Map to accompany problem number 1.

down the forecast for the day in question. Finally, record what actually occurred on that day. Contrast the forecast seven days ahead with what actually took place. How accurate (or inaccurate) was the seven-day forecast for the day you selected? How accurate was the five-day forecast for this day? The two-day forecast?

3. Using Box 12–4 as a guide, calculate the precipitation probability for the following situations:

   a. There is a 50 percent chance that a storm will move into the forecast area and that it will affect 20 percent of the area.

   b. There is a 90 percent chance that a storm will move into the forecast area and that it will affect 100 percent of the area.

   c. There is a 50 percent chance that a storm will move into the forecast area and that it will affect 50 percent of the area.

Location	Temperature (°F)	Pressure (MB)	Wind direction	Sky cover (tenths)
Wilmington, N.C.	57	1009	SW	7
Philadelphia, Pa.	59	1001	S	10
Hartford, Conn.	47	1001	SE	Sky obscured
International Falls, Minn.	−12	1008	NE	0
Pittsburgh, Pa.	52	995	WSW	10
Duluth, Minn.	−1	1006	N	0
Sioux City, Iowa	11	1010	NW	0
Springfield, Mo.	35	1011	WNW	2
Chicago, Ill.	34	985	NW	10
Madison, Wis.	23	995	NW	10
Nashville, Tenn.	40	1008	SW	10
Louisville, Ky.	40	1002	SW	5
Indianapolis, Ind.	35	994	W	10
Atlanta, Ga.	49	1010	SW	7
Huntington, W.Va.	52	998	SW	6
Toronto, Canada	44	985	E	9
Albany, N.Y.	50	998	SE	7
Savanna, Ga.	63	1012	SW	10
Jacksonville, Fla.	66	1013	WSW	10
Norfolk, Va.	67	1005	S	10
Cleveland, Ohio	49	988	SW	4
Little Rock, Ark.	37	1014	WSW	0
Cincinnati, Ohio	41	997	WSW	10
Detroit, Mich.	44	984	SW	10
Montreal, Canada	42	993	E	10
Quebec, Canada	34	999	NE	Sky obscured

TABLE 12-1 Weather data for a typical March day

Atmospheric Science Online

The Atmosphere 10e web site uses the resources and flexibility of the Internet to aid in your study of the topics in this chapter. Written and developed by meteorology instructors, this site will help improve your understanding of meteorology. Visit **http://www .prenhall.com/lutgens** and click on the cover of *The Atmosphere 10e* to find:

- **Online review quizzes**
- **Critical thinking exercises**
- **Links to chapter-specific web resources**
- **Internet-wide key term searches**

http://www.prenhall.com/lutgens

TABLE A-1 The international system of units (SI)

I. Basic units

Quantity	Unit	SI symbol
Length	meter	m
Mass	kilogram	kg
Time	second	s
Electric current	ampere	A
Thermodynamic temperature	kelvin	K
Amount of substance	mole	mol
Luminous intensity	candela	cd

II. Prefixes

Prefix	Factor by which unit is multiplied	Symbol
tera	10^{12}	T
giga	10^{9}	G
mega	10^{6}	M
kilo	10^{3}	k
hecto	10^{2}	h
deka	10	da
deci	10^{-1}	d
centi	10^{-2}	c
milli	10^{-3}	m
micro	10^{-6}	μ
nano	10^{-9}	n
pico	10^{-12}	p
femto	10^{-15}	f
atto	10^{-18}	a

III. Derived units

Quantity	Units	Expression
Area	square meter	m^2
Volume	cubic meter	m^3
Frequency	hertz (Hz)	s^{-1}
Density	kilogram per cubic meter	kg/m^3
Velocity	meter per second	m/s
Angular velocity	radian per second	rad/s
Acceleration	meter per second squared	m/s^2
Angular acceleration	radian per second squared	rad/s^2
Force	newton (N)	$kg \cdot ms^2$
Pressure	newton per square meter	N/m^2
Work, energy, quantity of heat	joule (J)	$N \cdot m$
Power	watt (W)	J/s
Electric charge	coulomb (C)	$A \cdot s$
Voltage, potential difference, electromotive force	volt (V)	W/A
Luminance	candela per square meter	cd/m^2

TABLE A-2 Metric–English conversion

When you want to convert:	Multiply by:	To find:
Length		
inches	2.54	centimeters
centimeters	0.39	inches
feet	0.30	meters
meters	3.28	feet
yards	0.91	meters
meters	1.09	yards
miles	1.61	kilometers
kilometers	0.62	miles
Area		
square inches	6.45	square centimeters
square centimeters	0.15	square inches
square feet	0.09	square meters
square meters	10.76	square feet
square miles	2.59	square kilometers
square kilometers	0.39	square miles
Volume		
cubic inches	16.38	cubic centimeters
cubic centimeters	0.06	cubic inches
cubic feet	0.028	cubic meters
cubic meters	35.3	cubic feet
cubic miles	4.17	cubic kilometers
cubic kilometers	0.24	cubic miles
liters	1.06	quarts
liters	0.26	gallons
gallons	3.78	liters
Masses and Weights		
ounces	28.33	grams
grams	0.035	ounces
pounds	0.45	kilograms
kilograms	2.205	pounds

Temperature

When you want to convert degrees Fahrenheit (°F) to degrees Celsius (°C), subtract 32 degrees and divide by 1.8 (also see Table A–3).

When you want to convert degrees Celsius (°C) to degrees Fahrenheit (°F), multiply by 1.8 and add 32 degrees (see also Table A–3).

When you want to convert degrees Celsius (°C) to degrees Kelvin (K), delete the degree symbol and add 273.

When you want to convert degrees Kelvin (K) to degrees Celsius (°C), add the degree symbol and subtract 273.

TABLE A-3 Temperature conversion table. (To find either the Celsius or the Fahrenheit equivalent, locate the known temperature in the center column. Then read the desired equivalent value from the appropriate column.)

°C		°F	°C		°F	°C		°F	°C		°F
−40.0	−40	−40	−17.2	+1	33.8	5.0	41	105.8	27.2	81	177.8
−39.4	−39	−38.2	−16.7	2	35.6	5.6	42	107.6	27.8	82	179.6
−38.9	−38	−36.4	−16.1	3	37.4	6.1	43	109.4	28.3	83	181.4
−38.3	−37	−34.6	−15.4	4	39.2	6.7	44	111.2	28.9	84	183.2
−37.8	−36	−32.8	−15.0	5	41.0	7.2	45	113.0	29.4	85	185.0
−37.2	−35	−31.0	−14.4	6	42.8	7.8	46	114.8	30.0	86	186.8
−36.7	−34	−29.2	−13.9	7	44.6	8.3	47	116.6	30.6	87	188.6
−36.1	−33	−27.4	−13.3	8	46.4	8.9	48	118.4	31.1	88	190.4
−35.6	−32	−25.6	−12.8	9	48.2	9.4	49	120.2	31.7	89	192.2
−35.0	−31	−23.8	−12.2	10	50.0	10.0	50	122.0	32.2	90	194.0
−34.4	−30	−22.0	−11.7	11	51.8	10.6	51	123.8	32.8	91	195.8
−33.9	−29	−20.2	−11.1	12	53.6	11.1	52	125.6	33.3	92	197.6
−33.3	−28	−18.4	−10.6	13	55.4	11.7	53	127.4	33.9	93	199.4
−32.8	−27	−16.6	−10.0	14	57.2	12.2	54	129.2	34.4	94	201.2
−32.2	−26	−14.8	−9.4	15	59.0	12.8	55	131.0	35.0	95	203.0
−31.7	−25	−13.0	−8.9	16	60.8	13.3	56	132.8	35.6	96	204.8
−31.1	−24	−11.2	−8.3	17	62.6	13.9	57	134.6	36.1	97	206.6
−30.6	−23	−9.4	−7.8	18	64.4	14.4	58	136.4	36.7	98	208.4
−30.0	−22	−7.6	−7.2	19	66.2	15.0	59	138.2	37.2	99	210.2
−29.4	−21	−5.8	−6.7	20	68.0	15.6	60	140.0	37.8	100	212.0
−28.9	−20	−4.0	−6.1	21	69.8	16.1	61	141.8	38.3	101	213.8
−28.3	−19	−2.2	−5.6	22	71.6	16.7	62	143.6	38.9	102	215.6
−27.8	−18	−0.4	−5.0	23	73.4	17.2	63	145.4	39.4	103	217.4
−27.2	−17	+1.4	−4.4	24	75.2	17.8	64	147.2	40.0	104	219.2
−26.7	−16	3.2	−3.9	25	77.0	18.3	65	149.0	40.6	105	221.0
−26.1	−15	5.0	−3.3	26	78.8	18.9	66	150.8	41.1	106	222.8
−25.6	−14	6.8	−2.8	27	80.6	19.4	67	152.6	41.7	107	224.6
−25.0	−13	8.6	−2.2	28	82.4	20.0	68	154.4	42.2	108	226.4
−24.4	−12	10.4	−1.7	29	84.2	20.6	69	156.2	42.8	109	228.2
−23.9	−11	12.2	−1.1	30	86.0	21.1	70	158.0	43.3	110	230.0
−23.3	−10	14.0	−0.6	31	87.8	21.7	71	159.8	43.9	111	231.8
−22.8	−9	15.8	0.0	32	89.6	22.2	72	161.6	44.4	112	233.6
−22.2	−8	17.6	+0.6	33	91.4	22.8	73	163.4	45.0	113	235.4
−21.7	−7	19.4	1.1	34	93.2	23.3	74	165.2	45.6	114	237.2
−21.1	−6	21.2	1.7	35	95.0	23.9	75	167.0	46.1	115	239.0
−20.6	−5	23.0	2.2	36	96.8	24.4	76	168.8	46.7	116	240.8
−20.0	−4	24.8	2.8	37	98.6	25.0	77	170.6	47.2	117	242.6
−19.4	−3	26.6	3.3	38	100.4	25.6	78	172.4	47.8	118	244.4
−18.9	−2	28.4	3.9	39	102.2	26.1	79	174.2	48.3	119	246.2
−18.3	−1	30.2	4.4	40	104.0	26.7	80	176.0	48.9	120	248.0
−17.8	0	32.0									

TABLE A-4 Wind-conversion table (Wind-speed units: 1 mile per hour = 0.868391 knot = 1.609344 km/h = 0.44704 m/s)

Miles per hour	Knots	Meters per second	Kilometers per hour	Miles per hour	Knots	Meters per second	Kilometers per hour
1	0.9	0.4	1.6	51	44.3	22.8	82.1
2	1.7	0.9	3.2	52	45.2	23.2	83.7
3	2.6	1.3	4.8	53	46.0	23.7	85.3
4	3.5	1.8	6.4	54	46.9	24.1	86.9
5	4.3	2.2	8.0	55	47.8	24.6	88.5
6	5.2	2.7	9.7	56	48.6	25.0	90.1
7	6.1	3.1	11.3	57	49.5	25.5	91.7
8	6.9	3.6	12.9	58	50.4	25.9	93.3
9	7.8	4.0	14.5	59	51.2	26.4	95.0
10	8.7	4.5	16.1	60	52.1	26.8	96.6
11	9.6	4.9	17.7	61	53.0	27.3	98.2
12	10.4	5.4	19.3	62	53.8	27.7	99.8
13	11.3	5.8	20.9	63	54.7	28.2	101.4
14	12.2	6.3	22.5	64	55.6	28.6	103.0
15	13.0	6.7	24.1	65	56.4	29.1	104.6
16	13.9	7.2	25.7	66	57.3	29.5	106.2
17	14.8	7.6	27.4	67	58.2	30.0	107.8
18	15.6	8.0	29.0	68	59.1	30.4	109.4
19	16.5	8.5	30.6	69	59.9	30.8	111.0
20	17.4	8.9	32.2	70	60.8	31.3	112.7
21	18.2	9.4	33.8	71	61.7	31.7	114.3
22	19.1	9.8	35.4	72	62.5	32.2	115.9
23	20.0	10.3	37.0	73	63.4	32.6	117.5
24	20.8	10.7	38.6	74	64.3	33.1	119.1
25	21.7	11.2	40.2	75	65.1	33.5	120.7
26	22.6	11.6	41.8	76	66.0	34.0	122.3
27	23.4	12.1	43.5	77	66.9	34.4	123.9
28	24.3	12.5	45.1	78	67.7	34.9	125.5
29	25.2	13.0	46.7	79	68.6	35.3	127.1
30	26.1	13.4	48.3	80	69.5	35.8	128.7
31	26.9	13.9	49.9	81	70.3	36.2	130.4
32	27.8	14.3	51.5	82	71.2	36.7	132.0
33	28.7	14.8	53.1	83	72.1	37.1	133.6
34	29.5	15.2	54.7	84	72.9	37.6	135.2
35	30.4	15.6	56.3	85	73.8	38.0	136.8
36	31.3	16.1	57.9	86	74.7	38.4	138.4
37	32.1	16.5	59.5	87	75.5	38.9	140.0
38	33.0	17.0	61.2	88	76.4	39.3	141.6
39	33.9	17.4	62.8	89	77.3	39.8	143.2
40	34.7	17.9	64.4	90	78.2	40.2	144.8
41	35.6	18.3	66.0	91	79.0	40.7	146.5
42	36.5	18.8	67.6	92	79.9	41.1	148.1
43	37.3	19.2	69.2	93	80.8	41.6	149.7
44	38.2	19.7	70.8	94	81.6	42.0	151.3
45	39.1	20.1	72.4	95	82.5	42.5	152.9
46	39.9	20.6	74.0	96	83.4	42.9	154.5
47	40.8	21.0	75.6	97	84.2	43.4	156.1
48	41.7	21.5	77.2	98	85.1	43.8	157.7
49	42.6	21.9	78.9	99	86.0	44.3	159.3
50	43.4	22.4	80.5	100	86.8	44.7	160.9

B EXPLANATION AND DECODING OF THE DAILY WEATHER MAP

GEODe Introduction to the Atmosphere

▶ In the Lab: Reading Weather Maps

Weather maps showing the development and movement of weather systems are among the most important tools used by the weather forecaster. Of the several types of maps used, some portray conditions near the surface of Earth and others depict conditions at various heights in the atmosphere. Some cover the entire Northern Hemisphere and others cover only local areas as required for special purposes. The maps used for daily forecasting by the National Weather Service (NWS) are similar in many respects to the printed Daily Weather Map. At NWS offices, maps showing conditions at Earth's surface are drawn four times daily. Maps of upper-level temperature, pressure, and humidity are prepared twice each day.

Principal Surface Weather Map

To prepare the surface map and present the information quickly and pictorially, two actions are necessary: (1) weather observers at many places must go to their posts at regular times each day to observe the weather and send the information to the offices where the maps are drawn; (2) the information must be quickly transcribed to the maps. In order for the necessary speed and economy of space and transmission time to be realized, codes have been devised for sending the information and for plotting it on the maps.

Codes and Map Plotting

A great deal of information is contained in a brief coded weather message. If each item were named and described in plain language, a very lengthy message would be required, one confusing to read and difficult to transfer to a map. A code permits the message to be condensed to a few five-figure numeral groups, each figure of which has a meaning, depending on its position in the message. People trained in the use of the code can read the message as easily as plain language (see Figure B–1).

The location of the reporting station is printed on the map as a small circle (the station circle). A definite arrangement of the data around the station circle, called

the *station model,* is used. When the report is plotted in these fixed positions around the station circle on the weather map, many code figures are transcribed exactly as sent. Entries in the station model that are not made in code figures or actual values found in the message are usually in the form of symbols that graphically represent the element concerned. In some cases, certain of the data may or may not be reported by the observer, depending on local weather conditions. Precipitation and clouds are examples. In such cases, the absence of an entry on the map is interpreted as nonoccurrence or nonobservance of the phenomena. The letter *M* is entered where data are normally observed but not received.

Both the code and the station model are based on international agreements. These standardized numerals and symbols enable a meteorologist of one country to use the weather reports and weather maps of another country even though that person does not understand the language. Weather codes are, in effect, an international language that permits complete interchange and use of worldwide weather reports so essential in present-day activities.

The boundary between two different air masses is called a *front.* Important changes in weather, temperature, wind direction, and clouds often occur with the passage of a front. Half circles or triangular symbols or both are placed on the lines representing fronts to indicate the kind of front. The side on which the symbols are placed indicates the direction of frontal movement. The boundary of relatively cold air of polar origin advancing into an area occupied by warmer air, often of tropical origin, is called a *cold front.* The boundary of relatively warm air advancing into an area occupied by colder air is called a *warm front.* The line along which a cold front has overtaken a warm front at the ground is called an *occluded front.* A boundary between two air masses, which shows at the time of observation little tendency to advance into either the warm or cold areas, is called a *stationary front.* Air-mass boundaries are known as surface fronts when they intersect the ground and as *upper-air fronts* when they do not. Surface fronts are drawn in solid black; fronts aloft are drawn in outline only. Front symbols are given in Table B–1.

A front that is disappearing or weak and decreasing in intensity is labeled *frontolysis.* A front that is forming is la-

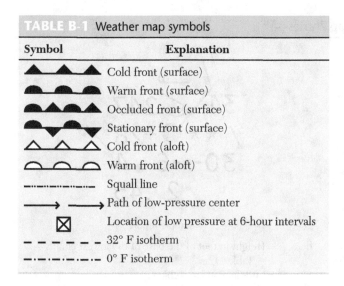

beled *frontogenesis*. A *squall line* is a line of thunderstorms or squalls usually accompanied by heavy showers and shifting winds (Table B–1).

The paths followed by individual disturbances are called *storm tracks* and are shown by arrows (Table B–1). A symbol (a box containing an X) indicates past positions of a low-pressure center at six-hour intervals. HIGH (H) and LOW (L) indicate the centers of high and low barometric pressure. Solid lines are isobars and connect points of equal sea-level barometric pressure. The spacing and orientation of these lines on weather maps are indications of speed and direction of windflow. In general, wind direction is parallel to these lines with low pressure to the left of an observer looking downwind. Speed is directly proportional to the closeness of the lines (called *pressure gradient*). Isobars are labeled in millibars.

Isotherms are lines connecting points of equal temperature. Two isotherms are drawn on the large surface weather map when applicable. The freezing, or 32° F, isotherm is drawn as a dashed line, and the 0° F, isotherm is drawn as a dash–dot line (Table B–1). Areas where precipitation is occurring at the time of observation are shaded.

Auxiliary Maps

500-Millibar Map

Contour lines, isotherms, and wind arrows are shown on the insert map for the 500-millibar contour level. Solid lines are drawn to show height above sea level and are labeled in feet. Dashed lines are drawn at 5° intervals of temperature and are labeled in degrees Celsius. True wind direction is shown by "arrows" that are plotted as flying with the wind. The wind speed is shown by flags and feathers. Each flag represents 50 knots, each full feather represents 10 knots, and each half feather represents 5 knots.

Temperature Map (Highest and Lowest)

Temperature data are entered from selected weather stations in the United States. The figure entered above the station dot shows the maximum temperature for the 12-hour period ending 7:00 P.M. EST of the previous day. The figure entered below the station dot shows the minimum temperature during the 12 hours ending at 7:00 A.M. EST. The letter *M* denotes missing data.

Precipitation Map

Precipitation data are entered from selected weather stations in the United States. When precipitation has occurred at any of these stations in the 24-hour period ending at 7:00 A.M. EST, the total amount, in inches and hundredths, is entered above the station dot. When the figures for total precipitation have been compiled from incomplete data and entered on the map, the amount is underlined. *T* indicates a trace of precipitation (less than 0.01 inch) and the letter *M* denotes missing data. The geographical areas where precipitation has fallen during the 24 hours ending at 7:00 A.M. EST are shaded. Dashed lines show depth of snow on ground in inches as of 7:00 A.M. EST.

Symbol station model

Sample report

N	Total cloud cover—Table E
dd	Wind direction
ff	Wind speed in knots or mi/hr—Table F
VV	Visibility in miles
ww	Present weather—Table H
W	Past weather—Table H
PPP	Barometric pressure reduced to sea level (add an initial 9 or 10 and place a decimal point to the left of last number)
TT	Current air temperature in °F
N_h	Fraction of sky covered by low or middle clouds—Table E (ranges from 0 for no clouds to 9 for sky obscured)
C_L	Low clouds or clouds with vertical development—Table C

h	Height in feet of the base of the lowest clouds—Table D
C_M	Middle clouds—Table C
C_H	High clouds—Table C
T_dT_d	Dewpoint temperature in °F
a	Pressure tendency—Table A
pp	Pressure change in mb in preceding 3 hrs (+28 = +2.8)
RR	Amount of precipitation in last 6 hr
R_t	Time precipitation began or ended (0 = none; 1 = <1 hr ago; 2 = 1–2 hr ago; 3 = 2–3 hr ago; 4 = 3–4 hr ago; 5 = 4–5 hr ago; 6 = 5–6 hr ago; 7 = 6–12 hr ago; 8 = >12 hr ago; 9 = unknown)

TABLE A Air pressure tendency

⟋	Rising, then falling; same as or higher than 3 hrs ago
⟍	Rising, then steady; or rising, then rising more slowly
/	Rising steadily, or unsteadily
✓	Falling or steady, then rising; or rising, then rising more rapidly
—	Steady; same as 3 hrs ago
⟍	Falling, then rising; same as or lower than 3 hrs ago
⟍	Falling, then steady; or falling, then falling more slowly
\	Falling steadily, or unsteadily
⟍	Steady or rising, then falling; or falling, then falling more rapidly

Barometric pressure now higher than 3 hours ago

Barometric pressure now lower than 3 hours ago

TABLE B Cloud abbreviations

St	stratus
Fra	fractus
Sc	stratocumulus
Ns	nimbostratus
As	altostratus
Ac	altocumulus
Ci	cirrus
Cs	cirrostratus
Cc	cirrocumulus
Cu	cumulus
Cb	cumulonimbus

TABLE C Cloud Types

Low clouds and clouds of vertical development

Cu of fair weather, little vertical development and seemingly flattened

Cu of considerable development, generally towering, with or without other Cu or Sc, bases all at same level

Cb with tops lacking clear-cut outlines, but distinctly not cirriform or anvil shaped; with or without Cu, Sc, or St

Sc formed by spreading out of Cu; Cu often present also

Sc not formed by spreading out of Cu

St or StFra, but no StFra of bad weather

StFra and/or CuFra of bad weather (scud)

Cu and Sc (not formed by spreading out of Cu) with bases at different levels

Cb having a clearly fibrous (cirriform) top, often anvil shaped, with or without Cu, Sc, St, or scud

Middle Clouds

Thin As (most of cloud layer semitransparent)

Thick As, greater part sufficiently dense to hide Sun (or Moon), or Ns

Thin Ac, mostly semitransparent; cloud elements not changing much and at a single level

Thin Ac in patches; cloud elements continually changing and/or occurring at more than one level

Thin Ac in bands or in a layer gradually spreading over sky and usually thickening as a whole

Ac formed by the spreading out of Cu or Cb

Double-layered Ac, or a thick layer of Ac, not increasing; or Ac with As and/or Ns

Ac in the form of Cu-shaped tufts or Ac with turrets

Ac of a chaotic sky, usually at different levels; patches of dense Ci usually present also

High Clouds

Filaments of Ci, or "mares' tails," scattered and not increasing

Dense Ci in patches or twisted sheaves, usually not increasing, sometimes like remains of Cb; or towers or tufts

Dense Ci, often anvil shaped, derived from or associated with Cb

Ci, often hook shaped, gradually spreading over the sky and usually thickening as a whole

Ci and Cs, often in converging bands, or Cs alone; generally overspreading and growing denser; the continuous layer not reaching 45° altitude

Ci and Cs, often in converging bands, or Cs alone; generally overspreading and growing denser; the continuous layer exceeding 45° altitude

Veil of Cs covering the entire sky

Cs not increasing and not covering entire sky

Cc alone or Cc with some Ci or Cs, but the Cc being the main cirriform cloud

TABLE D — Height of base of lowest cloud

Code	Feet	Meters
0	0–149	0–49
1	150–299	50–99
2	300–599	100–199
3	600–999	200–299
4	1000–1999	300–599
5	2000–3499	600–999
6	3500–4999	1000–1499
7	5000–6499	1500–1999
8	6500–7999	2000–2499
9	8000 or above or no clouds	2500 or above or no clouds

TABLE E — Cloud cover

○	No clouds
◔	One-tenth or less
	Two-tenths or three-tenths
	Four-tenths
◐	Five-tenths
	Six-tenths
	Seven-tenths or eight-tenths
	Nine-tenths or overcast with openings
●	Completely overcast (ten-tenths)
⊗	Sky obscured

TABLE F — Wind speed

Symbol	Knots	Miles per hour	Kilometers per hour
◎	1–2	1–2	1–3
	3–7	3–8	4–13
	8–12	9–14	14–19
	13–17	15–20	20–32
	18–22	21–25	33–40
	23–27	26–31	41–50
	28–32	32–37	51–60
	33–37	38–43	61–69
	38–42	44–49	70–79
	43–47	50–54	80–87
	48–52	55–60	88–96
	53–57	61–66	97–106
	58–62	67–71	107–114
	63–67	72–77	115–124
	68–72	78–83	125–134
	73–77	84–89	135–143
	103–107	119–123	192–198

TABLE G — Fronts

Fronts are shown on surface weather maps by the symbols below. (Arrows—not shown on maps—indicate direction of motion of front.)

↓ ▼▼▼	Cold front (surface)
↑ ●●●	Warm front (surface)
↑ ●▲●▲	Occluded front (surface)
●▼●▼	Stationary front (surface)
↑ ◠◠◠	Warm front (aloft)
↓ ▽▽▽	Cold front (aloft)

TABLE H   Weather conditions

Cloud development NOT observed or NOT observable during past hour	Clouds generally dissolving or becoming less developed during past hour	State of sky on the whole unchanged during past hour	Clouds generally forming or developing during past hour	Visibility reduced by smoke
Light fog (mist)	Patches of shallow fog at station, NOT deeper than 6 feet on land	More or less continuous shallow fog at station, NOT deeper than 6 feet on land	Lightning visible, no thunder heard	Precipitation within sight, but NOT reaching the ground
Drizzle (NOT freezing) or snow grains (NOT falling as showers) during past hour, but NOT at time of observation	Rain (NOT freezing and NOT falling as showers) during past hour, but NOT at time of observation	Snow (NOT falling as showers) during past hour, but NOT at time of observation	Rain and snow or ice pellets (NOT falling as showers) during past hour, but NOT at time of observation	Freezing drizzle or freezing rain (NOT falling as showers) during past hour, but NOT at time of observation
Slight or moderate dust storm or sandstorm has decreased during past hour	Slight or moderate dust storm or sandstorm, no appreciable change during past hour	Slight or moderate dust storm or sandstorm has begun or increased during past hour	Severe dust storm or sandstorm, has decreased during past hour	Severe dust storm or sandstorm, no appreciable change during past hour
Fog or ice fog at distance at time of observation, but NOT at station during past hour	Fog or ice fog in patches	Fog or ice fog, sky discernible, has become thinner during past hour	Fog or ice fog, sky NOT discernible, has become thinner during past hour	Fog or ice fog, sky discernible, no appreciable change during past hour
Intermittent drizzle (NOT freezing), slight at time of observation	Continuous drizzle (NOT freezing), slight at time of observation	Intermittent drizzle (NOT freezing), moderate at time of observation	Continuous drizzle (NOT freezing), moderate at time of observation	Intermittent drizzle (NOT freezing), heavy at time of observation
Intermittent rain (NOT freezing), slight at time of observation	Continuous rain (NOT freezing), slight at time of observation	Intermittent rain (NOT freezing), moderate at time of observation	Continuous rain (NOT freezing), moderate at time of observation	Intermittent rain (NOT freezing), heavy at time of observation
Intermittent fall of snowflakes, slight at time of observation	Continuous fall of snowflakes, slight at time of observation	Intermittent fall of snowflakes, moderate at time of observation	Continuous fall of snowflakes, moderate at time of observation	Intermittent fall of snowflakes, heavy at time of observation
Slight rain shower(s)	Moderate or heavy rain shower(s)	Violent rain shower(s)	Slight shower(s) of rain and snow mixed	Moderate or heavy shower(s) of rain and snow mixed
Moderate or heavy shower(s) of hail, with or without rain, or rain and snow mixed, not associated with thunder	Slight rain at time of observation; thunderstorm during past hour, but NOT at time of observation	Moderate or heavy rain at time of observation; thunderstorm during past hour, but NOT at time of observation	Slight snow, or rain and snow mixed, or hail at time of observation; thunderstorm during past hour, but NOT at time of observation	Moderate or heavy snow, or rain and snow mixed, or hail at time of observation; thunderstorm during past hour, but NOT at time of observation

TABLE H   Weather conditions

Haze	Widespread dust in suspension in the air, NOT raised by wind, at time of observation	Dust or sand raised by wind at time of observation	Well developed dust whirl(s) within past hour	Dust storm or sandstorm within sight of or at station during past hour
Precipitation within sight, reaching the ground but distant from station	Precipitation within sight, reaching the ground, near to but NOT at station	Thunderstorm, but no precipitation at the station	Squall(s) within sight during past hour or at time of observation	Funnel cloud(s) within sight of station at time of observation
Showers of rain during past hour, but NOT at time of observation	Showers of snow, or of rain and snow, during past hour, but NOT at time of observation	Showers of hail, or of hail and rain, during past hour, but NOT at time of observation	Fog during past hour, but NOT at time of observation	Thunderstorm (with or without precipitation) during past hour, but NOT at time of observation
Severe dust storm or sandstorm has begun or increased during past hour	Slight or moderate drifting snow, generally low (less than 6 ft)	Heavy drifting snow, generally low	Slight or moderate blowing snow, generally high (more than 6 ft)	Heavy blowing snow, generally high
Fog or ice fog, sky NOT discernible, no appreciable change during past hour	Fog or ice fog, sky discernible, has begun or become thicker during past hour	Fog or ice fog, sky NOT discernible, has begun or become thicker during past hour	Fog depositing rime, sky discernible	Fog depositing rime, sky NOT discernible
Continuous drizzle (NOT freezing), heavy at time of observation	Slight freezing drizzle	Moderate or heavy freezing drizzle	Drizzle and rain, slight	Drizzle and rain, moderate or heavy
Continuous rain (NOT freezing), heavy at time of observation	Slight freezing rain	Moderate or heavy freezing rain	Rain or drizzle and snow, slight	Rain or drizzle and snow, moderate or heavy
Continuous fall of snowflakes, heavy at time of observation	Ice prisms (with or without fog)	Snow grains (with or without fog)	Isolated starlike snow crystals (with or without fog)	Ice pellets or snow pellets
Slight snow shower(s)	Moderate or heavy snow shower(s)	Slight shower(s) of snow pellets, or ice pellets with or without rain, or rain and snow mixed	Moderate or heavy shower(s) of snow pellets, or ice pellets, or ice pellets with or without rain or rain and snow mixed	Slight shower(s) of hail, with or without rain or rain and snow mixed, not associated with thunder
Slight or moderate thunderstorm without hail, but with rain, and/or snow at time of observation	Slight or moderate thunderstorm, with hail at time of observation	Heavy thunderstorm, without hail, but with rain and/or snow at time of observation	Thunderstorm combined with dust storm or sandstorm at time of observation	Heavy thunderstorm with hail at time of observation

C RELATIVE HUMIDITY AND DEW-POINT TABLES

TABLE C-1	Relative humidity (percent)

Dry bulb (°C) / Dry-bulb (air) temperature

Depression of web-bulb temperature
(Dry-bulb temperature minus wet-bulb temperature = depression of the wet bulb)

Dry bulb (°C)	1	2	3	4	5	6	7	8	9	10	11	12	13	14	15	16	17	18	19	20	21	22
−20	28																					
−18	40																					
−16	48	0																				
−14	55	11																				
−12	61	23																				
−10	66	33	0																			
−8	71	41	13																			
−6	73	48	20	0																		
−4	77	54	32	11																		
−2	79	58	37	20	1																	
0	81	63	45	28	11																	
2	83	67	51	36	20	6																
4	85	70	56	42	27	14																
6	86	72	59	46	35	22	10	0														
8	87	74	62	51	39	28	17	6														
10	88	76	65	54	43	33	24	13	4													
12	88	78	67	57	48	38	28	19	10	2												
14	89	79	69	60	50	41	33	25	16	8	1											
16	90	80	71	62	54	45	37	29	21	14	7	1										
18	91	81	72	64	56	48	40	33	26	19	12	6	0									
20	91	82	74	66	58	51	44	36	30	23	17	11	5									
22	92	83	75	68	60	53	46	40	33	27	21	15	10	4	0							
24	92	84	76	69	62	55	49	42	36	30	25	20	14	9	4	0						
26	92	85	77	70	64	57	51	45	39	34	28	23	18	13	9	5						
28	93	86	78	71	65	59	53	45	42	36	31	26	21	17	12	8	4					
30	93	86	79	72	66	61	55	49	44	39	34	29	25	20	16	12	8	4				
32	93	86	80	73	68	62	56	51	46	41	36	32	27	22	19	14	11	8	4			
34	93	86	81	74	69	63	58	52	48	43	38	34	30	26	22	18	14	11	8	5		
36	94	87	81	75	69	64	59	54	50	44	40	36	32	28	24	21	17	13	10	7	4	
38	94	87	82	76	70	66	60	55	51	46	42	38	34	30	26	23	20	16	13	10	7	5
40	94	89	82	76	71	67	61	57	52	48	44	40	36	33	29	25	22	19	16	13	10	7

*To determine the relative humidity, find the air (dry-bulb) temperature on the vertical axis (far left) and the depression of the wet bulb on the horizontal axis (top). Where the two meet, the relative humidity is found. For example, when the dry-bulb temperature is 20°C and a wet-bulb temperature is 14°C, then the depression of the wet-bulb is 6°C (20°C−14°C). From Table C-1, the relative humidity is 51 percent and from Table C-2, the dew point is 10°C.

TABLE C-2 Dew-point temperature (°C)*

Dry bulb (°C)

Dry-bulb temperature minus wet-bulb temperature = depression of the wet bulb

Dry bulb	1	2	3	4	5	6	7	8	9	10	11	12	13	14	15	16	17	18	19	20	21	22
−20	−33																					
−18	−28																					
−16	−24																					
−14	−21	−36																				
−12	−18	−28																				
−10	−14	−22																				
−8	−12	−18	−29																			
−6	−10	−14	−22																			
−4	−7	−12	−17	−29																		
−2	−5	−8	−13	−20																		
0	−3	−6	−9	−15	−24																	
2	−1	−3	−6	−11	−17																	
4	1	−1	−4	−7	−11	−19																
6	4	1	−1	−4	−7	−13	−21															
8	6	3	1	−2	−5	−9	−14															
10	8	6	4	1	−2	−5	−9	−14	−18													
12	10	8	6	4	1	−2	−5	−9	−16													
14	12	11	9	6	4	1	−2	−5	−10	−17												
16	14	13	11	9	7	4	1	−1	−6	−10	−17											
18	16	15	13	11	9	7	4	2	−2	−5	−10	−19										
20	19	17	15	14	12	10	7	4	2	−2	−5	−10	−19									
22	21	19	17	16	14	12	10	8	5	3	−1	−5	−10	−19								
24	23	21	20	18	16	14	12	10	8	6	2	−1	−5	−10	−18							
26	25	23	22	20	18	17	15	13	11	9	6	3	0	−4	−9	−18						
28	27	25	24	22	21	19	17	16	14	11	9	7	4	1	−3	−9	−16					
30	29	27	26	24	23	21	19	18	16	14	12	10	8	5	1	−2	−8	−15				
32	31	29	28	27	25	24	22	21	19	17	15	13	11	8	5	2	−2	−7	−14			
34	33	31	30	29	27	26	24	23	21	20	18	16	14	12	9	6	3	−1	−5	−12	−29	
36	35	33	32	31	29	28	27	25	24	22	20	19	17	15	13	10	7	4	0	−4	−10	
38	37	35	34	33	32	30	29	28	26	25	23	21	19	17	15	13	11	8	5	1	−3	−9
40	39	37	36	35	34	32	31	30	28	27	25	24	22	20	18	16	14	12	9	6	2	−2

Dew point temperatures

APPENDIX

D LAWS RELATING TO GASES

Kinetic Energy

All moving objects, by virtue of their motion, are capable of doing work. We call this energy of motion, or *kinetic energy*. The kinetic energy of a moving object is equal to one-half its mass (M) multiplied by its velocity (v) squared. Stated mathematically:

$$\text{Kinetic energy} = \tfrac{1}{2} M v^2$$

Therefore, by doubling the velocity of a moving object, the object's kinetic energy will increase four times.

First Law of Thermodynamics

The first law of thermodynamics is simply the thermal version of the law of conservation of energy, which states that energy cannot be created or destroyed, only transformed from one form to another. Meteorologists use the first law of thermodynamics along with the principles of kinetic energy extensively in analyzing atmospheric phenomena. According to the kinetic theory, the temperature of a gas is proportional to the kinetic energy of the moving molecules. When a gas is heated, its kinetic energy increases because of an increase in molecular motion. Further, when a gas is compressed, the kinetic energy will also be increased and the temperature of the gas will rise. These relationships are expressed in the first law of thermodynamics, as follows: The temperature of a gas may be changed by the addition or subtraction of heat, or by changing the pressure (compression or expansion), or by a combination of both. It is easy to understand how the atmosphere is heated or cooled by the gain or loss of heat. However, when we consider rising and sinking air, the relationships between temperature and pressure become more important. Here an increase in temperature is brought about by performing work on the gas and not by the addition of heat. This phenomenon is called the *adiabatic form* of the first law of thermodynamics.

Boyle's Law

About 1600, the Englishman Robert Boyle showed that if the temperature is kept constant when the pressure exerted on a gas is increased, the volume decreases. This principle, called *Boyle's law,* states: At a constant temperature, the volume of a given mass of gas varies inversely with the pressure. Stated mathematically:

$$P_1 V_1 = P_2 V_2$$

The symbols P_1 and V_1 refer to the original pressure and volume, respectively, and P_2 and V_2 indicate the new pressure and volume, respectively, after a change occurs. Boyle's

law shows that if a given volume of gas is compressed so that the volume is reduced by one-half, the pressure exerted by the gas is doubled. This increase in pressure can be explained by the kinetic theory, which predicts that when the volume of the gas is reduced by one-half, the molecules collide with the walls of the container twice as often. Because density is defined as the mass per unit volume, an increase in pressure results in increased density.

Charles's Law

The relationships between temperature and volume (hence, density) of a gas were recognized about 1787 by the French scientist Jacques Charles, and were stated formally by J. Gay-Lussac in 1802. *Charles's law* states: At a constant pressure, the volume of a given mass is directly proportional to the absolute temperature. In other words, when a quantity of gas is kept at a constant pressure, an increase in temperature results in an increase in volume and vice versa. Stated mathematically:

$$\frac{V_1}{V_2} = \frac{T_1}{T_2}$$

where V_1 and T_1 represent the original volume and temperature, respectively, and V_2 and T_2 represent the final volume and temperature, respectively. This law explains the fact that a gas expands when it is heated. According to the kinetic theory, when heated, particles move more rapidly and therefore collide more often.

The Ideal Gas Law or Equation of State

In describing the atmosphere, three variable quantities must be considered: pressure, temperature, and density (mass per unit volume). The relationships among these variables can be found by combining in a single statement the laws of Boyle and Charles as follows:

$$PV = RT \text{ or } P = \rho RT$$

where P is pressure, V volume, R the constant of proportionality, T absolute temperature, and ρ density. This law, called the *ideal gas law,* states:

1. When the volume is kept constant, the pressure of a gas is directly proportional to its absolute temperature.

2. When the temperature is kept constant, the pressure of a gas is proportional to its density and inversely proportional to its volume.

3. When the pressure is kept constant, the absolute temperature of a gas is proportional to its volume and inversely proportional to its density.

APPENDIX
E NEWTON'S LAWS OF MOTION

Because air is composed of atoms and molecules, its motion is governed by the same natural laws that apply to all matter. Simply put, when a force is applied to air, it will be displaced from its original position. Depending on the direction from which the force is applied, the air may move horizontally to produce winds, or in some situations vertically to generate convective flow. To better understand the forces that produce global winds, it is helpful to become familiar with Newton's first two laws of motion.

Newton's first law of motion states that an object at rest will remain at rest, and an object in motion will continue moving at a uniform speed and in a straight line unless a force is exerted upon it. In simple terms this law states that objects at rest tend to stay at rest, and objects in motion tend to continue moving at the same rate in the same direction. The tendency of things to resist change in motion (including a change in direction) is known as inertia.

You have experienced Newton's first law if you have ever pushed a stalled auto along flat terrain. To start the automobile moving (accelerating) requires a force sufficient to overcome its inertia (resistance to change). However, once this vehicle is moving, a force equal to that of the frictional force between the tires and the pavement is enough to keep it moving.

Moving objects often deviate from straight paths or come to rest, whereas objects at rest begin to move. The changes in motion we observe in daily life are the result of one or more applied forces.

Newton's second law of motion describes the relationship between the forces that are exerted on objects and the observed accelerations that result. Newton's second law states that the acceleration of an object is directly proportional to the net force acting on that body and inversely proportional to the mass of the body. The first part of Newton's second law means that the acceleration of an object changes as the intensity of the applied force changes.

We define acceleration as the rate of change in velocity. Because velocity describes both the speed and direction of a moving body, the velocity of something can be changed by changing its speed or its direction or both. Further, the term acceleration refers both to decreases and increases in velocity.

For example, we know that when we push down on the gas pedal of an automobile, we experience a positive acceleration (increase in velocity). On the other hand, using the brakes retards acceleration (decreases velocity).

In the atmosphere, three forces are responsible for changing the state of motion of winds. These are the pressure-gradient force, the Coriolis force, and friction. From the preceding discussion, it should be clear that the relative strengths of these forces will determine to a large degree the role of each in establishing the flow of air. Further, these forces can be directed in such a way as to increase the speed of airflow, decrease the speed of airflow, or, in many instances, just change the direction of airflow.

F CLIMATE DATA

The following climate data are for 51 representative stations (Table F–1) from around the world. Temperatures are given in degrees Celsius and precipitation in millimeters. Names and locations are given in Table F–2 along with the elevation (in meters) of each station and its Köppen classification. This format was selected so that you can use the data in exercises to reinforce your understanding of climatic controls and classification. For example, after classifying a station using Table 15–1 p. 000, write out a likely location based on such items as mean annual temperature, annual temperature range, total precipitation, and seasonal precipitation distribution. Your location need not be a specific city; it could be a description of the station's setting, such as "middle-latitude continental" or "subtropical with a strong monsoon influence." It would also be a good idea to list the reasons for your selection. You may then check your answer by examining the list of stations in Table F–2.

If you simply wish to examine the data for a specific place or data for a specific climatic type, consult the list at the end of this appendix.

TABLE F-1 Selected climate data for the world

	J	F	M	A	M	J	J	A	S	O	N	D	YR.
1.	1.7	4.4	7.9	13.2	18.4	23.8	25.8	24.8	21.4	14.7	6.7	2.8	13.8
	10	10	13	13	20	15	30	32	23	18	10	13	207
2.	−10.4	−8.3	−4.6	3.4	9.4	12.8	16.6	14.9	10.8	5.5	−2.3	−6.4	3.5
	18	25	25	30	51	89	64	71	33	20	18	15	459
3.	10.2	10.8	13.7	17.9	22.2	25.7	26.7	26.5	24.2	19.0	13.3	10.0	18.4
	66	84	99	74	91	127	196	168	147	71	53	71	1247
4.	−23.9	−17.5	−12.5	−2.7	8.4	14.8	15.6	12.8	6.4	−3.1	−15.8	−21.9	−3.3
	23	13	18	8	15	33	48	53	33	20	18	15	297
5.	−17.8	−15.3	−9.2	−4.4	4.7	10.9	16.4	14.4	10.3	3.3	−3.6	−12.8	−0.3
	58	58	61	48	53	61	81	71	58	61	64	64	738
6.	−8.2	−7.1	−2.4	5.4	11.2	14.7	18.9	17.4	12.7	7.4	−0.4	−4.6	5.4
	21	23	29	35	52	74	39	40	35	29	26	21	424
7.	12.8	13.9	15.0	15.0	17.8	20.0	21.1	22.8	22.2	18.3	17.2	15.0	17.6
	69	74	46	28	3	3	0	0	5	10	28	61	327
8.	18.9	20.0	21.1	22.8	25.0	26.7	27.2	27.8	27.2	25.0	21.1	20.0	23.6
	51	48	58	99	163	188	172	178	241	208	71	43	1520
9.	−4.4	−2.2	4.4	10.6	16.7	21.7	23.9	22.7	18.3	11.7	3.8	−2.2	10.4
	46	51	69	84	99	97	97	81	97	61	61	51	894
10.	−5.6	−4.4	0.0	6.1	11.7	16.7	20.0	18.9	15.5	10.0	3.3	−2.2	7.5
	112	96	109	94	86	81	74	61	89	81	107	99	1089
11.	−2.1	0.9	4.7	9.9	14.7	19.4	24.7	23.6	18.3	11.5	3.4	−0.2	10.7
	34	30	40	45	36	25	15	22	13	29	33	31	353
12.	12.8	13.9	15.0	16.1	17.2	18.8	19.4	22.2	21.1	18.8	16.1	13.9	15.9
	53	56	41	20	5	0	0	2	5	13	23	51	269
13.	−0.1	1.8	6.2	13.0	18.7	24.2	26.4	25.4	21.1	14.9	6.7	1.6	13.3
	50	52	78	94	95	109	84	77	70	73	65	50	897
14.	2.7	3.2	7.1	13.2	18.8	23.4	25.7	24.7	20.9	15.0	8.7	3.4	13.9
	77	63	82	80	105	82	105	124	97	78	72	71	1036
15.	12.8	15.0	18.9	21.1	26.1	31.1	32.7	33.9	31.1	22.2	17.7	13.9	23.0
	10	9	6	2	0	0	6	13	10	10	3	8	77

TABLE F-1 Continued

	J	F	M	A	M	J	J	A	S	O	N	D	YR.
16.	25.6	25.6	24.4	25.0	24.4	23.3	23.3	24.4	24.4	25.0	25.6	25.6	24.7
	259	249	310	165	254	188	168	117	221	183	213	292	2619
17.	25.9	25.8	25.8	25.9	26.4	26.6	26.9	27.5	27.9	27.7	27.3	26.7	26.7
	365	326	383	404	185	132	68	43	96	99	189	143	2433
18.	13.3	13.3	13.3	13.3	13.9	13.3	13.3	13.3	13.9	13.3	13.3	13.9	13.5
	99	112	142	175	137	43	20	30	69	112	97	79	1115
19.	25.9	26.1	25.2	23.9	22.3	21.3	20.8	21.1	21.5	22.3	23.1	24.4	23.2
	137	137	143	116	73	43	43	43	53	74	97	127	1086
20.	13.8	13.5	11.4	8.0	3.7	1.2	1.4	2.9	5.5	9.2	11.4	12.9	7.9
	21	16	18	13	25	15	15	17	12	7	15	18	171
21.	1.5	1.3	3.1	5.8	10.2	12.6	15.0	14.7	12.0	8.3	5.5	3.3	7.8
	179	139	109	140	83	126	141	167	228	236	207	203	1958
22.	−0.5	0.2	3.9	9.0	14.3	17.7	19.4	18.8	15.0	9.6	4.7	1.2	9.5
	41	37	30	39	44	60	67	65	45	45	44	39	556
23.	6.1	5.8	7.8	9.2	11.6	14.4	15.6	16.0	14.7	12.0	9.0	7.0	10.8
	133	96	83	69	68	56	62	80	87	104	138	150	1126
24.	10.8	11.6	13.6	15.6	17.2	20.1	22.2	22.5	21.2	18.2	14.4	11.5	16.6
	111	76	109	54	44	16	3	4	33	62	93	103	708
25.	−9.9	−9.5	−4.2	4.7	11.9	16.8	19.0	17.1	11.2	4.5	−1.9	−6.8	4.4
	31	28	33	35	52	67	74	74	58	51	36	36	575
26.	8.0	9.0	10.9	13.7	17.5	21.6	24.4	24.2	21.5	17.2	12.7	9.5	15.9
	83	73	52	50	48	18	9	18	70	110	113	105	749
27.	−9.0	−9.0	−6.6	−4.1	0.4	3.6	5.6	5.5	3.5	−0.6	−4.5	−7.6	−1.9
	202	180	164	166	197	249	302	278	208	183	190	169	2488
28.	−2.9	−3.1	−0.7	4.4	10.1	14.9	17.8	16.6	12.2	7.1	2.8	0.1	6.6
	43	30	26	31	34	45	61	76	60	48	53	48	555
29.	12.8	13.9	17.2	18.9	22.2	23.9	25.5	26.1	25.5	23.9	18.9	15.0	20.3
	66	41	20	5	3	0	0	0	3	18	46	66	268
30.	24.6	24.9	25.0	24.9	25.0	24.2	23.7	23.8	23.9	24.2	24.2	24.7	24.4
	81	102	155	140	133	119	99	109	206	213	196	122	1675
31.	21.1	20.4	20.9	21.7	23.0	26.0	27.3	27.3	27.5	27.5	26.0	25.2	24.3
	0	2	0	0	1	15	88	249	163	49	5	6	578
32.	20.4	22.7	27.0	30.6	33.8	34.2	33.6	32.7	32.6	30.5	25.5	21.3	28.7
	0	0	0	0	0	2	1	11	2	0	0	0	16
33.	17.8	18.1	18.8	18.8	17.8	16.2	14.9	15.5	16.8	18.6	18.3	17.8	17.5
	46	51	102	206	160	46	18	25	25	53	109	81	922
34.	20.6	20.7	19.9	19.2	16.7	13.9	13.9	16.3	19.1	21.8	21.4	20.9	18.7
	236	168	86	46	13	8	0	3	8	38	94	201	901
35.	11.7	13.3	16.7	18.6	19.2	20.0	20.3	20.5	20.5	19.1	15.9	12.9	17.4
	20	41	179	605	1705	2875	2455	1827	1231	447	47	5	11437
36.	26.2	26.3	27.1	27.2	27.3	27.0	26.7	27.0	27.4	27.4	26.9	26.6	26.9
	335	241	201	141	116	97	61	50	78	91	151	193	1755
37.	−0.8	2.6	5.3	8.5	13.1	17.0	17.2	17.3	15.3	11.5	5.7	0.3	9.4
	0	0	1	1	18	72	157	151	68	4	1	0	473
38.	24.5	25.8	27.9	30.5	32.7	32.5	30.7	30.1	29.7	28.1	25.9	24.6	28.6
	24	7	15	25	52	53	83	124	118	267	308	157	1233
39.	−18.7	−18.1	−16.7	−11.7	−5.0	0.6	5.3	5.8	1.4	−4.2	−12.3	−15.8	−7.5
	8	8	8	8	15	20	36	43	43	33	13	12	247
40.	−21.9	−18.6	−12.5	−5.0	9.7	15.6	18.3	16.1	10.3	0.8	−10.6	−18.4	−1.4
	15	8	8	13	30	51	51	51	28	25	18	20	318
41.	−4.7	−1.9	4.8	13.7	20.1	24.7	26.1	24.9	19.9	12.8	3.8	−2.7	11.8
	4	5	8	17	35	78	243	141	58	16	10	3	623

TABLE F-1 Continued

	J	F	M	A	M	J	J	A	S	O	N	D	YR.
42.	24.3	25.2	27.2	29.8	29.5	27.8	27.6	27.1	27.6	28.3	27.7	25.0	27.3
	8	5	6	17	260	524	492	574	398	208	34	3	2530
43.	25.8	26.3	27.8	28.8	28.2	27.4	27.1	27.1	26.7	26.5	26.1	25.7	27.0
	6	13	12	65	196	285	242	277	292	259	122	37	1808
44.	3.7	4.3	7.6	13.1	17.6	21.1	25.1	26.4	22.8	16.7	11.3	6.1	14.7
	48	73	101	135	131	182	146	147	217	220	101	60	1563
45.	−15.8	−13.6	−4.0	8.5	17.7	21.5	23.9	21.9	16.7	6.1	−6.2	−13.0	5.3
	8	15	15	33	25	33	16	35	15	47	22	11	276
46.	−46.8	−43.1	−30.2	−13.5	2.7	12.9	15.7	11.4	2.7	−14.3	−35.7	−44.5	−15.2
	7	5	5	4	5	25	33	30	13	11	10	7	155
47.	19.2	19.6	18.4	16.4	13.8	11.8	10.8	11.3	12.6	16.3	15.9	17.7	15.2
	84	104	71	109	122	140	140	109	97	106	81	79	1242
48.	28.2	27.9	28.3	28.2	26.8	25.4	25.1	25.8	27.7	29.1	29.2	28.7	27.6
	341	338	274	121	9	1	2	5	17	66	156	233	1562
49.	21.9	21.9	21.2	18.3	15.7	13.1	12.3	13.4	15.3	17.6	19.4	21.0	17.6
	104	125	129	101	115	141	94	83	72	80	77	86	1205
50.	−7.2	−7.2	−4.4	−0.6	4.4	8.3	10.0	8.3	5.0	1.1	−3.3	−6.1	0.7
	84	66	86	62	89	81	79	94	150	145	117	79	1132
51.	−4.4	−8.9	−15.5	−22.8	−23.9	−24.4	−26.1	−26.1	−24.4	−18.8	−10.0	−3.9	−17.4
	13	18	10	10	10	8	5	8	10	5	5	8	110

TABLE F-2 Locations and climate classifications for Table F–1

Station No.	City	Location	Elevation (m)	Köppen classification
		North America		
1	Albuquerque, N.M.	lat. 35°05′N long. 106°40′W	1593	BWk
2	Calgary, Canada	lat. 51°03′N long. 114°05′W	1062	Dfb
3	Charleston, S.C.	lat. 32°47′N long. 79°56′W	18	Cfa
4	Fairbanks, Alaska	lat. 64°50′N long. 147°48′W	134	Dfc
5	Goose Bay, Canada	lat. 53°19′N long. 60°33′W	45	Dfb
6	Lethbridge, Canada	lat. 49°40′N long. 112°39′W	920	Dfb
7	Los Angeles, Calif.	lat. 34°00′N long. 118°15′W	29	BSk
8	Miami, Fla.	lat. 25°45′N long. 80°11′W	2	Am
9	Peoria, Ill.	lat. 40°45′N long. 89°35′W	180	Dfa
10	Portland, Me.	lat. 43°40′N long. 70°16′W	14	Dfb
11	Salt Lake City, Utah	lat. 40°46′N long. 111°52′W	1288	BSk
12	San Diego, Calif.	lat. 32°43′N long. 117°10′W	26	BSk

Station No.	City	Location	Elevation (m)	Köppen classification
13	St. Louis, Mo.	lat. 38°39′N long. 90°15′W	172	Cfa
14	Washington, D.C.	lat. 38°50′N long. 77°00′W	20	Cfa
15	Yuma, Ariz.	lat. 32°40′N long. 114°40′W	62	BWh
		South America		
16	Iquitos, Peru	lat. 3°39′S long. 73°18′W	115	Af
17	Manaus, Brazil	lat. 3°01′S long. 60°00′W	60	Am
18	Quito, Ecuador	lat. 0°17′S long. 78°32′W	2766	Cfb
19	Rio de Janeiro, Brazil	lat. 22°50′S long. 43°20′W	26	Aw
20	Santa Cruz, Argentina	lat. 50°01′S long. 60°30′W	111	BSk
		Europe		
21	Bergen, Norway	lat. 60°24′N long. 5°20′E	44	Cfb
22	Berlin, Germany	lat. 52°28′N long. 13°26′E	50	Cfb
23	Brest, France	lat. 48°24′N long. 4°30′W	103	Cfb
24	Lisbon, Portugal	lat. 38°43′N long. 9°05′W	93	Csa
25	Moscow, Russia	lat. 55°45′N long. 37°37′E	156	Dfb
26	Rome, Italy	lat. 41°52′N long. 12°37′E	3	Csa
27	Santis, Switzerland	lat. 47°15′N long. 9°21′E	2496	ET
28	Stockholm, Sweden	lat. 59°21′N long. 18°00′E	52	Dfb
		Africa		
29	Benghazi, Libya	lat. 32°06′N long. 20°06′E	25	BSh
30	Coquilhatville, Zaire	lat. 0°01′N long. 18°17′E	21	Af
31	Dakar, Senegal	lat. 14°40′N long. 17°28′W	23	BSh
32	Faya, Chad	lat. 18°00′N long. 21°18′E	251	BWh
33	Nairobi, Kenya	lat. 1°16′S long. 36°47′E	1791	Csb
34	Harare, Zimbabwe	lat. 17°50′S long. 30°52′E	1449	Cwb

TABLE F-2 Continued

TABLE F-2 Continued

Station No.	City	Location	Elevation (m)	Köppen classification
		Asia		
35	Cherrapunji, India	lat. 25°15′N long. 91°44′E	1313	Cwb
36	Djakarta, Indonesia	lat. 6°11′S long. 106°45′E	8	Am
37	Lhasa, Tibet	lat. 29°40′N long. 91°07′E	3685	Cwb
38	Madras, India	lat. 13°00′N long. 80°11′E	16	Aw
39	Novaya Zemlya, Russia	lat. 72°23′N long. 54°46′E	15	ET
40	Omsk, Russia	lat. 54°48′N long. 73°19′E	85	Dfb
41	Beijing, China	lat. 39°57′N long. 116°23′E	52	Dwa
42	Rangoon, Myanmar	lat. 16°46′N long. 96°10′E	23	Am
43	Ho Chi Minh City, Viet Nam	lat. 10°49′N long. 106°40′E	10	Aw
44	Tokyo, Japan	lat. 35°41′N long. 139°46′E	6	Cfa
45	Urumchi, China	lat. 43°47′N long. 87°43′E	912	Dfa
46	Verkhoyansk, Russia	lat. 67°33′N long. 133°23′E	137	Dfd
		Australia and New Zealand		
47	Auckland, New Zealand	lat. 37°43′S long. 174°53′E	49	Csb
48	Darwin, Australia	lat. 12°26′S long. 131°00′E	27	Aw
49	Sydney, Australia	lat. 33°52′S long. 151° 179E	42	Cfb
		Greenland		
50	Ivigtut, Greenland	lat. 61°12′N long. 48° 109W	29	ET
		Antarctica		
51	McMurdo Station, Antarctica	lat. 77°53′S long. 167°00′E	2	EF

Glossary

Absolute Humidity The mass of water vapor per volume of air (usually expressed as grams of water vapor per cubic meter of air).

Absolute Instability The condition of air that has an environmental lapse rate that is greater than the dry adiabatic rate (1°C per 100 meters).

Absolute Stability The condition of air that has an environmental lapse rate that is less than the wet adiabatic rate.

Absolute Zero The zero point on the Kelvin temperature scale, representing the temperature at which all molecular motion is presumed to cease.

Acid Precipitation Rain or snow with a pH value that is less than the value for uncontaminated rain.

Adiabatic Temperature Change The cooling or warming of air caused when air is allowed to expand or is compressed, not because heat is added or subtracted.

Advection Horizontal convective motion, such as wind.

Advection Fog Fog formed when warm moist air is blown over a cool surface and chilled below the dew point.

Aerosols Tiny solid and liquid particles suspended in the atmosphere.

Aerovane A device that resembles a wind vane with a propeller at one end. Used to indicate wind speed and direction.

Air A mixture of many discrete gases, of which nitrogen and oxygen are most abundant, in which varying quantities of tiny solid and liquid particles are suspended.

Air Mass A large body of air, usually 1600 kilometers or more across, that is characterized by homogeneous physical properties at any given altitude.

Air-Mass Thunderstorm A localized thunderstorm that forms in a warm, moist, unstable air mass. Most frequent in the afternoon in spring and summer.

Air-Mass Weather The conditions experienced in an area as an air mass passes over it. Because air masses are large and relatively homogeneous, air-mass weather will be fairly constant and may last for several days.

Air Pollutants Airborne particles and gases occurring in concentrations that endanger the health and well-being of organisms or disrupt the orderly functioning of the environment.

Air Pressure The force exerted by the weight of a column of air above a given point.

Albedo The reflectivity of a substance, usually expressed as a percentage of the incident radiation reflected.

Aleutian Low A large cell of low pressure centered over the Aleutian Islands of the North Pacific during the winter.

Altimeter An aneroid barometer calibrated to indicate altitude instead of pressure.

Altitude (of the Sun) The angle of the Sun above the horizon.

Analog Method A statistical approach to weather forecasting in which current conditions are matched with records of similar past weather events with the idea that the succession of events in the past will be paralleled by current conditions.

Anemometer An instrument used to determine wind speed.

Aneroid Barometer An instrument for measuring air pressure; it consists of evacuated metal chambers that are very sensitive to variations in air pressure.

Annual Mean Temperature An average of the 12 monthly means.

Annual Temperature Range The difference between the warmest and coldest monthly means.

Anticyclone An area of high atmospheric pressure characterized by diverging and rotating winds and subsiding air aloft.

Anticyclonic Flow Winds blow out and flow clockwise about an anticyclone (high) in the Northern Hemisphere, and they blow out and flow counterclockwise about an anticyclone in the Southern Hemisphere.

Aphelion The point in the orbit of a planet that is farthest from the Sun.

Apparent Temperature The air temperature perceived by a person.

Arctic (A) Air Mass A bitterly cold air mass that forms over the frozen Arctic Ocean.

Arctic Sea Smoke A dense and often extensive steam fog occurring over high-latitude ocean areas in winter.

Arid *See* Desert.

Atmosphere The gaseous portion of a planet, the planet's envelope of air; one of the traditional subdivisions of Earth's physical environment.

Atmospheric Window Refers to the fact that the troposphere is transparent (i.e., does not absorb) to terrestrial radiation between 8 and 11 micrometers in length.

Aurora A bright and ever-changing display of light caused by solar radiation interacting with the upper atmosphere in the region of the poles. It is called *aurora borealis* in the Northern Hemisphere and *aurora australis* in the Southern Hemisphere.

Automated Surface Observing System (ASOS) A widely used, standardized set of automated weather instruments that provide routine surface observations.

Autumnal Equinox *See* Equinox.

Azores High The name given to the subtropical anticyclone when it is situated over the eastern part of the North Atlantic Ocean.

Backing Wind Shift A wind shift in a counterclockwise direction, such as a shift from east to north.

Barograph A recording barometer.

Barometric Tendency *See* Pressure Tendency.

Beaufort Scale A scale that can be used for estimating wind speed when an anemometer is not available.

Bergeron Process A theory that relates the formation of precipitation to supercooled clouds, freezing nuclei, and the different saturation levels of ice and liquid water.

Bermuda High The name given to the subtropical high in the North Atlantic during the summer when it is centered near the island of Bermuda.

Bimetal Strip A thermometer consisting of two thin strips of metal welded together, which have widely different coefficients of thermal expansion. When temperature changes, the two metals expand or contract unequally and cause changes in the curvature of the element. Commonly used in thermographs.

Biosphere The totality of life forms on Earth.

Blackbody A material that is able to absorb 100 percent of the radiation that strikes it.

Blizzard A violent and extremely cold wind laden with dry snow picked up from the ground.

Bora In the region of the eastern shore of the Adriatic Sea, a cold, dry northeasterly wind that blows down from the mountains.

Buys Ballot's Law With your back to the wind in the Northern Hemisphere, low pressure will be to your left and high pressure to your right. The reverse is true in the Southern Hemisphere.

Calorie The amount of heat required to raise the temperature of 1 gram of water 1°C.

Ceiling The height ascribed to the lowest layer of clouds or obscuring phenomena when the sky is reported as broken, overcast, or obscured and the clouds are not classified "thin" or "partial." The ceiling is termed *unlimited* when the foregoing conditions are not present.

Celsius Scale A temperature scale (at one time called the centigrade scale) devised by Anders Celsius in 1742 and used where the metric system is in use. For water at sea level, 0° is designated the ice point and 100° the steam point.

Chinook The name applied to a foehn wind in the Rocky Mountains.

Circle of Illumination The line (great circle) separating daylight from darkness on Earth.

Cirrus One of three basic cloud forms; also one of the three high cloud types. They are thin, delicate ice-crystal clouds often appearing as veil-like patches or thin, wispy fibers.

Climate A description of aggregate weather conditions; the sum of all statistical weather information that helps describe a place or region.

Climate Change A study dealing with variations in climate on many different time scales from decades to millions of years, and the possible causes of such variations.

Climate-Feedback Mechanisms Because the atmosphere is a complex interactive physical system, several different possible outcomes may result when one of the system's elements is altered. These various possibilities are called *climate-feedback mechanisms*.

Climate System The exchanges of energy and moisture occurring among the atmosphere, hydrosphere, lithosphere, biosphere, and cryosphere.

Closed System A system that is self contained with regard to matter—that is, no matter enters or leaves.

Cloud A form of condensation best described as a dense concentration of suspended water droplets or tiny ice crystals.

Cloud Condensation Nuclei Microscopic particles that serve as surfaces on which water vapor condenses.

Cloud Seeding The introduction into clouds of particles (most commonly dry ice or silver iodide) for the purpose of altering the cloud's natural development.

Clouds of Vertical Development A cloud that has its base in the low height range but extends upward into the middle or high altitudes.

Cold Front The discontinuity at the forward edge of an advancing cold air mass that is displacing warmer air in its path.

Cold-Type Occluded Front A front that forms when the air behind the cold front is colder than the air underlying the warm front it is overtaking.

Cold Wave A rapid and marked fall of temperature. The National Weather Service applies this term to a fall of temperature in 24 hours equaling or exceeding a specified number of degrees and reaching a specified minimum temperature or lower. These specifications vary for different parts of the country and for different periods of the year.

Collision–Coalescence Process A theory of raindrop formation in warm clouds (above 0°C) in which large cloud droplets ("giants") collide and join together with smaller droplets to form a raindrop. Opposite electrical charges may bind the cloud droplets together.

Condensation The change of state from a gas to a liquid.

Conditional Instability The condition of moist air with an environmental lapse rate between the dry and wet adiabatic rates.

Conduction The transfer of heat through matter by molecular activity. Energy is transferred during collisions among molecules.

Constant-Pressure Surface A surface along which the atmospheric pressure is everywhere equal at any given moment.

Continental (c) Air Mass An air mass that forms over land; it is normally relatively dry.

Continental Climate A climate lacking marine influence and characterized by more extreme temperatures than in marine climates; therefore, it has a relatively high annual temperature range for its latitude.

Contrail A cloudlike streamer frequently observed behind aircraft flying in clear, cold, and humid air and caused by the addition to the atmosphere of water vapor from engine exhaust gases.

Controls of Temperature Those factors that cause variations in temperature from place to place, such as latitude and altitude.

Convection The transfer of heat by the movement of a mass or substance. It can only take place in fluids.

Convection Cell Circulation that results from the uneven heating of a fluid; the warmer parts of the fluid expand and rise because of their buoyancy, and the cooler parts sink.

Convergence The condition that exists when the wind distribution within a given region results in a net horizontal inflow of air into the area. Because convergence at lower levels is associated with an upward movement of air, areas of convergent winds are regions favorable to cloud formation and precipitation.

Cooling Degree-Days Each degree of temperature of the daily mean above 65°F is counted as one cooling degree-day. The amount of energy required to maintain a certain temperature in a building is proportional to the cooling degree-days total.

Coriolis Effect The deflective effect of Earth's rotation on all free-moving objects, including the atmosphere and oceans. Deflection is to the right in the Northern Hemisphere and to the left in the Southern Hemisphere.

Corona A bright, whitish disk centered on the Moon or Sun that results from diffraction when the objects are veiled by a thin cloud layer.

Country Breeze A circulation pattern characterized by a light wind blowing into a city from the surrounding countryside. It is best developed on clear and otherwise calm nights when the urban heat island is most pronounced.

Cryosphere Collective term for the ice and snow that exist on Earth. One of the *spheres* of the climate system.

Cumulus One of three basic cloud forms; also the name given one of the clouds of vertical development. Cumulus are billowy, individual cloud masses that often have flat bases.

Cumulus Stage The initial stage in thunderstorm development in which the growing cumulonimbus is dominated by strong updrafts.

Cup Anemometer See Anemometer.

Cyclogenesis The process that creates or develops a new cyclone; also the process that produces an intensification of a preexisting cyclone.

Cyclone An area of low atmospheric pressure characterized by rotating and converging winds and ascending air.

Cyclonic Flow Winds blow in and counterclockwise about a cyclone (low) in the Northern Hemisphere and in and clockwise about a cyclone in the Southern Hemisphere.

Daily Mean Temperature The mean temperature for a day that is determined by averaging the hourly readings or, more commonly, by averaging the maximum and minimum temperatures for a day.

Daily Temperature Range The difference between the maximum and minimum temperatures for a day.

Dart Leader *See* Leader.

Deposition The process whereby water vapor changes directly to ice without going through the liquid state.

Desert One of the two types of dry climate—the driest of the dry climates.

Dew A form of condensation consisting of small water drops on grass or other objects near the ground that forms when the surface temperature drops below the dew point. Usually associated with radiation cooling on clear, calm nights.

Dew Point The temperature to which air has to be cooled in order to reach saturation.

Diffraction The slight bending of light as it passes sharp edges.

Diffused Light Solar energy is scattered and reflected in the atmosphere and reaches Earth's surface in the form of diffuse blue light from the sky.

Discontinuity A zone characterized by a comparatively rapid transition of meteorological elements.

Dispersion The separation of colors by refraction.

Dissipating Stage The final stage of a thunderstorm that is dominated by downdrafts and entrainment leading to the evaporation of the cloud structure.

Diurnal Daily, especially pertaining to actions that are completed within 24 hours and that recur every 24 hours.

Divergence The condition that exists when the distribution of winds within a given area results in a net horizontal outflow of air from the region. In divergence at lower levels, the resulting deficit is compensated for by a downward movement of air from aloft; hence, areas of divergent winds are unfavorable to cloud formation and precipitation.

Doldrums The equatorial belt of calms or light variable winds lying between the two trade-wind belts.

Doppler Radar A type of radar that has the capacity of detecting motion directly.

Drizzle Precipitation from stratus clouds consisting of tiny droplets.

Dry Adiabatic Rate The rate of adiabatic cooling or warming in unsaturated air. The rate of temperature change is 1°C per 100 meters.

Dry Climate A climate in which yearly precipitation is not as great as the potential loss of water by evaporation.

Dryline A narrow zone in the atmosphere along which there is an abrupt change in moisture as when dry continental tropical air converges with humid maritime tropical air. The denser cT air acts to lift the less dense mT air producing clouds and storms.

Dry-Summer Subtropical Climate A climate located on the west sides of continents between latitudes 30° and 45°. It is the only humid climate with a strong winter precipitation maximum.

Dynamic Seeding A type of cloud seeding that uses massive seeding, a process resulting in an increase of the release of latent heat and causing the cloud to grow larger.

Easterly Wave A large migratory wavelike disturbance in the trade winds that sometimes triggers the formation of a hurricane.

Eccentricity The variation of an ellipse from a circle.

Electromagnetic Radiation *See* Radiation.

Elements (atmospheric) Those quantities or properties of the atmosphere that are measured regularly and that are used to express the nature of weather and climate.

El Niño The name given to the periodic warming of the ocean that occurs in the central and eastern Pacific. A major El Niño episode can cause extreme weather in many parts of the world.

Entrainment The infiltration of surrounding air into a vertically-moving air column. For example, the influx of cool, dry air into the downdraft of a cumulonimbus cloud; a process that acts to intensify the downdraft.

Environmental Lapse Rate The rate of temperature decrease with height in the troposphere.

Equatorial Low A quasi-continuous belt of low pressure lying near the equator and between the subtropical highs.

Equinox The point in time when the vertical rays of the Sun are striking the equator. In the Northern Hemisphere, March 20 or 21 is the *vernal* or *spring equinox* and September 22 or 23 is the *autumnal equinox*. Lengths of daylight and darkness are equal at all latitudes at equinox.

Evaporation The process by which a liquid is transformed into gas.

Eye A roughly circular area of relatively light winds and fair weather at the center of a hurricane.

Eye Wall The doughnut-shaped area of intensive cumulonimbus development and very strong winds that surrounds the eye of a hurricane.

Fahrenheit Scale A temperature scale devised by Gabriel Daniel Fahrenheit in 1714 and used in the English system. For water at sea level, 32° is designated the ice point and 212° the steam point.

Fall Wind *See* Katabatic Wind.

Fata Morgana A mirage most frequently observed in coastal areas in which extreme towering occurs.

Fixed Points Reference points, such as the steam point and the ice point, used in the construction of temperature scales.

Flash The total discharge of lightning, which is usually perceived as a single flash of light but which actually consists of several flashes (*see* Stroke).

Foehn A warm, dry wind on the ice side of a mountain range that owes its relatively high temperature largely to adiabatic heating during descent down mountain slopes.

Fog A cloud with its base at or very near Earth's surface.

Forecasting Skill *See* Skill.

Freezing The change of state from a liquid to a solid.

Freezing Nuclei Solid particles that have a crystal form resembling that of ice; they serve as cores for the formation of ice crystals.

Freezing Rain *See* Glaze.

Front A boundary (discontinuity) separating air masses of different densities, one warmer and often higher in moisture content than the other.

Frontal Fog Fog formed when rain evaporates as it falls through a layer of cool air.

Frontal Wedging The lifting of air resulting when cool air acts as a barrier over which warmer, lighter air will rise.

Frontogenesis The beginning or creation of a front.

Frontolysis   The destruction and dying of a front.

Frost   Occurs when the temperature falls to 0°C or below (*See* White Frost).

Fujita Intensity Scale (F-scale)   A scale developed by T. Theodore Fujita for classifying the severity of a tornado, based on the correlation of wind speed with the degree of destruction.

Geosphere   The solid Earth, the largest of Earth's four major spheres.

Geostationary Satellite   A satellite that remains over a fixed point because its rate of travel corresponds to Earth's rate of rotation. Because the satellite must orbit at distances of about 35,000 kilometers, images from this type of satellite are not as detailed as those from polar satellites.

Geostrophic Wind   A wind, usually above a height of 600 meters, that blows parallel to the isobars.

Glaze   A coating of ice on objects formed when supercooled rain freezes on contact. A storm that produces glaze is termed an "icing storm."

Global Circulation   The general circulation of the atmosphere; the average flow of air over the entire globe.

Glory   A series of rings of colored light most commonly appearing around the shadow of an airplane that is projected on clouds below.

Gradient Wind   The curved airflow pattern around a pressure center resulting from a balance among pressure-gradient force, Coriolis force, and centrifugal force.

Greenhouse Effect   The transmission of shortwave solar radiation by the atmosphere coupled with the selective absorption of longer-wavelength terrestrial radiation, especially by water vapor and carbon dioxide, resulting in warming of the atmosphere.

Growing Degree-Days   A practical application of temperature data for determining the approximate date when crops will be ready for harvest.

Gust Front   The boundary separating the cold downdraft from a thunderstorm and the relatively warm, moist surface air. Lifting along this boundary may initiate the development of thunderstorms.

Hadley Cell   The thermally driven circulation system of equatorial and tropical latitudes consisting of two convection cells, one in each hemisphere. The existence of this circulation system was first proposed by George Hadley in 1735 as an explanation for the trade winds.

Hail   Precipitation in the form of hard, round pellets or irregular lumps of ice that may have concentric shells formed by the successive freezing of layers of water.

Halo   A narrow whitish ring of large diameter centered around the Sun. The commonly observed *22° halo* subtends an angle of 22° from the observer.

Heat   The kinetic energy of random molecular motion.

Heat Budget   The balance of incoming and outgoing radiation.

Heating Degree-Day   Each degree of temperature of the daily mean below 65°F is counted as one heating degree-day. The amount of heat required to maintain a certain temperature in a building is proportional to the heating degree-days total.

Heterosphere   A zone of the atmosphere beyond about 80 kilometers where the gases are arranged into four roughly spherical shells, each with a distinctive composition.

High Cloud   A cloud that normally has its base above 6000 meters; the base may be lower in winter and at high-latitude locations.

Highland Climate   Complex pattern of climate conditions associated with mountains. Highland climates are characterized by large differences that occur over short distances.

Homosphere   A zone of atmosphere extending from Earth's surface to about 80 kilometers that is uniform in terms of the proportions of its component gases.

Horse Latitudes   A belt of calms or light variable winds and subsiding air located near the center of the subtropical high.

Humid Continental Climate   A relatively severe climate characteristic of broad continents in the middle latitudes between approximately 40° and 50° north latitude. This climate is not found in the Southern Hemisphere, where the middle latitudes are dominated by the oceans.

Humidity   A general term referring to water vapor in the air.

Humid Subtropical Climate   A climate generally located on the eastern side of a continent and characterized by hot, sultry summers and cool winters.

Hurricane   A tropical cyclonic storm having minimum winds of 119 kilometers per hour; also known as *typhoon* (western Pacific) and *cyclone* (Indian Ocean).

Hurricane Warning   A warning issued when sustained winds of 119 kilometers per hour or higher are expected within a specified coastal area in 24 hours or less.

Hurricane Watch   An announcement aimed at specific coastal areas that a hurricane poses a possible threat, generally within 36 hours.

Hydrologic Cycle   The continuous movement of water from the oceans to the atmosphere (by evaporation), from the atmosphere to the land (by condensation and precipitation), and from the land back to the sea (via stream flow).

Hydrophobic Nuclei   Particles that are not efficient condensation nuclei. Small droplets will form on them whenever the relative humidity reaches 100 percent.

Hydrosphere   The water portion of our planet; one of the traditional subdivisions of Earth's physical environment.

Hydrostatic Equilibrium   The balance maintained between the force of gravity and the vertical pressure gradient that does not allow air to escape to space.

Hygrometer   An instrument designed to measure relative humidity.

Hygroscopic Nuclei   Condensation nuclei having a high affinity for water, such as salt particles.

Hypothesis   A tentative explanation that is tested to determine if it is valid.

Ice Cap Climate   A climate that has no monthly means above freezing and supports no vegetative cover except in a few scattered high mountain areas. This climate, with its perpetual ice and snow, is confined largely to the ice sheets of Greenland and Antarctica.

Icelandic Low   A large cell of low pressure centered over Iceland and southern Greenland in the North Atlantic during the winter.

Ice Point   The temperature at which ice melts.

Ideal Gas Law   The pressure exerted by a gas is proportional to its density and absolute temperature.

Inclination of the Axis   The tilt of Earth's axis from the perpendicular to the plane of Earth's orbit (plane of the ecliptic). Currently, the inclination is about 23 1/2° away from the perpendicular.

Inferior Mirage   A mirage in which the image appears below the true location of the object.

Infrared Radiation   Radiation with a wavelength from 0.7 to 200 micrometers.

Interference   Occurs when light rays of different frequencies (i.e., colors) meet. Such interference results in the cancellation or subtraction of some frequencies, which is responsible for the colors associated with coronas.

Internal Reflection   Occurs when light that is traveling through a transparent material, such as water, reaches the opposite surface and is reflected back into the material. This is an important factor in the formation of such optical phenomena as rainbows.

Intertropical Convergence Zone (ITCZ)   The zone of general convergence between the Northern and Southern Hemisphere trade winds.

Ionosphere   A complex atmospheric zone of ionized gases extending between 80 and 400 kilometers, thus coinciding with the lower thermosphere and heterosphere.

Isobar   A line drawn on a map connecting points of equal barometric pressure, usually corrected to sea level.

Isohyet   A line connecting places having equal rainfall.

Isotachs   Lines of equal wind speed.

Isotherm   A line connecting points of equal air temperature.

ITCZ   *See* Intertropical Convergence Zone.

Jet Streak   Areas of higher-velocity winds found within the jet stream.

Jet Stream   Swift geostrophic airstreams in the upper troposphere that meander in relatively narrow belts.

Jungle   An almost impenetrable growth of tangle vines, shrubs, and short trees characterizing areas where the tropical rain forest has been cleared.

Katabatic Wind   The flow of cold, dense air downslope under the influence of gravity; the direction of flow is controlled largely by topography.

Kelvin Scale   A temperature scale (also called the *absolute scale*) used primarily for scientific purposes and having intervals equivalent to those on the Celsius scale but beginning at absolute zero.

Köppen Classification   Devised by Wladimir Köppen, a system for classifying climates that is based on mean monthly and annual values of temperature and precipitation.

Lake-Effect Snow   Snow showers associated with a *cP* air mass to which moisture and heat are added from below as it traverses a large and relatively warm lake (such as one of the Great Lakes), rendering the air mass humid and unstable.

Land Breeze   A local wind blowing from the land toward the sea during the night in coastal areas.

La Niña   An episode of strong trade winds and unusually low sea–surface temperatures in the central and eastern Pacific. The opposite of *El Niño*.

Lapse Rate   *See* Environmental Lapse Rate; Normal Lapse Rate.

Latent Heat   The energy absorbed or released during a change of state.

Latent Heat of Condensation   The energy released when water vapor changes to the liquid state. The amount of energy released is equivalent to the amount absorbed during evaporation.

Latent Heat of Vaporization   The energy absorbed by water molecules during evaporation. It varies from about 600 calories per gram for water at 0°C to 540 calories per gram at 100°C.

Law of Conservation of Angular Momentum   The product of the velocity of an object around a center of rotation (axis) and the distance of the object from the axis is constant.

Leader   The conductive path of ionized air that forms near a cloud base prior to a lightning stroke. The initial conductive path is referred to as a *step leader* because it extends itself earthward in short, nearly invisible bursts. A *dart leader*, which is continuous and less branched than a step leader, precedes each subsequent stroke along the same path.

Lifting Condensation Level   The height at which rising air that is cooling at the dry adiabatic rate becomes saturated and condensation begins.

Lightning   A sudden flash of light generated by the flow of electrons between oppositely charged parts of a cumulonimbus cloud or between the cloud and the ground.

Liquid-in-Glass Thermometer   A device for measuring temperature that consists of a tube with a liquid-filled bulb at one end. The expansion or contraction of the fluid indicates temperature.

Long-Range Forecasting   Estimating rainfall and temperatures for a period beyond 3 to 5 days, usually for 30-day periods. Such forecasts are not as detailed or reliable as those for shorter periods.

Longwave Radiation   A reference to radiation emitted by Earth. Wavelengths are roughly 20 times longer than those emitted by the Sun.

Looming   A mirage that allows objects that are below the horizon to be seen.

Low Cloud   A cloud that forms below a height of about 2000 meters.

Macroscale Winds   Such phenomena as cyclones and anticyclones, which persist for days or weeks and have a horizontal dimension of hundreds to several thousands of kilometers; also, features of the atmospheric circulation that persist for weeks or months and have horizontal dimensions of up to 10,000 kilometers.

Marine Climate   A climate dominated by the ocean; because of the moderating effect of water, sites having this climate are considered relatively mild.

Marine West Coast Climate   A climate found on windward coasts from latitudes 40° to 65° and dominated by maritime air masses. Winters are mild and summers are cool.

Maritime (m) Air Mass   An air mass that originates over the ocean. These air masses are relatively humid.

Mature Stage   The second of the three stages of a thunderstorm. This stage is characterized by violent weather as downdrafts exist side by side with updrafts.

Maximum Thermometer   A thermometer that measures the maximum temperature for a given period in time, usually 24 hours. A constriction in the base of the glass tube allows mercury to rise but prevents it from returning to the bulb until the thermometer is shaken or whirled.

Mediterranean Climate   A common name applied to the dry-summer subtropical climate.

Melting   The change of state from a solid to a liquid.

Mercury Barometer   A mercury-filled glass tube in which the height of the column of mercury is a measure of air pressure.

Mesocyclone   A vertical cylinder of cyclonically rotating air (3 to 10 kilometers in diameter) that develops in the updraft of a severe thunderstorm and that often precedes the development of damaging hail or tornadoes.

Mesopause   The boundary between the mesosphere and the thermosphere.

Mesoscale Convective Complex (MCC)   A slow-moving roughly circular cluster of interacting thunderstorm cells covering an area of thousands of square kilometers that may persist for 12 hours or more.

Mesoscale Winds   Small convective cells that exist for minutes or hours, such as thunderstorms, tornadoes, and land and sea breezes. Typical horizontal dimensions range from 1 to 100 kilometers.

Meteorology   The scientific study of the atmosphere and atmospheric phenomena; the study of weather and climate.

Microburst   Small (less than 4 kilometers across), short-lived, straight-line downbursts of wind that occur beneath some thunderstorms.

Microscale Winds Phenomena such as turbulence, with life spans of less than a few minutes that affect small areas and are strongly influenced by local conditions of temperature and terrain.

Middle Cloud A cloud occupying the height range from 2000 to 6000 meters.

Middle-Latitude (Midlatitude) Cyclone Large low-pressure center with diameter often exceeding 1000 kilometers that moves from west to east and may last from a few days to more than a week and usually has a cold front and a warm front extending from the central area of low pressure.

Midlatitude Jet Stream A jet stream that migrates between the latitudes of 30° and 70°.

Milankovitch Cycles Systematic changes in three elements of Earth's orbit—eccentricity, obliquity, and precession. Named for Yugoslavian astronomer Milutin Milankovitch.

Millibar The standard unit of pressure measurement used by the National Weather Service. One millibar (mb) equals 100 newtons per square meter.

Minimum Thermometer A thermometer that measures the minimum temperature for a given period of time, usually 24 hours. By checking the small dumbbell-shaped index, the minimum temperature can be read.

Mirage An optical effect of the atmosphere caused by refraction in which the image of an object appears displaced from its true position.

Mistral A cold northwest wind that blows into the western Mediterranean basin from higher elevations to the north.

Mixing Depth The height to which convectional movements extend above Earth's surface. The greater the mixing depths, the better the air quality.

Mixing Ratio The mass of water vapor in a unit mass of dry air; commonly expressed as grams of water vapor per kilogram of dry air.

Model A term often used synonymously with hypothesis but is less precise because it is sometimes used to describe a theory as well.

Monsoon The seasonal reversal of wind direction associated with large continents, especially Asia. In winter, the wind blows from land to sea; in summer, it blows from sea to land.

Monthly Mean Temperature The mean temperature for a month that is calculated by averaging the daily means.

Mountain Breeze The nightly downslope winds commonly encountered in mountain valleys.

Multiple Vortex Tornado Tornadoes that contain several smaller intense whirls called suction vortices that orbit the center of the larger tornado circulation.

National Weather Service (NWS) The federal agency responsible for gathering and disseminating weather-related information.

Negative-Feedback Mechanism As used in climatic change, any effect that is opposite of the initial change and tends to offset it.

Newton A unit of force used in physics. One newton is the force necessary to accelerate 1 kilogram of mass 1 meter per second per second.

Normal Lapse Rate The average drop in temperature with increasing height in the troposphere; about 6.5°C per kilometer.

Nor'easter The term used to describe the weather associated with an incursion of *mP* air into the Northeast from the North Atlantic; strong northeast winds, freezing or near-freezing temperatures, and the possibility of precipitation make this an unwelcome weather event.

Nowcasting Short-term weather forecasting techniques that are generally applied to predicting severe weather.

Numerical Weather Prediction (NWP) Forecasting the behavior of atmospheric disturbances based upon the solution of the governing fundamental equations of hydrodynamics, subject to the observed initial conditions. Because of the vast number of calculations involved, high-speed computers are always used.

Obliquity The angle between the planes of Earth's equator and orbit.

Occluded Front A front formed when a cold front overtakes a warm front.

Occlusion The overtaking of one front by another.

Ocean Current The mass movement of ocean water that is either wind-driven or initiated by temperature and salinity conditions that alter the density of seawater.

Open System One in which both matter and energy flow into and out of the system. Most natural systems are of this type.

Orographic Lifting Mountains or highlands acting as barriers to the flow of air force the air to ascend. The air cools, adiabatically, and clouds and precipitation may result.

Outgassing The release of gases dissolved in molten rock.

Overrunning Warm air gliding up a retreating cold air mass.

Oxygen-Isotope Analysis A method of deciphering past temperatures based on the precise measurement of the ratio between two isotopes of oxygen, ^{16}O and ^{18}O. Analysis is commonly made of seafloor sediments and cores from ice sheets.

Ozone A molecule of oxygen containing three oxygen atoms.

Paleoclimatology The study of ancient climates; the study of climate and climate change prior to the period of instrumental records using proxy data.

Paleosol Old, buried soil that may furnish some evidence of the nature of past climates because climate is the most important factor in soil formation.

Parcel An imaginary volume of air enclosed in a thin elastic cover. Typically it is considered to be a few hundred cubic meters in volume and is assumed to act independently of the surrounding air.

Parhelia *See* Sun dogs.

Perihelion The point in the orbit of a planet closest to the Sun.

Permafrost The permanent freezing of the subsoil in tundra regions.

Persistence Forecast A forecast that assumes that the weather occurring upstream will persist and move on and will affect the areas in its path in much the same way. Persistence forecasts do not account for changes that might occur in the weather system.

pH Scale A 0 to 14 scale that is used for expressing the exact degree of acidity or alkalinity of a solution. A pH of 7 signifies a neutral solution. Values below 7 signify an acid solution, and values above 7 signify an alkaline solution.

Photochemical Reaction A chemical reaction in the atmosphere triggered by sunlight, often yielding a secondary pollutant.

Photosynthesis The production of sugars and starches by plants using air, water, sunlight, and chlorophyll. In the process, atmospheric carbon dioxide is changed to organic matter and oxygen is released.

Photosynthesis The production of sugars and starches by plants using air, water, sunlight, and chlorophyll. In the process, atmospheric carbon dioxide is changed to organic matter and oxygen is released.

Plane of the Ecliptic Plane of Earth's orbit around the Sun.

Plate Tectonics Theory A theory that states the outer portion of Earth is made up of several individual pieces, called *plates,* which move in relation to one another upon a partially molten zone below. As plates move, so do continents, which explains some climatic changes in the geologic past.

Polar (P) Air Mass A cold air mass that forms in a high-latitude source region.

Polar Climates Climates in which the mean temperature of the warmest month is below 10°C; climates that are too cold to support the growth of trees.

Polar Easterlies In the global pattern of prevailing winds, winds that blow from the polar high toward the subpolar low. These winds, however, should not be thought of as persistent winds, such as the trade winds.

Polar Front The stormy frontal zone separating air masses of polar origin from air masses of tropical origin.

Polar Front Theory A theory developed by J. Bjerknes and other Scandinavian meteorologists in which the polar front, separating polar and tropical air masses, gives rise to cyclonic disturbances that intensify and move along the front and pass through a succession of stages.

Polar High Anticyclones that are assumed to occupy the inner polar regions and are believed to be thermally induced, at least in part.

Polar Satellite Satellites that orbit the poles at rather low altitudes of a few hundred kilometers and require only 100 minutes per orbit.

Positive-Feedback Mechanism As used in climatic change, any effect that acts to reinforce the initial change.

Potential Energy Energy that exists by virtue of a body's position with respect to gravitation.

Precession The slow migration of Earth's axis that traces out a cone over a period of 26,000 years.

Precipitation Fog See Frontal Fog.

Pressure Gradient The amount of pressure change occurring over a given distance.

Pressure Tendency The nature of the change in atmospheric pressure over the past several hours. It can be a useful aid in short-range weather prediction.

Prevailing Westerlies The dominant west-to-east motion of the atmosphere that characterizes the regions on the poleward side of the subtropical highs.

Prevailing Wind A wind that consistently blows from one direction more than from any other.

Primary Pollutant A pollutant emitted directly from an identifiable source.

Prognostic Chart A computer-generated forecast showing the expected pressure pattern at a specified future time. Anticipated positions of fronts are also included. They usually represent the graphical output associated with a numerical weather prediction model.

Proxy Data Data gathered from natural recorders of climate variability such as tree rings, ice cores, and ocean-floor sediments.

Psychrometer Device consisting of two thermometers (wet bulb and dry bulb) that is rapidly whirled and, with the use of tables, yields the relative humidity and dew point.

Radiation The wavelike energy emitted by any substance that possesses heat. This energy travels through space at 300,000 kilometers per second (the speed of light).

Radiation Fog Fog resulting from radiation cooling of the ground and adjacent air; primarily a nighttime and early morning phenomenon.

Radiosonde A lightweight package of weather instruments fitted with a radio transmitter and carried aloft by a balloon.

Rainbow A luminous arc formed by the refraction and reflection of light in drops of water.

Rain Shadow Desert A dry area on the lee side of a mountain range.

Rawinsonde A radiosonde that is tracked by radio-location devices in order to obtain data on upper-air winds.

Reflection, Law of The angle of incidence (incoming ray) is equal to the angle of reflection (outgoing ray).

Refraction The bending of light as it passes obliquely from one transparent medium to another.

Relative Humidity The ratio of the air's water-vapor content to its water vapor capacity.

Return Stroke Term applied to the electric discharge resulting from the downward (earthward) movement of electrons from successively higher levels along the conductive path of lightning.

Revolution The motion of one body about another, as Earth about the Sun.

Ridge An elongate region of high atmospheric pressure.

Rime A delicate accumulation of ice crystals formed when supercooled fog or cloud droplets freeze on contact with objects.

Rossby Waves Upper-air waves in the middle and upper troposphere of the middle latitudes with wavelengths of from 4000 to 6000 kilometers; named for C. G. Rossby, the meteorologist who developed the equations for parameters governing the waves.

Rotation The spinning of a body, such as Earth, about its axis.

Saffir–Simpson Scale A scale, from 1 to 5, used to rank the relative intensities of hurricanes.

Santa Ana The local name given a foehn wind in southern California.

Saturation The maximum possible quantity of water vapor that the air can hold at any given temperature and pressure.

Saturation Vapor Pressure The vapor pressure, at a given temperature, wherein the water vapor is in equilibrium with a surface of pure water or ice.

Savanna A tropical grassland, usually with scattered trees and shrubs.

Sea Breeze A local wind blowing from the sea during the afternoon in coastal areas.

Secondary Pollutant A pollutant that is produced in the atmosphere by chemical reactions occurring among primary pollutants.

Semiarid See Steppe.

Severe Thunderstorm A thunderstorm that produces frequent lightning, locally damaging wind, or hail that is 2 centimeters or more in diameter. In the middle latitudes, most thunderstorms form along or ahead of cold fronts.

Shortwave Radiation Radiation emitted by the Sun.

Siberian High The high-pressure center that forms over the Asian interior in January and produces the dry winter monsoon for much of the continent.

Skill An index of the degree of accuracy of a set of forecasts as compared to forecasts based on some standard, such as chance or climatic data.

Sleet Frozen or semifrozen rain formed when raindrops pass through a subfreezing layer of air.

Smog A word currently used as a synonym for general air pollution. It was originally created by combining the words "smoke" and "fog."

Snow Precipitation in the form of white or translucent ice crystals, chiefly in complex branched hexagonal form and often clustered into snowflakes.

Solstice The point in time when the vertical rays of the Sun are striking either the Tropic of Cancer (summer solstice in the Northern Hemisphere) or the Tropic of Capricorn (winter solstice in the Northern Hemisphere). Solstice represents the longest or shortest day (length of daylight) of the year.

Source Region The area where an air mass acquires its characteristic properties of temperature and moisture.

Southern Oscillation The seesaw pattern of atmospheric pressure change that occurs between the eastern and western Pacific. The interaction of this effect and that of El Niño can cause extreme weather events in many parts of the world.

Specific Heat The amount of heat needed to raise 1 gram of a substance 1°C at sea-level atmospheric pressure.

Specific Humidity The mass of water vapor per unit mass of air, including the water vapor (usually expressed as grams of water vapor per kilogram of air).

Speed Divergence The divergence of air aloft that results from the variations in velocity occurring along the axis of a jet stream. On passing from a zone of lower wind speed to one of faster speed, air accelerates and therefore experiences divergence.

Squall Line Any nonfrontal line or narrow band of active thunderstorms.

Stable Air Air that resists vertical displacement. If it is lifted, adiabatic cooling will cause its temperature to be lower than the surrounding environment; and if it is allowed, it will sink to its original position.

Standard Atmosphere The idealized vertical distribution of atmospheric pressure (as well as temperature and density), which is taken to represent average conditions in the real atmosphere.

Standard Rain Gauge Having a diameter of about 20 centimeters, this gauge funnels rain into a cylinder that magnifies precipitation amounts by a factor of 10, allowing for accurate measurement of small amounts.

Static Seeding The most commonly used technique of cloud seeding; based on the assumption that cumulus clouds are deficient in freezing nuclei and that the addition of nuclei will spur additional precipitation formation.

Stationary Front A situation in which the surface position of a front does not move; the flow on either side of such a boundary is nearly parallel to the position of the front.

Statistical Methods (in forecasting) Methods in which tables or graphs are prepared from a long series of observations to show the probability of certain weather events under certain conditions of pressure, temperature, or wind direction.

Steam Fog Fog having the appearance of steam: produced by evaporation from a warm water surface into the cool air above.

Steam Point The temperature at which water boils.

Step Leader See Leader.

Steppe One of the two types of dry climate; a marginal and more humid variant of the desert that separates it from bordering humid climates. Steppe also refers to the short-grass vegetation associated with this semiarid climate.

Storm Surge The abnormal rise of the sea along a shore as a result of strong winds.

Stratopause The boundary between the stratosphere and the mesosphere.

Stratosphere The zone of the atmosphere above the troposphere characterized at first by isothermal conditions and then a gradual temperature increase. Earth's ozone is concentrated here.

Stratus One of three basic cloud forms; also the name given one of the low clouds. Stratus clouds are sheets or layers that cover much or all of the sky.

Stroke One of the individual components that make up a flash of lightning. There are usually three to four strokes per flash, roughly 50 milliseconds apart.

Subarctic Climate A climate found north of the humid continental climate and south of the polar climate and characterized by bitterly cold winters and short cool summers. Places within this climatic realm experience the highest annual temperature ranges on Earth.

Sublimation The process whereby a solid changes directly to a gas without going through the liquid state.

Subpolar Low Low pressure located at about the latitudes of the Arctic and Antarctic circles. In the Northern Hemisphere, the low takes the form of individual oceanic cells; in the Southern Hemisphere, there is a deep and continuous trough of low pressure.

Subsidence An extensive sinking motion of air, most frequently occurring in anticyclones. The subsiding air is warmed by compression and becomes more stable.

Subtropical High Not a continuous belt of high pressure, but rather several semipermanent anticyclonic centers characterized by subsidence and divergence located roughly between latitudes 25° and 35°.

Summer Solstice See Solstice.

Sun Dogs Two bright spots of light, sometimes called "mock suns," that sit at a distance of 22° on either side of the Sun.

Sun Pillar Shafts of light caused by reflection from ice crystals that extend upward or, less commonly, downward from the Sun when the Sun is near the horizon.

Sunspot A dark area on the Sun associated with powerful magnetic storms that extend from the Sun's surface deep into the interior.

Supercell A type of thunderstorm that consists of a single, persistent, and very powerful cell (updraft and downdraft) and that often produces severe weather, including hail and tornadoes.

Supercooled The condition of water droplets that remain in the liquid state at temperatures well below 0°C.

Superior Mirage A mirage in which the image appears above the true position of the object.

Synoptic Weather Forecasting A system of forecasting based on careful studies of synoptic weather charts over a period of years; from such studies a set of empirical rules is established to aid the forecaster in estimating the rate and direction of weather-system movements.

Synoptic Weather Map A weather map describing the state of the atmosphere over a large area at a given moment.

Taiga The northern coniferous forest; also a name applied to the subarctic climate.

Temperature A measure of the degree of hotness or coldness of a substance.

Temperature Gradient The amount of temperature change per unit of distance.

Temperature Inversion A layer in the atmosphere of limited depth where the temperature increases rather than decreases with height.

Theory A well-tested and widely accepted view that explains certain observable facts.

Thermal An example of convection that involves the upward movements of warm, less dense air. In this manner, heat is transported to greater heights.

Thermal Low An area of low atmospheric pressure created by abnormal surface heating.

Thermistor An electric thermometer consisting of a conductor whose resistance to the flow of current is temperature-dependent; commonly used in radiosondes.

Thermocouple An electric thermometer that operates on the principle that differences in temperature between the junction of two unlike metal wires in a circuit will induce a current to flow.

Thermograph An instrument that continuously records temperature.

Thermometer An instrument for measuring temperature; in meteorology, generally used to measure the temperature of the air.

Thermosphere The zone of the atmosphere beyond the mesosphere in which there is a rapid rise in temperature with height.

Thunder The sound emitted by rapidly expanding gases along the channel of a lightning discharge.

Thunderstorm A storm produced by a cumulonimbus cloud and always accompanied by lightning and thunder. It is of relatively short duration and usually accompanied by strong wind gusts, heavy rain, and sometimes hail.

Tipping-Bucket Gauge A recording rain gauge consisting of two compartments ("buckets"), each capable of holding 0.025 centimeter of water. When one compartment fills, it tips and the other compartment takes its place.

Tornado A violently rotating column of air attended by a funnel-shaped or tubular cloud extending downward from a cumulonimbus cloud.

Tornado Warning A warning issued when a tornado has actually been sighted in an area or is indicated by radar.

Tornado Watch A forecast issued for areas of about 65,000 square kilometers, indicating that conditions are such that tornadoes may develop; they are intended to alert people to the possibility of tornadoes.

Towering A mirage in which the size of an object is magnified.

Trace of Precipitation An amount less than 0.025 centimeter.

Trade Winds Two belts of winds that blow almost constantly from easterly directions and are located on the equatorward sides of the subtropical highs.

Transpiration The release of water vapor to the atmosphere by plants.

Trend Forecast A short-range forecasting technique that assumes that the weather occurring upstream will persist and move on to affect the area in its path.

Tropic of Cancer The parallel of latitude, 23 1/2° north latitude, marking the northern limit of the Sun's vertical rays.

Tropic of Capricorn The parallel of latitude, 23 1/2° south latitude, marking the southern limit of the Sun's vertical rays.

Tropical (T) Air Mass A warm-to-hot air mass that forms in the subtropics.

Tropical Depression By international agreement, a tropical cyclone with maximum winds that do not exceed 61 kilometers per hour.

Tropical Disturbance A term used by the National Weather Service for a cyclonic wind system in the tropics that is in its formative stages.

Tropical Rain Forest A luxuriant broadleaf evergreen forest; also the name given the climate associated with this vegetation.

Tropical Storm By international agreement, a tropical cyclone with maximum winds between 61 and 115 kilometers per hour.

Tropical Wet and Dry A climate that is transitional between the wet tropics and the subtropical steppes.

Tropopause The boundary between the troposphere and the stratosphere.

Troposphere The lowermost layer of the atmosphere marked by considerable turbulence and, in general, a decrease in temperature with increasing height.

Trough An elongate region of low atmospheric pressure.

Tundra Climate Found almost exclusively in the Northern Hemisphere or at high altitudes in many mountainous regions. A treeless climatic realm of sedges, grasses, mosses, and lichens dominated by a long, bitterly cold winter.

Ultraviolet Radiation Radiation with a wavelength from 0.2 to 0.4 micrometer.

Unstable Air Air that does not resist vertical displacement. If it is lifted, its temperature will not cool as rapidly as the surrounding environment and so it will continue to rise on its own.

Upslope Fog Fog created when air moves up a slope and cools adiabatically.

Upwelling The process by which deep, cold, nutrient-rich water is brought to the surface, usually by coastal currents that move water away from the coast.

Urban Heat Island Refers to the fact that temperatures within a city are generally higher than in surrounding rural areas.

Valley Breeze The daily upslope winds commonly encountered in a mountain valley.

Vapor Pressure That part of the total atmospheric pressure attributable to its water-vapor content.

Veering Wind Shift A wind shift in a clockwise direction, such as a shift from east to south.

Vernal Equinox *See* Equinox.

Virga Wisps or streaks of water or ice particles falling out of a cloud but evaporating before reaching Earth's surface.

Visibility The greatest distance that prominent objects can be seen and identified by unaided, normal eyes.

Visible Light Radiation with a wavelength from 0.4 to 0.7 micrometer.

Warm Front The discontinuity at the forward edge of an advancing warm air mass that is displacing cooler air in its path.

Warm-Type Occluded Front A front that forms when the air behind the cold front is warmer than the air underlying the warm front it is overtaking.

Water Hemisphere A term used to refer to the Southern Hemisphere, where the oceans cover 81 percent of the surface (compared to 61 percent in the Northern Hemisphere).

Wavelength The horizontal distance separating successive crests or troughs.

Weather The state of the atmosphere at any given time.

Weather Analysis The stage prior to developing a weather forecast. This stage involves collecting, compiling, and transmitting observational data.

Weather Forecasting Predicting the future state of the atmosphere.

Weather Modification Deliberate human intervention to influence and improve atmospheric processes.

Weighting Gauge A recording precipitation gauge consisting of a cylinder that rests on a spring balance.

Westerlies *See* Prevailing Westerlies.

Wet Adiabatic Rate The rate of adiabatic temperature change in saturated air. The rate of temperature change is variable, but it is always less than the dry adiabatic rate.

White Frost Ice crystals that form on surfaces instead of dew when the dew point is below freezing.

Wind Air flowing horizontally with respect to Earth's surface.

Windchill A measure of apparent temperature that uses the effects of wind and temperature on the cooling rate of the human body. The windchill chart translates the cooling power of the atmosphere with the wind to a temperature under nearly calm conditions.

Wind Vane An instrument used to determine wind direction.

Winter Solstice *See* Solstice.

World Meteorological Organization (WMO) Established by the United Nations, the WMO consists of more than 130 nations and is responsible for gathering needed observational data and compiling some general prognostic charts.

INDEX

Lutgens/Tarbuck/Tasa GEODe: Atmosphere, Tenth Edition CD-ROM

Frederick K. Lutgens and Edward J. Tarbuck
Illustrated by Dennis Tasa
ISBN 0-13-187471-3
©2007 Pearson Education, Inc.
Pearson Prentice Hall
Pearson Education, Inc.
Upper Saddle River, NJ 07458
All rights reserved.
Pearson Prentice Hall™ is a trademark of Pearson Education, Inc.

LICENSE AGREEMENT

Pearson Education, Inc.

YOU SHOULD CAREFULLY READ THE FOLLOWING TERMS AND CONDITIONS BEFORE BREAKING THE SEAL ON THE PACKAGE. AMONG OTHER THINGS, THIS AGREEMENT LICENSES THE ENCLOSED SOFTWARE TO YOU AND CONTAINS WARRANTY AND LIABILITY DISCLAIMERS. BY BREAKING THE SEAL ON THE PACKAGE, YOU ARE ACCEPTING AND AGREEING TO THE TERMS AND CONDITIONS OF THIS AGREEMENT. IF YOU DO NOT AGREE TO THE TERMS OF THIS AGREEMENT, DO NOT BREAK THE SEAL. YOU SHOULD PROMPTLY RETURN THE PACKAGE UNOPENED.

LICENSE.
Subject to the provisions contained herein, Prentice-Hall, Inc. ("PH") hereby grants to you a non-exclusive, non-transferable license to use the object code version of the computer software product ("Software") contained in the package on a single computer of the type identified on the package.

SOFTWARE AND DOCUMENTATION.
PH shall furnish the Software to you on media in machine-readable object code form and may also provide the standard documentation ("Documentation") containing instructions for operation and use of the Software.

LICENSE TERM AND CHARGES.
The term of this license commences upon delivery of the Software to you and is perpetual unless earlier terminated upon default or as otherwise set forth herein.

TITLE.
Title, and ownership right, and intellectual property rights in and to the Software and Documentation shall remain in PH and/or in suppliers to PH of programs contained in the Software. The Software is provided for your own internal use under this license. This license does not include the right to sublicense and is personal to you and therefore may not be assigned (by operation of law or otherwise) or transferred without the prior written consent of PH.You acknowledge that the Software in source code form remains a confidential trade secret of PH and/or its suppliers and therefore you agree not to attempt to decipher or decompile, modify, disassemble, reverse engineer or prepare derivative works of the Software or develop source code for the Software or knowingly allow others to do so. Further, you may not copy the Documentation or other written materials accompanying the Software.

UPDATES.
This license does not grant you any right, license, or interest in and to any improvements, modifications, enhancements, or updates to the Software and Documentation. Updates, if available, may be obtained by you at PH's then current standard pricing, terms, and conditions.

LIMITED WARRANTY AND DISCLAIMER.
PH warrants that the media containing the Software, if provided by PH, is free from defects in material and workmanship under normal use for a period of sixty (60) days from the date you purchased a license to it.

THIS IS A LIMITED WARRANTY AND IT IS THE ONLY WARRANTY MADE BY PH. THE SOFTWARE IS PROVIDED 'AS IS' AND PH SPECIFICALLY DISCLAIMS ALL WARRANTIES OF ANY KIND, EITHER EXPRESS OR IMPLIED, INCLUDING, BUT NOT LIMITED TO, THE IMPLIED WARRANTY OF MERCHANTABILITY AND FITNESS FOR A PARTICULAR PURPOSE. FURTHER, COMPANY DOES NOT WARRANT, GUARANTY OR MAKE ANY REPRESENTATIONS REGARDING THE USE, OR THE RESULTS OF THE USE, OF THE SOFTWARE IN TERMS OF CORRECTNESS, ACCURACY, RELIABILITY, CURRENTNESS, OR OTHERWISE AND DOES NOT WARRANT THAT THE OPERATION OF ANY SOFTWARE WILL BE UNINTERRUPTED OR ERROR FREE. COMPANY EXPRESSLY DISCLAIMS ANY WARRANTIES NOT STATED HEREIN. NO ORAL OR WRITTEN INFORMATION OR ADVICE GIVEN BY PH, OR ANY PH DEALER, AGENT, EMPLOYEE OR OTHERS SHALL CREATE, MODIFY OR EXTEND A WARRANTY OR IN ANY WAY INCREASE THE SCOPE OF THE FOREGOING WARRANTY, AND NEITHER SUBLICENSEE OR PURCHASER MAY RELY ON ANY SUCH INFORMATION OR ADVICE. If the media is subjected to accident, abuse, or improper use; or if you violate the terms of this Agreement, then this warranty shall immediately be terminated. This warranty shall not apply if the Software is used on or in conjunction with hardware or programs other than the unmodified version of hardware and programs with which the Software was designed to be used as described in the Documentation.

LIMITATION OF LIABILITY.
Your sole and exclusive remedies for any damage or loss in any way connected with the Software are set forth below. UNDER NO CIRCUMSTANCES AND UNDER NO LEGAL THEORY, TORT, CONTRACT, OR OTHERWISE, SHALL PH BE LIABLE TO YOU OR ANY OTHER PERSON FOR ANY INDIRECT, SPECIAL, INCIDENTAL, OR CONSEQUENTIAL DAMAGES OF ANY CHARACTER INCLUDING, WITHOUT LIMITATION, DAMAGES FOR LOSS OF GOODWILL, LOSS OF PROFIT, WORK STOPPAGE, COMPUTER FAILURE OR MALFUNCTION, OR ANY AND ALL OTHER COMMERCIAL DAMAGES OR LOSSES, OR FOR ANY OTHER DAMAGES EVEN IF PH SHALL HAVE BEEN INFORMED OF THE POSSIBILITY OF SUCH DAMAGES, OR FOR ANY CLAIM BY ANY OTHER PARTY. PH'S THIRD PARTY PROGRAM SUPPLIERS MAKE NO WARRANTY, AND HAVE NO LIABILITY WHATSOEVER, TO YOU. PH's sole and exclusive obligation and liability and your exclusive remedy shall be: upon PH's election, (i) the replacement of your defective media; or (ii) the repair or correction of your defective media if PH is able, so that it will conform to the above warranty; or (iii) if PH is unable to replace or repair, you may terminate this license by returning the Software. Only if you inform PH of your problem during the applicable warranty period will PH be obligated to honor this warranty. You may contact PH to inform PH of the problem as follows:

SOME STATES OR JURISDICTIONS DO NOT ALLOW THE EXCLUSION OF IMPLIED WARRANTIES OR LIMITATION OR EXCLUSION OF CONSEQUENTIAL DAMAGES, SO THE ABOVE LIMITATIONS OR EXCLUSIONS MAY NOT APPLY TO YOU. THIS WARRANTY GIVES YOU SPECIFIC LEGAL RIGHTS AND YOU MAY ALSO HAVE OTHER RIGHTS WHICH VARY BY STATE OR JURISDICTION.

MISCELLANEOUS.
If any provision of this Agreement is held to be ineffective, unenforceable, or illegal under certain circumstances for any reason, such decision shall not affect the validity or enforceability (i) of such provision under other circumstances or (ii) of the remaining provisions hereof under all circumstances and such provision shall be reformed to and only to the extent necessary to make it effective, enforceable, and legal under such circumstances. All headings are solely for convenience and shall not be considered in interpreting this Agreement. This Agreement shall be governed by and construed under New York law as such law applies to agreements between New York residents entered into and to be performed entirely within New York, except as required by U.S. Government rules and regulations to be governed by Federal law.

YOU ACKNOWLEDGE THAT YOU HAVE READ THIS AGREEMENT, UNDERSTAND IT, AND AGREE TO BE BOUND BY ITS TERMS AND CONDITIONS. YOU FURTHER AGREE THAT IT IS THE COMPLETE AND EXCLUSIVE STATEMENT OF THE AGREEMENT BETWEEN US THAT SUPERSEDES ANY PROPOSAL OR PRIOR AGREEMENT, ORAL OR WRITTEN, AND ANY OTHER COMMUNICATIONS BETWEEN US RELATING TO THE SUBJECT MATTER OF THIS AGREEMENT.

U.S. GOVERNMENT RESTRICTED RIGHTS.
Use, duplication or disclosure by the Government is subject to restrictions set forth in subparagraphs (a) through (d) of the Commercial Computer-Restricted Rights clause at FAR 52.227-19 when applicable, or in subparagraph (c) (1) (ii) of the Rights in Technical Data and Computer Software clause at DFARS 252.227-7013, and in similar clauses in the NASA FAR Supplement.

PROGRAM INSTRUCTIONS
Windows
To start the GEODe Atmosphere program simply insert GEODe Atmosphere CD-ROM into your CD-ROM drive. The GEODe Atmosphere program will automatically start.

It is recommended that the display be set to "millions of colors."

If your display is larger than 640 x 480 pixels, there will be a black border around the 640 x 480 display window.

Macintosh
To start the GEODe Atmosphere program simply insert GEODe Atmosphere CD-ROM into your CD-ROM drive. The GEODe Atmosphere program will automatically start (if the AutoPlay feature in the QuickTime Settings control panel is checked.)
If the AutoPlay feature is not enabled:
1) double-click the GEODe Atmosphere CD-ROM icon on your desktop,
2) open (double-click) the "Program" folder,
3) double-click the GEODe Atmosphere application icon to start the program.
It is recommended that the display be set to "millions of colors."
If your display is larger than 640 x 480 pixels, there will be a black border around the 640 x 480 display window.

MINIMUM SYSTEM REQUIREMENTS
Windows
Processor: 166 MHz Intel Pentium processor or greater
(Windows XP requires a 233 MHz processor)
RAM:
Windows 98 - 32 MB of RAM
Windows NT - 32 MB of RAM
Windows 2000 - 64 MB of RAM
Windows ME - 32 MB of RAM
Windows XP - 128 MB of RAM
Operating System:Windows 98, NT4, 2000, ME, XP
Monitor resolution: 640 x 480 pixels; millions of colors
Required third-party software: QuickTime(TM)
Required hardware: CD drive, sound card, speakers

Macintosh
Processor: 120 MHz PowerPC
RAM: In addition to the RAM required by the operating system, this application requires 10 MBytes of RAM (16 MBytes recommended).
Operating System: MAC OS 8.1 to 9.1 (OS X 10.2.x using Classic Mode).
Monitor resolution: 640 x 480 pixels; millions of colors
Required third-party software: QuickTime™
Required hardware: CD drive, speakers

TECHNICAL SUPPORT
If you are having problems with this software, call (800) 677-6337 between 8:00 a.m. through 8:00 p.m. Monday through Friday and 5:00 p.m. through 12:00 a.m. Saturday and Sunday Eastern Standard Time. You can also get support by filling out the web form located at http://247.prenhall.com/mediaform Our technical staff will need to know certain things about your system in order to help us solve your problems more quickly and efficiently. If possible, please be at your computer when you call for support. You should have the following information ready:

Textbook ISBN
CD-Rom/Diskette ISBN
corresponding product and title
computer make and model
Operating System (Windows or Macintosh) and Version
RAM available
hard disk space available
Sound card? Yes or No
printer make and model
network connection
detailed description of the problem, including the exact wording of any error messages.

NOTE: Pearson does not support and/or assist with the following:
third-party software (i.e. Microsoft including Microsoft Office Suite, Apple, Borland, etc.)
homework assistance
Textbooks and CD-Rom's purchased used are not supported and are non-replaceable. To purchase a new CD-Rom contact Pearson Individual Order Copies at 1-800-282-0693